KEYS TO THE TREMATODES OF ANIMALS AND MAN

KEYS TO THE TREMATODES OF ANIMALS AND MAN

by K. I. Skrjabin and others

ENGLISH TRANSLATION EDITED BY

Hisao P. Arai
UNIVERSITY OF ALBERTA, CALGARY, AND CENTER FOR ZOONOSES RESEARCH,
UNIVERSITY OF ILLINOIS

TRANSLATED BY

Raymond W. Dooley
CENTER FOR ZOONOSES RESEARCH AND AGRICULTURAL EXPERIMENT STATION,
UNIVERSITY OF ILLINOIS

UNIVERSITY OF ILLINOIS PRESS, URBANA, 1964

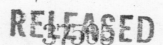

Academician K. I. Skrjabin and his staff prepared the original work
from which these keys have been drawn at the Helminthological Laboratory, Academy of Sciences of the USSR. It was originally published,
in twenty volumes, as TREMATODY ZHIVOTNYKH I CHELOVEKA, Izdatelstvo Akademii Nauk SSSR, Moskva, 1947 through 1962. Four more
volumes are scheduled.

CONTENTS

INTRODUCTION

This volume is a translation of the keys to the trematodes in the first 20 volumes of *Trematody Zhivotnykh i Cheloveka (Trematodes of Animals and Man)*, edited by Academician K. I. Skrjabin. This series of volumes is a monumental compendium on these important parasites, many of which are zoonotic agents. The series is published by the USSR Academy of Science. The first volume appeared in 1947, and subsequent volumes have appeared periodically since then. At present, 20 volumes containing approximately 14,000 pages have been published, and the work is still incomplete.

These books will serve as a base-line for trematode taxonomic and epidemiologic work for many decades, and non-Russian helminthologists are greatly handicapped by not having ready access to them. It would be desirable to have complete English translations made, but the task seems beyond present capabilities. The next best thing is to have keys to the different groups and species of trematodes translated, and that is what are presented herein.

This translation is published in the hope that it will aid zoologists to a better understanding of the trematode parasites of vertebrates. The taxonomy of a group of animals must be known before the results of other studies on that group can be interpreted meaningfully. For this reason, workers in disciplines other than taxonomic parasitology can profit from this book.

In the introduction in his first volume, Skrjabin (1947) stated that his work was undertaken to alleviate the lack of a comprehensive source of information on the digenetic trematodes. He had planned to compile this information in eight to ten volumes, restricting them primarily to information at the generic level. However, he has included descriptions of all known species together with their synonymies, host lists, distributional data, and, in many cases, available information on life history studies.

There is no apparent attempt in the first twenty volumes to offer a complete presentation of a group, i.e., to treat the larger taxa in their entirety. It appears that, when any given compilation was completed, it was included in the volume currently being processed for publication. For example, studies on the family Dinuridae have now appeared in five different volumes. This multiple treatment of groups indicates that the ideas and concepts of Skrjabin and his co-workers on the relationships between taxa are being continually modified. For these reasons and on the basis of what has been presented to date, it is not possible to glean a concise classification of the Digenea or to obtain other indications of basic relationships between lower taxonomic groupings. It is possible that this synthesis and further concepts of phylogeny will be presented in subsequent volumes; the twenty which have appeared so far do not include all of the digenetic trematodes.

The following procedure was used in preparing the manuscript: 1) Dooley wrote the initial translations by hand. 2) Arai typed and edited the first draft. 3) Dooley and Arai edited the first typewritten draft, Dooley reading from the text and Arai proofing the copy. 4) Arai and Lanko typed the second draft. 5) Dooley and Arai edited the second typewritten draft, Dooley reading from the text and Arai proofing the copy. 6) Dooley re-edited the second typewritten draft against the text to insure accuracy. 7) Arai re-edited the second typewritten draft for content. 8) Tudor typed the third draft. 9) Arai and Dooley individually edited the final draft.

In translating, Dooley used Whitfield's (1958) transliterated form of the Cyrillic alphabet. The choice is one of convenience; however, I believe that the relative lack of diacritical marks in the form presently used will minimize subsequent typographical errors. In other transliterated forms of the Cyrillic alphabet, such as that used by the Library of Congress, many of the last ten letters have marks which are not included on standard typewriters.

In the initial translation, Dooley translated on a word-for-word basis. In the first editing, I altered the construction of many lines to the extent that, in some cases, the only resemblance to the original is in content or meaning. The translations of the reference citations were kept as close to the original as possible. Changes in structure were made only where the original construction was extremely awkward in its English form. Initially, an attempt was made to correct, complete, or revise the citations; however, because of time limitations and the general unavailability of the original literature, the majority of the references are presented as they appeared. Only the citations given in Cyrillic are included; the reader is referred to Skrjabin's volumes for numerous other references which are given in English, French, or German.

The illustrations included are those of typical species of the genus represented. In some cases, however, when these illustrations were not available in the Russian volumes, the figure of another species from these volumes was substituted.

Since I believe that the present publication should be used in conjunction with the Russian series, the format follows the chronological order in which the keys and references appeared originally, i.e., each part contains the keys and references in the same order as they appeared in each volume of the series. The volumes and pages in the Russian work are indicated by the numbers following the title of a key or the title of a group of reference citations.

I wish to acknowledge the invaluable aid of Drs.

Carl A. Brandly, Norman D. Levine, and Francis J. Kruidenier of the Center for Zoonoses Research, University of Illinois. Without their timely suggestions and assistance, the completion of this work would have been rendered infinitely more difficult. Acknowledgement is also made to the University Research Board, University of Illinois, for financial aid in the preparation of the manuscript and in publication of this work. To Academician K. I. Skrjabin and his co-workers and to other helminthologists whose original research made possible the Russian compendium on the digenetic trematodes, I owe an extreme debt of gratitude. I am further indebted for secretarial assistance extended by many individuals, especially Miss Joyce Lanko and Mrs. Harriet Tudor.

Grants from the Research Board of the University of Illinois have aided in the translation and publication of this work.

Hisao P. Arai
Calgary, Alberta
July, 1963

PART I

KEY TO THE SUBPHYLA OF THE PHYLUM
PLATHELMINTHES SCHNEIDER, 1873 (I:10)

K. I. Skrjabin

1 (2) Majority of forms parasitic (all cestodes,
trematodes and few turbellarians); circulatory system or proboscis lacking; anal pore usually lacking
(with rare exceptions); animals usually hermaphroditic (with several exceptions); ciliated adult forms
occurring only in Turbellaria.
                    Platodes Leuckart, 1854
2 (1) Free-living organisms; circulatory system
present; special proboscis present; anal pore present; majority with sexes separate; bodies covered
with cilia.   Nemertarii Poche, 1925

KEY TO THE CLASSES OF THE SUBPHYLUM
PLATODES LEUCKART, 1854 (I:10)

K. I. Skrjabin

1 (2) Adults mostly covered with cilia; mainly
free-living organisms, more rarely parasitic forms.
                    Turbellaria Ehrenberg, 1831
2 (1) Adults lacking cilia; all forms parasitic.
3 (4) Special digestive apparatus (oral orifice,
pharynx, esophagus, intestine) present, occasionally
apparatus strongly reduced (with only oral orifice
and pharynx); larva of miracidium type (body wholly
covered with cilia and lacking hooklets), or larva
lacking cilia, or only partially covered.
                    Trematoda Rudolphi, 1808
4 (3) Special digestive apparatus lacking; larva of
onchosphere type (with six embryonic hooklets) or
lycophore type (having 10 embryonic hooklets)
                    Cestoidea Rudolphi, 1808

KEY TO THE SUBCLASSES OF THE CLASS
TREMATODA RUDOLPHI, 1808 (I:11)

K. I. Skrjabin

1 (2) Trematodes with two excretory pores, opening dorsally; uterus short, usually containing only
one egg; development direct; usually ecto-parasitic.
                    Monogenea Carus, 1863
2 (1) Trematodes with single excretory pore, at
posterior end of body; uterus with numerous coils,
containing many eggs; development including intermediate host; usually endoparasitic.
                    Digenea Carus, 1863

KEY TO THE SUB-SUBCLASSES OF
DIGENETIC TREMATODES (I:36)

K. I. Skrjabin

1 (2) Oral orifice on ventral surface; cephalic part
equipped with organ of fixation, not playing part of
mouth. Gasterostomatoinei Skrjabin and Schulz, 1937
2 (1) Oral orifice opening on cephalic end of parasite, either terminally or sub-terminally.
        Prosostomatoinei Skrjabin and Schulz, 1937

KEY TO THE SUPERORDERS OF SUB-SUBCLASS
PROSOSTOMATOINEI SKRJABIN AND SCHULZ,
1937 (I:36)

K. I. Skrjabin

1 (2) Fixatory apparatus consisting of ventral disc,
composed of numerous sucking locules; development
direct, without parthenogenesis.
        Aspidogasteriformes Skrjabin and Schulz, 1937
2 (1) Ventral fixatory disc lacking; suckers serving
as organs of adhesion; one (oral) or two (oral and
ventral) suckers present, rarely organs of adhesion
completely lacking; development with alternation of
generations.
        Fascioliformes Skrjabin and Schulz, 1937

KEY TO THE ORDERS OF TREMATODES
RELATED TO THE SUPERORDER
FASCIOLIFORMES SKRJABIN AND SCHULZ,
1937 (I:37)

K. I. Skrjabin

1 (2) Excretory pore opening dorso-medially, near
anterior end of body; uterus composed of two descending loops and three ascending ones.
        Heronimata Skrjabin and Schulz, 1937
2 (1) Excretory pore at considerable distance from
cephalic end of body, usually near posterior end;
uterus differently constructed.
3 (4) In addition to uterine pore, two vaginal pores
present, opening laterally in anterior part of body.
        Faustulata Skrjabin and Schulz, 1937
4 (3) Female genital pore represented only by pore
of uterus; vaginal openings on lateral sides of body
lacking.
5 (16) Hermaphroditic trematodes.
6 (7) Esophagus long, anteriorly broadened, posteriorly constricted, passing into un-paired intestine;
genital pore slightly anterior to posterior end of
body; anterior section of body with special branching
tentacles.   Alcicornata Skrjabin and Schulz, 1937
7 (6) Esophagus and intestine differently constructed; anterior tentacles lacking.
8 (9) Parasites in blood of fishes and reptiles;

pharynx lacking; uterus short or with only ootype, containing single egg.

Sanguinicolata Skrjabin and Schula, 1937

9 (8) Parasites not found in blood of fishes; pharynx usually present, rarely lacking; uterus differently constructed.

10 (11) On ventral surface of body there protrudes a special "organ of Brandes" of varying structure, an accessory organ of fixation and, apparently of external digestion.   Strigeata LaRue, 1926

11 (10) Organ of Brandes lacking.

12 (13) Ventral sucker and pharynx lacking; gonads in posterior part of body; testes extra-cecal; eggs usually with filaments.

Notocotylata Skrjabin and Schulz, 1933

13 (12) Ventral sucker present.

14 (15) Ventral sucker at posterior pole of body or else caudo-ventral; pharynx usually absent, rarely present; special lymphatic system present; eggs lacking filaments.

Paramphistomatata Skrjabin and Schulz, 1937

15 (14) Ventral sucker situated ventrally, relatively near oral sucker; oral sucker sometimes lacking; relative positions of gonads varied.

Fasciolata Skrjabin and Schulz, 1937

16 (5) Trematodes with sexes separate.

17 (18) Males and females without any trace of hermaphroditism; intestinal ceca joined; free-swimming in blood of host.

Schistosomatata Skrjabin and Schulz, 1937

18 (17) Males and females characterized by rudimentary hermaphroditism; intestinal ceca not joining; paired in cysts.

Didymozoata Skrjabin and Schulz, 1937

KEY TO THE GENERA OF THE FAMILY BIVESICULIDAE YAMAGUTI, 1938 (I:46)

K. I. Skrjabin

1 (2) Uterus reaching posterior end of body; intestinal ceca and vitellaria extending only to anterior border of testis.   Bivesicula Yamaguti, 1934 (fig. 1)

2 (1) Uterus not extending beyond level of testis; intestinal ceca and vitellaria extending posteriorly beyond anterior border of testis.

Bivesiculoides Yamaguti, 1938 (fig. 2)

KEY TO THE SPECIES OF THE GENUS CATHAEMASIA LOOSS, 1899 (I:57)

K. I. Skrjabin

1 (6) Scales on ventral surface of cuticle extending nearly to posterior end of body.

2 (5) Testes lobed, not dendritic.

3 (4) Esophagus present; vitellaria originating at middle of ventral sucker; eggs 0.10 x 0.055 mm. Hosts: storks and herons.

C. hians (Rudolphi, 1819) (fig. 3)

4 (3) Esophagus lacking; vitellaria originating at

level of posterior edge of ventral sucker; eggs: 0.072 - 0.083 x 0.0416 mm. Host: Hydrochelidon nigra.

C. fodicans M. Braun, 1901

5 (2) Testes dendritic; eggs: 0.057 - 0.062 x 0.037 mm. Host: ibis, Tantalus ibis.

C. famelica Odhner, 1926

6 (1) Scales on ventral surface of cuticle located only in anterior part of body, extending to level of ventral sucker; testes dendritic; eggs very large, 0.16 - 0.17 x 0.10 mm. Host: Leptoptilus crumenifer.   C. spectabilis Odhner, 1926

KEY TO THE SUBFAMILIES OF THE FAMILY CLINOSTOMATIDAE LÜHE, 1901 (I:64)

K. I. Skrjabin

1 (2) Cirrus sac not containing pars prostatica; uterus saccular. Parasites of birds.

Clinostomatinae Pratt, 1902

2 (1) Cirrus sac containing pars prostatica; uterus tubular. Parasites of reptiles.

3 (4) Cirrus sac large, elongate, sharply curved; eggs with miracidia when ejected from uterus. Esophageal parasites of crocodiles.

Opisthophallinae Travassos, 1926

4 (3) Cirrus sac small, only slightly bent, not forming sharply curved configuration; eggs leave uterus without miracidia. Intestinal parasites of snakes and crocodiles.

Harmotrematinae Yamaguti, 1933

KEY TO THE GENERA OF THE SUBFAMILY CLINOSTOMATINAE PRATT, 1902 from Baer (1933) (I:65)

1 (2) Intestines with long lateral diverticula, which are sometimes sub-branched.

Euclinostomum Travassos, 1938 (fig. 4)

2 (1) Intestines with short lateral diverticula, never sub-branched.

3 (4) Body length reaching several centimeters; vitellaria not reaching level of anterior half of body.

Ithyoclinostomum Witenberg, 1926 (fig. 5)

4 (3) Body not reaching several centimeters in length; vitellaria extending into anterior half of body.

Clinostomum Leidy, 1856 (fig. 6)

KEY TO THE SPECIES OF THE GENUS CLINOSTOMUM LEIDY, 1856 from Baer (1933) (I:65)

1 (2) Vitellaria extending into zone anterior to ventral sucker.   C. sorbens M. Braun, 1899

2 (1) Vitellaria not passing into zone anterior to ventral sucker.

3 (6) Gonads medial in equatorial region of body.

4 (5) Vitallaria radially situated.

C. foliiforme M. Braun, 1899

5 (4) Vitellaria not radially situated.

C. complanatum (Rudolphi, 1899) (fig. 6)

6 (3) Gonads in posterior half or posterior third of body.

7 (8) Uterus with lateral out-growths.
C. detruncatum M. Braun, 1899

8 (7) Uterus without lateral out-growths.

9 (12) Ventral sucker more distal than oral sucker from posterior limit of mature uterus.

10 (11) Gonads far from equator of body.
C. heluans M. Braun, 1899

11 (10) Gonads near equator of body.
C. attenuatum Cort, 1913

12 (9) Ventral sucker nearer than oral sucker to posterior limit of mature uterus.

13 (16) Small parasites, body not exceeding 5 mm. in length.

14 (15) Oral sucker 0.16 mm. in diameter.
C. lambitans M. Braun, 1899

15 (14) Oral sucker 0.40 mm. in diameter.
C. hornum Nicoll, 1914

16 (13) Large parasites, body reaching 11 mm. in length.

17 (18) Vitelline reservoir present.
C. lophophallum Baer, 1932

18 (17) Vitelline reservoir lacking.

19 (20) Ventral sucker at posterior border of anterior third of body.   C. intermedialis Lamont, 1920

20 (19) Ventral sucker at posterior border of anterior fourth of body. C. phalacrocoracis Dubois, 1930

KEY TO THE SPECIES OF THE GENUS CLINOSTOMUM FOR WHICH ONLY METACERCARIA ARE KNOWN from Baer (1933) (I:77)

1 (2) Uterus extending to posterior border of anterior testis.   C. dictyotum (Monticelli, 1893)

2 (1) Uterus not reaching level of posterior border of anterior testis.

3 (4) Pharynx present; uteroductus entering uterus at midpoint of length of uterus.
C. chrysichthys Dubois, 1929

4 (3) Pharynx lacking; uteroductus entering uterus at base of uterus.
C. piscidium Southwell and Prashad, 1918

KEY TO THE SPECIES OF THE GENUS EUCLINOSTOMUM TRAVASSOS, 1928 (I:81)

K. I. Skrjabin

1 (2) Adult stages known; uterus reaching level of ventral sucker.
E. heterostomum (Rudolphi, 1809) (fig. 4)

2 (1) Adult stages unknown; only metacercaria known; uterus not extending to level of ventral sucker.

3 (4) Gonads situated in posterior third of body. Supplementary host: fish, Clarias angolense
E. clarias (Dubois, 1929)

4 (3) Gonads in middle third of body. Supplementary host: fish, Ophiocephalus striatus.
E. multicaecum Tubangui and Masilungan, 1935

KEY TO THE GENERA OF THE SUBFAMILY OPISTHOPHALLINAE TRAVASSOS, 1926 from Baer (1933) (I:82)

1 (2) Genital pore between testes.
Odhneriotrema Travassos, 1928 (fig. 7)

2 (1) Genital pore posterior to both testes.
Opisthophallus Baer, 1923

KEY TO THE SPECIES OF THE GENUS ODHNERIOTREMA TRAVASSOS, 1928 (I:86)

K. I. Skrjabin

1 (2) Genital pore near level of anterior edge of posterior testis; ovary mid-way between testes, slightly nearer to anterior testis. Parasites of oral cavities of alligators.
O. incommodum (Leidy, 1856)

2 (1) Genital pore at level of anterior edge of ovary; ovary directly anterior to posterior testis. Esophageal parasites of caiman.
O. microcephala (Travassos, 1922) Travassos, 1928 (fig. 7)

KEY TO THE SPECIES OF THE GENUS HARMOTREMA NICOLL, 1914 (I:89)

K. I. Skrjabin

1 (2) Testes and ovary lobed; genital pore between ventral sucker and posterior end of body; vitellaria originating mid-way between intestinal bifurcation and ventral sucker.
H. infecundum Nicoll, 1914 (fig. 8)

2 (1) Testes and ovary entire.

3 (4) Genital pore post-equatorial; vitellaria well-developed, extending from anterior edge of ventral sucker to posterior end of body.
H. rudolphii Tubangui and Masilungan, 1936

4 (3) Genital pore pre-equatorial.

5 (6) Vitellaria inter-cecal from posterior edge of ventral sucker to posterior end of body; testes small: 0.17-0.23 x 0.13-0.17 mm. (anterior testis); ovary: 0.22-0.17 x 0.10-0.15 mm.; eggs: 0.108-0.115 x 0.069-0.077 mm.
H. eugari Tubangui and Masilungan, 1936

6 (5) Vitellaria partially extra-cecal in region between ventral sucker and posterior end of body; testes large: 0.5-0.55 x 0.44-0.6 mm. (anterior testis); ovary: 0.16-0.25 x 0.23-0.31 mm.; eggs: 0.128-0.129 x 0.075-0.078 mm.
H. laticaudae Yamaguti, 1933

KEY TO THE GENERA OF THE FAMILY EUCOTYLIDAE SKRJABIN, 1924 (I:107)

K. I. Skrjabin

1 (2) Triangular cephalic end separated from body by muscular shoulder; esophagus present; testes symmetrical.   Eucotyle Cohn, 1904 (fig. 9)

2 (1) Cephalic end without muscular shoulder, tapering gradually into remainder of body.
3 (4) Esophagus present; testes oblique, palmate.
Tanaisia Skrjabin, 1924 (fig. 10)
4 (3) Esophagus lacking; testes entire, symmetrical.   Tamerlania Skrjabin, 1924 (fig. 11)

KEY TO THE SPECIES OF THE GENUS EUCOTYLE COHN, 1904 (I:107)

K. I. Skrjabin

1 (4) Vitellaria reaching only to posterior border of testes.
2 (3) Body 5.6 mm. long, 1.1 mm. wide; testes occupying entire width of body; lateral edges of testes contacting each other medially; uterus occupying entire space posterior to testes.
E. zakharowi Skrjabin, 1920
3 (2) Body 2.4 mm. long, 0.387 mm. wide; testes separated by intercecal space; uterus weakly developed.   E. wehri Price, 1930
4 (1) Vitellaria extending posterior to testes.
5 (6) Intestines straight, not forming medial curve in area of testes; testes elongate, entire, exclusively extra-cecal.   E. nephritica (Creplin, 1846) (fig. 9)
6 (5) Intestines with medial curve in region of testis.
7 (10) Testes lobed; seminal vesicle medial.
8 (9) Testes bifurcated at each end; ovary larger than testes.   E. hassalli Price, 1930
9 (8) Testes irregularly shaped; seminal vesicle larger than ovary.   E. cohni Skrjabin, 1924
10 (7) Testes entire; seminal vesicle sinistral, larger than ovary; ovary medial, entire.
E. popowi Skrjabin and Evranova, 1942

KEY TO THE SPECIES OF THE GENUS TAMERLANIA SKRJABIN, 1924 (I:120)

K. I. Skrjabin

1 (2) Vitellaria in anterior and middle thirds of body; oral sucker reaching 0.40 x 0.50 mm.
T. bragai Santos, 1934
2 (1) Vitellaria in middle third of body; oral sucker: 0.15-0.30 mm.
3 (4) Vitellaria of unequal size: right 0.9 mm. in length; left: 0.6 mm.; body 2.5 mm. long; ovary triangular.   T. meruli Neslobinsky, 1926
4 (3) Vitellaria of equal size; body exceeding 2.5 mm. in length; ovary round or oval.
5 (6) Vitellaria reaching 1.7 mm. in length; ovary round or slightly oval; eggs: 0.042 x 0.024 mm.
T. zarudnyi Skrjabin, 1924 (fig. 11)
6 (5) Vitellaria reaching 1.3 mm. in length; width of ovary considerably exceeding length (0.05 x 0.09 mm.); eggs: 0.030 x 0.021 mm.
T. melospizae Penner, 1939

LITERATURE ON THE TREMATODES OF THE

FAMILY EUCOTYLIDAE SKRJABIN, 1924 (I:130)

Skrjabin, K. I. 1920. Helminthological notes. Izvestiya Donskogo Veterinarnogo Instituta. 2(2):1-7.
Strom, Zh. K. 1932. On the trematode fauna of Tadzhikistan. *In:* Materials on the parasitology and fauna of southern Tadzhikistan. Trudy Tadzhikskoy Komplexnoy Expeditsii. No. 10:219-254.

KEY TO THE GENERA OF THE FAMILY MEGAPERIDAE MANTER, 1934 (I:134)

K. I. Skrjabin

1 (2) Greater part of testes extra-cecal; anterior border of testes anterior to intestinal bifurcation; medial edges of testes not contacting; ovary tri-lobed; prepharynx weakly developed, or altogether absent.
Megapera Manter, 1934 (fig. 12)
2 (1) Testes against intestinal ceca, not extending externally beyond lateral edges; testes located posterior to intestinal bifurcation, anterior portions contiguous along medial line of body; ovary round; prepharynx well-developed.
Thysanopharynx Manter, 1933 (fig. 13)

LITERATURE ON THE TREMATODES OF THE FAMILY MESOTRETIDAE POCHE, 1925 (I:146)

Strom, Zh. K. 1935. On the trematode fauna of Tadzhikistan. *In:* Materials on the parasitology and fauna of southern Tadzhikistan. Trudy Tadzhikskoy Komplexnoy Expeditsii. No. 10:219-254.

KEY TO THE SPECIES OF THE GENUS NOTOPORUS YAMAGUTI, 1938 (I:150)

K. I. Skrjabin

1 (2) Pigmented eye-spots present; vitellaria not reaching pharynx; genital pore at level of center of ventral sucker.   N. trachuri Yamaguti, 1938
2 (1) Pigmented eye-spots lacking; vitellaria reaching pharynx; genital pore at level of anterior edge of ventral sucker. N. leiognathi Yamaguti, 1938 (fig. 14)

KEY TO THE SPECIES OF THE GENUS OMMATOBREPHUS NICOLL, 1914 (I:156)

K. I. Skrjabin

1 (2) Oral sucker considerably smaller than ventral (0.18 and 0.53 mm. in diameter, respectively); eggs exceptionally large, 0.095 x 0.056 mm. Host: Uromastix (N. Africa).
O. singularis Nicoll, 1914 (fig. 15)
2 (1) Oral sucker two times smaller than ventral (0.215 and 0.435 mm. respectively); eggs: 0.070-0.078 x 0.035-0.042 mm. Hosts: Zamenis mucosus, Tropidonotus piscator, Ptyas mucosus, and Varanus benegalensis from India.   O. lobatum Mehra, 1928

KEY TO THE GENERA OF THE FAMILY ORCHIPEDIDAE SKRJABIN, 1925 (I:165)

K. I. Skrjabin

1 (2) Body sub-divided into two parts by constriction; genital pore near intestinal bifurcation; ventral sucker in anterior part of body; vitellaria forming two supplementary rows in inter-cecal zone. Tracheal parasites of birds.

Orchipedum Braun, 1901 (fig. 16)

2 (1) Body not sub-divided; genital pore posterior to intestinal bifurcation; ventral sucker passing into posterior half of body; vitellaria not forming supplementary rows in intercecal zone. Parasites of nasal cavities of mammals.

Mammorchipedum Skrjabin, 1947 (fig. 17)

KEY TO THE SPECIES OF THE GENUS ORCHIPEDUM BRAUN, 1901 modified by Zhukova (1937) from K. I. Skrjabin (1925) (I:166)

1 (6) Vitellaria originating at level of posterior edge of ventral sucker.

2 (3) Ovary posterior to ventral sucker, at distance equal to space between suckers, medial rows of vitellaria continuous.   O. armenicum Skrjabin, 1925

3 (2) Ovary directly posterior to ventral sucker; medial rows of vitellaria in separate clusters.

4 (5) With about fifty testes; eggs: 0.062 mm. long.

O. tracheicola Braun, 1901 (fig. 16)

5 (4) With about one hundred and twenty-five testes; eggs: 0.081-0.0845 mm. long.

O. centorchis Witenberg, 1922

6 (1) Vitellaria originating anterior to ventral sucker.

7 (8) Ovary directly posterior to ventral sucker; ovary always smaller than each individual testis.

O. turkestanicum Skrjabin, 1913

8 (7) Ovary well separated from ventral sucker; ovary always larger than each individual testis.

O. formosum Sonsino, 1890

Note: O. conjunctum Strom and O. akhtari Bhalerao, 1942 omitted from key.

LITERATURE ON THE TREMATODES OF THE FAMILY ORCHIPEDIDAE SKRJABIN, 1925 (I:181)

Skrjabin, K. I. 1913. Parasitic worms of birds of Turkestan, A. Trematodes, 2. Orchipedinae. Arkhiv Veterinarnykh Nauk. 43(4):399-344.

Skrjabin, K. I. 1925. A new trematode from the trachea of birds, Orchipedum armeniacum. Russky Zhurnal Tropicheskoy Meditsiny. 3(1-3):61-64.

Zhukova, E. V. 1937. On the characteristics of the trematodes of the genus Orchipedum. Sbornik Rabot po Gelmintologii, Posvyaschenny 30-letiyu Deyatelnosti K. I. Skrjabina. pp. 221-225.

Strom, Zh. K. 1942. Two new species of trematodes of birds of Uzbekistan. Rukopis.

KEY TO THE GENERA OF THE FAMILY PHILOPHTHALMIDAE TRAVASSOS, 1918 (I:186)

K. I. Skrjabin

1 (4) Cirrus sac elongate, passing beyond posterior edge of ventral sucker.

2 (3) Testes symmetrical; rudimentary collar present along lateral margins of oral sucker. Parasites of intestine and fabrician bursa of birds.

Parorchis Nicoll, 1907 (fig. 18)

3 (2) Testes medial, tandem or slightly oblique; oral collar absent. Parasites of the conjunctiva of eye.   Philophthalmus Looss, 1898 (fig. 19)

4 (1) Cirrus sac not extending beyond posterior edge of ventral sucker.

5 (6) Testes symmetrical. Cloacal parasites of birds.   Cloacitrema Yamaguti, 1935 (fig. 20)

6 (5) Testes oblique.

7 (8) Body sub-divided by deep constriction into anterior and posterior sections. Parasites of conjunctiva of eyes of birds.

Ophthalmotrema Sobolev, 1943 (fig. 21)

8 (7) Body not sub-divided into anterior and posterior sections. Cloacal parasites of birds.

Pygorchis Looss, 1899 (fig. 22)

LITERATURE ON THE TREMATODES OF THE FAMILY PHILOPHTHALMIDAE TRAVASSOS, 1918 (I:212)

Skrjabin, K. I. 1924. Proctobium gedoelsti n. sp., a new trematode from sandpiper. Trudy Gosudarstvennogo Instituta Experimentalnoy Veterinarii. 2(1):1-4.

Sobolev, A. 1943. Paths of evolution of trematodes of the family Philophthalmidae. Doklady Akad. Nauk SSSR. 40(9):430-432.

LITERATURE ON THE TREMATODES OF THE FAMILY PSILOSTOMATIDAE ODHNER, 1913 (I:259)

Schulz, R. S. and M. I. Dobrova 1933. Materials on the knowledge of the parasitic worms of water rats of the lower Volga region. Vestnik Mikrobiologii, Epidemiologii, i Parazitologii. 12(4):329-331.

LITERATURE ON THE TREMATODES OF THE FAMILY RENICOLIDAE DOLLFUS, 1939 (I:277)

Rayevsky, V. A. 1937. A new trematode, Renicola paraquinta n. sp. from gull (Larus ridibundus). Sbornik Rabot po Gelmintologii, Posvyaschenny 30-letiyu Deyatelnosti K. I. Skrjabina. pp. 565-568.

Sokolova-Andronova, E. V. 1937. Trematodes of kidneys of birds of the Far East. Sbornik Rabot po Gelmintologii, Posvyaschenny 30-letiyu Deyatelnosti K. I. Skrjabina. pp. 571-572.

Sudarikov, V. E. 1947. (No title given). Rukopis.

KEY TO THE GENERA OF THE FAMILY STOMYLOTREMATIDAE POCHE, 1925 (I:283)

K. I. Skrjabin

1 (2) Genital pore at right edge of anterior half of body; ventral sucker in posterior half of body; ovary at level of pharynx; vitellaria lateral, forming single rows of large follicles, rows extending posteriorly into posterior half of body.

Stomylotrema Looss, 1900 (fig. 23)

2 (1) Genital pore at left edge of anterior half of body; ventral sucker usually equatorial, sometimes slightly displaced anteriorly; ovary at level of ventral sucker; vitellaria occupying wide field, concentrated in anterior half of body.

Laterotrema Semenov, 1928 (fig. 24)

KEY TO THE SPECIES OF THE GENUS STOMYLOTREMA LOOSS, 1900 (I:283)

K. I. Skrjabin

1 (2) Considerable number of vitelline follicles on each side of body; eggs: 0.034 x 0.019 mm.

S. perpastum Braun, 1902 (fig. 23)

2 (1) Number of vitelline follicles constant, seven on poral side and nine on aporal side.

3 (4) Vitellaria horseshoe-shaped; eggs exceptionally small: 0.019 x 0.014-0.018 mm.

S. bijugum M. Braun, 1901

4 (3) Vitellaria of different shape; egg length exceeding 0.02 mm.

5 (10) Testes partially extra-cecal.

6 (7) Vitellaria extending to posterior end of body; eggs: 0.0228 x 0.014 mm. Parasites of Caprimulgus sp. and Squatarola helvetica. S. fastosum Braun, 1901

7 (6) Vitellaria extending to level of middle of ventral sucker; egg length exceeding 0.025 mm.

8 (9) Intestinal ceca at level of testes, bending medially; eggs: 0.028 x 0.021 mm. Parasites of passerine birds (thrushes).

S. gratiosus Travassos, 1922

9 (8) Intestinal ceca straight; eggs: 0.032-0.033 x 0.017-0.018 mm. Parasites of snipes.

S. spasskii Sobolev, 1943

10 (5) Testes inter-cecal.

11 (12) Oral sucker slightly larger than ventral; cirrus sac S-shaped; eggs: 0.0228-0.025 x 0.011-0.014 mm. Parasites of swallows (Brazil).

S. tagax Braun, 1901

12 (11) Oral sucker slightly smaller than ventral; cirrus sac straight.

13 (16) Vitellaria extending posteriorly beyond posterior border of ventral sucker.

14 (15) Cirrus sac 1.166 mm. long; oral and ventral suckers exceeding 1.0 mm. in diameter. Parasites of storks.   S. pictum (Creplin, 1837)

15 (14) Cirrus sac 0.8 mm. long; diameters of oral and ventral suckers less than 1.0 mm. Parasites of Artamus fuscus.   S. travassosi Mehra, 1938

16 (13) Vitellaria not passing posteriorly beyond posterior edge of ventral sucker.

17 (18) Eggs: 0.032-0.034 x 0.020 mm.; oral sucker without cylindrical outgrowth protruding into aperture of sucker. Parasites of Hypotaenidia (Philippines).

S. rotunda Tubangui, 1928

18 (17) Eggs: 0.0228 x 0.014 mm.; oral sucker with cylindrical outgrowth protruding into aperture of sucker. Parasites of ibises (Brazil).

S. vicarium Braun, 1901

KEY TO THE SUBGENERA OF THE GENUS LATEROTREMA SEMENOV, 1928 (I:295)

K. I. Skrjabin

1 (2) Uterine loops in posterior part of body and passing in lesser quantities anterior to ventral sucker; ovary anterior to right testis, not directly in contact.   Laterotrema (Semenov, 1928) (fig. 24)

2 (1) Uterine loops confined wholly within posterior half of body, posterior to ventral sucker; ovary in contact with right testis.

Pseudolaterotrema Yamaguti, 1939

KEY TO THE SUBFAMILIES OF THE FAMILY ECHINOSTOMATIDAE DIETZ, 1909 from Skrjabin and Schulz (1938) (I:312)

1 (12) Anal appendage absent.

2 (9) Cephalic collar with spines present.

3 (4) Oral sucker wholly reduced; pharynx only muscular organ in cephalic end. Liver parasites of birds.   Pegosomatinae Skrjabin and Schulz, 1938

4 (3) Oral sucker present. Parasites of digestive tracts, more rarely of fabrician bursa of birds and mammals.

5 (6) Cirrus sac extending beyond posterior edge of ventral sucker; single row of spines on cephalic collar; ventral cylinder of cephalic collar lacking; pars prostatica present.   Himasthlinae Odhner, 1911

6 (5) Cirrus sac not passing beyond posterior edge of ventral sucker.

7 (8) Cephalic spines forming single or double row, not interrupted dorsally; ventral cylinder of cephalic collar present; pars prostatica present or absent.

Echinostomatinae Odhner, 1911

8 (7) Cephalic spines in single row, interrupted dorsally; ventral cylinder of cephalic collar lacking; pars prostatica present.

Echinochasminae Odhner, 1911

9 (2) Cephalic collar with spines wholly reduced.

10 (11) Canal of Mesaulus running from posterior edge of ventral sucker to posterior end of body, straight; ventral sucker sessile.

Cotylotretinae Skrjabin and Schulz, 1938

11 (10) Canal of Mesaulus absent; ventral sucker pedunculate. Parasites of beavers.

Stephanoproraoidinae Skrjabin and Schulz, 1938

12 (1) Constricted anal appendage present, more or less sharply delineated from body.

13 (14) Body sub-divided into three sections: narrowly tapering anterior and posterior sections extending from leaf-shaped middle section; cephalic collar weakly developed, with well developed spines; ventral sucker in posterior half of body. Parasites of birds. Chaunocephalinae Travassos, 1922

14 (13) Body sub-divided into two sections: expanded, leaf-shaped anterior part, and elongate anal appendage; cephalic collar lacking; corner spines present, lateral to flattened cephalic end; ventral sucker at boundary of anterior and posterior sections of body. Sodaliinae Skrjabin and Schulz, 1938

KEY TO THE GENERA OF THE SUBFAMILY ECHINOSTOMATINAE ODHNER, 1911 (I:315)

E. Ya. Bashkirova

1 (20) Cephalic collar well developed.
2 (5) Cephalic collar with dorsal and ventral cavity.
3 (4) Cephalic collar with weakly expressed dorsal cavity; cephalic spines forming single, dorsally continuous row. Nephrostomum Dietz, 1909 (fig. 25)
4 (3) Cephalic collar with deep, narrow dorsal cavity; cephalic spines forming single row, interrupted dorsally. Patagifer Dietz, 1909 (fig. 26)
5 (2) Cephalic collar with ventral cavity only, (dorsal cavity lacking).
6 (19) Cephalic collar reniform, with well-developed dorso-ventral lobes, and continuous, double row of spines.
7 (12) Uterus well developed; eggs numerous.
8 (9) Posterior part of body serrated laterally; each lateral projection with spine.
Prionosoma Dietz, 1909 (fig. 27)
9 (8) Posterior part of body not serrated laterally.
10 (11) Body without sharply constricted area anterior to ventral sucker, but rather broadly rounded, so that width of body anterior to ventral sucker considerably exceeds width of cephalic collar; suckers very close together.
Skrjabinophora Baschkirova, 1941 (fig. 28)
11 (10) Body anterior to ventral sucker constricted so that width less than that of cephalic collar; suckers not close together.
Echinostoma Rudolphi, 1819 (fig. 29)
12 (7) Uterus weakly developed, with few eggs.
13 (14) Small parasites with thick bodies, testes usually transversely elongate, oblique or symmetrical. Petasiger Dietz, 1909 (fig. 30)
14 (13) Parasites of medium or large dimensions; testes usually longitudinally elongate, tandem.
15 (16) Parasites with massive bodies; testes extensively lobed. Paryphostomum Dietz, 1909 (fig. 31)
16 (15) Parasites with thin, delicate bodies; testes entire, or slightly indented.
17 (18) Vitellaria usually displaced toward posterior end of body. Euparyphium Dietz, 1909 (fig. 32)
18 (17) Vitellaria extending anteriorly to level of ventral sucker.
Echinoparyphium Dietz, 1909 (fig. 33)

19 (6) Cephalic collar half-moon shaped, with weakly expressed ventral lobes; cephalic spines forming single dorsally continuous row.
Drepanocephalus Dietz, 1909 (fig. 34)
20 (1) Cephalic collar weakly developed.
21 (22) Cephalic collar transversely oval, covered with spines in double, dorsally continuous row; suckers close together.
Hypoderaeum Dietz, 1909 (fig. 35)
22 (21) Cephalic collar rudimentary, composed of two weakly expressed protuberances lateral to large oral sucker; cephalic spines in double, dorsally interrupted row; suckers not close together.
Microparyphium Dietz, 1909 (fig. 36)

KEY TO THE GENERA OF THE SUBFAMILY HIMASTHLINAE ODHNER, 1911 (I:342)

E. Ya. Bashkirova

1 (12) Eggs without filaments.
2 (7) Cephalic spines forming single row.
3 (4) Groups of ventral corner spines present; uterus with numerous eggs.
Himasthla Dietz, 1909 (fig. 37)
4 (3) Groups of ventral corner spines absent; uterus with few eggs.
5 (6) Testes lobed; vitellaria extending anteriorly to level of testes. Cleophora Dietz, 1909 (fig. 38)
6 (5) Testes entire; vitellaria usually extending anteriorly to level of cirrus sac, but infrequently extending only to level of testes.
Acanthoparyphium Dietz, 1909 (fig. 39)
7 (2) Cephalic spines forming double row.
8 (11) Testes lobed, or branched.
9 (10) Testes lobed; vitellaria extending anteriorly to cirrus sac.
Artyfechinostomum Lane, 1915 (fig. 40)
10 (9) Testes branched; vitellaria extending anteriorly to ventral sucker.
Reptiliotrema Baschkirova, 1941 (fig. 41)
11 (8) Testes round; vitellaria not extending beyond level of testes anteriorly.
Pelmatostomum Dietz, 1909 (fig. 42)
12 (1) Eggs with filaments; vitellaria extending anteriorly to level of testes.
Aporchis Stossich, 1909 (fig. 43)

KEY TO THE GENERA OF THE SUBFAMILY ECHINOCHASMINAE ODHNER, 1911 (I:356)

E. Ya. Bashkirova

1 (2) Male genital pore at tip of special papilla.
Allechinostomum Odhner, 1911 (fig. 44)
2 (1) Genital papilla lacking.
3 (4) Parasites with narrow, elongate bodies; testes longitudinally elongate; anterior boundary of vitellaria reaching only to level of testes.
Mesorchis Dietz, 1909 (fig. 45)
4 (3) Parasites of small or medium dimensions,

with broad, posteriorly-rounded bodies; testes round or transversely elongate; anterior boundary of vitellaria variable in position.

5 (6) Anterior part of body elongate; testes round; vitellaria extending anteriorly to level of ventral sucker.   Heterechinostomum Odhner, 1911

6 (5) Anterior part of body not elongate; testes transversely elongate; anterior boundary of vitellaria variable in position.

Echinochasmus Dietz, 1909 (fig. 47)

KEY TO THE SUBGENERA OF THE GENUS ECHINOCHASMUS DIETZ, 1909 (I:364)

E. Ya. Bashkirova

1 (4) Vitellaria well-developed, right and left groups of vitelline follicles merging at point anterior to intestinal bifurcation.

2 (3) Vitellaria originating at level of pharynx, and extending posteriorly to posterior end of body. Parasites of fabrician bursae (rarely of intestines) of birds.   Episthmium (Lühe, 1909) Baschkirova, 1941

3 (2) Vitellaria originating at level of intestinal bifurcation, and extending to posterior end of body. Intestinal parasites of mammals.

Episthochasmus (Verma, 1935) Baschkirova, 1941

4 (1) Vitelline follicles not merging anterior to intestinal bifurcation.

5 (6) Vitellaria originating at level of ventral sucker, and extending to posterior end of body. Intestinal parasites of birds and mammals.

Echinochasmus (Dietz, 1909) Baschkirova, 1941
(fig. 47)

6 (5) Vitellaria originating at level of testes, extending to posterior end of body. Intestinal parasites of birds.   Monilifer (Dietz, 1909) Baschkirova, 1941

KEY TO THE GENERA OF THE SUBFAMILY CHAUNOCEPHALINAE TRAVASSOS, 1922 (I:377)

E. Ya. Bashkirova

1 (2) Anterior part of body greatly constricted; globular swelling present anterior to ventral sucker; uterus long, occupying entire anterior part of body.
Balfouria Leiper, 1908 (fig. 48)

2 (1) Anterior part of body globular; uterus short, posterior to ventral sucker.

Chaunocephalus Dietz, 1909 (fig. 49)

KEY TO THE GENERA OF THE SUBFAMILY COTYLOTRETINAE SKRJABIN AND SCHULZ, 1938 (I:383)

E. Ya. Bashkirova

1 (2) Ventral sucker unusually large, occupying nearly entire width of body; cephalic collar absent; cuticular armament lacking.
Cotylotretus Odhner, 1902 (fig. 50)

2 (1) Ventral sucker small; cephalic collar lacking spines, represented by two small protuberances along sides of oral sucker; cuticular armament present. Pseudoechinostomum Odhner, 1911 (fig. 51)

LITERATURE ON THE TREMATODES OF THE FAMILY ECHINOSTOMATIDAE DIETZ, 1909 (I:384-389)

Soloviev, P. F. 1912. Parasitic worms of birds of Turkestan. Ezhegodnik Zoologicheskogo Muzeya Imperatorskoy Akad. Nauk. 17(2):86-115.

Skrjabin, K. I. 1915. Trematodes of birds of the Urals. Ezhegodnik Zoologicheskogo Muzeya Akad. Nauk SSSR. 20(3):395-417.

Skrjabin, K. I. 1916. On the knowledge of the helminth fauna of domestic animals of Turkestan. Dissertatsiya, Yuriev.

Skrjabin, K. I. 1919. Trematodes of the fabrician bursa of birds of the Don region. Trudy Obschestva Veterinarnikh Vrachey Vsevelikogo Voyska Donskogo. No. 1:15-29.

Skrjabin, K. I. and G. T. Lindtrop. 1919. Intestinal trematodes of dogs of the Don district. Izvestiya Donskogo Veterinarnogo Instituta. 1(1):30-43.

Skrjabin, K. I. and N. P. Zakharov. 1919. Results of the initial research on the helminth fauna of the Don district. Trudy Obschestva Veterinarnykh Vrachey Donskoy Oblasti. No. 1:1-25.

Skrjabin, K. I. 1920. Helminthological notes. On the knowledge of the helminth fauna of birds of Russia. Izvestiya Donskogo Veterinarnogo Instituta. 2(2):1-7.

Skrjabin, K. I. 1923. Trematodes of poultry. Trudy Gelmintologicheskogo Instituta Experimentalnoy Veterinarii. 1(2):193-256.

Kalantaryan, E. V. 1924. On the knowledge of the trematodes of birds in the vicinity of Erevan. Trudy Tropicheskogo Instituta Armenii. 1:74-75.

Isaychikov, I. M. 1925. A new representative of avian trematodes of the genus Echinoparyphium Dietz, 1909. Uchenye Trudy Sibirskogo Veterinarnogo Instituta. No. 6:5-16.

Petrov, A. M. 1926. On the fauna of parasitic worms of domestic and wild geese of the Don district. Trudy Gosudarstvennogo Instituta Experimentalnoy Veterinarii. 3(1):99-113.

Ivanitsky, S. V. 1927-28. On the trematode fauna of vertebrates of the Ukraine. Veterinarne Dilo. No. 5(42):36-42.; No. 2(51):30-48.

Isaychikov, I. M. 1927. A rare parasite of Crimean birds. Trudy Sibirskogo Veterinarnogo Instituta. No. 9:111-115.

Kurova, O. A. 1927. On the knowledge of the trematodes of the family Echinostomatidae from birds of Turkestan. Ezhegodnik Zoologicheskogo Muzeya Akad. Nauk SSSR. 27(2-3):113.

Pukhov, V. I. 1928. On the fauna of parasitic worms of coots. Rukopis, VIGIS, Moskva.

Semenov, V. D. 1927. Trematodes of birds of western U.S.S.R. Sbornik Rabot po

Gelmintologii, Posvyaschenny K. I. Skrjabinu. pp. 221-271.

Scherbovich, I. A. 1928. On the fauna of trematodes and cestodes of birds of the Far East of the U.S.S.R. Rukopis, VIGIS, Moskva.

Murashkintsev, N. S. 1930. A new trematode from domestic hen. Rukopis, VIGIS, Moskva.

Skrjabin, K. I. 1932. Helminth infestations of pigeons. Selkhozgiz, Moskva. 124 pp.

Skvortsov, A. A. 1934. On the study of the helminth fauna of water rats. Vestnik Mikrobiologii, i Parazitologii, Saratov. 13(4):317-326.

Burdelev, T. E. 1938. A new species of trematode, Echinoparyphium syrdariensis from domestic hen. Sbornik Rabot po Gelmintologii, Posvyaschenny 30-letiyu Deyatelnosti Akademika K. I. Skrjabina. pp. 63-65.

Efimov, A. V. 1937. The helminth fauna of several farm animals of the Tatar Republic. Rukopis, VIGIS, Moskva.

Palimpsestov, A. M. 1937. On the agents of helminthiases of domestic animals in the Mordovian Autotomy, Kuybyshev and Orenburg districts. Sbornik Rabot po Gelminthologii, Posvyaschenny 30-letiyu Deyatelnosti Akademika K. I. Skrjabina. pp. 454-458.

Fedyushin, A. V. 1937. The helminth fauna of geese and ducks of western Siberia, with reference to the problem of utilizing natural bodies of water for purposes of poultry production. Sbornik Rabot po Gelmintologii, Posvyaschenny 30-letiyu Deyatelnosti Akademika K. I. Skrjabina pp. 167-177.

Elperin, M. A. 1937. A new species of trematode from Falco tinunculus, Echinoparyphium jubilarum. Rukopis, VIGIS, Moskva.

Vildanov, M. G. 1938. The helminth fauna of poultry of the Bashkir A.S.S.R. Trudy Bashkirskoy Gelminthologicheskoy Expeditsii. pp. 360-371.

Gnedina, M. P. 1938. On the trematode fauna of birds of the Moscow Zoological Park. Rukopis, VIGIS, Moskva.

Gorshkov, I. P. 1938. On the knowledge of the helminth fauna of domestic geese of the Omsk and Chelyabinsk districts. Sbornik Rabot po Gelmintologii, Posvyaschenny 30-letiyu Deyatelnosti Akademika K. I. Skrjabina. pp. 191-202.

Matevosyan, I. M. 1938. The helminth fauna of wild birds of Bashkiria. Trudy Bashkirskoy Gelmintologicheskoy Expeditsii. pp. 372-391.

Skrjabin, K. I. 1938. Echinostoma paraulum, a new parasite of man. Meditsinskaya Parazitologiya i Parazitarnye Bolezni. 7(1):129-138.

Strom, Zh. K. 1938. On the trematode fauna of animals of the Lenkoran region (Azerbaydzhan). Rukopis, VIGIS, Moskva.

Bashkirova, E. Ya. 1941. Echinostomatids of birds of the U.S.S.R., and a review of their life cycles. Trudy Bashkirskoy Nauchno-Issledovatelskoy Veterinarnoy Stantsii. 3:243-300.

KEY TO THE SPECIES OF THE GENUS

ECHINOSTOMA RUDOLPHI, 1809 (of birds)
(I:393)

K. I. Skrjabin, A. M. Petrov, and E. Ya. Bashkirova

1 (4) Less than thirty cephalic spines present.
2 (3) Twenty-seven cephalic spines present; body dimension: 9.5-10 x 1.25 mm. Host: Strix aluco, others (Central Europe). E. stridulae (Reich, 1801)
3 (2) Twenty-nine cephalic spines present; body dimensions: 2.08 x 0.60 mm. Host: Labivanellus lobatus (Australia). E. ignavum Nicoll, 1914
4 (1) More than thirty cephalic spines present.
5 (12) Not more than thirty-three cephalic spines present.
6 (7) Thirty-one cephalic spines present; length of spines: 0.034-0.055 mm. Hosts: Ephippiorhynchus senegalensis, others (Egypt).
E. sudanense Odhner, 1911
7 (6) Thirty-three cephalic spines present.
8 (9) Ventral corner spines larger than dorsal spines; dorsal spine sizes: 0.048 x 0.021 mm., ventral corner spine dimensions: 0.108 x 0.034 mm. Host: Plotus surinamensis (Brazil).
E. operosum Dietz, 1909
9 (8) Ventral corner spines larger than dorsal, or equal in length to dorsal spines.
10 (11) Ventral corner spines nearly equal in size to dorsal spines; length of corner spines: 0.125-0.133 mm.; dorsal spines: 0.125 mm.; body length: 9.0-9.8 mm.; testes entire. Host: Capella gallinago (USSR). E. stantschinskii Semenov, 1927
11 (12) Ventral corner spines smaller than dorsal; length of ventral corner spines: 0.127 mm.; length of dorsal spines: 0.159 mm.; body length; 19.8 mm.; testes with deep transverse groove. Host: Netta rufina (USSR). E. rufinae Kurova, 1922
12 (5) More than thirty-three cephalic spines present.
13 (32) Not more than thirty-seven cephalic spines (thirty-five or thirty-seven) present.
14 (19) Thirty-five cephalic spines present.
15 (18) Ventral corner spines and dorsal spines of collar nearly equal in dimensions.
16 (17) Body length: 3.75 mm.; vitellaria merging posterior to testes; egg dimensions: 0.086-0.093 x 0.053-0.057 mm. Host: Amblycercus solitarius (Brazil). E. distinctum Dietz, 1909
17 (16) Body length: 5.7 mm.; vitellaria not merging posterior to testes; egg dimensions: 0.091-0.109 x 0.067-0.072 mm. Host: black-winged plover (India). E. skattacharyai Verma, 1936
18 (15) Ventral corner spines larger than dorsal spines; length of ventral: 0.102-0.109 mm.; length of dorsal spines: 0.075-0.095 mm.; testes sausage-shaped. Hosts: Crotophaga ani and C. major (Brazil). E. uncatum Dietz, 1909
19 (14) Thirty-seven cephalic spines present.
20 (23) Vitellaria merging posterior to testes.
21 (22) Body length: 21-26 mm.; six spines on each corner lobe of collar; testes slightly lobed, up

to 1.30 mm. in length. Hosts: hens, ducks, others (Japan).   E. miyagawai Ishii, 1932

22 (21) Body length: 7.8-9.8 mm.; five spines present on each corner lobe of collar; testes deeply-lobed, transversely elongate, up to 0.62 mm. in length. Hosts: Columba livia, Streptopelia chinensis, others (Formosa, USSR).   E. robustum Yamaguti, 1935

23 (20) Vitellaria not merging posterior to testes.

24 (27) Body spines lacking.

25 (26) Body length 2.70-3.30 mm.; five corner spines present on each lobe of collar, dimensions: 0.048-0.060 x 0.01-0.012 mm.; diameter of ovary: 0.07-0.09 mm. Host: Milvus milvus (Central Europe).   E. echinocephalum (Rudolphi, 1819)

26 (25) Body length: 86 mm.; four corner spines on each lobe of collar, dimensions: 0.075-0.078 x 0.022-0.024 mm.; diameter of ovary: 0.27-0.31 mm. Host: Rallus aquaticus indicus (Japan).
                    E. ralli Yamaguti, 1934

27 (24) Body spines present.

28 (29) Testes with central constriction; cephalic spine length reaching 0.075 mm. Parasites of ducks (wild and domestic), pigeons, Podiceps cristatus, others (Central Europe, U.S.S.R., etc.).
                    E. paraulum Dietz, 1909

29 (28) Testes lacking central constriction.

30 (31) Dimensions of cephalic spines: 0.01-0.112 x 0.03-0.035 mm.; testes in anterior half of body. Host: Carphibis spinicollis (Australia).
                    E. acuticauda Nicoll, 1914

31 (30) Dimensions of cephalic spines: 0.049-0.119 x 0.009-0.035 mm.; testes in posterior half of body. Various hosts (Europe, Asia, America).
                    E. revolutum (Fröhlich, 1802) (fig. 29)

32 (13) More than thirty-seven cephalic spines present.

33 (42) Not more than forty-one cephalic spines (thirty-nine or forty-one) present.

34 (37) Thirty-nine cephalic spines present.

35 (36) Cuticular spines present; length of cephalic spines: 0.101-0.130 mm.; egg dimensions: 0.128 x 0.072 mm. Host: Tringa glareola (USSR).
                    E. uralensis Skrjabin, 1915

36 (35) Cuticular spines absent; length of cephalic spines: 0.047-0.075 mm.; egg dimensions: 0.084-0.087 x 0.048-0.050 mm. Host: Porphryio martinicus (Brazil).   E. aphilactum Dietz, 1909

37 (34) Cephalic spines forty-one in number.

38 (41) Spines present on body.

39 (40) Cuticular spines extending to level of testes; length of cephalic spines: 0.060-0.095 mm.; testes long, sinuous. Hosts: Tinamus variegatus, etc.   E. siticulosum Dietz, 1909

40 (39) Cuticular spines extending to ventral sucker; length of cephalic spines: 0.028-0.053 mm.; testes imperfectly circular, lobed. Host: Netta rufina (USSR).   E. turkestanicum Kurova, 1923

41 (38) Spines on body lacking; length of cephalic spines: 0.061-0.068 mm.; testes elongate, root-like. Host: Porphyrio parvus (Brazil).
                    E. alepidotum Dietz, 1909

42 (33) More than forty-one cephalic spines present.

43 (48) Not more than forty-five cephalic spines (forty-three or forty-five) present.

44 (47) Forty-three cephalic spines present.

45 (46) Body length 8.5 mm.; ventral corner spines larger than dorsal cephalic spines; length of ventral spines: 0.148 mm.; cuticle armed; length of genital bursa: 0.34 mm. Host: Limosa limosa (USSR).
                    E. academica Skrjabin, 1915

46 (45) Body length: 17.10 mm.; ventral corner spines (0.053 mm. in length) shorter than dorsal spines; cuticular armament lacking; length of genital bursa: 1.14 mm. Host: Corvus corone (USSR).
                    E. coronale Kurova, 1923

47 (44) Forty-five cephalic spines present; body length; 19.10-21.23 mm.; vitellaria merging posterior to testes. Hosts: Coot and domestic goose (USSR).   E. dietzi Skrjabin, 1923

48 (43) Forty-seven to fifty-one cephalic spines present.

49 (60) Forty-seven cephalic spines present.

50 (53) Testes with special shape (elongate, twisted along longitudinal axis).

51 (52 Length of cephalic spines: 0.100-0.115 mm.; eggs: 0.120-0.130 x 0.07-0.075 mm. Host: Porphyrio melanotus (Australia).
                    E. hilliferum Nicoll, 1914

52 (51) Length of cephalic spines: 0.073-0.094 mm.; eggs: 0.107-0.110 x 0.051-0.064 mm. Host: Corvus corone cornix (USSR).
                    E. travassosi Skrjabin, 1924

53 (50) Testes elongate, either entire or with indentations.

54 (57) Cephalic spines large.

55 (56) Length of cephalic spines: 0.077-0.147 mm.; spines present on body; length of testes: 0.77-1.20 mm. Host: Geronticus coerulescens (Brazil).
                    E. necopinum Dietz, 1909

56 (55) Length of cephalic spines: 0.068-0.156 mm.; spines on body lacking; length of testes: 1.50-2.28 mm. Host: Grus grus (Central Europe).
                    E. sarcinum Dietz, 1909

57 (54) Cephalic spines small.

58 (59) Length of cephalic spines: 0.033-0.057 mm.; transverse diameter of ventral sucker: 0.072-0.073 mm.; length of testes: 0.55-0.60 mm. Host: Gallinula chloropus, others (Europe).
                    E. chloropodis (Zeder, 1800)

59 (58) Cephalic spines 0.048-0.084 mm. long; transverse diameter of ventral sucker: 1.25 mm.; length of testes: 1.38-1.80 mm. Host: Corvus corone (Japan).   E. corvi Yamaguti, 1935

60 (49) More than forty-seven cephalic spines present.

61 (64) Forty-nine cephalic spines present.

62 (63) Body dimensions: 7.0-13.5 x 0.35-1.30 mm.; diameter of oral sucker: 0.16-0.19 mm.; ventral sucker: 0.52-0.73 mm.; length of testes: 0.52-0.83 mm. Host: Hydropsalis torquata, others (Brazil).   E. condiguum Dietz, 1909

63 (62) Body dimensions: 11.76 x 2.07 mm.;

diameter of oral sucker: 0.42 mm.; of ventral: 1.20 mm.; length of testes: 1.20-1.44 mm. Host: domestic hen (USSR).   E. coecale Muraschkinzew, 1937

64 (61) Fifty-one cephalic spines present; length of spines: 0.060-0.112 mm. Host: Fulica armillata (Brazil).   E. transfretanum Dietz, 1909

KEY TO THE SPECIES OF THE GENUS ECHINOPARYPHIUM DIETZ, 1909 from Baschkirova (1941) (I:421)

1 (36) Parasites of birds.

2 (29) More than thirty-three spines present on cephalic collar.

3 (10) Thirty-seven cephalic spines present.

4 (9) Body spines present.

5 (6) Body length not exceeding 3 mm.; length of cephalic spines: 0.028-0.049 mm. Hosts: Vanellus vanellus, others (Europe).   E. aconiatum Dietz, 1909

6 (5) Body length not less than 5 mm.

7 (8) Maximum body width: up to 0.38 mm.; length of cirrus sac: up to 0.250 mm. Hosts: Helodromus ochropus, Vanellus vanellus.
E. politum Skrjabin, 1915

8 (7) Maximal body width up to 1.44 mm.; length of cirrus sac up to 0.781 mm. Host: Mareca penelope.
E. nordiana Baschkirova, 1941

9 (4) Body spines absent; maximal body width: 0.75 mm. Host: Columba livia.
E. schulzi Mathevossian, 1939

10 (3) More than thirty-seven spines present on cephalic collar.

11 (14) Forty-one cephalic spines present.

12 (13) Oral and aboral spines of cephalic collar of equal length; length of cirrus sac: 0.11-0.13 mm. Host: Helodromus ochropus.
E. clerci Skrjabin, 1915

13 (12) Oral spines smaller than aboral spines (oral: 0.040-0.059 mm.; aboral: 0.058-0.067 mm.); length of cirrus sac: 0.36-0.38 mm. Host: domestic hen.   E. vestsibiricum Issaitschikov, 1924

14 (11) More than forty-one cephalic spines present.

15 (22) Forty-three cephalic spines present.

16 (21) Oral and aboral cephalic spines of unequal dimensions.

17 (18) Body length not exceeding 3 mm.; length of ventral sucker: 0.33 mm. Host: Phoenicopterus roseus (Egypt).   E. elegans (Looss, 1899) (fig. 33)

18 (17) Body length not less than 4.5 mm.

19 (20) Body dimensions: 4.55 x 0.962 mm.; length of pharynx: 0.087 mm.; testes irregularly oval. Host: domestic hen. E. syrdariensis Burdelev, 1937

20 (15) Body dimensions: 6.00-8.20 x 0.920-1.20 mm.; length of pharynx: 0.132-0.154 mm.; testes elongate, oval. Host: Mergellus albellus.
E. syrdariensis aquatica Baschkirova, 1941

21 (16) Oral and aboral spines of equal size; body length: 1.76-2.52 mm. Hosts: anatids, sandpipers, others (Central Europe). E. cinctum (Rudolphi, 1802)

22 (15) Forty-five cephalic spines present.

23 (28) Body covered with spines.

24 (25) Spines limited to anterior portion of body; length of ventral sucker: 0.33-0.36 mm. Hosts: doves, pigeons, galliformes, others (Europe).
E. recurvatum (Linstow, 1873)

25 (24) Entire body covered with spines.

26 (27) Length of cephalic, corner spines: 0.035 mm.; length of oral sucker: 0.06 mm. Host: Parra africana (Egypt).   E. niloticum Odhner, 1911

27 (26) Length of corner, cephalic spines: 0.087 mm.; length of oral sucker: 0.119 mm. Host: Helodromus ochropus (USSR).
E. mordwilkoi Skrjabin, 1915

28 (23) Body not covered with spines: body length: up to 3.0 mm.; oral and aboral spines unequal in size. Hosts: geese, doves, pigeons, others.
E. baculus (Diesing, 1850)

29 (2) Not more than thirty-three cephalic spines present.

30 (33) Thirty-three cephalic spines present.

31 (32) Entire body armed with spines; length of ventral sucker: 0.651-0.8 mm. Host: Theresticus hagedash (Egypt).   E. volvulus Odhner, 1911

32 (31) Body armed with spines anteriorly; length of ventral sucker: 0.32 mm. Host: Buteo buteo, others (Central Europe).   E. agnatum Dietz, 1909

33 (30) Less than thirty-three cephalic spines present.

34 (35) Twenty-seven cephalic spines present; body not armed with spines. Host: Cerchneis tinnunculus.
E. jubilarum Elperin, 1937

35 (34) Nineteen cephalic spines present; body armed with spines anteriorly. Host: Podiceps ruficollis japonicus (Japan).   E. brevicauda Ishii, 1935

36 (1) Parasites of mammals.

37 (40) Thirty-seven cephalic spines present.

38 (39) Body dimensions: 3.3-4.3 x 0.56-0.7 mm.; dimensions of ovary: 0.16-0.19 x 0.14-0.15 mm. Host: Ondatra zibethica (America).
E. condiguum Barker and Bastron, 1915

39 (38) Body dimensions: 8.91-9.59 x 1.15-1.44 mm.; dimensions of ovary: 0.27-0.42 x 0.23-0.48 mm. Host: Arvicola terrestris.
E. sisjakovi Skvortzov, 1934

40 (36) Thirty-five cephalic spines present; body not armed with spines. Host: Rattus norvegicus (Japan).   E. japonicum Ando and Ozaki, 1923

KEY TO THE SPECIES OF THE GENUS HYPODERAEUM DIETZ, 1909 from Baschkirova (I:442)

1 (4) Not less than forty-seven cephalic spines present.

2 (3) Vitellaria lateral and merging at point posterior to testes; body length: up to 7 mm.; forty-nine cephalic spines present; ratio of sucker dimensions: 1.5. Host: Querquedula crecca (USSR).
H. gnedini Baschkirova, 1941

3 (2) Vitellaria not merging posterior to testes; body length up to 12 mm.; forty-seven to fifty-three cephalic spines present; sucker ratio: 1.4. Hosts:

various Anatidae, others (Central Europe, Asia).
                    H. conoideum (Bloch, 1782) (fig. 35)
    4 (1) Forty-three cephalic spines present; body
length up to 13 mm.; dimensions of genital bursa:
1.10-1.32 x 0.517 mm. Hosts: Erolia ferruginosa,
Nyroca marila.   H. vigi Baschkirova, 1941

KEY TO THE SPECIES OF THE GENUS
PARYPHOSTOMUM DIETZ, 1909 from Baschkirova
(I:446)

    1 (8) Twenty-seven cephalic spines present.
    2 (3) Testes with four to six lobes, rosette-shaped.
Host: Phalacrocorax carbo (USSR, Central Europe).
                    P. radiatum (Dujardin, 1845) (fig. 31)
    3 (2) Testes lobed, with one lobe directed poste-
riorly.
    4 (5) Body length not exceeding 2.5 mm.; cephalic
spines in a double row. Host: Phalacrocorax africanus (Egypt).   P. lobulatum Odhner, 1911
    5 (4) Body length not less than 3.5 mm.
    6 (7) Testes with five to seven lobes; cephalic
spines 0.108-0.142 mm. long. Hosts: Catharista
atrata, others (Brazil).   P. segregatum Dietz, 1909
    7 (6) Testes cardiform, tri-lobed; cephalic spines
0.064-0.121 mm. long. Host: Dendrocygna javanica,
others (India, USSR).   P. testitrifolium Gogate, 1934
    8 (1) More than twenty-seven spines present.
    9 (10) Thirty-five cephalic spines present; body
length up to 19 mm. Host: sandpipers (India).
                    P. pentalobum Verma, 1936
    10 (9) Thirty-seven cephalic spines present; body
length up to 11 mm. Hosts: Anas platyrhyncha and
Anser indicus (India).   P. novum Verma, 1936

KEY TO THE SUBGENERA OF THE GENUS
PETASIGER DIETZ, 1909 from Baschkirova
(1941) (I:454)

    1 (2) Testes tandem.
                    Petasiger (Dietz, 1909) (fig. 30)
    2 (1) Testes oblique, nearly symmetrical or sym-
metrical.   Neopetasiger Baschkirova, 1941

KEY TO THE SPECIES OF THE SUBGENUS
PETASIGER (DIETZ, 1909) from Baschkirova (I:454)

    1 (4) Cephalic spines in double row.
    2 (3) Twenty-seven cephalic spines present; vitel-
laria extending from intestinal bifurcation or anterior
edge of ventral sucker to posterior end of body.
Hosts: Phalacrocorax carbo, P. pygmaeus (Central
Europe).   P. exaeretus Dietz, 1909 (fig. 30)
    3 (2) Nineteen to twenty-one spines present on ce-
phalic collar; vitellaria extending from anterior edge
of ventral sucker to posterior end of body. Host:
Colymbus nigricans (Germany).
                    P. pungens Linstow, 1883
    4 (1) Cephalic spines in single row.
    5 (6) Testes lobed, transversely elongate; vitellaria
extending from anterior edge of ventral sucker to

posterior end of body. Host: Podiceps ruficollis
japonicus (Japan).   P. lobatus Yamaguti, 1933
    6 (5) Testes entire, imperfectly round; vitellaria
extending from intestinal bifurcation to posterior end
of body. Host: Podiceps cristatus (Hungary).
                    P. megacanthum Kotlan, 1923

KEY TO THE SPECIES OF THE SUBGENUS
NEOPETASIGER BASCHKIROVA, 1941 from
Baschkirova (I:456)

    1 (12) Cephalic spines in a single row.
    2 (7) Testes oblique.
    3 (6) Nineteen spines present.
    4 (5) Vitellaria confluent medially at level of intes-
tinal bifurcation; testes near posterior end of body.
Host: Podiceps ruficollis (Japan).
                    P. (N.) grandivesicularis Ishii, 1935
    5 (4) Vitellaria not confluent anterior to ventral
sucker; testes midway between center of ventral
sucker and posterior end of body. Host: Columbus
auritus (America).   P. (N.) nitidus Linton, 1928
    6 (3) Twenty-three spines present; vitellaria ex-
tending from posterior edge of ventral sucker to posterior end of body, filling all space posterior to
testes. Host: Dendrocygna javanica (India).
                    P. (N.) minutissimus Gogate, 1934
    7 (2) Testes symmetrical.
    8 (11) Nineteen spines present.
    9 (10) Scales present on surface of anterior part of
body; vitellaria weakly developed, lateral, not filling
space posterior to testes. Hosts: Podiceps cristatus,
P. griseigena (Switzerland, USSR).
                    P. (N.) neocomense Fuhrmann, 1927
    10 (9) Scales lacking on anterior portion of body;
vitellaria well-developed, extending from intestinal
bifurcation to posterior end of body, filling space
posterior to testes. Host: Querquedula crecca
(USSR).   P. (N.) skrjabini Baschkirova, 1941
    11 (8) Nineteen to twenty-two cephalic spines pres-
ent; testes oblique or symmetrical; vitellaria extending from anterior edge of ventral sucker to posterior
end of body. Host: Puffinus kuhli (Italy).
                    P. (N.) magniovatus (Stossich, 1898)
    12 (1) Twenty-seven cephalic spines present, in
double row; testes small, oblique. Host: Phalacrocorax carbo (Egypt).
                    P. (N.) variospinosum Odhner, 1911

KEY TO THE SPECIES OF THE GENUS
PATAGIFER DIETZ, 1909 from Baschkirova (I:458)

    1 (4) Width of cephalic collar less than width of an-
terior portion of body.
    2 (3) Fifty to fifty-two cephalic spines present;
length of corner cephalic spines: 0.09-0.0119 mm.;
of lateral spines: 0.07-0.102 mm.; of dorsal spines:
0.025 mm. Host: Podiceps ruficollis (Japan).
                    P. parvispinosus Yamaguti, 1933
    3 (2) Fifty-two to fifty-eight cephalic spines pres-
ent; spine lengths: corner, 0.067 mm.; dorsal,

0.027-0.034 mm.; lateral, 0.047-0.108 mm. Host: Geronticus coerulescens. P. consimilis Dietz, 1909

4 (1) Width of cephalic collar exceeding width of anterior portion of body.

5 (6) Fifty-two to sixty-two spines present; spine lengths: corner, 0.081-0.143 mm.; dorsal, 0.024-0.110 mm.; lateral, 0.074-0.165 mm. Hosts: Plegadis falcinellus, Platalea leucorodia, others (Europe, Asia, America).
P. bilobus Dietz, 1909 (fig. 26)

6 (5) Sixty to sixty-two cephalic spines present; spine lengths: corner, 0.156 mm.; dorsal, 0.03 mm.; lateral, 0.024-0.027 mm. Host: glossy ibis (India).
P. westley Verma, 1936

KEY TO THE GENERA OF THE SUBFAMILY ECHINOCHASMINAE ODHNER, 1911 from Baschkirova (I:466)

1 (2) Male genital pore at tip of special papilla.
Allechinostomum Odhner, 1911 (fig. 44)

2 (1) Genital papilla absent.

3 (4) Parasites with narrow, elongate bodies; testes longitudinally elongate; anterior border of vitellaria reaching only to level of testes.
Mesorchis Dietz, 1909 (fig. 45)

4 (3) Small or medium sized parasites with broadly rounded posterior portion of body; testes round or transversely elongate; anterior border of vitellaria variable in position.

5 (6) Anterior portion of body elongate; testes round; vitellaria reaching ventral sucker anteriorly.
Heterechinostomum Odhner, 1911

6 (5) Anterior portion of body not elongate; testes transversely elongate; position of anterior border of vitellaria variable.
Echinochasmus Dietz, 1909 (fig. 47)

KEY TO THE SUBGENERA OF THE GENUS ECHINOCHASMUS DIETZ, 1909 from Baschkirova (I:469)

1 (4) Vitellaria well developed; lateral groups of follicles merging medially anterior to intestinal bifurcation.

2 (3) Vitellaria originating at level of pharynx and extending to posterior end of body. Parasites of fabrician bursa, more rarely of intestines, of birds.
Episthmium (Lühe, 1909) Baschkirova, 1941

3 (2) Vitellaria originating at level of intestinal bifurcation and extending to posterior end of body. Intestinal parasites of mammals.
Episthochasmus (Verma, 1935) Baschkirova, 1941

4 (1) Vitelline follicles not merging medially anterior to intestinal bifuraction.

5 (6) Vitellaria originating at level of ventral sucker and extending to posterior end of body. Intestinal parasites of mammals and birds.
Echinochasmus (Dietz, 1909) Baschkirova, 1941 (fig. 47)

6 (5) Vitellaria originating at level of testes and

extending to posterior end of body. Intestinal parasites of birds.
Monilifer (Dietz, 1909) Baschkirova, 1941

KEY TO THE SPECIES OF THE SUBGENUS ECHINOCHASMUS (DIETZ, 1909) from Baschkirova (I:469)

1 (16) Twenty-four cephalic spines present.

2 (5) Body length not exceeding 1 mm.

3 (4) Cuticular spines usually limited to anterior portion of body. Hosts: Ardea cinerea, A. ralloides, Nyticorax nycticorax.
E. (E.) beleocephalus (Linstow, 1873)

4 (3) Cuticular spines covering entire body. Hosts: predatory birds, Milvus parasiticus, M. aegypticus, others, as well as of mammals.
E. (E.) liliputanum (Looss, 1896)

5 (2) Body length exceeding 1 mm.

6 (7) Body length up to 2 mm.; cephalic spines: 0.021-0.035 mm. long, partially in double alternating row. Hosts: Ardea grayi, Nycticorax nycticorax (India).
E. (E.) bagulai Verma, 1935

7 (6) Body length exceeding 2 mm.

8 (9) Body length not exceeding 3 mm.; length of spines up to 0.054 mm. Hosts: Milvus parasiticus, M. korschun, Circus aeroginosus.
E. (E.) euryporus (Looss, 1896)

9 (8) Body length exceeding 3 mm.

10 (13) Corner spines of cephalic collar not in distinct ventral groups.

11 (12) Testes large, up to 0.63 mm. in length; eggs: 0.103-0.105 mm. long. Hosts: mammals (dogs, cats, foxes) (Hungary, USSR).
E. (E.) perfoliatus (Ratz, 1908)

12 (11) Testes small, up to 0.25 mm. in length, eggs: 0.08 mm. long. Host: Podiceps ruficollis (India).
E. (E.) ruficapensis Verma, 1935

13 (10) Corner spines of cephalic collar in distinct ventral groups.

14 (15) Two spines isolated on each ventral corner lobe of cephalic collar; sucker ratio: 1:5. Hosts: Botaurus stellaris, Phalacrocorax carbo, others (Hungary, USSR). E. (E.) amphibolus Kotlan, 1922

15 (14) Three spines isolated on each ventral corner lobe of cephalic collar; sucker ratio: approximately 1:3. Hosts: Podiceps cristatus, P. griseigena (Europe, USSR).
E. (E.) coaxatus Dietz, 1909 (fig. 47)

16 (1) Different number of cephalic spines present.

17 (20) Less than twenty-four cephalic spines present.

18 (19) Twenty cephalic spines present, with three spines located on each ventral corner lobe of cephalic collar. Host: Podiceps cristatus (USSR).
E. (E.) dietzevi Issaitschikov, 1927

19 (18) Twenty-two cephalic spines present, with two spines on each ventral corner lobe of cephalic collar. Host: Pelecanus crispus (USSR).
E. (E.) muraschkinzevi Baschkirova, 1941

20 (17) More than twenty-four spines present.

21 (22) Thirty cephalic spines present. Host: white rat (Japan).   E. (E.) rugosus Yamaguti, 1933

22 (21) Thirty-two cephalic spines present. Host: white rat (Japan).

E. (E.) redioduplicatus Yamaguti, 1933

KEY TO THE SPECIES OF THE SUBGENUS EPISTHMIUM (LÜHE, 1909) BASCHKIROVA, 1941 from Baschkirova (I:479)

1 (8) Cephalic collar well developed; cephalic spines relatively large.

2 (7) Twenty-four cephalic spines present.

3 (6) Cuticular spines covering entire body.

4 (5) Cirrus sac large, extending posteriorly beyond middle of ventral sucker; body length up to 2.5 mm. Intestinal parasites of Hieraciea orientalis (Australia).   E. (E.) prosthovitellatus (Nicoll, 1914)

5 (4) Cirrus sac small; body length up to 4.1 mm. Parasites of fabrician bursa of birds: Ardea cinerea, Botaurus stellaris, Circus aeruginosus, Porzana porzana.   E. (E.) intermedius Skrjabin, 1919

6 (3) Cuticular spines covering only anterior half of body (to level of testes); body length up to 8.0 mm. Parasites of fabrician bursa of Milvus parasiticus, Ibis hagedash.   E. (E.) africanum (Stiles, 1901)

7 (2) Twenty to twenty-four cephalic spines present; body length up to 3 mm. Parasites of fabrician bursa of birds: Ardea cinerea, A. purpurea (USSR).

E. (E.) bursicola (Creplin, 1837)

8 (1) Cephalic collar weakly developed, with very small spines.

9 (10) Diameter of ventral sucker: 0.34 mm.; testes: 0.4 x 0.5 mm. and 0.5 x 0.3 mm. Host: domestic hen (fabrician bursa) (Brazil).

E. (E.) oscari Travassos, 1903

10 (9) Diameter of ventral sucker: 0.64 mm.; testes: 0.1 x 0.6 and 1.0 x 0.7 mm. Hosts (fabrician bursa): Ardea cocoi, Euxenura maguari (Brazil).

E. (E.) proximum Travassos, 1923

KEY TO THE GENERA OF THE SUBFAMILY CHAUNOCEPHALINAE TRAVASSOS, 1922 from Baschkirova (I:483)

1 (2) Anterior portion of body greatly constricted; with globular swelling of body directly anterior to ventral sucker; uterus long and filling entire anterior portion of body.   Balfouria Leiper, 1908 (fig. 48)

2 (1) Anterior portion of body wholly globular; uterus short, posterior to ventral sucker.

Chaunocephalus Dietz, 1909 (fig. 49)

KEY TO THE SPECIES OF THE GENUS CHAUNOCEPHALUS DIETZ, 1909 from Baschkirova (I:483)

1 (10) Cephalic spines not more than twenty-seven.

2 (3) Twenty-three cephalic spines present; length

of cephalic spines: 0.12-0.23 mm. Host: Euxenura maguari (Brazil).   C. paduriformis Travassos, 1922

3 (2) Twenty-seven cephalic spines present.

4 (7) Width of cephalic collar not exceeding 0.700 mm.

5 (6) Body dimensions: 4.4-8.8 x 0.3-0.4 mm.; length of cephalic spines: 0.088-0.210 mm.; diameter of oral sucker: 0.30-0.33 mm. Hosts: black-necked stork and black-necked gull (India).

C. similiferox Verma, 1936

6 (5) Body dimensions: 3.15-7.24 x 0.70-1.88 mm.; length of cephalic spines: 0.077-0.165 mm.; diameter of oral sucker: 0.110-0.176 mm. Host: Ciconia ciconia (USSR).

C. ferox orientalis Baschkirova, 1941

7 (4) Width of cephalic collar not less than 1 mm.

8 (9) Dimensions of body: 5.5-5.8 x 1.87-2.29 mm.; length of cephalic spines: 0.04-0.185 mm.; diameter of oral sucker: 0.130-0.150 mm. Hosts: white stork, black stork, bittern (Europe).

C. ferox (Rudolphi, 1795) (fig. 49)

9 (8) Dimensions of body: 4-4.5 x 2.45-2.85 mm.; length of cephalic spines: 0.090-0.240 mm.; diameter of oral sucker: 0.384-0.400 mm. Host: Euxenura maguari (Brazil).

C. geraldi Gedoelst, 1913

10 (1) Twenty-nine cephalic spines present; length of cephalic spines: 0.098-0.033 mm. Host: Ciconia nigra (USSR).   C. schulzi Gnedina, 1941

LIST OF SUPPLEMENTARY ILLUSTRATIONS

Atractotrematidae Yamaguti, 1939
   Atractotrema fusum Goto and Ozaki, 1929 (fig. 775)
Collyriclidae Ward, 1919
   Collyriclum faba (Bremser, 1831) (fig. 776)
Mesotretidae Poche, 1925
   Mesotretes peregrinus M. Braun, 1900 (fig. 777)
Opisthogonoporidae Yamaguti, 1937
   Opisthogonoporus amadai Yamaguti, 1937 (fig. 778)
Psilostomatidae Odhner, 1913
   Psilostomum brevicolle (Creplin, 1829) (fig. 779)
   Apopharynx bolodes (Braun, 1902) (fig. 780)
   Lyperorchis lyperorchis Travassos, 1925 (fig. 781)
   Psilotrema marki Skwortzow, 1934 (fig. 782)
   Psilochasmus oxyurus (Creplin, 1825) (fig. 783)
   Skrjabinomerus desmane Sobolev, Maschkov and
      Maschkov, 1939 (fig. 784)
   Sphaeridiotrema globulus (Rudolphi, 1819) (fig. 785)
   Testifrondosa cristata Bhalerao, 1924 (fig. 786)
Renicolidae Dollfus, 1939
   Renicola pinguis (Mehlis, 1831) (fig. 787)
Echinostomatidae Dietz, 1909
   Pegosomum saginatum (Ratz, 1898) (fig. 788)
   Sodalis spatulatus (Rudolphi, 1819) (fig. 789)
   Stephanoproraoides lawi Price, 1934 (fig. 790)
Cathaemasiidae Poche, 1925
   Cathaemasioides callis Freitas, 1940 (fig. 791)

PART II

KEY TO THE FAMILIES OF THE SUPERFAMILY FASCIOLOIDEA STILES AND GOLDBERGER, 1910 (II:11)

K. I. Skrjabin

1 (2) Egg with thin shell, oval-shaped in cross section; lacking seminal receptacle; excretory bladder branched. Parasites of bile ducts and intestines of terrestrial mammals.   Fasciolidae Railliet, 1895

2 (1) Egg with thick shell, triangular in cross section; seminal receptacle present; excretory bladder simple. Parasites of bile ducts, nasal cavity, and intestines of marine mammals: cetaceans and pinnipeds.   Campulidae Odhner, 1926

KEY TO THE SUBFAMILIES OF THE FAMILY FASCIOLIDAE RAILLIET, 1895 (II:12)

K. I. Skrjabin

1 (4) Testes always dendritically branched; ovary usually branched, rarely compact.

2 (3) Intestinal ceca with numerous lateral, external diverticula; cephalic protuberance clearly expressed.   Fasciolinae Stiles & Hassall, 1898

3 (2) Intestinal ceca smooth, without diverticula; cephalic protuberance not developed.
                    Fasciolopsinae Odhner, 1911

4 (1) Ovary and testes compact, round, not branched.   Protofasciolinae Skrjabin, 1948

KEY TO THE GENERA OF THE SUBFAMILY FASCIOLINAE STILES AND HASSALL, 1898 (II:12)

K. I. Skrjabin

1 (2) Vitellaria ventral and dorsal to intestinal ceca.   Fasciola Linnaeus, 1758 (fig. 52)

2 (1) Vitellaria only ventral to intestinal ceca.
                    Fascioloides Ward, 1917

KEY TO THE SPECIES OF THE GENUS FASCIOLA LINNAEUS, 1758 (II:15)

K. I. Skrjabin

1 (2) Body almost circular in form. Parasites of bile ducts of elephants.   F. jacksoni (Cobbold, 1869)

2 (1) Body elongate, not spherical.

3 (4) Length of ribbon-shaped body 3-4 times greater than width; sides run parallel; "shoulders" sometimes present, not fully developed, sometimes lacking completely; intestinal ceca with numerous, medially branching diverticula.
                    F. gigantica (Cobbold, 1885)

4 (3) Leaf-shaped body, relatively broad; conical cephalic protuberance sharply delimited from remaining body by special shoulders; medial diverticula of ceca few and small.

5 (6) Body completely covered with spines.
                    F. halli Sinitsin, 1933

6 (5) Several body regions free of spines.

7 (8) Dorsal and ventral surfaces of posterior portion of body lacking spines.
                    F. hepatica Linnaeus, 1758 (fig. 52)

8 (7) Posterior part of body lacking spines only on dorsal surface.   F. californica Sinitsin, 1933

KEY TO THE SPECIES OF THE GENUS FASCIOLOIDES WARD, 1917 (II:44)

K. I. Skrjabin

1 (2) Body very large, broad; conical cephalic protuberance not sharply developed; length of esophagus 3.5 times greater than length of pharynx.
                    F. magna (Bassi, 1875)

2 (1) Body narrow, awl-shaped; conical cephalic protuberance large, sharply protruding; esophagus rudimentary. Parasites of hippopotamus.
                    F. nyanzi (Leiper, 1910)

KEY TO THE GENERA OF THE SUBFAMILY FASCIOLOPSINAE ODHNER, 1910 (II:49)

K. I. Skrjabin

1 (2) Cephalic protuberance lacking; ovary lobed, dendritic. Intestinal parasites of omnivores, dogs and man.   Fasciolopsis Looss, 1899 (fig. 54)

2 (1) Cephalic protuberance sharply developed; ovary compact, entire. Parasites of the bile ducts of ruminants (elk).
                    Parafasciolopsis Ejsmont, 1932 (fig. 55)

LITERATURE ON FASCIOLIASIS (II:114-117)

Vasilieva, A. 1926. Distomum hepaticum in an eleven year old girl. Trudy Detskoy Kliniki. SAGU za 1924-1925 Akad. god.

Vasilieva, A. P. 1927. Distomatiases of the liver of children in Turkestan. Russky Zhurnal Tropicheskoy Meditsiny. 5(1):36-43.

Gorshkov, I. A. and E. E. Shumakovich. 1936. Methods of de-helminthization of manure of farm animals. Trudy Vsesoyuznogo Instituta Gelmintologii im. Akademika K. I. Skrjabina. 1:149-182.

Gusynin, I. A. 1928a. On the question of treating fascioliasis of sheep with carbon tetrachloride. Vestnik Sovremennoy Veterinarii. 4(18):562-567.

Gusynin, I. A. 1928b. On the question of methods of introducing medicinal substances into small animals. Vestnik Sovremennoy Veterinarii. 4(16):508-511.

Gusynin, I. A. 1929a. Results of the first extensive experiments in the U.S.S.R. in treating fascioliasis of sheep with carbon tetrachloride. Vestnik Sovremennoy Veterinarii. 5(7-8):181-187.

Gusynin, I. A. 1929b. The efficacy of carbon tetrachloride in treating fascioliasis of short-horned cattle. Vestnik Sovremennoy Veterinarii. 5(11):272-274.

Gusynin, I. A. 1930. Results of the first extensive experiment in treating fascioliasis of long-horned cattle, carried out in North Osetiya, in October of 1929. Vestnik Sovremennoy Veterinarii. 6(17-18): 419-423.

Davtyan, E. A. 1937. Experiments in treating fascioliasis of long-horned cattle with hexachlorethane. Trudy Nauchno-Issledovatelskogo Veterinarnogo Instituta SSR Armenii. No. 2:1-34.

Dinnik, Yu. A. 1930. Experiment in malacological investigation of an area, with reference to the study of the epizootology of fascioliasis. Vestnik Sovremennoy Veterinarii. No. 15-16:398-400.

Domontovich, M. K. 1915. Experiments and observations on adolescaria (the encystment of cercaria). *In:* Sinitsyn, D. F. Liver fluke in the Moscow District. Moskva. 42 pp.

Elmanov, N. V. 1929. Carbon tetrachloride and its use in treating fascioliasis of sheep. Sbornik Rabot Kursantov-Vetvrachey Sozyva (1927-1928 gg.). 1(1):82-103.

Ershov, V. S. 1929. Work of the 57th Union Helminthological Expedition in the Vyatka Province. 15-1 X 1928 g. Izdatelstvo Vyatsk, Okr. Bet. Otd., Vyatka. 79 pp.

Zhadin, V. I. and V. Ya. Pankratova. 1931. Researches on the biology of molluscan transmitting agents of fascioliasis and an elaboration of measures of controlling them. Raboty Okskoy Biologicheskoy Stantsii. 6(1-3):79-158.

Zhadin, V. I. 1926. Our Fresh-water molluscs. Guide to the molluscs. Izdatelstvo Okskoy Biologicheskoy Stantsii.

Zhadin, V. I. 1926. On the biology of drained bodies of water. Russky Gidrobiologichesky Zhurnal. :17

Zhadin, V. I. 1930. How to control the transmitting agents of fascioliasis. Vestnik Sovremennoy Veterinarii. 6(22):525-526.

Zhadin, V. I. 1933. Freshwater molluscs of the U.S.S.R. OGIZ. Lensnabtekhizdat. 233 pp.

Ilinsky, N. I. and M. A. Palimpsestov. 1929. Fascioliasis of long-horned cattle in the Astrakhan province, and experiments in its treatment by the Railliet method. Vestnik Sovremennoy Veterinarii. 5(1):11-13.

Ilinsky, N. I. and M. A. Palimpsestov. 1929. Carbon tetrachloride as a means of treating fascioliasis of long-horned cattle. Vestnik Sovremennoy Veterinarii. 5(15):369-371; 5(16):392-394.

Kevorkov, N. 1933. Materials on the investigation of trematodiases in Central Asia. Za Sotsialisticheskoye Zdravookhranenie Uzbekistana. pp. 71-75.

Kovalevsky, I. 1885. A case from practice (distomatiasis in horned cattle). Arkhiv Veterinarnykh Nauk. 1:34-36.

Kulagin, S. M. 1927. Further observations on worm infestations in the school population of the city of Ivanovo-Voznesensk. Sev. Med. Zhurnal. No. 1:28-33.

Kulagin, S. M. 1927. Trematodiasis and trichostrongyliasis among the population of Ivanovo-Voznesensk. Sev. Med. Sbornik. 1(3):354-355.

Lapidus, S. S. 1925. Treatment of distomatiasis in sheep, goats, and long-horned cattle. Vestnik Sovremennoy Veterinarii. No. 11:17-18.

Lebedev, P. T. 1929. Therapeutic and toxic properties of extracts from Filicus maris obtained from Russian stock in the treatment of fascioliasis in sheep. Sbornik Rabot Kursantov-Vetvrachey Sozyva 1927-1928 gg. 1(1):104-133.

Malygin, S. A. 1934. On the question of fascioliasis of lungs of long-horned cattle. Trudy Vyatskogo Gosudarstvennogo Veterinarnogo Instituta. 1(2):110-112.

Marek, J. 1916. Liver fluke disease, its treatment and prevention. Arkhiv Veterinarnykh Nauk. 46(11): 1429-1462.

Mozgov, I. E. 1931. On the question of treatment of fascioliasis of long-horned cattle. Veterinarny Spetsialist na Sotsialisticheskoy Stroyke. 7(1-2):26-30.

Neller. 1928. Liver fluke disease of domestic animals (its essence, significance, and control. Noyaya Deryevnya. 54 pp.

Pavlova, O. N. 1927. On the symptoms and therapy of hepatic distomiasis. Meditsinskaya Mysl Uzbekistana. No. 2:39-46.

Palimpsestov, M. A. 1929. The efficacy of carbon tetrachloride on Fasicola gigantica Cobb., 1856 in the de-helminthization of long-horned cattle. Rabota 74-y Soyuznoy Gelmintologicheskoy Expeditsii v Astrakhanskom Okruge Nizhne-Volozhskovo Kraya. pp. 41-48.

Palimpsestov, M. A. 1930. Liver fluke disease (fascioliasis) in domestic animals, and measures of control. Astrakhan. 43 pp.

Palimpsestov, M. A. 1931. Experiments in massive de-helminthization of Fasciola gigantica Cobb., 1856 in long-horned cattle. Veterinarny Spetsialist na Sotsialisticheskoy Stroyke. 7(1-2):31-46.

Petrov, A. M. 1913. On the pathological anatomy of distomatiasis in man and domestic animals. Sbornik Trudov Kharkovskogo Veterinarnogo Instituta. 11(1-4):27-95.

Petrov, A. M., M. K. Dzhavadov, and A. D. Gaibov. 1936. Distribution of fascioliasis, echinococcosis, anoplocephalidiasis, and dictyocaulosis in ruminants of Azerbaydzhan. Trudy Tropicheskogo Instituta. Narkomz. Azerbaydzh. SSR. 2:257-262.

Pigulevsky, S. V. 1927. A case of discovering Fasciola gigantica Cobbold in an Uzbek infant in Old Tashkent. Meditsinskaya Mysl Uzbekistana. Nos. 6-7:59-61.

Poddubsky, I. V. 1929. On the question of treating fascioliasis in sheep with dystol. Sbornik Rabot Kursantov-Vetvrachey Sozyva 1927-1928 gg. 1(1):63-81.

Podyapolskaya, V. P. 1927. On helminthiases of man in the U.S.S.R. Sbornik Rabot po Gelmintologii, Posvyaschenny Prof. K. I. Skrjabinu. pp. 155-179.

Potudin, M. I. 1929. Experiment on the efficacy of carbon tetrachloride in the treatment of fascioliasis of sheep in rural economy. Vestnik Sovremennoy Veterinarii. 5(22):563-564.

Pukhov, V. I. 1934. Expeditionary work of 1931. Trudy Severno-Kavkazkogo Nauchno-Issledovatelskogo Veterinarnogo Prof. Instituta. No. 2:154-158.

Pukhov, V. I. 1934. Study of living conditions of a small pond and elaboration of means of regulation for prophylactic control of fascioliasis. Trudy Severno-Kavkazkogo Nauchno-Issledovatelskogo Veterinarnogo Prof. Instituta. No. 2:132-149.

Pukhov, V. I. and A. Z. Efimov. 1934. Description of cercariae. Trudy Severno-Kavkazkogo Nauchno-Issledovatelskogo Veterinarnogo Prof. Instituta. No. 2:149-150.

Pukhov, V. I., A. Z. Efimov, and E. E. Krivoshta. 1934. Laboratory work on the effects of various chemical substances on a small pond. Trudy Severno-Kavkazkogo Nauchno-Issledovatelskogo Veterinarnogo Prof. Instituta. No. 2:158-166.

Pukhov, V. I., E. E. Krivoshta, and A. Z. Efimov. 1934. Survey of current chemical means of controlling molluscs from the point of view of their practical significance. Trudy Severno-Kavkazkogo Nauchno-Issledovatelskogo Veterinarnogo Prof. Instituta. No. 2:166-176.

Pukhov, V. I. and G. D. Nikiforov. 1934. Experiments in infecting sheep with larval forms obtained from molluscs of the genera Limnea and Planorbis. Trudy Severno-Kavkazkogo Nauchno-Issledovatelskogo Veterinarnogo Prof. Instituta. No. 2:151-154.

Semenov, G. M. 1925. On the question of the worm fauna and the distribution of worms among the population of Tashkent. Turkestany Meditsinsky Zhurnal. No. 9:

Semenov, G. M. 1926. A new finding of Fasciola hepatica in Tashkent. Byulleten Nauchnoy Konferentsii pri Uzbekistanskom Krayevom Bakteriologichkom Institute, Tashkent. No. 1:

Semenov, G. M. 1927. Materials for the study of distomatosis in Central Asia. Vrachebnaya Gazeta. 31(7):509-510.

Semenov, G. M. 1927. General summary of distomatosis caused by Fasciola hepatica with reference to its distribution in Central Asia. Meditsinskaya Mysl Uzbekistana. No. 2:13-29.

Semenov, G. M. and D. A. Kogan. 1927. A case of human infection with Fasciola hepatica and treating it with small doses of an emetic of chlorohydrate. Meditsinskaya Mysl Uzbekistana. No. 2:30-38.

Sinitsyn, D. F. 1913. On the plan of work in the search for rational measures for controlling distomatosis in sheep. Zhurnal Zased. Komissii 9/IV

1913 g. po Voprosy ob Izyskaniyakh Rationalnykn Mer Borby s Pechenochnoy Glistnoy Boleznyu Ovets v Moskovskoy Gubernii Veterinarnaya Khronika Khersonskoy Gubernii, god. 23-i, Iyun.-Avgust. pp. 149-159.

Sinitsyn, D. F. 1915. The fluke, Fasciola hepatica L., in the Moscow Province. Prilozhenie k No. 14 Dokladov Gub. Zemsk. Upr., Moskva. 42 pp.

Skvortsov, A. A. 1931. Experiment on the study of the ecology of the molluscan transmitting agent in fascioliasis, and its control. Rukopis, VIG.

Skvortsov, A. A. 1931. On the biology of Fasciola hepatica. Rukopis, VIG.

Skrjabin, K. I. 1916. On the knowledge of the helminth fauna of domestic animals of Turkestan. Dissertatsiya, Yuriev.

Skrjabin, K. I. 1927. The Fourth Russian Helminthological Expedition into the Don district (Novocherkassk). Deyatelnosti 28-y Gelmintologicheskoy Expeditsii v SSSR. pp. 32-40.

Skrjabin, K. I. 1929. Helminth infestations in sheep and their economic importance in sheep raising. Moskva. 114 pp.

Skrjabin, K. I. and V. S. Ershov. 1934. Helminthiases of the horse. Selkhozgiz, Moskva-Leningrad. 408 pp.

Skrjabin, K. I. and R. Ed. S. Schulz. 1926. Work of the expedition for study of helminth diseases in coal-miners of the Artemovsky region of the Donets basin. Sbornik Rabot 25-y Soyuznoy Gelmintologicheskoy Expeditsii Artemovskom Okruge Donbassa. Izdatelstvo Artemovskogo Okrugzdrava, Moskva. pp. 8-45.

Skrjabin, K. I. and R. Ed. S. Schulz. 1926. Hepatic helminthiases of man caused by trematodes. In: Trematodiases of man. Moskva. pp. 57-68.

Skrjabin, K. I. and R. Ed. S. Schulz. 1928. Hepatic trematodiases of man. Second Ed. Moskva. 43 pp.

Skrjabin, K. I. and R. Ed. S. Schulz. 1929. Helminthiases of man, Part I. Gosmedizdat, Moskva-Leningrad. 375 pp.

Skrjabin, K. I. and R. Ed. S. Schulz. 1931. Trematodology. Selkhozgiz, Moskva. 47 pp.

Skrjabin, K. I. and R. Ed. S. Schulz. 1935. Fascioliases of animals and the means of control. Izdatelstvo Uchebnogo Kombinata Narkomzema USSR, Moskva. 174 pp.

Skrjabin, K. I., R. Ed. S. Schulz, and V. P. Podyapolskaya. 1927. Work of the 35th Union Helminthological Expedition in Central Asia. Gigiena i Epidemiologiya. No. 3:88-90.

Solonitsyn, I. A. and E. A. Davtyan. 1933. Tetrachlorethylene as an anti-helminthic in veterinary medicine. Uchenye Zapiski Kazanskogo Veterinarnogo Instituta.

Soshestvensky, N. A. 1929. Fascioliasis of sheep and long-horned cattle. Treatment and symptoms of disease. Izdatelstvo Osoaviakhima, Moskva. 38 pp.

Soshestvensky, N. A. and I. A. Gusynin. 1929. Treatment of fascioliasis of long-horned cattle.

Vestnik Sovremennoy Veterinarii. 5(19):482-485; 5(20):504-507; 5(21):536-538.

Tarnogradsky, D. A. and K. K. Popov. 1933. On the biology and distribution of the transmitting agent of fascioliasis, Limnea trunculata Müll. in the northern Caucasus. Rabota Severo-Kavkazskoy Gidrobiologicheskoy Stantsii. 1(1); 148 pp.

Shepetov, and Nechayev, 1928. Meliorative works in the Tversk Province for systematic sanitization of a region and for controlling helminth and protozoan diseases of animals. Veterinarny Truzhenik. Nos. 8-9:

Schulz, R. Ed. S. 1931. Carbon tetrachloride in veterinary helminthological practice. Selkhozgiz, Moskva. 112 pp.

Schulz, R. Ed. S. and V. S. Sutyagin. 1935. On the question of treating fascioliasis in long-horned cattle with filitsilen. Trudy Vsesoyuznogo Veterinarnogo Zootekhnicheskogo Instituta. 1(2):

Schulz, R. Ed. S. and E. A. Davtyan. 1935. Is tetrachlorethylene effective in the treatment of fascioliasis? Khim-Farmak. Promyshl.

Schulz, R. Ed. S. and E. A. Davtyan. 1935. Is tetrachlorethylene effective as an anti-helminthic in fascioliasis? Trudy Nauchno-Issledovatelskogo Veterinarnogo Instituta SSR Armenii. No. 1:92-95.

Schulz, R. Ed. S., Z. A. Rayevskaya, and L. A. Losev. 1930. Experiments in enacting measures of controlling fascioliasis in long-horned cattle on collective farms. Vestnik Sovremennoy Veterinarii. 6(15-16):395-398.

Yaguzhinsky, S. N. 1932. On the biology of Chaetogaster limnaei K. Bauer in connection with its feeding on cercariae. Zapiski Bolshevskoy Biologicheskoy Stantsii. Nos. 5-6:31-36.

KEY TO THE SUBFAMILIES OF THE FAMILY CAMPULIDAE ODHNER, 1926 (II:129)

K. I. Skrjabin

1 (2) Two testes; seminal receptacle and cirrus sac present; blind anterior out-growths of intestine present (excepting Synthesium). Parasites of liver and intestine. Campulinae Stunkard and Alvey, 1929.

2 (1) Testes of numerous follicles; seminal receptacle and cirrus sac absent; anterior intestinal diverticula lacking. Parasites of nasal cavities.
                              Nasitrematinae Ozaki, 1935

KEY TO THE GENERA OF THE SUBFAMILY CAMPULINAE STUNKARD AND ALVEY, 1929 (II:129-130)

K. I. Skrjabin

1 (6) Cirrus unarmed.
2 (3) Body elongate, 60-80 mm. long; ovary deeply lobed; vitellaria forming more or less rectangular groups of follicles.
      Lecithodesmus M. Braun, 1902 (fig. 56)

3 (2) Body shorter, less than 20 mm. long; ovary not lobed; vitellaria of different structure.
4 (5) Oral sucker larger than ventral sucker; eggs round in cross section.
      Zalophotrema Stunkard and Alvey, 1929 (fig. 57)
5 (4) Oral and ventral suckers of almost equal dimensions; eggs triangular in cross section.
              Campula Cobbold, 1858 (fig. 58)
6 (1) Cirrus armed.
7 (12) Vitelline follicles not clustered in separate groups.
8 (9) Intestine lacking anterior diverticula; vagina armed; testes deeply lobed.
      Synthesium Stunkard and Alvey, 1929 (fig. 59)
9 (8) Intestine with anterior diverticula.
10 (11) Prepharynx present; testes not deeply lobed.
       Orthosplanchnus Odhner, 1905 (fig. 60)
11 (10) Prepharynx absent; testes entire.
       Oshmarinella Skrjabin, 1947 (fig. 61)
12 (7) Vagina unarmed; vitelline follicles in distinctly separate groups. Intestinal parasites of toothed whales and liver parasites of pinnipeds.
      Odhneriella Skrjabin, 1915 (fig. 62)

KEY TO THE SPECIES OF THE GENUS CAMPULA COBBOLD, 1858 (II:130-131)

K. I. Skrjabin

1 (4) Testes entire.
2 (3) Suckers close together; testes pre-equatorial. Host: Delphinus delphis.
              C. rochebruni (Poirier, 1886)
3 (2) Suckers significantly apart; testes in posterior third of body. Host: Delphinus delphis.
              C. delphini (Poirier, 1886)
4 (1) Testes lobed.
5 (6) Intestinal ceca equipped with anal pore; cirrus sac reaching posterior edge of ventral sucker. Host: Phocaena phocaena.
              C. oblonga Cobbold, 1858 (fig. 58)
6 (5) Intestinal ceca without anal pores.
7 (8) Cirrus sac not reaching posterior edge of ventral sucker; prepharyngeal pouch absent. Host: Delphinus delphini.   C. palliata (Looss, 1885)
8 (7) Cirrus sac extending to posterior edge of ventral sucker; prepharyngeal pouch present. Host: Neophocaena phocaenoides.   C. folium Ozaki, 1935

KEY TO THE SPECIES OF THE GENUS ODHNERIELLA SKRJABIN, 1915 (II:145)

K. I. Skrjabin

1 (2) Body 9 mm. long. Liver parasites of walruses (Odobaenus rosmarus).
              O. rossica Skrjabin, 1915 (fig. 62)
2 (1) Body up to 60 mm. long. Intestinal parasites of Delphinopterus leucos.
              O. seymouri (Price, 1932)

KEY TO THE SPECIES OF THE GENUS ORTHOSPLANCHNUS ODHNER, 1905 (II:149)

K. I. Skrjabin

1 (2) Vitellaria reaching anteriorly to level of posterior end of pharynx. Hosts: Erignathus barbatus, Phoca hispida, others.
O. arcticus Odhner, 1905 (fig. 60)

2 (1) Vitellaria not reaching level of pharynx.

3 (4) Vitelline follicles originating at level of anterior edge of ventral sucker. Hosts: Odobaenus rosmarus and Erignathus barbatus.
O. fraterculus Odhner, 1905

4 (3) Vitellaria not reaching posterior edge of ventral sucker. Host: Neophocaena phocaenoides.
O. elongatus Ozaki, 1935

LITERATURE ON THE TREMATODES OF THE FAMILY CAMPULIDAE ODHNER, 1926 (II:162)

Skrjabin, K. I. 1915. Odhneriella rossica n. g., n. sp., the agent of liver fluke disease in walrus. Arkhiv Veterinarnykh Nauk. 45(11):1058-1064.

Skrjabin, K. I. and R. Ed. S. Schulz. 1935. Fascioliasis in animals and the means of control. Izdatelstvo Uchebnogo Kombinata Narkomzema USSR, Moskva. 174 pp.

Skrjabin, K. I. 1947. Oshmarinella sobolevi n. g., n. sp., a new trematode from the liver of whales. Doklady Akad. Nauk SSSR. 57(8):857-859.

KEY TO THE SUBFAMILIES OF THE FAMILY BRACHYLAEMIDAE STILES AND HASSALL, 1898 (II:169)

K. I. Skrjabin

1 (2) Width of body several times greater than length; genital pores lateral; uterus slightly sinuous, tubular, transversely directed, without ascending or descending limbs. Parasites of mammals.
Moreauinae Johnston, 1915

2 (1) Length of body exceeding width; uterus with ascending and descending loops, situated mainly along longitudinal axis of body.

3 (6) Genital pores opening on ventral side of body; excretory bladder opening near posterior end of body.

4 (5) Testes tandem; genital pores medial, or slightly to side of medial line. Parasites of birds and insectivorous mammals.
Brachylaeminae Stiles and Hassall, 1898

5 (4) Testes oblique; genital pores medial or nearly lateral. Parasites of ruminants and rodents.
Hasstilesiinae Orloff, Erschoff and Badanin, 1934

6 (3) Genital pores sometimes on dorsal side, sometimes at posterior end of body; excretory bladder opening dorsally, posterior to ventral sucker; siphons of excretory system extracecal.
Leucochloridiinae Sinitsin, 1931

KEY TO THE TRIBES OF THE SUBFAMILY BRACHYLAEMINAE STILES AND HASSALL, 1898 from Witenberg (1925) (II:170)

1) Posterior border of vitellaria at level of anterior edge of anterior testis.

a) Body ribbon or thread-shaped; bend of uterus located posterior to the ventral sucker.
Ithyogonimea Witenberg, 1925

b) Body tongue-shaped; bend of uterus anterior to ventral sucker.   Harmostomea Witenberg, 1925
(Today, it is necessary to call this tribe Brachylaemea)

2) Posterior border of vitellaria at level of or posterior to ovary.

a) Body tongue-shaped; suckers weakly developed; posterior ends of vitellaria at level of ovary.
Urotocea Witenberg, 1925

b) Body oval; suckers well developed; posterior ends of vitellaria at level of posterior part of posterior testis or at posterior end of body.
Leucochloridiea Witenberg, 1925

KEY TO THE GENERA OF THE TRIBE BRACHYLAEMEA SKRJABIN, 1948 (II:170-171)

K. I. Skrjabin

1 (2) Genital pores opening in space between testes.
Glaphyrostomum Braun, 1901 (fig. 63)

2 (1) Genital pores opening at some other site.

3 (4) Genital pores opening posterior to posterior testis.   Panopistus Sinitsin, 1931

4 (3) Genital pores opening at level of anterior testis or more anteriorly.

5 (8) Genital pores situated anterior to anterior testis.

6 (7) Siphons of excretory system extra-cecal.
Ectosiphonus Sinitsin, 1931 (fig. 65)

7 (6) Siphons of excretory system intercecal.
Entosiphonus Sinitsin, 1931 (fig. 66)

8 (5) Genital pores at level of anterior testis.

9 (10) Genital pores at the level of anterior edge of anterior testis; intestinal ceca straight; uterine loops not evenly distributed.
Brachylaemus Dujardin, 1843 (fig. 67)

10 (9) Genital pore posterior to anterior edge of anterior testis; intestinal ceca sinuous; snake-like uterus composed of two central trunks, ascending and descending along axis of body, with branches returning in transverse direction.
Postharmostomum Witenberg, 1923 (fig. 68)

KEY TO THE GENERA OF THE TRIBE ITHYOGONIMEA WITENBERG, 1925 (II:242)

K. I. Skrjabin

1 (2) Gonads in posterior-most part of body; ventral sucker not displaced anteriorly; genital pore at level of anterior edge of posterior testis. Parasites of mammals.   Ithyogonimus Lühe, 1899 (fig. 69)

2 (1) Gonads slightly more anterior in position; ventral sucker displaced anteriorly; genital pore anterior to anterior testis. Parasites of birds.
Scaphiostomum Braun, 1901 (fig. 70)

KEY TO THE SPECIES OF THE GENUS ITHYOGONIMUS LÜHE, 1899 (II:245)

K. I. Skrjabin

1 (2) Ventral sucker exceptionally small: 0.1-0.12 mm. in diameter, almost three times smaller than oral sucker.   I. talpe (Goeze, 1782)
2 (1) Ventral sucker reaching 0.32-0.51 mm. in diameter; larger than oral sucker which reaches 0.25-0.48 mm.   I. lorum (Dujardin, 1845) (fig. 69)

KEY TO THE SPECIES OF THE GENUS UROTOCUS LOOSS, 1899 (II:252)

K. I. Skrjabin

1 (2) Body elongate, oval; ventral sucker present; posterior testis in space between blind ends of the intestine. Parasites in fabrician bursa of thrushes, Turdus pilaris.
U. rossitensis (Mühling, 1898) (fig. 71)
2 (1) Body fusiform; ventral sucker absent; posterior testis anterior to blind ends of intestine. Parasites in fabrician bursa of Oporonis philadelphia (N. America).   U. fusiformis (McIntosh, 1935)

KEY TO THE GENERA OF THE SUBFAMILY HASSTILESIINAE ORLOFF, ERSCHOFF AND BADANIN, 1934 (II:292)

K. I. Skrjabin

1 (2) Genital pore medial; testes separate from each other; anterior testis anterior to ovary. Parasites of rodents (N. America).
Hasstilesia Hall, 1916 (fig. 72)
2 (1) Genital pore near lateral edge of body; testes nearly adjacent; anterior testis posterior to ovary. Parasites of ruminants (Uzbekistan and Khirgizia).
Skrjabinotrema Orloff, Erschoff and Badanin, 1934
(fig. 73)

KEY TO THE SPECIES OF THE GENUS HASSTILESIA HALL, 1916 (II:295)

K. I. Skrjabin

1 (2) Oral sucker 0.10-0.12 mm.; testes 0.105-0.140 mm. long; cirrus 0.14 mm. long.
H. texensis Chandler, 1929
2 (1) Oral sucker 0.088-0.11 mm.; testes 0.236-0.248 mm. long; cirrus 0.080 mm. long.
H. tricolor (Stiles and Hassall, 1894) (fig. 72)

KEY TO THE SPECIES OF THE GENUS

RHOPALIAS STILES AND HASSALL, 1898 (II:307-308)

K. I. Skrjabin

1 (4) Body length greater than 5 mm.
2 (3) Proboscis very long, reaching 1.3 mm.; each proboscis armed with longitudinal rows of 10-12 spines; largest spine reaching length of 0.062 mm.; length of body 6-9 mm.
R. coronatus (Rudolphi, 1819) (fig. 74)
3 (2) Proboscis short, reaching 0.26 mm., armed with 7-8 spines; spines not in rows; largest spines reaching length of 0.073 mm.; length of body 10-12 mm.   R. baculifer Braun, 1901
4 (1) Body length less than 5 mm.
5 (6) Length of proboscis about 0.26 mm., armed with numerous spines reaching 0.036-0.041 mm. in length; body length 2-3 mm.
R. horridus (Diesing, 1850)
6 (5) Proboscis 0.28-0.32 mm. long, armed with ten spines; spines in two groups: five spines on the dorsal side, five on ventral; length of largest spine reaching 0.125 mm.; body length 4.0-4.75 mm.
R. macracanthus Chandler, 1932

KEY TO THE GENERA OF THE FAMILY RHYTIDODIDAE ODHNER, 1926 (II:316)

K. I. Skrjabin

1 (2) Large trematodes, exceeding 19 mm. in length; vitellaria posterior to ventral sucker.
Rhytidodes Looss, 1901 (fig. 75)
2 (1) Small trematodes, body length less than 4 mm.; vitellaria entering into zone anterior to ventral sucker.   Rhytidodoides Price, 1939 (fig. 76)

KEY TO THE SPECIES OF THE GENUS RHYTIDODOIDES PRICE, 1939 (II:325)

K. I. Skrjabin

1 (2) Genital pore posterior to intestinal bifurcation; testes tandem, posterior smaller than anterior.
R. intestinalis Price, 1939 (fig. 76)
2 (1) Genital pore slightly anterior to intestinal bifurcation; testes oblique, posterior larger than anterior.   R. similis Price, 1939

KEY TO THE GENERA OF THE FAMILY SPHAEROSTOMATIDAE THAPAR AND DAYAL, 1934 (II:328)

K. I. Skrjabin

1 (2) Genital sucker absent; testis and ovary simple, round.
Sphaerostomum Stiles and Hassall, 1898 (fig. 77)
2 (1) Genital sucker present; testes and ovary more lobular.
Cotylogonoporum Thapar and Dayal, 1934 (fig. 78)

KEY TO THE SUBFAMILIES OF THE FAMILY LECITHODENDRIIDAE ODHNER, 1911 (II:339)

T. S. Skarbilovich

1 (4) Genital pore medial.
2 (3) Genital pore anterior to ventral sucker. Hosts: mammals (Chiroptera), more rarely birds.
Lecithodendriinae Looss, 1902
3 (2) Genital pore near posterior edge of or posterior to ventral sucker. Hosts: mammals.
Gyrabascinae Macy, 1935
4 (1) Genital pore lateral, at edge of body.
5 (6) Genital pore anterior to ventral sucker, between two suckers; cirrus sac present. Hosts: amphibians and reptiles.   Pleurogenetinae Looss, 1899
6 (5) Genital pore at level of ventral sucker or posterior to it; cirrus sac absent. Hosts: mammals (rodents, Chiroptera).
Allassogonoporinae Skarbilovich, 1943

KEY TO THE GENERA OF THE TRIBE LECITHODENDRIEA SKARBILOVICH, 1943 (II:339-340)

T. S. Skarbilovich

1 (24) Intestinal ceca short.
2 (15) Vitellaria in anterior part of body.
3 (7) Ovary lobed.
4 (12) Spines absent on suckers and atrium.
5 (6) Body oval or pyriform, longitudinally elongate; pseudo-bursa present.
Paralecithodendrium (Odhner, 1911) (fig. 79)
6 (5) Body square, transversely elongate; cirrus sac lacking.   Castroia Travassos, 1928 (fig. 80)
7 (3) Ovary entire.
8 (11) Ovary and testes anterior to ventral sucker; ovary anterior to testes.
9 (10) Cirrus sac large, with proximal portion anterior to ventral sucker, distal portion posterior to ventral sucker.   Glyptoporus Macy, 1936 (fig. 81)
10 (9) Cirrus sac small, anterior to ventral sucker.
Travassodendrium Skarbilovich, 1943 (fig. 82)
11 (8) Ovary posterior to ventral sucker, posterior to testes.   Prosthodendrium Dollfus, 1931 (fig. 83)
12 (4) Suckers, and sometimes atrium, armed with spines.
13 (14) Vitellaria in clusters; spines present in or on atrium.   Acanthatrium Faust, 1919 (fig. 84)
14 (13) Vitellaria in two transverse rows of follicles; spines present on oral sucker.
Skrjabinodendrium Skarbilovich, 1943 (fig. 85)
15 (2) Vitellaria in middle or posterior portion of body.
16 (23) Vitellaria equatorially located in body, in small group of follicles.
17 (20) Vitellaria posterior to testes and ovary; ovary posterior to testes.
18 (19) Vitellaria in rosette configuration, in middle of body. Lecithodendrium (Lecithodendrium) (fig. 86)

19 (18) Vitellaria in compact masses extending along sides of body.
Lecithodendrium (Mesodendroides)
20 (17) Vitellaria anterior to ovary and testes; ovary anterior to testes.
21 (22) Body oval; cuticle spinose.
Pycnoporus Looss, 1899 (fig. 87)
22 (21) Body cylindrical; cuticle smooth.
Lecithoporus Mehra, 1935 (fig. 88)
23 (16) Vitellaria in small follicles, in posterior region of body, extending along body to posterior end.
24 (1) Intestinal ceca long.
Anchitrema Looss, 1899 (fig. 89)

KEY TO THE SPECIES OF THE GENUS CASTROIA TRAVASSOS, 1928 (II:364)

T. S. Skarbilovich

1 (2) Suckers equal in size.
C. silvae Travassos, 1928 (fig. 80)
2 (1) Oral sucker smaller than ventral.
C. amplicava Travassos, 1928

KEY TO THE SUBGENERA OF THE GENUS ACANTHATRIUM FAUST, 1919 (II:402)

T. S. Skarbilovich

1 (2) Vitellaria in clusters, in anterior portion of body, anterior to testes.
Acanthatrium (Acanthatrium) Skarbilovich, 1947 (fig. 84)
2 (1) Vitellaria in large follicles or compact masses, posterior to testes.
Acanthatrium (Mesothatrium) Skarbilovich, 1947

KEY TO THE GENERA OF THE TRIBE PHANEROPSOLEA SKARBILOVICH, 1943 (II:446)

T. S. Skarbilovich

1 (14) Genital pore medial, at level of pharynx, or between two suckers.
2 (9) Vitellaria in clusters, in anterior portion of body.
3 (8) Cirrus sac elongate.
4 (5) Genital pore opening near pharynx.
Phaneropsolus Looss, 1899 (fig. 90)
5 (4) Genital pore opening half-way between suckers.
6 (7) Cirrus sac superimposed on ventral sucker and partially anterior to it.
Pleuropsolus Mehra, 1935 (fig. 91)
7 (6) Cirrus sac not reaching ventral sucker.
Loxogenes Stafford, 1905 (fig. 92)
8 (3) Cirrus sac spherical.
Chiroptodendrium Skarbilovich, 1943 (fig. 93)
9 (2) Vitellaria in posterior region of body, of different shape.
10 (13) Cirrus sac short, not extending beyond ventral sucker.

11 (12) Intestinal ceca long; testes anterior to ventral sucker.   Eumegacetes Looss, 1900 (fig. 94)
12 (11) Intestinal ceca absent; testes posterior to ventral sucker.
                    Anenterotrema Stunkard, 1938 (fig. 95)
13 (10) Cirrus sac long, extending beyond level of ventral sucker; seminal vesicle straight.
                    Exotidendrium Mehra, 1935 (fig. 96)
14 (1) Genital pore sinistral, mid-way between ventral sucker and pharynx.
                    Mosesia Travassos, 1928 (fig. 97)

KEY TO THE SPECIES OF THE GENUS EUMEGACETES LOOSS, 1900 from Kurashvili (1940) (II:458-459)

1 (10) Vitellaria extending anteriorly to level of testes or to level of oral sucker.
2 (9) Loops of uterus narrow and of equal thickness throughout.
3 (6) Middle region of testes in pre-equatorial zone.
4 (5) Cirrus sac not reaching ventral sucker.
                    E. emendatus Braun, 1901 (fig. 94)
5 (4) Cirrus sac reaching ventral sucker and partially covered by it.
                    E. emendatus ibericus Kurashvili, 1940
6 (3) Posterior region of testes in equatorial zone.
7 (8) Ovary displaced from posterior portion of body toward ventral sucker.
                    E. medioximus Braun, 1901
8 (7) Ovary in posterior portion of body, with posterior edge at level of blind ends of intestines.
                    E. perodiosus Travassos, 1922
9 (2) Loops of uterus not of equal thickness; terminal portions consisting of massive, saccular loops, remaining loops thin.   E. artamii Mehra, 1935
10 (1) Vitellaria not extending to level of testes, scarcely reaching middle or posterior portions of ventral sucker.   E. brauni Mehra, 1935
11 (12) Cirrus sac transversely oriented; testes situated at level of cirrus sac.
                    E. contribulans Braun, 1901
12 (11) Cirrus sac longitudinally oriented; testes at level of posterior portion of cirrus sac.
                    E. komarovi Skrjabin, 1948

KEY TO THE SPECIES OF THE GENUS MOSESIA TRAVASSOS, 1928 (II:484)

T. S. Skarbilovich

1 (2) Ventral sucker larger than oral; genital pore at level of anterolateral edge of ventral sucker; seminal receptacle large; ovary and testes with large lobes; intestinal ceca not extending beyond level of middle of ventral sucker; vitellaria extending beyond level of posterior ends of intestine.
                    M. mosesi (Travassos, 1921) (fig. 97)
2 (1) Oral sucker larger than ventral; genital pore anterior to ventral sucker; seminal receptacle smaller; gonads, with irregular outline, without clear

subdivision into lobes; intestinal ceca extending considerably beyond posterior edge of ventral sucker; vitellaria not reaching level of posterior ends of intestinal ceca.   M. chordeilesia McMullen, 1936

KEY TO THE TRIBES OF THE SUBFAMILY GYRABASCINAE MACY, 1935 (II:486)

T. S. Skarbilovich

1 (2) Genital pore equatorial, far posterior to ventral sucker; cirrus sac lacking.
                    Gyrabascea Skarbilovich, 1943
2 (1) Genital pore equatorial, near posterior edge of ventral sucker; cirrus sac present.
                    Limatulea Skarbilovich, 1943

KEY TO THE GENERA OF THE TRIBE GYRABASCEA SKARBILOVICH, 1943 (II:486)

T. S. Skarbilovich

1 (4) Ovary entire.
2 (3) Esophagus present; intestinal ceca broad, situated in region of ventral sucker.
                    Gyrabascus Macy, 1935 (fig. 98)
3 (2) Esophagus absent; intestinal ceca narrow, situated in region of oral sucker.
                    Ophiosacculus Macy, 1935 (fig. 99)
4 (1) Ovary lobed.
    Echinuscodendrium Skarbilovich, 1943 (fig. 100)

KEY TO THE GENERA OF THE TRIBE LIMATULEA SKARBILOVICH, 1943 (II:497)

T. S. Skarbilovich

1 (6) Intestinal ceca short.
2 (5) Loops of uterus few, in posterior part of body, not extending to ventral sucker; testes symmetrical, along sides of body.
3 (4) Cirrus sac with S-curve, near ventral sucker.
                    Limatulum Travassos, 1921 (fig. 101)
4 (3) Cirrus sac nearly surrounding sucker.
                    Basantisia Pande, 1938 (fig. 102)
5 (2) Uterine loops numerous, filling entire body, extending beyond ventral sucker to vitellaria; testes oblique, with right testis lower.
                    Postorchigenes Tubangui, 1928 (fig. 103)
6 (1) Intestinal ceca long.
7 (10) Vitellaria of small follicles, not covering intestinal bifurcation.
8 (11) Intestinal ceca long, extending to end of body.
9 (12) Testes small, symmetrical, at some distance from each other.   Parabascus Looss, 1907 (fig. 104)
10 (7) Vitellaria of large follicles, covering intestinal bifurcation and forming arch.
11 (8) Intestinal ceca of medium length, extending only slightly beyond posterior border of testes.
12 (9) Testes large, symmetrical, close to each other.   Parabascoides Stunkard, 1938 (fig. 105)

KEY TO THE TRIBES OF THE SUBFAMILY PLEUROGENETINAE LOOSS, 1899 (II:516)

T. S. Skarbilovich

1 (2) Genital pore at edge of body, anterior to ventral sucker.   Pleurogenea Skarbilovich, 1943
2 (1) Genital pore at edge of body, at level of ventral sucker.   Brandesiea Skarbilovich, 1943

KEY TO THE GENERA OF THE TRIBE PLEUROGENEA SKARBILOVICH, 1943 (II:516-517)

T. S. Skarbilovich

1 (12) Vitellaria restricted to anterior half of body.
2 (11) Cirrus sac present.
3 (6) Intestinal ceca long, extending beyond ventral sucker.
4 (5) Testes posterior to intestinal ceca.
          Pleurogenes Looss, 1896 (fig. 106)
5 (4) Testes anterior to intestinal ceca, near intestinal bifurcation.
          Mehraorchis Srivastava, 1934 (fig. 107)
6 (3) Intestinal ceca short.
7 (10) Testes posterior to intestinal ceca and to cirrus sac.
8 (9) Cirrus sac crossing corresponding intestinal cecum.   Pleurogenoides Travassos, 1921 (fig. 108)
9 (8) Cirrus sac not crossing corresponding intestinal ceca, adjacent to external wall of cecum.
          Sonsinotrema Balozet and Callot, 1938 (fig. 109)
10 (7) Testes anterior to cirrus sac and intestinal ceca.   Prosotocus Looss, 1899 (fig. 110)
11 (2) Cirrus sac absent.
          Ganeo Klein, 1905 (fig. 111)
12 (1) Vitellaria dispersed throughout body.
          Cryptotropa Strand, 1931 (fig. 112)

KEY TO THE GENERA OF THE TRIBE BRANDESIEA SKARBILOVICH, 1943 (II:567)

T. S. Skarbilovich

1 (2) Uterus with many loops, filling both posterior and anterior portions of body; vitellaria in region of oral sucker.   Brandesia Stossich, 1899 (fig. 113)
2 (1) Uterus with few loops, located in posterior portion of body, posterior to ventral sucker; vitellaria in middle portion of body, near ventral sucker.
          Leyogonimus Gynezinskaia, 1947 (fig. 114)

KEY TO THE GENERA OF THE SUBFAMILY ALLASSOGONOPORINAE SKARBILOVICH, 1947 (II:577)

1 (2) Genital pore posterior to ventral sucker. Parasites of rodents and of Chiroptera.
          Allassogonoporus Olivier, 1938 (fig. 115)

2 (1) Genital pore at level of ventral sucker. Parasites of Chiroptera.
          Myotitrema Macy, 1940 (fig. 116)

LITERATURE ON THE TREMATODES OF THE FAMILY LECITHODENDRIIDAE ODHNER, 1911 (II:586-587)

Ginetsinskaya, T. A. 1947. A new genus for the species Distomum polyoon Braun, 1902, Leyogonimus n. g. Rukopis.

Kirshenblat, Ya. D. 1941. A new genus of trematodes in rodents. Soobscheniya Akad. Nauk Gruz. SSR. 2(6):

Kurashvili, B. E. 1941. On the study of the helminth fauna of birds of Georgia. Trudy Zoologicheskogo Instituta Akad. Nauk. 4:53-100.

Skarbilovich, T. S. 1943. On the revision of the systematics of trematodes of the family Lecithodendriidae Odhner, 1911. Doklady Akad. Nauk SSSR. 38(7):223-224.

Skrjabin, K. I. 1915. On the biology of the trematode, Lecithodendrium chilostomum (Mehlis, 1831). Vestnik Obschestvennoy Veterinarii. 27(11):409-412.

Skrjabin, K. I. 1916. Parasitic trematodes and nematodes collected by Prof. V. A. Dogiel and I. I. Sokolov in British East Africa and Uganda. Nauchnye Rezultaty Zoologicheskoy Expeditsii Prof. V. A. Dogielya i I. I. Sokolova v Britanskuyu Vostochnuyu Afriku i Ugandu v 1914 Godu. Petrograd. 1(14):1-157.

Skrjabin, K. I. 1948. A new species of the genus Eumegacetes, E. komarovi nov. sp. Rukopis.

Shaldybin, L. S. 1948. On the trematode fauna of chiropterans. Rukopis.

Strom, Zh. K. 1935. On the trematode fauna of Tadzhikistan. In: Materials on the parasitology and fauna of southern Tadzhikistan. Trudy Tadzhikskoy Komplexnoy Expeditsii. No. 10:219-254.

Strom, Zh. K. 1940. On the trematode fauna of wild animals of Kirgizia. Parazitologichesky Sbornik Zoologicheskogo Instituta Akad. Nauk SSSR. 8:189-224.

LIST OF SUPPLEMENTARY ILLUSTRATIONS

Fasciolidae Railliet, 1895
  Protofasciola robusta (Lorenz, 1881) (fig. 792)
Campulidae
  Nasitrema spathulatum Ozaki, 1935 (fig. 793)
Brachylaemidae Stiles and Hassall, 1898
  Leucochloridium macrostomum (Rudolphi, 1802) (fig. 794)
  Moreania mirabilis Johnston, 1915 (fig. 795)
Lecithodendriidae Odhner, 1911
  Leucochloridiomorpha constantiae (Müller, 1935) (fig. 796)

PART III

KEY TO THE FAMILIES OF THE ORDER PARAMPHISTOMOIDEA RUDOLPHI, 1801 from Stiles and Goldberger (1910) (III:8)

1 (2) Body usually flat, divided into anterior and posterior sections; ventral pouch lacking.
> Gastrodiscidae Stiles and Goldberger, 1910

2 (1) Body usually conical, not divided into anterior and posterior sections.

3 (4) Ventral pouch lacking.
> Paramphistomatidae Fischoeder, 1901

4 (3) Ventral pouch present.
> Gastrothylacidae Stiles and Goldberger, 1910

KEY TO THE FAMILIES OF THE ORDER AMPHISTOMATA FUKUI, 1929 from Fukui (1929) (III:10)

1 (2) Genital pores in posterior region of body: Parasites of reptiles.   Opisthoporidae Fukui, 1929

2 (1) Genital pores in anterior region of body.

3 (4) Excretory system in form of rosette-like diverticula, with saccular part and eight main canals; posterior sucker lacking: Parasites of reptiles.
> Angiodictyidae Looss, 1902

4 (3) Excretory system without rosette-like diverticula, bladder simple; posterior sucker present.

5 (6) Ovary usually posterior to testes, never anterior; seminal receptacle lacking: Parasites of all classes of vertebrates.
> Paramphistomatidae Fischoeder, 1901

6 (5) Ovary anterior to testes; seminal receptacle present. Parasites of fishes (Spaceroides, Tachysurus, Siganus).   Opistholebetidae Fukui, 1929

KEY FOR THE CLASSIFICATION OF AMPHISTOME PHARYNGEAL TYPES from Näsmark (1937) (III:14)

1 (8) Pharynx without bulb.

2 (5) Pharynx equipped with primary pharyngeal sac.

3 (4) Posterior pharyngeal sphincter well-developed.
Types: Pseudocladorchis, Scleroporum, Stichorchis

4 (3) Posterior pharyngeal sphincter lacking, or else represented by isolated insignificant circular muscle fibers.   Types: Cladorchis, Microrchis

5 (2) Pharynx lacking primary pharyngeal sacs.

6 (7) Middle layer of circular muscle present.
> Types: Explanatum, Pisum, Liorchis

7 (6) Middle layer of circular muscle lacking.
> Types: Paramphistoma, Calicophoron, Ijimai, Scolicocoelium

8 (1) Pharynx with pharyngeal bulb.

9 (12) Secondary pharyngeal sacs present, united with pharyngeal bulb.

10 (11) Anterior pharyngeal sphincter present.
> Types: Brumptia, Gastrodiscus

11 (10) Anterior pharyngeal sphincter lacking.
> Types: Pseudodiscus, Watsonius

12 (9) Secondary pharyngeal sacs associated with pharyngeal bulb lacking.   Type: Stephanopharynx

KEY TO THE TYPES OF GENITAL CLOACAE IN REPRESENTATIVES OF THE SUBFAMILY PARAMPHISTOMATINAE NÄSMARK (III:15)

K. I. Skrjabin

1 (2) Genital cloaca equipped with genital sucker.
> Type: Cotylophoron

2 (1) Genital cloaca without genital sucker.

3 (4) Genital cloaca with papillose genital sphincter.
Types: Microbothrium, Calicophoron, Bothriophoron, Clavula, Streptocoelium, Gigantocotyle, Scoliocoelium

4 (3) Genital cloaca without genital sphincter.

5 (6) Papillae on sphincters present.
> Types: Hippopotamus, Gigantoatrium, Minutum, Watsonius, Ishikawai, Explanatum, Pisum, Stephanopharynx, Liorchis

6 (5) Papillae on sphincters lacking.
> Types: Sellsi, Buxifrons, Epiclitum, Gracile, Microatrium

KEY TO THE SUBFAMILIES OF THE FAMILY PARAMPHISTOMATIDAE FISCHOEDER, 1901 from Näsmark (1937) (III:15)

1 (8) Pharynx lacking pharyngeal bulb.

2 (5) Pharynx equipped with primary pharyngeal diverticula.

3 (4) Testes anterior to ovary.
> Parasites of fresh water fishes in South America.   Pseudocladorchinae Näsmark, 1937
> Parasites of turtles in the Mediterranean and in North America — also in snakes of North America.   Schizamphistomatinae Looss, 1912
> Parasites of beavers (Europe and North America) and of representatives of genus Dicotyles (South America).   Stichorchinae Näsmark, 1937
> Parasites of aquatic vertebrates of South America.   Cladorchinae Fischoeder, 1901
> Parasites of an Indian elephant (Japan).   Pfenderiinae Fukui, 1929
> Parasites of amphibians of all parts of world.   Diplodiscinae Cohn, 1904
> Parasites of ducks of America.   Zygocotylinae Stunkard, 1916

4 (3) Testes large, posterior to ovary.
> Parasites of Bos taurus, Dorcelaphus dicotomus (South America).   Balanorchinae Stunkard, 1917

5 (2) Pharynx lacking primary pharyngeal diverticula.

26

6 (7) Ventral pouch lacking.

Parasites of Artiodactyla (Africa, Asia, and Holarctic).   Paramphistomatinae Fischoeder, 1901

7 (6) Ventral pouch present.

Parasites of ungulates (Africa, Asia).

Gastrothylacinae Stiles and Goldberger, 1910

8 (1) Pharynx equipped with pharyngeal bulb.

9 (10) Pharynx equipped with secondary pharyngeal diverticula.

Parasites of elephants and rhinoceros (Central Africa).   Brumptinae Stunkard, 1925

Parasites of horses, elephants (India).

Pseudodiscinae Näsmark, 1937

Parasites of primates (West Africa, India).

Watsoniinae Näsmark, 1937

Parasites of horses, horned cattle, swine, also man (Asia, Africa).

Gastrodiscinae Monticelli, 1892

Parasites of horses and elephants (India).

Pseudodiscinae Näsmark, 1937

10 (9) Pharyngeal bulb very large; secondary pharyngeal diverticula lacking.

Parasites of Bos taurus, Redunca bohor, Cobus sp.

Stephanopharynginae Stiles and Goldberger, 1910

KEY TO THE SUPERFAMILIES OF THE SUBORDER PARAMPHISTOMATATA SKRJABIN AND SCHULZ, 1937 (III:28)

K. I. Skrjabin

1 (6) Ventral sucker near posterior end of body, terminal or subterminal; excretory bladder simple, excretory system lacking rosette-like diverticula.

2 (3) Seminal receptacle present; ovary anterior to testes.   Gyliauchenoidea Skrjabin, 1949

3 (2) Seminal receptacle lacking; ovary (with rare exceptions) posterior to testes.

4 (5) Oral sucker with diverticula, usually two, more rarely one.   Cladorchiodea Skrjabin, 1949

5 (4) Oral sucker lacking diverticula.

Paramphistomatoidea Stiles and Goldberger, 1910

6 (1) Ventral sucker lacking; excretory system with rosette-like diverticula, saccular portion and eight main canals; ovary anterior to, or posterior to, testes.   Microscaphidioidea Skrjabin, 1949

KEY TO THE FAMILIES OF THE SUPERFAMILY PARAMPHISTOMATOIDEA FISCHOEDER, 1901 (III:29)

K. I. Skrjabin

1 (2) Paramphistomatoidea with large, deep, ventral cavity, so-called "ventral chamber", opening in anterior part of body posterior to oral orifice, bottom of chamber reaching almost to level of posterior sucker; genital pores opening into ventral chamber.

Gastrothylacidae Stiles and Goldberger, 1910

2 (1) Paramphistomatoidea lacking "ventral chamber".   Paramphistomatidae Fischoeder, 1901

KEY TO THE SUBFAMILIES OF THE FAMILY PARAMPHISTOMATIDEA FISCHOEDER, 1901 from Maplestone (1923) (III:30)

1 (2) Oral diverticula lacking.

Paramphistomatinae Fischoeder, 1901

2 (1) Oral diverticula present.

3 (4) Oral diverticula double.

Cladorchinae Fischoeder, 1901

4 (3) Oral diverticulum single.

Stephanopharynginae Stiles and Goldberger, 1910

KEY TO THE GENERA OF THE FAMILY PARAMPHISTOMATIDAE FISCHOEDER, 1901 from Näsmark (1937) (III:32)

1 (10) Excretory duct crossing Laurer's canal.

2 (3) Posterior sucker of paramphistoma-type; ratio of diameter of posterior sucker to body-length: 1:3.6-1:7.6; average ratio of all representatives of genus: 1:4.55.

Paramphistomum Fischoeder, 1901 (fig. 117)

3 (2) Posterior sucker not of paramphistoma-type.

4 (5) Posterior sucker of pisum-type; ratio of diameter of posterior sucker to body-length: 1:3.8.

Ugandocotyle Nasmark, 1937 (fig. 118)

5 (4) Posterior sucker not of pisum-type.

6 (7) Posterior sucker and genital cloaca of calicophoron-type; ratio of diameter of posterior sucker to body-length: 1:3.0-1:3.4 (average: 1:3.17).

Calicophoron Näsmark, 1937 (fig. 119)

7 (6) Posterior sucker and genital cloaca not of calicophoron-type.

8 (9) Posterior sucker and genital cloaca of cotylophoron-type; ratio of diameter of posterior sucker to body-length: 1:2.7-1:4.9 (average: 1:3.72).

Cotylophoron Stiles and Goldberger, 1910 (fig. 120)

9 (8) Posterior sucker of explanatum, symmeri, or duplicitestorum-type; oral sucker always of explanatum-type; ratio of diameter of posterior sucker to body-length: 1:1.50-1:2.60 (average: 1:2.22).   Gigantocotyle Näsmark, 1937 (fig. 121)

10 (1) Excretory duct and Laurer's canal not crossing.

11 (16) Oral sucker smaller than posterior sucker.

12 (13) Posterior sucker of streptocoelium-type; ratio of diameter of posterior sucker to body-length: 1:6-1:7.2 (average: 1:6.48).

Ceylonocotyle Näsmark, 1937 (fig. 122)

13 (12) Posterior sucker not of streptocoelium-type.

14 (15) Posterior sucker of nilocotyle-type; ratio of diameter of posterior sucker to body-length: 1:2.8-1:10.5 (average: 1:5.43).

Nilocotyle Näsmark, 1937 (fig. 123)

15 (14) Posterior sucker of buxifrons-type; ratio of diameter of posterior sucker to body-length: 1:4-1:6 (average: 1:5).   Buxifrons Näsmark, 1937 (fig. 124)

16 (11) Oral sucker larger than posterior sucker; ratio of diameter of posterior sucker to body-length: 1:9.67; interrelation of excretory duct and Laurer's canal not clarified.
                    Macropharynx Näsmark, 1937 (fig. 125)

KEY TO THE SUBGENERA OF THE GENUS
PARAMPHISTOMUM FISCHOEDER, 1901
after Fukui (1929) (III:33)

1 (2) Genital sucker present.
          Cotylophoron Stiles and Goldberger, 1910
2 (1) Genital sucker absent.
3 (4) Testes tandem.
          Paramphistomum Fischoeder, 1901 (fig. 117)
4 (3) Testes differently arranged.
5 (6) Testes oblique.   Explanatum Fukui, 1929
6 (5) Testes contacting laterally.
                    Buxifrons Fukui, 1929

KEY TO THE SUBGENERA OF THE GENUS
PARAMPHISTOMUM FISCHOEDER, 1901
from Popova (1937) (III:33)

1 (2) Testes tandem; Laurer's canal may or may not intersect excretory duct or bladder; ventral chamber of genital sinus present or absent.
          Paramphistomum Stiles and Goldberger, 1910
                    (fig. 117)
2 (1) Testes oblique, surfaces adjacent or separated; Laurer's canal intersecting excretory bladder or duct, opening posterior to excretory pore; two pores may be in a row, almost confluent; ventral chamber of genital sinus lacking.
          Cauliorchis Stiles and Goldberger, 1910

KEY TO THE SPECIES OF THE GENUS
BUXIFRONS NÄSMARK, 1937 from Näsmark
(1937) (III:78)

1 (2) Body 2-4 mm. in length; ratio of diameter of ventral sucker to body length: 1:4.
                    B. buxifrons (Leiper, 1910) (fig. 124)
2 (1) Body 8-12 mm. in length; ratio of diameter of ventral sucker to body length: 1:6.
                    B. maxima Näsmark, 1937

KEY TO THE SPECIES OF THE GENUS
CALICOPHORON NÄSMARK, 1937 modified from
Näsmark (1937) (III:82)

K. I. Skrjabin

1 (6) Ventral sucker and genital cloaca of calicophoron-type.
2 (3) Oral sucker of calicophoron-type, reaching length of 1.7-2 mm.; ratio of length of oral sucker to body length: 1:5.1.
          C. calicophorum (Fischoeder, 1901) (fig. 119)
3 (2) Oral sucker of ijimai-type, reaching length of 0.95-1.10 mm.; ratio of length of oral sucker to body length: 1:9-9.2.

4 (5) Ventral sucker surrounded by folded, garland-like ridge; body swollen.   C. raja Näsmark, 1937
5 (6) Ventral sucker without such ridge, body form as in C. calicophorum.   C. ijimai (Fukui, 1922)
6 (1) Genital cloaca of calicophoron-type; type of ventral and oral suckers not clarified.
7 (8) Testes oblique.
                    C. crassum (Stiles and Goldberger, 1910)
8 (7) Testes not oblique.
9 (10) Testes symmetrical.
                    C. cauliorchis (Stiles and Goldberger, 1910)
10 (9) Testes tandem.
                    C. papillosum (Stiles and Goldberger, 1910)

KEY TO THE SPECIES OF THE GENUS
CEYLONCOTYLE NÄSMARK, 1937 modified from
Näsmark (1937) (III:103)

K. I. Skrjabin

1 (4) Esophagus with well-developed bulb; oral sucker with crude sphincter.
2 (3) Genital cloaca with genital sphincter.
                    C. scoliocoelium (Fischoeder, 1901) (fig. 122)
3 (2) Genital cloaca without genital sphincter.
                    C. dicranocoelium (Fischoeder, 1901)
4 (1) Esophagus without bulb; oral sucker without sphincter.
5 (6) Genital cloaca with genital sphincter; short esophagus without bulb, with special esophageal sphincter posteriorly.
                    C. streptocoelium (Fischoeder, 1901)
6 (5) Genital cloaca without genital sphincter; long esophagus without special esophageal sphincter posteriorly.   C. orthocoelium (Fischoeder, 1901)

KEY TO THE SPECIES OF THE GENUS
COTYLOPHORON STILES AND GOLDBERGER,
1910 modified from Näsmark (1937) (III:119-120)

K. I. Skrjabin

1 (4) Body comparatively broad, slightly flattened dorso-ventrally; ventral sucker ventral, subterminal; ratio of ventral sucker diameter to body-length: 1:2.7-1:2.9; testes oblique.
2 (3) Body reaching 5 mm.; aperture of ventral sucker usually surrounded by folded, garland-like ridge; color yellowish-brown; esophagus with well-developed bulb; ratio of oral sucker to diameter of genital sucker: 1:2.7.
                    C. cotylophorum (Fischoeder, 1901) (fig. 120)
3 (2) Body 3 mm. long; aperture of ventral sucker lacking folded ridge; body white or light yellow; esophagus without bulb; ratio of oral sucker to diameter of genital sucker: 1:1.07.
                    C. fulleborni Näsmark, 1937
4 (1) Body elongate, conical, not compressed dorso-ventrally; ventral sucker terminal; ratio of diameter of ventral sucker to body length: 1:3.7-1:4.9; testes tandem; body color white.

5 (6) Body 6 mm. long; esophagus without bulb, without traces of muscular thickenings; ratio of oral sucker to diameter of genital sucker: 1:1.83.
C. indicum Stiles and Goldberger, 1910

6 (5) Body about 10 mm. long; esophagus without bulb, with weakly developed, distinctly thickened esophageal muscles; ratio of oral sucker to diameter of genital sucker: 1:1.   C. jacksoni Näsmark, 1937

KEY TO THE SPECIES OF THE GENUS
GIGANTOCOTYLE NÄSMARK, 1937
modified from Näsmark (1937) (III:134-135)

K. I. Skrjabin

1 (6) Ventral sucker of explanatum-type.
2 (5) Testes oblique.
3 (4) Genital cloaca of explanatum-type.
G. explanatum (Creplin, 1847) (fig. 121)
4 (3) Genital cloaca of gigantocotyle-type.
G. gigantocotyle (Brandes, 1896)
5 (2) Testes tandem.
G. bathycotyle (Fischoeder, 1901)
6 (1) Ventral sucker not of explanatum-type.
7 (10) Ventral sucker of symmeri-type.
8 (9) Genital cloaca of gigantocotyle-type.
G. symmeri Näsmark, 1937
9 (8) Genital cloaca of explanatum-type.
G. formosanum (Fukui, 1929)
10 (7) Ventral sucker of duplicitestorum-type.
G. duplicitestorum Näsmark, 1937

KEY TO THE SPECIES OF THE GENUS
NILOCOTYLE NÄSMARK, 1937
modified from Näsmark (1937) (III:162)

K. I. Skrjabin

1 (6) Oral sucker with lip-like sphincter; oral sucker of dicranocoelium-type.
2 (5) Body length exceeding 2 mm.
3 (4) Body length about 2.24 mm.; esophageal bulb present; weakly developed microatrium-type genital cloaca present.   N. microatrium Näsmark, 1937
4 (3) Body length about 2.56 mm.; with well-developed esophageal bulb; genital cloaca of minutum-type.   N. praesphinctris Näsmark, 1937
5 (2) Body length 1.53 mm.; esophageal bulb very large; genital cloaca of buxifrons-type.
N. pygmaeum Näsmark, 1937
6 (1) Oral sucker without lip-like sphincter, of paramphistoma-type.
7 (8) Genital cloaca of gigantoatrium-type.
N. gigantoatrium Näsmark, 1937 (fig. 123)
8 (7) Genital cloaca of different type.
9 (12) Genital cloaca of sellsi-type.
10 (11) Body not flattened dorso-ventrally; without esophageal bulb; testes entire.
N. sellsi (Leiper, 1910)
11 (10) Body markedly flattened dorso-ventrally, equipped with lateral appendices at posterior end;

with esophageal bulb; tested lobed.
N. polycladiformae Näsmark, 1937
12 (9) Genital cloaca not of sellsi-type.
13 (16) Genital cloaca of hippopotami-type.
14 (15) Internal diameter of genital cloaca 0.088 mm.; ratio of genital cloaca diameter to length of oral sucker: 1:2.23; aperture of ventral sucker narrow; sucker cavity deep; esophageal bulb lacking.
N. hippopotami Näsmark, 1937
15 (14) Internal diameter of genital cloaca 0.068 mm.; ratio of cloaca diameter to length of oral sucker: 1:3.56; aperture of ventral sucker equal to internal diameter of genital cloaca; esophageal bulb well-developed.   N. circulare Näsmark, 1937
16 (13) Genital cloaca not of hippopotami-type.
17 (20) Genital cloaca of minutum-type.
18 (19) Oral sucker relatively large; ratio of oral sucker length to body length: 1:5.9-1:6.
N. minutum (Leiper, 1910)
19 (18) Oral sucker relatively small; ratio of sucker length to body length: 1:8.5.
N. leiperi Näsmark, 1937
20 (17) Genital cloaca not of minutum-type.
21 (22) Genital cloaca of wagandi-type; body without transverse, protruding ridges.
N. wagandi (Leiper, 1910)
22 (21) Genital cloaca of epiclitum-type; entire body equipped with system of protruding, annular ridges in parallel transverse rows.
N. paradoxus Näsmark, 1937

KEY TO THE GENERA OF THE FAMILY
GASTROTHYLACIDAE STILES AND GOLDBERGER,
1910 from Maplestone (1923) (III:184)

1 (2) Uterus passing transversely from one side of body to other side in equatorial zone of body.
Gastrothylax Poirier, 1883 (fig. 126)
2 (1) Uterus concentrated only in medial zone of body for entire length.
3 (4) Testes symmetrical.
Carmyerius Stiles and Goldberger, 1910 (fig. 127)
4 (3) Testes superimposed, medial.
Fischoederius Stiles and Goldberger, 1910 (fig. 128)

KEY TO THE SPECIES OF THE GENUS
CARMYERIUS STILES AND GOLDBERGER, 1910
from Maplestone (1923) (III:193)

1 (2) Genital pore external to pore of ventral chamber. Host: Limnotragus gratus.
C. exoporus Maplestone, 1923
2 (1) Genital pore within ventral chamber.
3 (4) Excretory duct and Laurer's canal uniting, forming common duct leading to exterior. Host: Cobus maria.   C. wenyoni (Leiper, 1908)
4 (3) Excretory duct and Laurer's canal not uniting.
5 (6) Transverse section of ventral pouch yielding five corners. Host: hippopotamus.
C. cruciformis (Leiper, 1910)

6 (5) Transverse section of ventral pouch not yielding five corners.

7 (8) Intestinal ceca reaching testes. Parasites of ruminants.   C. spatiosus (Brandes, 1898)

8 (7) Intestinal ceca not reaching beyond midpoint of body. Parasites of ruminants.

C. gregarius (Looss, 1896) (fig. 127)

KEY TO THE SPECIES OF THE GENUS FISCHOEDERIUS STILES AND GOLDBERGER, 1910 (III:209)

K. I. Skrjabin

1 (2) Intestinal ceca long, reaching at least to testes.   F. cobboldi (Poirier, 1883)

2 (1) Intestinal ceca short, never reaching beyond middle of body.

F. elongatus (Poirier, 1883) (fig. 128)

KEY TO THE FAMILIES OF THE SUPERFAMILY CLADORCHOIDEA SKRJABIN, 1949 from Skrjabin (1949) (III:222-223)

1 (2) Oral sucker equipped with single diverticulum; pharyngeal bulb and genital sucker lacking. Parasites of mammals (ruminants).

Stephanopharyngidae Skrjabin, 1949

2 (1) Oral sucker equipped with two diverticula.

3 (6) Pharyngeal bulb lacking.

4 (5) Body with two tab-like posterior appendages; genital sucker present. Parasites of mammals (elephants and rhinoceros).   Brumptidae Skrjabin, 1949

5 (4) Body without posterior appendages; genital sucker absent or present. Parasites of mammals and fishes.

Cladorchidae Southwell and Kirshner, 1937

6 (3) Pharyngeal bulb present.

7 (8) Body sub-divided into two distinct regions, anterior and posterior; genital sucker absent. Parasites of mammals.

Gastrodiscidae Stiles and Goldberger, 1910

8 (7) Body not sub-divided into two portions; ventral sucker with protuberance within cavity (similar to a second or auxilliary sucker); genital sucker present or absent (pharyngeal bulb absent in subfamily Opisthodiscinae). Parasites of amphibians, reptiles, fishes.   Diplodiscinae Skrjabin, 1949

KEY TO THE SUBFAMILIES OF THE FAMILY CLADORCHIDAE STILES AND GOLDBERGER, 1910 from Skrjabin (1949) (III:224)

1 (8) Genital sucker present.

2 (5) Ovary posterior to testes. Intestinal parasites of fishes.

3 (4) Anterior end of body separated from rest of body by transverse constriction; posterior portion of body with two rounded protuberances at each side of ventral sucker; cirrus sac lacking; testes extra-cecal,

in anterior part of body, symmetrical.

Kalitrematinae Travassos, 1933

4 (3) Anterior portion of body without constriction; posterior protuberances lacking; cirrus sac present; testes symmetrical, extra and inter-cecal, in equatorial zone of body.

Pseudocladorchinae Näsmark, 1937

5 (2) Parasites of mammals.

6 (7) Ovary anterior to testes; testes in posterior portion of body, symmetrical, inter-cecal; cirrus sac present.   Balanorchinae Stunkard, 1925

7 (6) Ovary posterior to testes; testes in equatorial zone, tandem or symmetrical, inter-cecal; cirrus sac present.   Cladorchinae Fischoeder, 1901

8 (1) Genital sucker lacking; ovary posterior to testes. Parasites of mammals.

9 (10) Large cirrus sac present; diverticula present in muscular wall of oral sucker, not protruding externally; testes symmetrical. Parasites of elephants.   Pfenderiinae Fukui, 1929

10 (9) Cirrus sac lacking; diverticula protruding externally in form of large muscular, lateral outgrowths of oral sucker; testes symmetrical. Parasites of horses and elephants.

Pseudodiscinae Näsmark, 1937

KEY TO THE GENERA OF THE SUBFAMILY CLADORCHINAE FISCHOEDER, 1901 (III:225)

K. I. Skrjabin

1 (4) Testes composed of complex bundles of branching, club-shaped appendices, symmetrical.

2 (3) Testes equatorial.

Cladorchis Fischoeder, 1901 (fig. 129)

3 (2) Testes in anterior half of body.

Taxorchis Fischoeder, 1901 (fig. 130)

4 (1) Testes compact, without sharply expressed lobes, lacking branching appendices, tandem.

Chiostichorchis Artigas and Pacheco, 1932 (fig. 131)

KEY TO THE SPECIES OF THE GENUS CLADORCHIS FISCHOEDER, 1901 (III:225)

K. I. Skrjabin

1 (2) Diameter of ventral sucker one-fifth body length; internal surface of sucker smooth.

C. pyriformis (Diesing, 1838) (fig. 129)

2 (1) Diameter of ventral sucker about 10/23 of body length; internal surface of sucker lined with papillae.   C. asper (Diesing, 1838)

KEY TO THE SPECIES OF THE GENUS STICHORCHIS FISCHOEDER, 1901 (III:244)

K. I. Skrjabin

1 (2) Oral diverticula large; intestinal ceca not reaching posterior end of body; genital sucker powerful.   S. giganteus (Diesing, 1835) (fig. 132)

2 (1) Oral diverticula short, in muscular wall of sucker; intestinal ceca reaching posterior end of body; genital sucker rudimentary.

S. subtriquetrus (Rudolphi, 1814)

KEY TO THE GENERA OF THE SUBFAMILY PFENDERIINAE FUKUI, 1929 (III:273)

K. I. Skrjabin

1 (2) Pharynx lacking; genital pore at level of intestinal bifurcation; posterior sucker terminal, with internal papillae; intestinal ceca long, sinuous.

Pfenderius Stiles and Goldberger, 1910 (fig. 133)

2 (1) Pharynx present; genital pore considerably anterior to intestinal bifurcation; posterior sucker subterminal, without papillae; intestinal ceca short.

Tugumaea Fukui, 1926 (fig. 134)

KEY TO THE SPECIES OF THE GENUS PFENDERIUS STILES AND GOLDBERGER, 1910 (III:274)

K. I. Skrjabin

1 (2) Body 4.5-5.5 mm. in length; genital pore 1-1.5 mm. from anterior end of body.

P. papillatus (Cobbold, 1882) (fig. 133)

2 (1) Body 2.3 mm. in length; genital pore 0.48 mm. from anterior end of body.

P. birmanicus Bhalerao, 1935

KEY TO THE SUBFAMILIES OF THE FAMILY DIPLODISCIDAE SKRJABIN, 1949 (III:309)

K. I. Skrjabin

1 (12) Genital sucker absent.

2 (3) Pharyngeal bulb elongate, cylindrical; oral diverticula rudimentary; cirrus sac rudimentary; vitellaria small, extra-cecal.

Nematophilinae Skrjabin, 1949

3 (2) Pharyngeal bulb round or pyriform.

4 (7) Cirrus sac absent.

5 (6) Posterior sucker equipped with two lateral papilla-like protuberances; genital pore posterior to intestinal bifurcation. Parasites of mammals, birds, fishes.

Zygocotylinae Stunkard, 1917

6 (5) Posterior sucker of usual structure, without lateral protuberances; genital pore anterior to intestinal bifurcation, directly posterior to oral sucker. Parasites of mammals, (including man).

Watsoniinae Näsmark, 1937

7 (4) Cirrus sac present.

8 (11) Ventral sucker with internal protuberance resembling accessory sucker.

9 (10) Mature individuals with one testis formed from merging of two testes in early growth; pharyngeal bulb present.   Diplodiscinae Cohn, 1904

10 (9) Two testes in both young and mature specimens; pharyngeal bulb lacking.

Opisthodiscinae Skrjabin, 1949

11 (8) Ventral sucker without supplementary internal protuberances in cavity; two testes in all stages; pharyngeal bulb present.

Schizamphistomatinae Looss, 1912

12 (1) Genital sucker present.

13 (14) Cirrus sac absent; oral diverticula small, protruding laterally. Parasites of fishes.

Dadayinae Fukui, 1929

14 (13) Cirrus sac present.

15 (16) Oral diverticula long, forming laterally protuberant appendages; testes inter-cecal, symmetrical. Parasites of turtles.

Helostomatinae Skrjabin, 1949

16 (15) Oral diverticula short, lateral; testes symmetrical, extra-cecal; genital sucker exceptionally large. Parasite of fishes.

Nicollodiscinae Skrjabin, 1949

KEY TO THE GENERA OF THE SUBFAMILY DIPLODISCINAE COHN, 1904 modified from Price (1937) (III:311)

K. I. Skrjabin

1 (4) Posterior sucker equipped with small central accessory sucker.

2 (3) Mature forms with two testes.

Megalodiscus Chandler, 1923 (fig. 135)

3 (2) Mature forms with single testis.

Diplodiscus Diesing, 1836 (fig. 136)

4 (1) Posterior sucker without accessory sucker.

5 (6) Testes medial; posterior sucker sub-divided.

Catadiscus Cohn, 1904 (fig. 137)

6 (5) Testes lateral; posterior sucker not sub-divided.   Dermatemytrema Price, 1937 (fig. 138)

KEY TO THE SPECIES OF THE GENUS DIPLODISCUS DIESING, 1936 (III:312)

K. I. Skrjabin

1 (8) Intestinal ceca long, reaching zone of ventral sucker.

2 (7) Genital pore at level of intestinal bifurcation or slightly posterior.

3 (6) Vitellaria anteriorly reaching esophageal bulb.

4 (5) Eggs relatively small.

D. subclavatus (Goeze, 1782) (fig. 136)

5 (4) Eggs relatively large.

D. japonicus (Yamaguti, 1936)

6 (3) Vitellaria anteriorly reaching oral diverticula.

D. mehrai Pande, 1937

7 (2) Genital pore considerably posterior to intestinal bifuraction.   D. amphichrus Tubangui, 1933

8 (1) Intestinal ceca short.

9 (10) Genital pore posterior to intestinal bifurcation.   D. megalochrus Johnston, 1912

10 (9) Genital pore at level of oral diverticula.

D. doyeri Ortlepp, 1926

KEY TO THE SPECIES OF THE GENUS
MEGALODISCUS CHANDLER, 1923 modified from
Bravo (1941) (III:345)

K. I. Skrjabin

1 (8) Intestinal ceca reaching ventral sucker.
2 (7) Vitellaria extending from posterior edge of
posterior testis to origin of ventral sucker.
3 (6) Vitellaria forming one group on each side of
body.
4 (5) Diameter of ventral sucker surpassing diameter of body. M. americanus Chandler, 1923 (fig. 135)
5 (4) Diameter of ventral sucker less than diameter
of body.   M. microphagus Ingles, 1936
6 (3) Vitellaria forming four groups, two on each
side of body.   M. intermedius (Hunter, 1930)
7 (2) Vitellaria extending from anterior edge of anterior testis to region posterior to ovary.
                            M. temperatus (Stafford, 1905)
8 (1) Intestinal ceca reaching anterior edge of
ovary.   M. rankini Bravo, 1941
    Note: M. montezuma Travassos, 1934 omitted from
key.

KEY TO THE GENERA OF THE SUBFAMILY
HELOSTOMATINAE SKRJABIN, 1949 (III:373)

K. I. Skrjabin

1 (2) Oral diverticula on long stalks; uterus forming dense loops in space between testes; testes symmetrical.   Helostomatis Fukui, 1929 (fig. 139)
2 (1) Oral diverticula large, without elongate
stalks; uterus in space between testes, not forming
dense loops; testes slightly oblique.
            Protocladorchis Willey, 1935 (fig. 140)

KEY TO THE SPECIES OF THE GENUS
HELOSTOMATIS FUKUI, 1929 (III:374)

K. I. Skrjabin

1 (2) Posterior sucker with three appendices on
posterior edge; ovary entire, round or oval; eggs:
0.145 mm. (length) x 0.064 mm. (width).
        H. helostomatis (MacCallum, 1905) (fig. 139)
2 (1) Posterior sucker round without appendices;
ovary tri-lobed; eggs: 0.078-0.082 mm. (length) x
0.042-0.044 mm. (width).   H. sakrei Bhalerao, 1937

KEY TO THE GENERA OF THE SUBFAMILY
NEMATOPHILINAE SKRJABIN, 1949 (III:385)

K. I. Skrjabin

1 (2) Vitelline follicles minute, distinct; testes
minute, stellate, with irregularly distributed branching arms. Parasites of turtles.
        Nematophila Travassos, 1934 (fig. 141)
2 (1) Vitelline follicles relatively large, not clearly

defined; testes rounded, entire or with large, rounded
lobes. Parasites of fishes.
        Orientodiscus Srivastava, 1938 (fig. 142)

KEY TO THE SPECIES OF THE GENUS
ORIENTODISCUS SRIVASTAVA, 1938 (III:389)

K. I. Skrjabin

1 (2) Testes and ovary lobular in mature and in
young specimens.
            O. lobatum Srivastava, 1938 (fig. 142)
2 (1) Testes and ovary spherical, entire in mature
and in young specimens.   O. jumnai Srivastava, 1938

KEY TO THE SPECIES OF THE GENUS
SCHIZAMPHISTOMOIDES STUNKARD, 1925 from
Price (1936) (III:455)

1 (2) Maximal body width at level of posterior
sucker; testes pre-equatorial. Parasites of marine
turtles, Chelone mydas.   S. spinulosum (Looss, 1901)
2 (1) Maximal body width anterior to posterior
sucker; testes equatorial or post-equatorial. Parasites of fresh-water turtles.
3 (4) Posterior sucker separated from body by
constriction; testes pre-equatorial. Parasites of
Pelomedusa galeata.
            S. constrictus Price, 1936 (fig. 143)
4 (3) Posterior sucker not separated from body by
constriction; testes equatorial. Parasites of Derma-
temys mawii.
        S. tabascensis Caballero and Sokoloff, 1934

KEY TO THE GENERA OF THE SUBFAMILY
WATSONIINAE NÄSMARK, 1937 (III:475)

K. I. Skrjabin

1 (2) Esophageal bulb absent; genital pore slightly
posterior to intestinal bifurcation; intestinal ceca
somewhat wavy in outline. Parasites of muskrats.
        Wardius Barker and East, 1915 (fig. 144)
2 (1) Esophageal bulb present.
3 (4) Genital pore anterior to intestinal bifurcation,
at level of middle of oral diverticula; intestinal ceca
straight. Parasites of man and monkeys.
        Watsonius Stiles and Goldberger, 1910 (fig. 145)
4 (3) Genital pore posterior to intestinal bifurcation;
intestinal ceca of wavy outline. Parasites of elephants.
        Hawkesius Stiles and Goldberger, 1910 (fig. 146)

KEY TO THE GENERA OF THE SUBFAMILY
ZYGOCOTYLINAE WARD, 1917 (III:487)

K. I. Skrjabin

1 (2) Lymphatic system of three pairs of longitudinal trunks: one dorsal, two ventral. Parasites of mammals and birds. Zygocotyle Stunkard, 1917 (fig. 147)

2 (1) Lymphatic system of two pairs of longitudinal trunks. Parasites of reptiles.

Stunkardia Bhalerao, 1931 (fig. 148)

KEY TO THE GENERA OF THE FAMILY GASTRODISCIDAE STILES AND GOLDBERGER, 1910 (III:504)

K. I. Skrjabin

1 (2) Anterior section of body flat, broad; posterior section narrow, spherical.

Homalogaster Poirier, 1882 (fig. 149)

2 (1) Anterior section of body narrow, conical; posterior section broad, thickened.

3 (4) Genital pore in anterior part of body; ventral surface of posterior section not covered with papillae.

Gastrodiscoides Leiper, 1913 (fig. 150)

4 (3) Genital pore in anterior part of posterior section of body; ventral surface of posterior section of body covered with papillae.

Gastrodiscus Leuckart, 1877 (fig. 151)

KEY TO THE SPECIES OF THE GENUS GASTRODISCUS LEUCKART, 1877 (III:505)

K. I. Skrjabin

1 (2) Genital pore displaced from anterior edge of posterior part of body by less than 1 mm., i.e., at level of esophagus.

G. aegyptiacus (Cobbold, 1876) (fig. 151)

2 (1) Genital pore displaced from anterior edge of posterior part of body by more than 1 mm., i.e., posterior to intestinal bifurcation.

G. secundus Looss, 1907

KEY TO THE GENERA OF THE FAMILY MICROSCAPHIIDAE TRAVASSOS, 1922 from Ruiz (1943) (III:523)

1 (12) Posterior end of body with two-pronged protuberance or with terminal cavities.

2 (3) Genital sucker present.

Denticauda Fukui, 1929

3 (2) Genital sucker absent.

4 (5) Four pairs of papillae present posteriorly.

Neoctangium Ruiz, 1943 (fig. 152)

5 (4) Papillae absent posteriorly.

6 (7) Vitellaria in three separate fields: two extra-cecal, one inter-cecal. Parasites of turtles.

Octangium Looss, 1902 (fig. 153)

7 (6) Vitellaria with different distribution.

8 (9) Vitellaria extra-cecally in two separate fields. Parasites of fishes.

Hexangitrema Price, 1937 (fig. 154)

9 (8) Vitellaria in V- or Y-shaped configurations.

10 (11) Loops of uterus inter-cecal and extra-cecal, posterior to intestinal ceca; vitellaria in Y-shaped configuration. Parasites of fishes.

Parabaris Travassos, 1922 (fig. 155)

11 (10) Loops of uterus inter-cecal only; vitellaria in V-shaped configuration. Parasites of turtles.

Octangioides Price, 1937 (fig. 156)

12 (1) Posterior end of body rounded, smooth, without protuberances.

13 (14) Ventral surface of body with longitudinal rows of glandular structures.

Deuterobaris Looss, 1900 (fig. 157)

14 (13) Ventral surface of body without longitudinal rows of glandular structures.

15 (16) Gonads posterior to intestinal ceca, in posterior third of body.

Hexangium Goto and Ozaki, 1929 (fig. 158)

16 (15) Gonads inter-cecal, in middle third of body.

17 (18) Oral diverticula long; esophagus equipped anteriorly with spine-like structures.

Microscaphidium Looss, 1900 (fig. 159)

18 (17) Oral diverticula rudimentary: esophagus un-armed.

19 (20) Body equipped with two lateral groups of vesicular structures.

Angiodictyum Looss, 1902 (fig. 160)

20 (19) Body lacking lateral vesicular structures.

Polyangium Looss, 1902 (fig. 161)

KEY TO THE SPECIES OF THE GENUS MICROSCAPHIDIUM LOOSS, 1899 (III:524)

K. I. Skrjabin

1 (2) Spinous section of esophagus extending to same level as diverticula of oral sucker; with six or seven (rarely eight) rosette-like diverticula of excretory pore. Intestinal parasites of Chelone mydas.

M. reticularis (van Beneden, 1859) (fig. 159)

2 (1) Spinous section of esophagus reaching only half length of diverticula of oral sucker; seven or eight rosette-like diverticula of excretory pore present. Intestinal parasites of Chelone mydas.

M. aberrans Looss, 1902

KEY TO THE SPECIES OF THE GENUS HEXANGIUM GOTO AND OZAKI, 1929 (III:541)

K. I. Skrjabin

1 (2) Testes oblique; body 8-10.3 mm. long. Parasites of Siganus fuscescens.

H. sigani Goto and Ozaki, 1929 (fig. 158)

2 (1) Testes symmetrical; body 4.17 mm. long. Parasites of Theuthis concalenata.

H. secundum Annereaux, 1947

KEY TO THE SPECIES OF THE GENUS OCTANGIUM LOOSS, 1902 (III:551)

K. I. Skrjabin

1 (2) Body length 7 mm., width 2 mm.; six or seven (rarely eight) rosette-like diverticula present in excretory pore. Intestinal parasites of

Chelone mydas (Mediterranean).

O. sagitta (Looss, 1899) (fig. 153)

2 (1) Body length less than 6 mm.

3 (4) Body length 5.5 mm., width 1.2 mm.; eggs: 0.07-0.075 mm. (length) x 0.045 mm. (width). Intestinal parasites of Chelone mydas (Japan).

O. takanoi Kobayashi, 1921

4 (3) Body length 3.4 mm., width 0.9 mm.; seven or eight rosette-like diverticula, present in excretory pore; eggs: 0.084 mm. (length) x 0.05 mm. (width). Intestinal parasites of Chelone mydas (Mediterranean).

O. hasta Looss, 1902

KEY TO THE SPECIES OF THE GENUS POLYANGIUM LOOSS, 1902 (III:562)

K. I. Skrjabin

1 (2) Pharyngeal bulb present at end of pharynx; body length 8-8.5 mm., width 1.4-1.6 mm.; eggs: 0.084 x 0.05 mm. Parasites of Chelone mydas (Mediterranean).

P. linguatula (Looss, 1899) (fig. 161)

2 (1) Pharyngeal bulb absent; body length 10-11mm., width 2 mm.; eggs: 0.070 x 0.04 mm. Parasites of Chelone mydas (Singapore).

P. miyajimai Kobayashi, 1921

Body length 10.2 mm., width 1.75 mm.; eggs: 0.072-0.099 x 0.0475-0.060 mm. Kidney parasites of birds, Colymbus arcticus.   P. colymbi (Poche, 1926)

KEY TO THE GENERA OF THE FAMILY GYLIAUCHENIDAE OZAKI, 1933 (III:576)

K. I. Skrjabin

1 (4) Prepharynx exceptionally long, forming several folds; vitellaria concentrated in anterior half of body.

2 (3) Testes oblique, anterior to ventral sucker; genital pore at level of intestinal ceca, or posterior to ceca; prepharynx forming several folds.

Gyliauchen Nicoll, 1915 (fig. 162)

3 (2) Testes symmetrical, posterior to ventral sucker; genital pore at level of pharynx; folds of prepharynx weakly developed.

Paragyliauchen Yamaguti, 1934 (fig. 163)

4 (1) Prepharynx long, straight, not forming folds; vitellaria in anterior and posterior body regions.

Telotrema Ozaki, 1933 (fig. 164)

LITERATURE ON THE TREMATODES OF THE SUBORDER PARAMPHISTOMATA SKRJABIN AND SCHULZ, 1937 (III:609-610)

Badanin, N. V. 1929. On the discovery of the human parasite, Gastrodiscus hominis, in wild boar in Kazakhstan. Russky Zhurnal Tropicheskoy Meditsiny. 7(8):514-516.

Belayeva, K., P. Kovylkova, and L. Kobaydova. 1937. On the fauna of the parasitic worms of Rana ridibunda in the vicinity of Tashkent. Trudy Sredne-

Aziatskogo Gosudarstvennogo Universiteta, seriya zoologiya, 8-a. No. 32; 7 pp.

Borisov, A. M. 1948. Pathological changes in the anatomy and histology of the intestine of beavers caused by the trematode, Stichorchis subtriquetrus (Rud., 1814). Parazitofauna i Zabolevaniya Dikikh Zhivotnykh, Moskva. pp. 195-198.

Bykovsky, B. E. 1933. Trematodes of amphibians in the vicinity of Kiev. Zoologischer Anzeiger. 102(1-2):44-58. (In German).

Vlasenko, N. 1930. On the trematode fauna of amphibians and reptiles in the vicinity of Kharkov. Trudy Kharkivskogo Tovaristva Doslidnikiv Prirodi. 53(1):49-57. (In Ukrainian).

Dogiel, V. A. 1947. Course in general parasitology. Second Ed. Uchpedgiz, Leningrad. 371 pp.

Dubinina (Gorbunova), M. N. 1945. Ecological research on the parasite fauna of Rana ridibunda of the Volga delta. Referaty Rabot Uchrezhdeny Otdeleniya Biologicheskikh Nauk Akad. Nauk SSSR za 1941-1943 gg. pp. 168-169.

Zhadin, V. 1921. Trematodes of amphibians and unionids in the vicinity of Murom. Raboty Okskoy Biologicheskoy Stantii 1(2-3):68-89.

Zmeev, G. and B. E. Bykhovsky. 1940. Parasites of amphibians of the Gissarskaya valley. Trudy Tadzhikikoy Bazy Akad. Nauk SSSR. 11:127-143.

Isaychikov, I. M. 1922. On the knowledge of the helminth fauna of amphibians of Russia. Centralblatt für Bakteriologie, Parasitenkunde, and Infektionskrankheiten. 57(11-13):272-274. (In German).

Isaychikov, I. M. 1923. On the knowledge of the helminth fauna of amphibians of Russia, II. Centralblatt für Bakteriologie, Parasitenkunde, und Infektionskrankheiten. 59(1-4):19-26. (In German).

Isaychikov, I. M. 1926. On the knowledge of the helminth fauna of amphibians of Russia. Trudy Sibirskogo Veterinarnogo Instituta. No. 7:61-159.

Isaychikov, I. M. and N. P. Zakharov. 1929. On the fauna of parasitic worms of Rana esculenta of the Don district. Russky Gidrobiologichsky Zhurnal. 8(1-3):49-54.

Layman, E. M. 1933. Several new facts concerning the ecology of trematodes of amphibians. Zoologischer Anzeiger. 101(7-8):199-201. (In German).

Moskalev, B. S. 1948. Experiments in testing antihelminthic preparations for combating stichorchiasis and ascariasis of beaver. Parazitofauna i Zaboleyvaniya Dikikh Zhivotnykh, Moskva. pp. 185-194.

Orlov, I. V. 1941. Study of the life cycle of the trematode, Stichorchis subtriquetrus, parasitic in beavers. Doklady Akad. Nauk SSSR. 31(6):641-643.

Orlov, I. V. 1948. Results of the work of the 209th Union Helminthological Expedition into the Voronezh Government Preserve in the summer of 1940. Parazitofauna i Zabolevaniya Dikikh Zhivotnykh, Moskva. pp. 105-113.

Orlov, I. V. 1948. On the study of the helminth fauna of beavers. Parazitofauna i Zabolevaniya Dikikh Zhivotnykh, Moskva. pp. 114-125.

Orlov, I. V. 1948. Sources of helminth infection in beavers under farm conditions in the Voronezh Preserve. Parazitofauna i Zabolevaniya Dikikh Zhivotnykh, Moskva. pp. 160-165.

Orlov, I. V. 1948. Elaboration of the means of diagnosing stichorchiasis in living beavers. Parazitofauna i Zabolevaniya Dikikh Zhivotnykh, Moskva. pp. 129-133.

Orlov, I. V. 1948. Study on the life cycle of the trematode of beavers, Stichorchis subtriquetris (Rudolphi, 1814). Parazitofauna i Zabolevaniya Dikikh Zhivotnykh, Moskva. pp. 134-152.

Orlov, I. V. 1948. Measures for protecting beavers from helminthiases. Parazitofauna i Zabolevaniya Dikikh Zhivotnykh, Moskva. pp. 174-184.

Orlov, I. V. and L. G. Dikesman. 1948. Distribution of larval stichorchiasis among molluscs of the Usmanka River. Parazitofauna i Zabolevaniya Dikikh Zhivotnykh, Moskva. pp. 153-159.

Popova, K. A. 1937. Paramphistomum (Cautiorchis) skrjabini n sp. from the rumen of long-horned cattle. In: Skrjabin, K. I. and R. Ed. S. Schulz, Helminthiases of long-horned cattle and their young. Selkhozgiz, Moskva. 723 pp.

Skrjabin, K. I. 1916. On the knowledge of the helminth fauna of domestic animals of Turkestan. Dissertatsiya, Yuriev.

Skrjabin, K. I. 1931. Helminth infestations of reindeer. Selkhozgiz, Moskva-Leningrad. 86 pp.

Skrjabin, K. I. and V. S. Ershov. 1933. Helminthaises of the horse. Selkhozgiz, Moskva-Leningrad. 408 pp.

Skrjabin, K. I., A. I. Petrov, I. V. Orlov, et al. 1941. Short course in the parasitology of domestic animals. Fifth Ed. Selkhozgiz, Moskva.

Skrjabin, K. I. and R. Ed. S. Schulz. 1940. Fundamental of general helminthology. Selkhozgiz, Moskva. 470 pp.

Skrjabin, K. I. and R. Ed. S. Schulz. 1937. Helminthology. Veterinary parasitology and infectious diseases of domestic animals. Second Ed. Selkhozgiz, Moskva. 418 pp.

Skrjabin, K. I. and R. Ed. S. Schulz. 1937. Helminthiases of long-horned cattle and their young. Selkhozgiz, Moskva. 723 pp.

Timofeev, N. E. 1900. Trematodes of amphibians and reptiles in the vicinity of Kharkov. Trudy Obschestva Ispytateley Prirody pri Kharkovskom Universitete. 34:37-66.

LIST OF SUPPLEMENTARY ILLUSTRATIONS

Cladorchidae Southwell and Kirschner, 1937
  Balanorchis anastrophus Fischoeder, 1901 (fig. 797)
  Cleptodiscus reticulatus Linton, 1910 (fig. 798)
  Kalitrema kalitrema Travassos, 1933 (fig. 799)
  Pseudocladorchis cylindricus (Diesing, 1836) (fig. 800)
  Pseudodiscus collinsi (Cobbold, 1875) (fig. 801)
Diplodiscidae Skrjabin, 1949
  Opisthodiscus diplodiscoides Cohn, 1904 (fig. 802)
  Dadayius marenzelleri (Daday, 1907) (fig. 803)
  Nicollodiscus gangeticus Srivastava, 1938 (fig. 804)
  Schizamphistomum scleroporum (Creplin, 1844) (fig. 805)
  Allassostoma magnum Stunkard, 1917 (fig. 806)
  Allassostomoides parvum (Stunkard, 1917) (fig. 807)
  Chiorchis fabaceus (Diesing, 1839) (fig. 808)
  Dadaytrema oxycephala (Diesing, 1836) (fig. 809)
  Microrchis megacotyle (Diesing, 1836) (fig. 810)
  Neocladorchis poonaensis Bhalerao, 1937 (fig. 811)
  Ophioxenos dienteros Sumwalt, 1926 (fig. 812)
  Travassosinia dilatata (Daday, 1907) (fig. 813)
  Quasichiorchis purvisi (Southwell and Kirshner, 1937) (fig. 814)
  Halltrema avitellina Lent and Freitas, 1939 (fig. 816)
Brumptidae Skrjabin, 1949
  Brumptia bicaudata (Poirier, 1908) (fig. 817)
Stephanopharyngidae Skrjabin, 1949
  Stephanopharynx compactus Fischoeder, 1901 (fig. 818)
Metacetabulidae Freitas and Lent, 1938
  Metacetabulum invaginatus Freitas and Leng, 1938 (fig. 819)

PART IV

KEY TO THE GENERA OF THE FAMILY CEPHALOGONIMIDAE NICOLL, 1914 (IV:6)

K. I. Skrjabin

1 (4) Genital pore terminal, anterior to subterminal oral sucker; eggs relatively elongate, narrow. Parasites of amphibians and reptiles.

2 (3) Body elongate; vitellaria extending anterior and posterior to ventral sucker; ventral sucker in anterior half of body.

   Cephalogonimus Poirier, 1886 (fig. 165)

3 (2) Body almost round; vitellaria concentrated only anterior to ventral sucker; ventral sucker equatorial.

   Paracephalogonimus Skrjabin and Petrow, 1950 (fig. 166)

4 (1) Genital pore lateral to oral sucker, at level of aperture; eggs short, broad. Parasites of fishes.

   Emoleptalea Looss, 1900 (fig. 167)

LITERATURE ON THE TREMATODES OF THE FAMILY CEPHALOGONIMIDAE (IV:41)

Dinnik, Yu. A. 1932. On the discovery of Cephalogonimus europaeus Blaizot, 1910 in the Caucasus. Trudy Sevanskoy Ozernoy Stantsii. 4(1-2):133-138.

KEY TO THE GENERA OF THE FAMILY LISSORCHIDAE POCHE, 1925 (IV:43)

K. I. Skrjabin

1 (2) Edges of oral and ventral suckers armed with large spines; ovary multi-lobed; esophagus lacking.
Lissorchis Magath, 1917 (fig. 168)
2 (1) Edges of oral and ventral suckers lacking spines; ovary tri-lobed; esophagus present.
Triganodistomum Simer, 1929 (fig. 169)

KEY TO THE SPECIES OF THE GENUS TRIGANODISTOMUM SIMER, 1929 from Fischthal (1942) (IV:48)

1 (2) Anterior border of vitellaria posterior to ventral sucker.   T. hypentelii Fischthal, 1942
2 (1) Anterior border of vitellaria at level of posterior half of ventral sucker.
3 (6) Seven to twelve vitelline follicles present on each side of body.
4 (5) Ovary deeply tri-lobed, resembling three separate structures; length of part of body posterior to most posterior testis roughly equal to length of three gonads taken together.
T. simeri Müller and Van Cleave, 1932
5 (4) Ovary slightly tri-lobed; length of body posterior to posterior testis only about one-quarter length of three gonads taken together.
T. mutabile (Cort, 1918)
6 (3) Sixteen to thirty-two vitelline follicles present on each side of body.
7 (8) Body long, 3.5 mm.; length of body section posterior to posterior testis approximately equal to length of both testes together.
T. attenuatum Müller and Van Cleave, 1932
8 (7) Body short, 1.0 mm.; length of body posterior to posterior testis roughly one-third length of both testes.   T. translucens Simer, 1929 (fig. 169)

KEY TO THE GENERA OF THE FAMILY UROTREMATIDAE POCHE, 1925 (IV:67)

K. I. Skrjabin

1 (2) Body reaching maximal width in posterior half; ovary and testes lobed.
Urotrematulum Macy, 1933 (fig. 170)
2 (1) Maximum body width in anterior part of body, sometimes at midpoint of body length; testes and ovary entire.   Urotrema Braun, 1900 (fig. 171)

KEY TO THE SPECIES OF THE GENUS

UROTREMA BRAUN, 1900 (IV:67)

K. I. Skrjabin

1 (4) Vitellaria reaching level of anterior testis.
2 (3) Body about 2 mm. long, with spines in anterior third of body. Parasites of Lasionycteris noctivagans.   U. minuta Macy, 1933
3 (2) Body 3-4 mm. long, with spines covering anterior two-thirds of body. Parasites of Lasiurus borealis, Nycteris humeralis and Eptesicus fuscus.
U. lasiurensis Alicata, 1932
4 (1) Vitellaria restricted, falling considerably short of level of anterior testis.
5 (6) Vitellaria originating at level of posterior edge of ventral sucker and extending for three-quarters of distance between ovary and anterior testis; oral sucker about 1 mm. Parasite of Molossus sp.   U. scabridum Braun, 1900 (fig. 171)
6 (5) Vitellaria extending to anterior edge of ventral sucker (one-quarter of distance between ovary and anterior testis); oral sucker about 5 mm. Parasites of muskrats.   U. shillingeri Price, 1931

KEY TO THE SUBFAMILIES OF THE FAMILY OPISTHORCHIDAE BRAUN, 1901 (IV:87-88)

K. I. Skrjabin and A. M. Petrov

1 (2) Gonotyl present; genital pore opening at base of gonotyl; oral sucker absent; vitellaria confluent in anterior part of body. Parasites of birds.
Pseudamphimerinae Skrjabin and Petrow, 1950
2 (1) Gonotyl lacking; oral sucker present.
3 (4) Body elongate, slender, of equal width at all points; testes removed from posterior end of body; vitellaria confluent posterior to ovary; uterus weakly developed, inter-cecal; excretory bladder dorsal to testes; seminal receptacle lacking. Parasites of porpoises.   Delphinicolinae Yamaguti, 1933
4 (3) Testes in posterior part of body; seminal receptacle present.
5 (6) Long prepharynx present, may considerably exceed length of pharynx; esophagus long; vitellaria in posterior half of body; intestinal ceca not reaching posterior end of body. Parasites of marine mammals and fishes.   Phocitrematinae Skrjabin, 1945
6 (5) Long prepharynx lacking.
7 (8) Parasites of reptiles; anterior end of body equipped with pre-oral lip and neck glands; vitellaria gathered into tubular lobules, filling space from ventral sucker to posterior end of body.
Oesophagicolinae Yamaguti, 1933
8 (7) Parasites of birds, mammals and fishes; pre-oral lip and neck glands lacking anteriorly.
9 (10) Intestinal ceca very broad, each reaching one-third of body width; oral and ventral suckers rudimentary; body long with parallel sides and truncated posterior end; excretory bladder saccular. Parasites of birds.   Plotnikoviinae Skrjabin, 1945
10 (9) Intestinal ceca of different construction.

11 (12) Excretory bladder ventral to testes; loops of uterus covering intestinal ceca, posterior to and anterior to ventral sucker. Parasites of mammals and birds. Metorchinae Lühe, 1909

12 (11) Excretory bladder S-shaped, lying between testes or else straight, dorsal to testes; loops of uterus and vitellaria not reaching anteriorly beyond ventral sucker. Parasites of mammals, birds and in exceptional cases, fishes.

Opisthorchinae Looss, 1899

KEY TO THE GENERA OF THE SUBFAMILY OPISTHORCHINAE LOOSS, 1899 (IV:88)

K. I. Skrjabin and A. M. Petrov

1 (4) Prepharynx elongate; cuticle of anterior part of body thickly armed with spines; testes tandem; excretory bladder straight, dorsal to testes.

2 (3) Body narrow, very long; intestinal ceca extending beyond boundary of posterior testis, reaching posterior end of body. Parasites of snakes.
Evranorchis Skrjabin, 1944 (fig. 172)

3 (2) Body of moderate length; intestinal ceca reaching level of middle of posterior testis, not reaching posterior end of body. Parasites of fishes.
Gomtia Thapar, 1930 (fig. 173)

4 (1) Elongate prepharynx lacking.

5 (10) Vitellaria on each side of body consisting of two groups of follicles, anterior group reaching to level of ovary, and posterior group, lateral or posterior to testes; excretory bladder S-shaped, passing in space between testes.

6 (7) Posterior group of follicles posterior to testes, occupying posterior-most region of body; oral sucker rudimentary.
Euamphimerus Yamaguti, 1941 (fig. 174)

7 (6) Posterior group of follicles posterior to ovary, lateral to testes, not reaching posterior-most extremity of body.

8 (9) Oral sucker larger than ventral.
Amphimerus Barker, 1911 (fig. 175)

9 (8) Oral sucker lacking.
Erschoviorchis Skrjabin, 1945 (fig. 176)

10 (5) Vitellaria not sub-divided into two groups, terminating at level of ovary, not entering posterior part of body; excretory bladder sometimes S-shaped, in space between testes, sometimes straight, lying dorsal to testes.

11 (14) Excretory bladder straight, dorsal to testes.

12 (13) Testes dendritic, branches partially extracecal.
Clonorchis Looss, 1907 (fig. 177)

13 (12) Testes lobed, inter-cecal.
Notaulus Skrjabin, 1913 (fig. 178)

14 (11) Excretory bladder S-shaped, in space between testes.
Opisthorchis R. Blanchard, 1895 (fig. 179)

KEY TO THE GENERA OF THE SUBFAMILY METORCHINAE LÜHE, 1909 (IV:204)

K. I. Skrjabin and A. M. Petrov

1 (2) Posterior end of body blunt, characterized by funnel-shaped or sucker-like indentation; vitellaria in middle part of body, not extending beyond anterior border of testes, not merging; medial edges of testes closely adjacent; uterus in middle part of body.
Pseudamphistomum Lühe, 1903 (fig. 180)

2 (1) Sucker-like indentation absent posteriorly.

3 (4) Vitellaria anterior to intestinal bifurcation, lateral to esophagus; intestinal ceca not reaching posterior end of body; uterine loops occupying nearly all space posterior to ventral sucker.
Holometra Looss, 1899 (fig. 181)

4 (3) Vitellaria differently distributed.

5 (6) Ventral sucker nearly adjacent to oral sucker, at level of pharynx; genital pore sharply displaced anteriorly; vitellaria originating posterior to ventral sucker, extending to posterior end of body, skirting blind ends of intestinal ceca, thence directing anteriorly, passing inter-cecally to level of posterior testis. Tubangorchis Skrjabin, 1943 (fig. 182)

6 (5) Ventral sucker not adjacent to oral sucker; vitellaria in anterior half of body, not passing beyond anterior edge of anterior testis.

7 (8) Loops of uterus extending posteriorly and entering space between testes.
Cladocystis Poche, 1926 (fig. 183)

8 (7) Uterus in anterior half of body, loops not descending into space between testes.

9 (12) Testes medial, tandem.

10 (11) Loops of uterus surrounding ventral sucker in shape of rosette.
Parametorchis Skrjabin, 1913 (fig. 184)

11 (10) Loops of uterus around ventral sucker not forming rosette.
Metametorchis Morosov, 1939 (fig. 185)

12 (9) Testes oblique or symmetrical.
Metorchis Looss, 1899 (fig. 186)

KEY TO THE SPECIES OF THE GENUS CLADOCYSTIS POCHE, 1926 (IV:231)

K. I. Skrjabin and A. M. Petrov

1 (2) Testes equal in size, lobed; ovary tri-lobed; cuticular spines lacking. Parasites of birds.
C. trifolium (Braun, 1901) (fig. 183)

2 (1) Testes unequal in size, entire; ovary entire; cuticular spines present. Parasites of fishes.
C. intestinalis Vaz, 1932

KEY TO THE SPECIES OF THE GENUS METAMETORCHIS (MOROSOV, 1939) SKRJABIN AND PETROV, 1950 (IV:238)

K. I. Skrjabin and A. M. Petrov

1 (4) Testes lobed; intestinal ceca sinuous.

2 (3) Length of body 3.0-3.5 mm.; trunk of excretory bladder narrow; uterus in transverse loops.
M. intermedius (Price, 1929)

3 (2) Length of body 5.0-7.0 mm.; trunk of excretory bladder wide; uterus not forming distinct transverse loops.
M. manitobensis (Allen and Wardle, 1934)

4 (1) Testes slightly indented or entire; intestinal ceca straight.

5 (6) Length of body 1.7-2.0 mm.; testes minute, lateral edges not reaching intestines; vitellaria not crossing into inter-cecal zone.
M. canadensis (Price, 1929)

6 (5) Body length 3.5 mm.; testes large, lateral edges touching intestinal ceca; anterior follicles of vitellaria crossing over into inter-cecal zone.
M. skrjabini (Morosov, 1939) (fig. 185)

KEY TO THE SPECIES OF THE GENUS PARAMETORCHIS SKRJABIN, 1913 (IV:249)

K. I. Skrjabin and A. M. Petrov

1 (2) Testes deeply lobed; intestinal ceca sinuous; vitellaria crossing into inter-cecal zone anteriorly, merging.
P. complexus (Stiles and Hassall, 1894) (fig. 184)

2 (1) Testes either entire or slightly indented; intestinal ceca straight; vitellaria restricted laterally.
P. noveboracensis Hung, 1926

KEY TO THE GENERA OF THE SUBFAMILY PHOCITREMATINAE SKRJABIN, 1945 (IV:270)

K. I. Skrjabin and A. M. Petrov

1 (2) Body fusiform, tapering anteriorly and posteriorly; cuticle armed with spines; loops of uterus extending anteriorly only to anterior edges of testes, not entering posterior end of body. Liver parasites of marine mammals.
Phocitrema Goto and Ozaki, 1930 (fig. 187)

2 (1) Body with narrowed anterior end, gradually broadening in posterior direction, with bluntly rounded posterior end, reaching maximal width at posterior end; cuticle smooth, without spines; loops of uterus reaching posterior end of body. Liver parasites of fishes.   Witenbergia Vaz, 1932 (fig. 188)

KEY TO THE GENERA OF THE FAMILY PACHYTREMATIDAE BAER, 1943 (IV:284)

K. I. Skrjabin and A. M. Petrov

1 (2) Oral sucker and pharynx rudimentary; genital pore at considerable distance from cephalic end, slightly pre-equatorial; esophagus elongate. Pancreatic parasties of birds.
Diasia Travassos, 1922 (fig. 189)

2 (1) Oral sucker and pharynx normally developed.

3 (4) Genital pore near anterior edge of ventral sucker, near oral sucker; loops of uterus posterior to ventral sucker; esophagus lacking or very short.
Pachytrema Looss, 1907 (fig. 190)

4 (3) Genital pore near anterior edge of ventral sucker, in posterior half of body; loops of uterus anterior to ventral sucker; esophagus short. Liver parasites of mammals.
Microtrema Kobayashi, 1920 (fig. 191)

KEY TO THE SPECIES OF THE GENUS PACHYTREMA LOOSS, 1907 (IV:284)

K. I. Skrjabin and A. M. Petrov

1 (6) Oral sucker larger than ventral.

2 (3) Vitellaria originating anterior to ventral sucker.   P. tringae Layman, 1926

3 (2) Vitellaria originating at level of ventral sucker or posterior to it.

4 (5) Ovary and testes at same level; body length: 4.5 mm.   P. proximum Travassos, 1921

5 (4) Ovary posterior to testes; body length: 8.5-13.5 mm.   P. magnum Travassos, 1921

6 (1) Oral sucker smaller than ventral; vitellaria originating at level of ventral sucker or posterior.

7 (10) Length of eggs exceeding 0.1 mm.

8 (9) Diameter of ventral sucker 0.3 mm.; egg: 0.11 x 0.044 mm.   P. calculus Looss, 1907 (fig. 190)

9 (8) Diameter of ventral sucker 0.43 mm.; egg: 0.11 x 0.055-0.060 mm.
P. paniceum Brinkmann, 1942

10 (7) Length of eggs 0.081 mm., width 0.042 mm.; diameter of ventral sucker 0.51 mm.
P. compositum Tscherbowitsch, 1946

KEY TO THE GENERA OF THE FAMILY RATZIIDAE BAER, 1943 (IV:312)

K. I. Skrjabin and A. M. Petrov

1 (2) Intestinal ceca not extending beyond level of posterior testis; uterus inter-cecal; testes tandem.
Ratzia Poche, 1926 (fig. 192)

2 (1) Intestinal ceca reaching posterior end of body; uterus with transverse loops crossing intestinal ceca; testes slightly oblique.
Cyclorchis Lühe, 1908 (fig. 193)

KEY TO THE SPECIES OF THE GENUS CYCLORCHIS LÜHE, 1908 from Price (1936) (IV:316)

1 (2) Proximal part of uterine canal passing between ovary and testes. Parasites of whales.
C. campula (Cobbold, 1876) (fig. 193)

2 (1) Proximal part of uterine canal not passing between ovary and testes; parasites of reptiles.

3 (4) Ventral sucker at posterior boundary of anterior fourth of body length; testes oblique. Parasites of Naja naja.   C. amphileucus (Looss, 1896)

4 (3) Ventral sucker at boundary of anterior and middle thirds of body; testes nearly symmetrical. Parasites of Varanus niloticus.
C. varani Price, 1936

LITERATURE ON THE TREMATODES OF THE SUPERFAMILY OPISTHORCHOIDEA FAUST, 1929
(IV:319-322)

Altgauzen, A. Ya. 1927. On five cases of discovery of distomatid eggs. Laboratoriya Praktika. No. 2:4-5.

Altgauzen, A. Ya. 1929. Trematodiasis (distomatosis) of the liver and bile ducts with special reference to opisthorchiases. Klinicheskaya Meditsina. 7(4):254-260.

Akhrem-Akhremovich, R. M. and A. P. Ananyina. 1940. Symptoms and therapy of opisthorchiasis. Meditsinskaya Parazitologiya i Parazitarnye Bolezni. 9(5):426-431.

Bol, B. K. and I. I. Yakovlev. 1932. Pathological anatomy of the liver of a cat with an opisthorchiasis infection. Meditsinskaya Parazitologiya i Parazitarnye Bolezni. 1(3-4):145.

Vinogradov, K. N. 1892. On a new species of distome (Distomum sibericum) in the human liver. Trudy Tomskogo Obschestva Estestvoispyteley. 3:116-130.

Vinogradov, K. N. 1892a. A second case of Distomum sibericum in the human liver. Trudy Tomskogo Obschestva Estestvoispyteley. 3:121-135.

Vinogradov, K. N. 1893. On the parasitic helminths of the human body, from materials based on pathological-anatomical autopsies at the Tomsk University. Izvestiya Imperatorskogo Tomskogo Universiteta. 5:348-360.

Golubeva, N. A. 1945. On the question of metabolism in Opisthorchis felineus. Meditsinskaya Parazitologiya i Parazitarnye Bolezni. 14(4):45-48.

Zheltikov, V. S. 1932. On the pathological anatomy of opisthorchiasis in the human liver. Meditsinskaya Parazitologiya i Parazitarnye Bolezni. 1(3-4):143-144.

Zhukova, E. V. 1934. A new trematode of domestic duck. Zoologichesky Zhurnal. 13(1):148-149.

Zerchaninov, L. K. 1938. Helminth and protozoan fauna of the population of the northern Sverdlovsk district. Meditsinskaya Parazitologiya i Parazitarnye Bolezni. 7(5):745-748.

Isaychikov, I. M. 1925. On the fauna of parasitic worms of domestic carnivores of western Siberia. Veterinarny Truzhenik. 1(5):1-8.

Kadenatsii, A. N. 1931. Opisthorchiasis of foxes. Okhotnik i Rybak Sibiri. No. 9:

Kadenatsii, A. N. 1931a. Helminth diseases of sables. Okhotnik i Rybak Sibiri. Nos. 11-12:

Kadenatsii, A. N. 1939. Helminth fauna of fur-bearing and commercial animals of the Far East. Dissertatsiya (Rukopis).

Kadenatsii, A. N. 1940. Clonorchiasis (a hepatic helminth disease of swine of the Khabarov region). Sovetskaya Veterinariya. 17(1):29.

Kaplan. 1925. (No title given.) Novaya Khirurgiya. No. 2:

Kondratiev, V. I. 1932. On the symptoms and therapy of opisthorchiasis. Meditsinskaya Parazitologiya i Parazitarnye Bolezni. 1(3-4):140-142.

Korenchevsky, V. G. 1905. A case of a liver infected with a Siberian distomatid. Russkaya Vrachebnaya Gazeta. 4(35):1089-1092.

Krasheninnikov, S. and A. Z. Efimov. 1937. On the question of the distribution of an opisthorchiasis epidemic among carnivorus animals in the Ukraine. Meditsinskaya Parazitologiya i Parazitarnye Bolezni. 6(1):138-140.

Krepkogorskaya, T. A. 1932. A case of opisthorchiasis in an infant in Khazakhstan. Meditsinskaya Parazitologiya i Parazitarnye Bolezni. 1(3-4):144.

Kurlov, M. G. 1911. On the distribution of flatworms in Tomsk. Sibirskaya Vrachebnaya Gazeta. 4(31):361-363.

Lifshits, M. 1927. Study of tumors of man.

Lyubavsky, A. D. 1932. Hepatic opisthorchiasis of polar foxes. Meditsinskaya Parazitologiya i Parazitarnye Bolezni. 1(3-4):145.

Lyublinsky, G. A. and O. P. Kulakovskaya. 1940. Degree of infestation and variability of Opisthorchis felineus. Meditskinskaya Parazitologiya i Parazitarnye Bolezni. 9(5):434-438.

Layman, E. M. 1926. Trematodes of bile ducts of the liver of Russian birds. Raboty Parazitologicheskoy Laboratorii I Moskovskogo Gosudarstvennogo Universiteta. pp. 59-72.

Malevitskaya, M. A. 1937. On the question of an opisthorchiasis epidemic in the Dnieper basin. Meditsinskaya Parazitologiya i Parazitarnye Bolezni. 6:135-136.

Mironova, M. N. 1938. Opisthorchiasis in the Dnieper district. Meditsinskaya Parazitologiya i Parazitarnye Bolezni. 7(1):139-140.

Morozov, F. N. 1939. Parasitic worms of fur-bearing animals of the family Mustelidae. Trudy Gorkovskogo Gosudarstvennogo Pedagogicheskogo Instituta. 4:3-44.

Okulova, R. K. 1929. From the statistics of the Tobolsk District Hospital on helminth diseases. Byulleten Obschestva Izucheniya Kraya pri Muzee Tobolskogo Severa. Nos. 1-2:24-25.

Pavlova, O. 1927. On the symptoms and therapy of hepatic distomatiasis. Meditsinskaya Mysl Uzbekistana. No. 2:118-119.

Paretskaya, M. S., S. M. Vishnevskaya, V. A. Zaturenskaya, and V. M. Geft. 1940. On the question of opisthorchiasis in the Poltavskaya district. Meditsinskaya Parazitologiya i Parazitarnye Bolezni. 9(1-2):144-145.

Pastor, E. A. 1898. A rare case of distomatiasis of the liver. Bolnichnaya Gazeta Botkina. 9(10):417-426.

Perevodchikova, L. N. 1940. Symptoms of opisthorchiasis. Meditsinskaya Parazitologiya i Parazitarnye Bolezni. 9(5):432-433.

Petrov, A. M. 1912. On the pathological anatomy of distomatosis. Dissertatsiya, Karkov.

Petrov, N. N. 1924. On the etiology of tumors. Vestnik Khirurgii. Nos. 10-11:126.

Petrov, A. M. 1927. Qualitative diversity of parasitic worms of domestic carnivores of the U.S.S.R.

Trudy 3-go Vserossiskogo Sezda Zoologov, Anatomov, i Gistologov. pp. 149-151.

Petrov, A. M. 1931. Helminth infestations of dogs; their sanitary and economic significance. Selkhozgiz, Moskva-Leningrad. 192 pp.

Petrov, A. M. 1941. Helminth diseases of fur-bearing animals. Izdatelstvo Mezhdunarodnaya Kniga, Moskva. 228 pp.

Plavinsky, Ya. V. 1911. On the question of pernicious anemia. Yubilarny Sbornik Posvyaschenny M. G. Kurlovu, Tomsk. pp. 1-20.

Platonov, N. V. and V. T. Frolova. 1931. On the question of helminth infections in the serving personnel of restaurants of Novosibirsk. Tropicheskaya Meditsina i Veterinariya. 9(1):28-31.

Plotnikov, N. N. 1940. Materials on the specific therapy of opisthorchiasis. Meditsinskaya Parazitologiya i Parazitarnye Bolezni. 9(5):419-426.

Plotnikov, N. N. 1941. Therapy of opisthorchiasis in cats with hexachlorethane. Doklady Akad. Nauk SSSR. 31(5):514-516.

Plotnikov, N. N. 1941. Opisthorchiasis in animals and its control. Veterinariya. No. 6:

Plotnikov, N. N. and L. K. Zerchaninov. 1931. On the fauna of parasitic worms in children of Tobolsk. Tropicheskaya Meditsina i Veterinariya. 9(10):493-494.

Plotnikov, N. N. and L. K. Zerchaninov. 1932. Materials on the biology of Opisthorchis felineus (Rivolta, 1884), and on the treatment of opisthorchiasis. Meditsinskaya Parazitologiya i Parazitarnye Bolezni. 1(3-4):130-139.

Podyapolskaya, V. P. 1927. On helminthiases of man in the U.S.S.R. Sbornik Rabot po Gelmintologii, Posvyaschenny Prof. K. I. Skrjabinu. pp. 155-179.

Romanov, F. I. 1901. Results of the pathological-anatomical autopsies conducted at the Tomsk University from 1890 to 1900. Izdatelstvo Tomskogo Universiteta.

Romanov, F. I. 1907. On the Siberian distomatid of Prof. K. N. Vinogradov (Distomum felineus Rivolta) from data obtained in the pathological-anatomical dissections conducted at the Tomsk University from 1892-1906. Russky Vrach. 6(39):1333-1338.

Ruditsky, M. G. 1926. On the significance of examining the duodenal juice in the laboratory diagnosis of parasitic diseases of the liver and bile ducts. Laboratornaya Praktika. No. 7:6-8.

Ruditsky, M. G. 1927. Distomatosis as an etiological agent of stone-less cholecystitis. Russkaya Klinika. 7:382-390.

Rufanov, I. G. 1925. Pancreatitis in connection with inflammatory processes in the bile ducts and gall bladder.

Savinykh, A. G. 1921. (No title given.) Novy Khirurgichesky Arkhiv. 47:241.

Savinykh, A. G. 1927. On the question of Opisthorchis felineus in the pancreas. Novy Khirurgichesky Arkhiv. 12(3):388.

Semenov, G. M. 1927. General summary on distomatosis caused by Fasciola hepatica L. in reference to its propagation in Central Asia. Meditsinskaya Mysl Uzbekistana. No. 2:13-29.

Semenov, G. M. and D. Kogan. 1927. A case of distomatosis caused by Fasciola hepatica and treating it with small doses of an emetic of chlorohydrate. Meditsinskaya Mysl Uzbekistana. No. 2:30-38.

Skrjabin, K. I. 1913. Metorchis pinguinicola nov. sp., a parasite of the gall bladder of penguins. Zhurnal Nauchnoy i Praktichnoy Veterinarnoy Meditsiny. 7(1):18-31.

Skrjabin, K. I. 1923. Trematodes of poultry. Trudy Gosudarstvennogo Instituta Experimentalnoy Veterinarii. 1(2):193-256.

Skrjabin, K. I. 1933. The statistics and geography of opisthorchiasis. Meditsinskaya Parazitologiya i Parazitarnye Bolezni. 1(3-4):122-124.

Skrjabin, K. I. 1932a. Opisthorchiasis as a sanitary and socio-economic problem of the Soviet North. Meditsinskaya Parazitologiya i Parazitarnye Bolezni. 1(3-4):120-121.

Skrjabin, K. I. 1932b. On the organization of the campaign against opisthorchiasis in the Tolbolsk North. Meditsinskaya Parazitologiya i Parazitarnye Bolezni. 1(3-4):129.

Skrjabin, K. I. 1944. Analysis of the generic components of the three trematode families: Opisthorchidae, Dicrocoeliidae, and Echinostomatidae. Doklady Akad. Nauk SSSR. 44(7):328-330.

Skrjabin, K. I. 1945. On the position of Hematotrephus fodiens Linton, 1928 in the systematics of the trematodes. Doklady Akad. Nauk SSSR. 48(1):75-76.

Skrjabin, K. I. 1945. On the revision of the systematics of trematodes of the family Opisthorchidae. Doklady Akad. Nauk SSSR. 49(2):155-156.

Skrjabin, K. I. and V. P. Baskakov. 1926. On the analysis of the helminth fauna in fishermen of the north Dvina Province. Russky Zhurnal Tropicheskoy Meditsiny. 4(8):23-30.

Skrjabin, K. I., A. M. Petrov, I. V. Orlov, et al. 1941. Short course in the parasitology of domestic animals. Selkhozgiz, Moskva.

Skrjabin, K. I. and V. P. Podyapolskaya. 1932. Opisthorchiasis infections as occurring in the populations of the minor nationalities of the Tobolsk North. Meditsinskaya Parazitologiya i Parazitarnye Bolezni. 1(3-4):124-127.

Skrjabin, K. I., V. P. Podyapolskaya, N. P. Shikovalova, and Z. G. Vasilkova. 1932. Opisthorchiasis of workers in the fish-canning factories of the Tobolsk North. Meditsinskaya Parazitologiya i Parazitarnye Bolezni. 1(3-4):127-128.

Skrjabin, K. I. and R. S. Schulz. 1926. Helminthiases of the liver of man caused by trematodes. Sbornik Rabot 25-y Soyuznoy Gelmintologicheskoy Expeditsii v Artemovskom Okruge Donbassa. pp. 57-68.

Skrjabin, K. I. and R. S. Shulz. 1928. Hepatic trematodiasis of man. Second Ed. Moskva. 43 pp.

Skrjabin, K. I. and R. S. Schulz. 1929. Helminthiases of man, Pt. I. Gosmedgiz, Moskva-Leningrad. 375 pp.

Skrjabin, K. I. and R. S. Schulz. 1932. Bibliography on opisthorchiasis. Meditsinskaya Parazitologiya i Parazitarnye Bolezni. 1(3-4):146-147.

Skrjabin, K. I. and R. S. Schulz. 1937. Helminthology. Veterinary parasitology and infectious diseases of domestic animals. Second Ed. Selkhozgiz, Moskva. 418 pp.

Sokolov. 1937. On the study of adenomas of the liver. Russky Arkhiv Patologii.

Soloviev, N. S. 1904. On the diagnosis of distomatosis in the liver of man. Sbornik Trudov Pamyati E. G. Salischeva, Tomsk. pp. 297-303.

Targonskaya, A. 1930. Two cases of opisthorchiasis of the liver. Vrachebnoye Delo. No. 1:54.

Finkelshtein, B. K. 1924. On the role of parasites in diseases of the bile ducts. Novy Khirurgichesky Arkhiv. Nos. 18-21:

Kholodkovsky, N. A. 1898. Atlas of human helminths. S.-Peterburg.

Kholodkovsky, N. A. 1879. Distomum felineum in the liver of man. Trudy Obschestva Estestvoispyteley. 27:185-189.

Chernyak, V. Z. 1934. Hepatic helminth diseases (pseudamphistomatosis) of Nyctereutes procyonodes Gray and silver foxes. Sbornik Rabot Leningradskogo Veterinarnogo Instituta. pp. 57-64.

Shakhmatov, A. P. 1927. Results of the Tomsk Helminthological Study. Sibirsky Meditsinsky Zhurnal. 3(4):48-56.

Strom, Zh. K. 1927. On hepatic pseudo-distomatosis. Vestnik Mikrobiologii i Epidemiologii. 6(4):433-438.

Shulman, E. S. 1926. On the fauna of parasitic worms in domestic carnivores of the Artemovsky region. Rabot 25-y Soyuznoy Gelmintologicheskoy Expeditsii v Artemovskomo Okruge Donabassa. pp. 78-81.

Shulman, E. S. and S. M. Vishnevskaya. 1940. Contributions on the study of the propagation of opisthorchiasis in the Ukraine. Materials on opisthorchiasis in the Kiev district. Meditsinskaya Parazatologiya i Parazitarnye Bolezni. 9(1-2):142-143.

Scherbovich, I. A. 1946. Trematodes of birds of the Far East. Sbornik Rabot po Gelmintologii, Posvyaschenny Akademiku K. I. Skrjabinu. pp. 196-300.

Elperin, M. A. 1937. On the question of the presence of opisthorchiasis in the Bug River basin. Meditsinskaya Parazitologiya i Parazitarnye Bolezni. 6:137.

Erlikh, I. S. 1929. Stool examinations for helminths of nursery teachers in Stavropol, with comparative evaluation of methods of examinations. Sovetskaya Meditsina na Severnom Kavkaze. No. 1:33-37.

KEY TO THE SUBFAMILIES AND TRIBES OF THE FAMILY CYCLOCOELIIDAE KOSSACK, 1911
modified from Witenberg (IV:351)

E. Ya. Bashkirova

A. Internal intestinal diverticula lacking.
Cyclocoeliinae
I. Ovary at level of posterior testis or anterior to it.
1. Gonads in triangular disposition.
(1) Testes at different levels; ovary and anterior testis on opposite sides.
a) Testes not separated by loops of uterus; loops of uterus often extending external to gonads.
Haematotrephea
b) Testes more or less separated by loops of uterus; loops not extending external to gonads.
Cyclocoelea
(2) Testes symmetrical within intestinal arch; ovary anterior to testes, medial.
2. Gonads aligned longitudinally; ovary may deviate toward side of anterior testis.   Hyptiasmea
II. Ovary within intestinal arch; testes anterior to ovary   Ophthalmophagea
B. Internal intestinal diverticula present.
Typhlocoelinae

KEY TO THE SPECIES OF THE SUBGENUS CYCLOCOELUM (BRANDES, 1892) WITENBERG, 1923 (IV:357)

E. Ya. Bashkirova

1 (14) Loops of uterus not extending beyond internal edges of intestinal ceca.
2 (3) Loops of uterus not extending to internal edges of intestinal ceca.   C. (C.) makii Yamaguti, 1933
3 (2) Loops of uterus reaching internal edges of intestinal ceca.
4 (5) Ovary on same level with posterior testis.
C. (C.) vogeli Szidat, 1932
5 (4) Ovary nearly equidistant from each testis.
6 (13) Vitellaria extending beyond internal edges of ceca, not separated from uterine loops by space.
7 (8) Loops of uterus reaching intestinal arch.
C. (C.) pseudomicrostomum Harrah, 1922
8 (7) Loops of uterus not reaching intestinal arch.
9 (10) Vitellaria anteriorly reaching level of pharynx.   C. (C.) obscurum (Leidy, 1887)
10 (9) Vitellaria anteriorly not reaching level of pharynx.
11 (12) Vitellaria extending anteriorly to intestinal bifurcation.   C. (C.) mutabile (Zeder, 1800) (fig. 194)
12 (11) Vitellaria falling considerably short of intestinal bifurcation.   C. (C.) theophili Dollfus, 1948
13 (6) Vitellaria not extending beyond internal edges of intestinal ceca.
C. (C.) capellum Khan, 1935
14 (1) Loops of uterus extending beyond internal edges of intestinal ceca.
15 (22) Loops of uterus not reaching external edges of intestinal ceca.
16 (17) Ovary and posterior testis at same level.
C. (C.) microstomum (Creplin)
17 (16) Ovary nearly equidistant from each testis.

18 (19) Vitellaria well developed, and may merge near intestinal arch.   C. (C.) phasidi Stunkard, 1929

19 (18) Vitellaria not merging near intestinal arch.

20 (21) Vitellaria extending beyond external edges of intestinal ceca, reaching internal edge.
C. (C.) macrorchis Harrah, 1922

21 (20) Vitellaria not extending beyond external edges of intestinal ceca.
C. (C.) orientale Skrjabin, 1913

22 (15) Loops of uterus reaching external edges of intestinal ceca.

23 (26) Vitellaria anteriorly reaching level of pharynx.

24 (25) Excretory bladder bicornate; pharynx smaller than oral sucker.
C. (C.) elongatum Harrah, 1921

25 (24) Excretory bladder simple, saccular; pharynx nearly equal in size to oral sucker.
C. (C.) sharadi Bhalerao, 1935

26 (23) Vitellaria anteriorly reaching intestinal bifurcation.

27 (34) Loops of uterus covering intestinal ceca.

28 (33) Vitellaria anteriorly reaching intestinal bifurcation or slightly beyond, not reaching level of pharynx.

29 (32) Testes separated by numerous loops of uterus.

30 (31) Loops of uterus reaching intestinal arch; vitellaria reaching mid-point of esophagus.
C. (C.) indicum Khan, 1935

31 (30) Loops of uterus not reaching intestinal arch; vitellaria extending only to intestinal bifurcation.   C. (C.) allahabadi Khan, 1935

32 (29) Testes entirely contiguous, or separated by few loops of uterus.
C. (C.) vicarium (Arnsdorff, 1908)

33 (28) Vitellaria anteriorly reaching level of pharynx.   C. (C.) halli Harrah, 1922

34 (27) Loops of uterus not covering intestinal ceca.

35 (36) Pharynx nearly twice as small as oral sucker; posterior testis filling intestinal arch.
C. (C.) obliquum Harrah, 1921

36 (35) Pharynx larger than oral sucker; posterior testis not filling intestinal arch.
C. (C.) erythropis Khan, 1935

KEY TO THE SPECIES OF THE SUBGENUS PSEUDHYPTIASMUS DOLLFUS, 1948 (IV:395)

E. Ya. Bashkirova

1 (4) Uterus restricted inter-cecally.

2 (3) Vitellaria anteriorly not reaching intestinal bifurcation; excretory bladder simple.
C. (P.) vagum Morishita, 1924

3 (2) Vitellaria anteriorly reaching level of pharynx; excretory bladder bicornate.
C. (P.) bivesiculatum Prudhoe, 1944

4 (1) Uterus reaching external edges of intestinal ceca.   C. (P.) straightum Khan, 1935

Note: C. (P.) dumetellae Zeliff, 1943 omitted from key

KEY TO THE SPECIES OF THE GENUS HAEMATOTREPHUS STOSSICH, 1902 (IV:411)

E. Ya. Bashkirova

1 (6) Loops of uterus transversely oriented, not forming arch in posterior region of body.

2 (3) Loops of uterus not passing beyond intestinal ceca.   H. capellae (Yamaguti, 1933)

3 (2) Loops of uterus passing beyond intestinal ceca.

4 (5) Vitellaria anteriorly reaching level of intestinal bifurcation.   H. nebularium (Khan, 1935)

5 (4) Vitellaria anteriorly reaching level of pharynx.   H. brasilianum (Stossich, 1902)

6 (1) Loops of uterus in posterior end of body forming arch above gonads.

7 (10) Loops of uterus passing beyond intestinal ceca.

8 (9) Loops of uterus laterally extending only to vitellaria.   H. tringae (Brandes, 1892)

9 (8) Loops of uterus laterally reaching edges of body.   H. similis Stossich, 1902 (fig. 195)

10 (7) Loops of uterus not passing beyond intestinal ceca.   H. kossacki (Witenberg, 1923)

KEY TO THE SPECIES OF THE GENUS UVITELLINA WITENBERG, 1923 (IV:420)

E. Ya. Bashkirova

1 (8) Posterior testis adjacent to internal wall of intestinal arch.

2 (5) Loops of uterus not extending posteriorly beyond anterior edge of anterior testis.

3 (4) Vitellaria extending anteriorly to level of intestinal bifurcation.   U. vanelli (Rudolphi, 1819)

4 (3) Vitellaria extending anteriorly only to level of pharynx.   U. dollfusi Shen, 1930

5 (2) Loops of uterus extending posteriorly beyond anterior edge of anterior testis.

6 (7) Posterior loops of uterus skirting gonads.
U. pseudocotylea Witenberg, 1923 (fig. 196)

7 (6) Posterior loops of uterus reaching anterior edge of posterior testis.   U. keri Yamaguti, 1933

8 (1) Posterior testis not adjacent to intestinal arch, remaining some distance from it.
U. adelphus (Johnston, 1916)

KEY TO THE GENERA OF THE TRIBE HYPTIASMEA WITENBERG, 1923 modified from Witenberg, 1923 (IV:430)

E. Ya. Bashkirova

1 (6) Intestinal ceca straight, or only slightly sinuous; genital pore anterior to pharynx.

2 (5) Loops of uterus reaching sides of body.

KEYS TO TREMATODES IN ANIMALS AND MAN 43

3 (4) Gonads aligned forming sharp angle with axis of body; loops of uterus not contacting one another posterior to posterior testis.

Hyptiasmus Kossack, 1911 (fig. 197)

4 (3) Gonads nearly medial, along axis of body; loops of uterus touching one another posterior to posterior testis. Transcoelum Witenberg, 1923 (fig. 198)

5 (2) Loops of uterus not reaching sides of body.

Prohyptiasmus Witenberg, 1923

6 (1) Intestinal ceca sinuous; genital pores at level of intestinal bifurcation.

Allopyge Johnston, 1913 (fig. 200)

KEY TO THE SPECIES OF THE GENUS HYPTIASMUS KOSSACK, 1911 (IV:435)

E. Ya. Bashkirova

1 (10) Testes relatively close together, within posterior third of body.

2 (7) Loops of uterus passing posteriorly beyond level of intestinal arch.

3 (4) Testes close together; intestinal arch considerably distant from sides of body.

H. arcuatus (Stossich, 1902) (fig. 197)

4 (3) Testes some distance from each other; intestinal arch separated from sides of body by small space.

5 (6) Gonads aligned; posterior testes occupying intestinal arch. H. laevigatus Kossack, 1911

6 (5) Gonads not aligned; posterior testis not occupying intestinal arch.

H. witenbergi Tretyakova, 1940

7 (2) Loops of uterus not passing posteriorly beyond level of intestinal arch.

8 (9) Excretory bladder two-branched; ovary and testes sub-equal. H. brumpti Dollfus, 1948

9 (8) Excretory bladder simple; ovary considerably larger than testes. H. theodori Witenberg, 1928

10 (1) Testes distant from one another, in posterior half of body. H. magniproles Witenberg, 1928

KEY TO THE SPECIES OF THE GENUS ALLOPYGE JOHNSTON, 1913 (IV:451)

E. Ya. Bashkirova

1 (4) Loops of uterus inter-cecal, not passing laterally beyond external walls of intestinal ceca.

2 (3) Genital pore anterior to intestinal bifurcation.

A. ominosus (Kossack, 1911)

3 (2) Genital pore posterior to intestinal bifurcation. A. undulatus Canavan, 1934

4 (1) Loops of uterus passing laterally beyond intestinal ceca. A. antigones Johnston, 1913 (fig. 200)
Note: A. adolphi Stossich omitted from key.

KEY TO THE SPECIES OF THE GENUS OPHTHALMOPHAGUS STOSSICH, 1902 (IV:460)

E. Ya. Bashkirova

1 (4) Testes nearly tandem.

2 (3) Intestinal ceca not sinuous; ovary in intestinal arch. O. singularis Stossich, 1902 (fig. 201)

3 (2) Intestinal ceca forming series of bends; ovary slightly anterior to intestinal arch.

O. magalhaesi Travassos, 1925

4 (1) Testes oblique.

5 (8) Esophagus S-shaped.

6 (7) Body cylindrical; loops of uterus not passing posteriorly beyond level of intestinal arch.

O. nasicola Witenberg, 1923

7 (6) Body pyriform; loops of uterus passing posteriorly beyond level of intestinal arch.

O. charadrii Yamaguti, 1934

8 (5) Esophagus short, straight.

O. skrjabinianum (Witenberg, 1923)

KEY TO THE SPECIES OF THE GENUS TYPHLOCOELUM STOSSICH, 1902 (IV:474)

E. Ya. Bashkirova

1 (4) Testes branched, not separated by loops of uterus.

2 (3) Vitellaria not merging along intestinal arch.

T. cucumerinum (Rudolphi, 1809) (fig. 202)

3 (2) Vitellaria merging along intestinal arch.

T. reticulare Johnston, 1913

4 (1) Testes lobed, separated by loops of uterus.

5 (6) Vitellaria extending beyond external walls of intestinal ceca, anteriorly reaching intestinal bifurcation. T. americanum Manter and Williams, 1928

6 (5) Vitellaria not extending beyond external walls of ceca, anteriorly not reaching intestinal bifurcation.

T. shovellus (Lal, 1936)

LITERATURE ON THE TREMATODES OF THE FAMILY CYCLOCOELIIDAE KOSSACK, 1911 (IV:491)

Witenberg, G. G. 1923. Trematodes of the family Cyclocoeliidae, and a new principle of their systematics. Trudy Gosudarstvennogo Instituta Experimentalnoy Veterinarii. 1(1):84-141.

Ginetsinskaya, T. A. 1947. On the rudimentary sucker of Cyclocoelum microstomum. Doklady Akad. Nauk SSSR. 58(3):509-512.

Ginetsinskaya, T. A. 1949. Life cycle of the trematode, Cyclocoelum microstomum (Creplin, 1829). Doklady Akad. Nauk SSSR. 66(6):1219-1222.

Dubinin, V. B. 1938. Variations in the parasite fauna of the glossy ibis, Plegadis falcinellus, in connection with age and migrations of the host. Trudy Astrakhanskogo Gosudarstvennogo Zapovednika. 2:108-212.

Ivanitskaya, V. V. 1920. Trematodes of the respiratory passages of birds of the Don region. Izvestiya Donskogo Veterinarnogo Instituta. 1(2):1-12.

Kalantaryan, E. V. 1924. On the knowledge of the trematodes of birds in the vicinity of Erevan. Trudy Tropicheskogo Instituta Armenii. 1:74-75.

Semenov, V. D. 1927. Trematodes of birds of the western U.S.S.R. Sbornik Rabot po Gelmintologii, Posvyaschenny Prof. K. I. Skrjabinu. pp. 221-271.

Skrjabin, K. I. 1913. On the knowledge of the helminth fauna of domestic animals of Turkestan. Dissertatsiya, Yuriev.

Skrjabin, K. I. 1914. Tracheophilus sisowi nov. gen., nov. sp., a new parasite from domestic duck. Uchenye Zapiski Kazanskogo Veterinarnogo Instituta. 31(2):115-128.

Skrjabin, K. I. 1920. The Third Don-Azov Helminthological Expedition. Izvestiya Donskogo Veterinarnogo Instituta. 1(2):1-9.

Skrjabin, K. I. 1927. The Fourth Russian Helminthological Expedition in the Don district. Deyatelnosti 28-y Gelmintogicheskoy Expeditsii v SSSR. pp. 32-40.

Skrjabin, K. I. 1946. The building of Soviet helminthology. Izdatelstvo Akad. Nauk SSSR. Moskva-Leningrad. 211 pp.

Tretiakova, O. N. 1940. The helminth fauna of domestic and game water-fowl of southern Zauralye (Trans-Ural region). Rukopis, VIGIS, Moskva.

LIST OF SUPPLEMENTARY ILLUSTRATIONS

PART V

KEY TO THE SUPERFAMILIES OF THE SUBORDER SCHISTOSOMATATA SKRJABIN AND SCHULZ, 1937 (V:9)

K. I. Skrjabin

1 (2) Diecious trematodes. Parasites of circulatory systems of warm-blooded vertebrates: mammals and birds.   Schistosomatoidea Stiles and Hassall, 1926

2 (1) Hermaphroditic trematodes. Parasites of circulatory systems of cold-blooded vertebrates: fishes and reptiles.   Sanguinicoloidea Skrjabin, 1951

KEY TO THE FAMILIES OF THE SUPERFAMILY SANGUINICOLOIDEA SKRJABIN, 1951 (V:13)

K. I. Skrjabin

1 (2) With two suckers, oral and ventral, or with one, oral; genital pore equatorial or slightly post-equatorial; with one or two intestinal ceca, posteriorly reaching end of body. Parasites of turtles.   Spirorchidae Stunkard, 1921

2 (1) Suckers lacking; genital pore in posterior part of body; intestinal ceca posteriorly usually not reaching end of body; intestinal ceca often in form of diverticula. Parasites of fishes, and rarely, of reptiles.   Sanguinicolidae Graff, 1907

KEY TO THE SUBFAMILIES OF THE FAMILY SPIRORCHIDAE STUNKARD, 1921 (V:18)

K. I. Skrjabin

1 (2) Genital pore and ovary nearly equatorial.   Hapalotrematinae Stunkard, 1921

2 (1) Genital pores and ovary in posterior half of body.

3 (6) Two intestinal ceca present, not uniting.

4 (5) Many testes present, all or majority located anterior to ovary.   Spirorchinae Stunkard, 1921

5 (4) Intestinal ceca of schistosomatid type, with anterior paired branches and single posterior branch; single testis present, spiral-shaped, in posterior half of body.   Neospirorchinae Skrjabin, 1951

6 (3) Single intestinal cecum present; single testis not divided into follicles, occupying almost entire length of body, lobed.   Unicaecuminae Mehra, 1934

KEY TO THE GENERA OF THE SUBFAMILY SPIRORCHINAE STUNKARD, 1921 (V:18)

K. I. Skrjabin

1 (4) Intestinal ceca turning anteriorly on leaving esophagus, returning to loop, passing posteriorly to posterior end of body; testes in single medial row.

2 (3) External seminal vesicle small; cirrus sac and glandular vesicle well-developed.   Hemiorchis Mehra, 1939 (fig. 203)

3 (2) External seminal vesicle well-developed; cirrus sac extremely small, with weak musculature; glandular vesicle weakly developed.   Plasmiorchis Mehra, 1934 (fig. 204)

4 (1) Intestinal ceca not forming anterior loops.

5 (10) All testes anterior to ovary.

6 (7) Ventral sucker lacking.   Spirorchis McCallum, 1918 (fig. 205)

7 (6) Ventral sucker present.

8 (9) Ovary lobed, not dendritic; intestinal ceca straight, without forming bends in area of ventral sucker.   Monticellius Mehra, 1939 (fig. 206)

9 (8) Ovary dendritic; intestinal ceca forming sharp bends in region of ventral sucker.

Learedius Price, 1934 (fig. 207)

10 (5) One or two testes, posterior to ovary.

11 (12) Ventral sucker present; cirrus sac well-developed.   Spirhapalum Ejsmont, 1927 (fig. 208)

12 (11) Ventral sucker lacking; cirrus sac weakly developed.   Diarmostorchis Ejsmont, 1927 (fig. 209)

KEY TO THE SPECIES OF THE GENUS SPIRORCHIS MAC CALLUM, 1918 (V:23)

K. I. Skrjabin

1 (6) Testes originating posterior to middle of body.

2 (5) With less than ten testes.

3 (4) Testes four or five; genital pore one-quarter of body length from posterior end of body.

S. parvus (Stunkard, 1923)

4 (3) Testes six; genital pore one-ninth of body length from posterior end of body.

S. elephantis (Cort, 1917)

5 (2) Testes ten; genital pore near posterior end of body.   S. haematobium (Stunkard, 1922)

6 (1) Testes originating anterior to middle of body.

7 (10) Genital pore one-seventh of body length from posterior end of body.

8 (9) Testes larger than ovary, indistinctly separated from each other.

S. innominata (Ward, 1921) (fig. 205)

9 (8) Testes smaller than ovary, distinctly separated from each other.   S. artericola (Ward, 1921)

10 (7) Genital pore one-quarter of body length from posterior end of body.

11 (14) Testes large.

12 (13) Testes originating directly posterior to intestinal bifurcation.   S. scripta Stunkard, 1923

13 (12) Testes originating at considerable distance posterior to intestinal bifurcation.

S. elegans Stunkard, 1923

14 (11) Testes small, not reaching more than half size of ovary.   S. picta Stunkard, 1923

Note: Spirorchis sp. Byrd, 1939 omitted from key.

KEY TO THE SPECIES OF THE GENUS HEMIORCHIS MEHRA, 1939 (V:68)

K. I. Skrjabin

1 (2) Testes transversely elongate, irregularly lobed; vitellaria inter-cecal, with small number of extra-cecal vitelline follicles.

H. hardelli (Mehra, 1934) (fig. 203)

2 (1) Testes oval, entire; vitellaria exclusively intercecal.   H. bengalensis Mehra, 1940

KEY TO THE SPECIES OF THE GENUS LEAREDIUS PRICE, 1934 (V:77)

K. I. Skrjabin

1 (2) With twenty-eight testes; eggs fusiform, with

polar appendices; eggs with appendices: 0.210 mm. (length)x 0.028 mm. (width).

L. learedi Price, 1934 (fig. 207)

2 (1) With thirty-five to forty-five testes; eggs fusiform with one long polar filament, and one short filament; eggs with filaments: 0.195-0.225 mm. (length) x 0.021-0.024 mm. (width).   L. orientalis Mehra, 1939

KEY TO THE SPECIES OF THE GENUS MONTICELLIUS MEHRA, 1939 (V:84)

K. I. Skrjabin

1 (2) Cuticular spines and tubercles lacking; vitellaria terminating posterior to ovary.

M. indicum Mehra, 1939 (fig. 206)

2 (1) Numerous cuticular tubercles present; vitellaria terminating at middle of ovary.

M. similis (Price, 1934)

KEY TO THE SPECIES OF THE GENUS PLASMIORCHIS MEHRA, 1934 (V:92)

K. I. Skrjabin

1 (2) Ventral sucker lacking in sexually mature specimens, naked area present on body marking former position of sucker.   P. pellucidus Mehra, 1934

2 (1) Ventral sucker present.

3 (4) With five to seven testes; intestinal ceca straight, lacking diverticula.

P. orientalis Mehra, 1934 (fig. 204)

4 (3) With large number of testes; intestinal ceca sinuous with small diverticula.

P. obscurum Mehra, 1934

Note: P. sanguinea (Sinha, 1934) omitted from key.

KEY TO THE GENERA OF THE SUBFAMILY HAPALOTREMATINAE STUNKARD, 1921 (V:109)

K. I. Skrjabin

1 (2) Testis single, spiral-shaped, posterior to compact ovary; esophageal diverticula present.

Vasotrema Stunkard, 1926 (fig. 210)

2 (1) With more than one testis.

3 (4) With many testes, forming two groups; ovary inter-testicular.   Hapalotrema Looss, 1899 (fig. 211)

4 (3) Two testes present; ovary inter-testicular.

5 (6) Cirrus sac and cirrus lacking; genital pore dorsal, anterior to anterior testis.

Hapalorhynchus Stunkard, 1922 (fig. 212)

6 (5) Cirrus sac and cirrus present.

7 (8) Genital pore dorsal, anterior to anterior testis.

Coeuritrema Mehra, 1933 (fig. 213)

8 (7) Genital pore ventral.

9 (10) Genital pore posterior to anterior testis.

Amphiorchis Price, 1934 (fig. 214)

10 (9) Genital pore anterior to anterior testis.

Enterohaematotrema Mehra, 1940 (fig. 215)

KEY TO THE SPECIES OF THE GENUS HAPALOTREMA LOOSS, 1899 (V:111)

K. I. Skrjabin

1 (2) Separate follicles of tested not clearly differentiated, forming two large compact masses: anterior mass and posterior mass; genital sucker well-developed.   H. synorchis Luhman, 1935
2 (1) Separate follicles of testes clearly differentiated; genital sucker lacking.
3 (4) Oral sucker considerably smaller than ventral.
H. loossi Price, 1934 (fig. 211)
4 (3) Oral and ventral suckers of equal size.
H. mistroides (Monticelli, 1896)

KEY TO THE SPECIES OF THE GENUS COEURITREMA MEHRA, 1933 (V:125)

K. I. Skrjabin

1 (2) Ventral sucker smaller than oral.
C. odhnerensis Mehra, 1933
2 (1) Ventral sucker larger than oral.
3 (4) Body narrow, tapering posteriorly; length of body reaching 3.16-3.45 mm.; seminal vesicle large, reaching 0.2 mm. in length. C. indicus (Thapar, 1933)
4 (3) Body broad, rounded posteriorly; length of body reaching 1.5-2.0 mm.; seminal vesicle small, reaching 0.048-0.57 mm. in length.
C. lyssimus Mehra, 1933 (fig. 213)

KEY TO THE SPECIES OF THE GENUS HAPALORHYNCHUS STUNKARD, 1922 (V:143)

K. I. Skrjabin

1 (2) Diameter of ventral sucker 0.6 mm.; vitellaria originating at level of intestinal bifurcation; ovary 0.1-0.12 x 0.06-0.07 mm.
H. gracilis Stunkard, 1922 (fig. 212)
2 (1) Diameter of ventral sucker: 0.13-0.14 mm.; vitellaria originating at some distance posterior to intestinal bifurcation; ovary 0.22 x 0.11 mm.
H. yoshidai Ozaki, 1939

KEY TO THE SPECIES OF THE GENUS VASOTREMA STUNKARD, 1926 (V:148)

K. I. Skrjabin

1 (2) Genital pore at level of ovary; intestinal ceca nearly reaching posterior end of body; body up to 3.0 mm. long.   V. robustum Stunkard, 1928
2 (1) Genital pore anterior to ovary, slightly posterior to ventral sucker; intestinal ceca terminating just short of posterior end of body; body length less than 2.0 mm.
3 (4) Esophageal diverticula well-developed; seminal vesicle of great dimensions, anterior to ovary, filling space between intestinal ceca, cirrus sac, and ovary.   V. amydae Stunkard, 1926 (fig. 210)
4 (3) Esophageal diverticula weakly developed; seminal vesicle small, posterior to ovary.
V. attenuatum Stunkard, 1928

LITERATURE ON THE TREMATODES OF THE FAMILY SPIRORCHIDAE STUNKARD, 1921 (V:164)

Skrjabin, K. I. and R. Ed. Schulz. 1937. Helminthiases of long-horned cattle and their young. Selkhozgiz, Moskva. 723 pp.

KEY TO THE GENERA OF THE FAMILY SANGUINICOLIDAE GRAFF, 1907 (V:167)

K. I. Skrjabin

1 (8) With many testes.
2 (5) Uterus short, without loops, consisting solely of metraterm; genital pore posterior to ovary.
3 (4) Cirrus sac with well-developed pars prostatica, sac modified into large, round organ; male genital pore considerably distant from femal genital pore. Parasites in body cavity of fishes.
Plehniella Szidat, 1951 (fig. 216)
4 (3) Cirrus sac rudimentary; male genital pore adjacent to female genital pore. Parasites in circulatory system of fresh-water fishes.
Sanguinicola Plehn, 1905 (fig. 217)
5 (2) Uterus elongate, with loops. Parasites of marine fishes.
6 (7) Genital pore anterior to ovary.
Aporocotyle Odhner, 1900 (fig. 218)
7 (6) Genital pore posterior to ovary.
Paradeontacylix McIntosh, 1934 (fig. 219)
8 (1) Testis single.
9 (10) Testis with two lateral lobes; lobes united by two transversely oblique bridges; ovary lateral; uterus usually both anterior and posterior to ovary.
Deontacylix Linton, 1910 (fig. 220)
10 (9) Testis entire, of net-like construction, originating posterior to intestinal bifurcation, terminating posteriorly at various levels.
Psettarium Goto and Ozaki, 1930 (fig. 221)

KEY TO THE SPECIES OF THE GENUS SANGUINICOLA PLEHN, 1905 modified from McIntosh (1934) (V:169)

K. I. Skrjabin

1 (2) Vitelline ducts double; with irregularly distributed cuticular spines.
S. occidentalis Van Cleave and Mueller, 1932
2 (1) Vitelline duct single; cuticular spines absent, or present in single row along edge of body.
3 (6) Body lacking cuticular spines, equipped with delicate bristles.
4 (5) Distance from oötype to posterior end of body one twenty-sixth of body length.
S. inermis Plehn, 1905 (fig. 217)
5 (4) Distance from oötype to posterior end of body

one-seventh of body length.
S. huronis Fischthal, 1949

6 (3) Body with simple row of cuticular spines.

7 (8) Cuticle equipped with delicate bristles.
S. intermedia Ejsmont, 1926

8 (7) Bristles on cuticle lacking.

9 (10) Intestine not forming lobes; six to seven pairs of testes present. S. chalmersi Odhner, 1924

10 (9) Intestine with lobes.

11 (14) Ten to twenty pairs of testes present.

12 (13) Ten pairs of testes present.
S. armata Plehn, 1905

13 (12) Twenty pairs of testes present.
S. volgensis (Rasin, 1929)

14 (11) Testes tubular, number beyond calculation.
S. argentinensis Szidat, 1951

KEY TO THE SPECIES OF THE GENUS PARADEONTACYLIX MCINTOSH, 1934 (V:204)

K. I. Skrjabin

1 (2) Ovary roughly cardiform, at point one-third of body length from posterior end.
P. sanguinicoloides McIntosh, 1934 (fig. 219)

2 (1) Ovary curved, at point one-ninth of body length from posterior end. P. odhneri (Layman, 1930)

KEY TO THE SPECIES OF THE GENUS PSETTARIUM GOTO AND OZAKI, 1930 (V:213)

K. I. Skrjabin

1 (2) Ovary compact, not subdivided into two parts, lateral; esophagus short, one-sixth of body length.
P. japonicum (Goto and Ozaki, 1929) (fig. 221)

2 (1) Ovary bipartite, medial.

3 (4) Body length: 1.125 mm., width: 0.167 mm.; posterior intestinal diverticula reaching length of 0.300-0.315 mm.; length of esophagus slightly less than one-half of body length.
P. cardiocolum Manter, 1947

4 (3) Body length: 3.483 mm., width: 0.412 mm.; posterior intestinal diverticula reaching length of 1.728 mm.; length of esophagus one-fourth of body length. P. tropicum Manter, 1940

LITERATURE ON THE TREMATODES OF THE FAMILY SANGUINICOLIDAE GRAFF, 1907 (V:223)

Layman, E. M. 1930. Parasitic worms of fishes of Peter the Great Bay. Izvestiya Tikhookeanskoy Nauchno-Promyslovoy Stantsii. 3(6):1-120.

Layman, E. M. 1949. Course in the diseases of fishes. Pischepromizdat, Moskva. 305 pp.

Malevitska, M. O. 1936. Trematodes (Trematoda) of pond carp fingerlings of several fish culture ponds of the Ukrainian S.S.R. Zbirnik Prats Zoologichnogo Muzeyu Akad. Nauk Ukr. SSR (18), Trudy Institutu Zoologii ta Biologii. 13:29-51. (In Ukrainian).

Malevitskaya, M. A. 1950. On the question of sanguinicoliasis of pond carp in fish culture ponds of the Ukrainian S.S.R. Trudy Nauchno-Issledovatelskogo Instituta Prudovogo i Ozerno-Rechnogo Rybnogo Khozyatstva. No. 7:138-141.

KEY TO THE SUBFAMILES OF THE FAMILY SCHISTOSOMATIDAE LOOSS, 1899 from Price (1929) (V:227)

1 (2) Females thin, with more or less cylindrical bodies; males larger than females, with thick bodies, with lateral regions forming gynecophoric canal; intestinal ceca usually uniting posterior to middle of body; testes anterior to intestinal arch.
Schistosomatinae Stiles and Hassall, 1898

2 (1) Females similar in form to males; male lacking well-developed gynecophoric canal; union of intestinal ceca anterior to middle of body; testes posterior to intestinal arch.

3 (4) Common intestinal cecum equipped with lateral, dendritically branching diverticula.
Dendritobilharziinae Mehra, 1940

4 (3) Common intestinal cecum simple, without diverticula.

5 (6) Female genital pore medial, near anterior end of body; oral sucker usually lacking; ventral sucker always present. Gigantobilharziinae Mehra, 1940

6 (5) Female genital pore opening posterior to ventral sucker; both suckers present.
Bilharziellinae Price, 1929

KEY TO THE GENERA OF THE SUBFAMILY SCHISTOSOMATINAE STILES AND HASSALL, 1898 (V:227)

K. I. Skrjabin

1 (2) Vitellaria and vitelline ducts paired, with narrow inter-cecal space present between lateral vitelline fields. Parasites of elephants.
Bivitellobilharzia Vogel and Minning, 1940 (fig. 222)

2 (1) Vitellaria and vitelline duct single.

3 (6) Testes more than sixty in number; ovary spiral-shaped.

4 (5) Not more than one hundred and twenty testes present; ovary in anterior third of body.
Ornithobilharzia Odhner, 1912 (fig. 223)

5 (4) Two hundred and thirty to two hundred and fifty testes present; ovary in posterior third of body.
Macrobilharzia Travassos, 1923 (fig. 224)

6 (3) Twenty or less testes present.

7 (8) Anterior end of gynecophoric canal near middle of body; testes in two rows, near anterior end of canal; genital pore directly anterior to anterior testis; intestinal ceca with short lateral diverticula; common intestinal cecum short in both sexes; ovary pre-equatorial. Schistosomatium Tanabe, 1923 (fig. 225)

8 (7) Anterior end of gynecophoric canal near ventral sucker; genital pore of male slightly posterior to ventral sucker; intestinal ceca without diverticula;

common intestinal cecum usually long; ovary pre- or post-equatorial.

9 (10) Less than ten testes present; ovary oval.
                    Schistosoma Weinland, 1858 (fig. 226)

10 (9) Eighteen to twenty testes present; ovary spiral-shaped.

11 (12) Anterior end of gynecophoric canal slightly posterior to ventral sucker; female lacking oral sucker; ovary in anterior portion of posterior third of body.   Austrobilharzia Johnston, 1917 (fig. 227)

12 (11) Anterior end of gynecophoric canal anterior to ventral sucker; female with oral sucker present; ovary pre-equatorial.
                    Microbilharzia Price, 1929 (fig. 228)

KEY TO THE SPECIES OF THE GENUS AUSTROBILHARZIA JOHNSTON, 1917 (V:280)

K. I. Skrjabin

1 (2) With eighteen to twenty testes; intestinal ceca with small diverticula. Parasites of gulls.
                    A. terrigalensis Johnston, 1917 (fig. 227)

2 (1) With twenty-eight testes; intestinal ceca without diverticula. Parasites of snipes.
                    A. bayensis Tubangui, 1933

KEY TO THE GENERA OF THE SUBFAMILY BILHARZIELLINAE PRICE, 1929 (V:348)

K. I. Skrjabin

1 (4) Body cylindrical or nearly cylindrical.

2 (3) Gynecophoric canal lacking; posterior end of male thread-like, widest in middle part of body. Trichobilharzia Skrjabin and Zakharow, 1920 (fig. 229)

3 (2) Gynecophoric canal well-developed; body of equal width throughout.
                    Pseudobilharziella Ejsmont, 1929 (fig. 230)

4 (1) Body flattened.

5 (6) Lateral edges of body not in-folded, without gynecophoric canal.
                    Bilharziella Looss, 1899 (fig. 231)

6 (5) Lateral edges of body folded internally, forming deep gynecophoric canal.   Chinchuta Lal, 1937

KEY TO THE SPECIES OF THE GENUS PSEUDOBILHARZIELLA EJSMONT, 1929
(for males) modified from Brackett (1942) (V:357)

K. I. Skrjabin

1 (6) Testes along sides of wavy, unpaired segment of intestine.

2 (3) Body length of male reaching 2.3 mm.
                    P. yokogawai (Oiso, 1927)

3 (2) Body length of male greater than 5 mm.

4 (5) Suckers small: oral reaching 0.045 mm. in diameter, ventral 0.064 mm.
                    P. kowalewskii Ejsmont, 1929 (fig. 230)

5 (4) Suckers large; oral reaching 0.15 mm. in di-

ameter, ventral 0.18-0.19 mm.
                    P. corvi Yamaguti, 1941

6 (1) Testes tandem; outline of unpaired segment of intestine more or less straight.

7 (8) Large forms, reaching 11-12 mm. in length, 0.15 mm. in width; testes large, reaching 0.08 x 0.06 mm.   P. filiformis Szidat, 1938

8 (7) Minute, very thin forms; bodies not exceeding 5-6 mm. in length.

9 (12) Body cylindrical, with equal diameter at all points.

10 (11) Seminal vesicle long, extending from ventral sucker to genital canal.
                    P. kegonsensis Brackett, 1942

11 (10) Seminal vesicle short, occupying only half distance from ventral sucker to genital canal.
                    P. burnetti Brackett, 1942

12 (9) Body with beaded outline, due to indentations between testes.

13 (14) Seminal vesicle extending from ventral sucker to genital canal, forming about ten loops; length of genital canal exceeding 0.25 mm.
                    P. waubesensis Brackett, 1942

14 (13) Seminal vesicle wide, forming only four to six loops; length of genital canal about 0.15 mm.
                    P. horiconensis Brackett, 1942

KEY TO THE SPECIES OF THE GENUS DENDRITOBILHARZIA SKRJABIN AND ZAKHAROW, 1920 (V:388)

K. I. Skrjabin

1 (4) Uterus long, containing many eggs.

2 (3) Eggs in uterus round, reaching 0.060-0.65 mm. in diameter, without spines, not containing miracidia, maturing in mucus layer of intestine to acquire spindle-shape.   D. anatinarum Cheatum, 1941

3 (2) Eggs oval-shaped with short sharp spines at one pole, length including spines: 0.027-0.033 mm., width: 0.015-0.018 mm.   D. asiatica Mehra, 1940

4 (1) Uterus short, with single egg.

5 (6) Body length of female reaching 1.56 mm., width 0.28 mm. Parasites of ducks.
                    D. pulverulenta (Braun, 1901) (fig. 233)

6 (5) Body length of female reaching 14.2 mm., width 1.41 mm. Parasites of pelicans.
                    D. loossi Skrjabin, 1924

KEY TO THE SPECIES OF THE GENUS GIGANTOBILHARZIA ODHNER, 1910 (for males)
modified from Brackett (1942) (V:397)

K. I. Skrjabin

1 (6) Gynecophoric canal present.

2 (5) Oral sucker present.

3 (4) Body length: 140-165 mm.; width: 0.25-0.35 mm.   G. acotylea Odhner, 1910

4 (3) Body length: 10 mm., width: 0.06 mm.
                    G. gyrauli (Brackett, 1940) (fig. 234)

5 (2) Oral sucker lacking. <u>G. lawayi</u> Brackett, 1942
6 (1) Gynecophoric canal lacking.
7 (8) Oral sucker present.

<u>G. monocotylea</u> Szidat, 1930
8 (7) Oral sucker absent. <u>G. egreta</u> Lal, 1937

LITERATURE ON THE TREMATODES OF THE FAMILY SCHISTOSOMATIDAE LOOSS, 1899 (V:410)

Boev, S. N. 1944. On the question of ornithobil-harziasis of domestic animals of Kazakhstan. Izvestiya Kazakhskogo Filiala Akad. Nauk SSSR, seriya zoologicheskaya. No. 3:130-131.

Zakharov, N. P. 1919. On the discovery of <u>Bilharziella polonica</u> in birds of the Don region. Trudy Obschestva Veterinarnykh Vrachey Donskoy Oblasti. No. 1:3-14.

Panova, L. G. 1926. Helminthology in Kazakhstan. Sbornik Rabot po Gelmintologii, Posvyaschenny Prof. K. I. Skrjabinu. pp. 121-137.

Popov. N. P. 1926. On the discovery of <u>Schistosomum turkestanicum</u> in a cat in Kazakhstan. Trudy Gosudarstvennogo Instituta Experimentalnoy Veterinarii. 4(1):141-144.

Skrjabin, K. I. 1913. <u>Schistosoma turkestanicum</u> n. sp., a new parasite from cattle of Russian Turkestan. Zeitschr. für Infektionskrankheiten, Parasitare Krankheiten and Hygiene der Haustiere. 13(7):458-468. (In German).

Skrjabin, K. I. 1911. Bilharziasis, a helminth disease of the blood of long-horned cattle in Turkestan. Arkhiv Veterinarnykh Nauk. 41(10):1167-1176.

Skrjabin, K. I. 1916. On the knowledge of the helminth fauna of domestic animals of Turkestan. Dissertatsiya, Yuriev.

Skrjabin, K. I. and N. P. Zakharov. 1919. Results of the initial investigation of the helminth fauna of the Don region. Trudy Obschestva Veterinarnykh Vrachey Donskoy Oblasti. No. 1:1-25.

Skrjabin, K. I. 1920. The second Don-Azov Helminthological Expedition. Izvestiya Donskogo Veterinarnogo Instituta. 1(2):1-18.

Skrjabin, K. I. 1924. On the fauna of parasitic worms in pelicans of Turkestan. Trudy Gosudarstvennogo Instituta Experimentalnoy Veterinarii. 2(1):4-5.

Skrjabin, K. I. and R. Ed. Schulz. 1937. Helminthiases of long-horned cattle and their young. Selkhozgiz, Moskva. 723 pp.

LITERATURE ON THE GENERAL STUDY OF SCHISTOSOMATIASIS (V:468)

Plotnikov, N. N. 1949. New developments in the chemotherapy of trematodiasis. Parazitologiya, No. 5, Gelmintologiya. pp. 28-35.

Skrjabin, K. I. and R. Ed. Schulz. 1937. Helminthiases of long-horned cattle and their young. Selkhozgiz, Moskva. 723 pp.

Skrjabin, K. I. and R. Ed. Schulz. 1940. Funda-mentals of general helminthology. Selkhozgiz, Moskva. 470 pp.

Shikhobalova, N. P. and E. S. Leykina. 1949. Contemporary state of the question of immuno-diagnosis of helminthiases. Parazitologiya, No. 5, Gelmintologiya. pp. 46-74.

Shikhobalova, N. P. 1950. Questions of immunity in helminthiases. Izdatelstvo Akad. Nauk SSSR, Moskva-Leningrad. 184 pp.

Schulz, R. Ed. S. and S. N. Boev. 1948. Post-imaginal dehelminthization. Izvestiya Akad. Nauk Kazak. SSR, seriya parazitologicheskays. No. 6:151-162.

LITERATURE ON THE CONNECTION BETWEEN SCHISTOSOMATIASIS AND NEOPIASMS (V:471)

Skrjabin, K. I. and R. Ed. S. Schulz. 1940. The role of helminths in the etiology of neoplasms. <i>In:</i> Fundamentals of general helminthology. Selkhozgiz, Moskva. 470 pp.

Smirnov, G. G. 1927. Cancerous tumors and animal parasites. Vestnik Mikrobiologii, Epidemiologii, i Parazitologii. 6(1):105-109.

LITERATURE ON SCHISTOSOMATID DERMATITIS (V:574-575)

Boev, S. N. 1944. On the question of ornithobil-harziasis of domestic ruminants of Kazakhstan. Izvestiya Kazakhskogo Filiala Akad. Nauk SSSR, seriya zoologicheskaya. No. 3:130-131.

Davtyan, E. A. and R. Ed. S. Schulz. 1949. Attempt at the systematization of the immunological states in helminthiases. Trudy Nauchno-Issledovatelskogo Veterinarnogo Instituta Armyansk. SSR. 6:145-150.

Panova, L. G. 1940. On the question of the distribution of ornithobilharziasis in long-horned cattle in Kazakhstan. Trudy Kazakhskogo Nauchno-Issledovatelskogo Veterinarnogo Instituta. 3:428-430.

Popov, N. P. 1926. On the discovery of <u>Schistosoma turkestanicum</u> in a cat in Kazakhstan. Trudy Gosudarstvennogo Instituta Experimentalnoy Veterinarii. 4(1):141-144.

Skrjabin, K. I. 1913. <u>Schistosoma turkestanicum</u> n. sp., a new parasite from cattle of Russian Turkestan. Zeitschr. für Infektionskrankheiten, parasitäre Krankheiten und Hygiene der Haustiere. 13(7):458-468. (In German).

Skrjabin, K. I. 1916. On the knowledge of the helminth fauna of domestic animals of Turkestan. Dissertatsiya, Yuriev.

Skrjabin, K. I. and N. P. Zakharov. 1920. Two new genera of trematodes from the blood of birds. (Materials on the knowledge of the helminth fauna of birds of Russia). Izvestiya Donskogo Veterinarnogo Instituta. 2(1):1-5.

Skrjabin, K. I., V. P. Podyapolskaya, and R. Ed. S. Schulz. 1929. Brief summary of the activities of the 60th Union Helminthological Expedition into the Far East region. Russky Zhurnal Tropicheskoy Meditsiny. 7(1):113-130.

Skrjabin, K. I. and R. Ed. S. Schulz. 1937. Helminthiases of long-horned cattle and their young. Selkhozgiz, Moskva. 723 pp.

Skrjabin, K. I. and R. Ed. S. Schulz. 1940. Fundamentals of general helminthology. Selkhozgiz, Moskva. 470 pp.

Schulz, R. Ed. S. and N. P. Shikhobalova. 1940. Immunization in helminthiases. *In:* Skrjabin, K. I. and R. Ed. S. Schulz, Fundamentals of general helminthology. Selkhozgiz, Moskva. pp. 313-370.

LITERATURE ON IMMUNITY FOR SCHISTOSOMATIASIS (V:610)

Davtyan, È. A. and R. Ed. S. Schulz. 1949. Attempt at systematization of immunological states in helminthiases. Trudy Nauchno-Issledovatelskogo Veterinarnogo Instituta. Armyansk. SSR. 6:145-150.

Kleynbock, M. P. 1949. The patho-morphology of the pancreas in eurytrematodiasis of domestic animals. Trudy Alma-Atinskogo Veterinarno-Zootekhnicheskogo Instituta. 6:341-355.

Shikhobalova, N. P. and E. S. Leykina. 1949. The contemporary state of the question of immunodiagnoses of helminthiases. Parazitologiya, No. 5, Gelmintologiya. pp. 46-74.

Schulz, R. Ed. S. and N. P. Shikhobalova. 1935. Immunity in helminthiases. Meditsinskaya Parazitologiya i Parazitarnye Bolezni. 4(4):258-280.

Schulz, R. Ed. S. and N. P. Shikhobalova. 1937. Allergic skin reactions in helminthiases. Meditsinskaya Parazitologiya i Parazitarnye Bolezni. 6(1):116-133.

Schulz, R. Ed. S. and N. P. Shikhobalova. 1940. Immunobiological diagnoses. *In:* Skrjabin, K. I. and R. Ed. S. Schulz, Fundamentals of general helminthology. Selkhozgiz, Moskva. pp. 401-433.

LIST OF SUPPLEMENTARY ILLUSTRATIONS

Spirorchidae Stunkard, 1921
  Neospirorchis schistosomatoides Price, 1934 (fig. 826)
  Unicaecum ruszkowskii Stunkard, 1925 (fig. 827)
Schistosomatidae Looss, 1899
  Heterobilharzia americana Price, 1929 (fig. 828)

PART VI

KEY TO THE FAMILIES OF THE SUBORDER ASPIDOGASTRATA FAUST, 1932 (VI:12)

K. I. Skrjabin

1 (2) Ventral sucking apparatus modified as disc of Baer, in a muscular disc distinct from body, with suckers concentrated in several longitudinal rows; life cycle direct, without intermediate hosts.
Aspidogastridae Poche, 1907
2 (1) Ventral sucking apparatus without disc distinct from body; numerous suckers present in single longitudinal row lying directly on ventral surface of body; life cycle with intermediate host, without larval alternation of generations in intermediate host.
Stichocotylidae Faust and Tang, 1936

KEY TO THE GENERA OF THE FAMILY ASPIDOGASTRIDAE POCHE, 1907 (VI:13-14)

K. I. Skrjabin

1 (2) With two intestinal ceca.
Zonocotyle Travassos, 1947 (fig. 235)
2 (1) Intestinal cecum single.
3 (4) Disc of Baer with single row of sucking locules; testis single. Macraspis Olsson, 1868 (fig. 236)
4 (3) Disc of Baer with three or four rows of sucking locules; one or two testes.

5 (10) Disc of Baer with sucking locules in three rows.
6 (7) With two testes.
Cotylogaster Monticelli, 1892 (fig. 237)
7 (6) With single testis.
8 (9) With cirrus sac.
Cotylaspis Leidy, 1857 (fig. 238)
9 (8) Cirrus sac lacking. Lissenmysia Sinha, 1935
10 (5) Sucking locules of disc of Baer in four rows.
11 (12) With two testes; numerous sucking locules present. Multicotyle Dawes, 1941 (fig. 240)
12 (11) With single testis.
13 (14) Papillae present in central portion of disc of Baer. Lophotaspis Looss, 1900 (fig. 241)
14 (13) Papillae lacking in central portion of disc of Baer.
15 (16) Mouth surrounded by lip-like appendices.
Lobatostoma Eckmann, 1932 (fig. 242)
16 (15) Mouth without lip-like appendices.
Aspidogaster K. Baer, 1827 (fig. 243)
Note: Platyaspis Monticelli, 1892 (-Cotylaspis Leidy, 1857) omitted from key.

KEY TO THE SPECIES OF THE GENUS ASPIDOGASTER K. BAER, 1827 (VI:14)

K. I. Skrjabin

1 (4) Number of lateral sucker-like locules on disc of Baer, less than twenty-five.

2 (3) Number of lateral locules on disc, twenty (nine pairs plus two). Parasites of fishes of the genus Barbus. A. enneatis Eckmann, 1932

3 (2) Number of lateral locules on disc: twenty-two (ten pairs plus two). Parasites of carp (Cyprinus carpio). A. decatis Eckmann, 1932

4 (1) More than twenty-five lateral sucker-like locules on disc.

5 (6) Parasites of molluscs.
A. conchicola K. Baer, 1827 (fig. 243)

6 (5) Parasites of fishes.
A. limacoides Diesing, 1834

KEY TO THE SPECIES OF THE GENUS COTYLAPSIS LEIDY, 1857 (VI:46)

K. I. Skrjabin

1 (2) Parasites of molluscs. Number of locules on disc, reaching twenty-nine.
C. insignis Leidy, 1857 (fig. 238)

2 (1) Parasites of turtles.

3 (4) Total number of locules on disc, fifty; eggs: 0.15 mm. (length) x 0.08 mm. (width). Parasites of Chelydra serpentina. C. stunkardi Rumbold, 1928

4 (3) Total number of locules on disc, less than forty.

5 (6) Number of locules on disc, thirty-two; eggs: 0.145-0.187 (length) x 0.071-0.086 mm. (width). Parasites of Malaclemys leseuri.
C. cokeri Barker and Parsons, 1914

6 (5) Less than thirty locules on disc.

7 (8) Twenty-seven locules on disc; eggs: 0.168-0.182 mm. (length) x 0.098-0.112 mm. (width). Parasites of Amyda tuberculata from China.
C. sinensis Faust and Tang, 1936

8 (7) Twenty-five locules on disc; eggs: 0.14 mm. (length) x 0.043 mm. (width). Parasites of Tetrathyra vaillandi from Africa. C. lenoiri (Poirier, 1886)

KEY TO THE SPECIES OF THE GENUS COTYLOGASTER MONTICELLI, 1892 (VI:75)

K. I. Skrjabin

1 (2) With twenty medial and fifty peripheral locules; vitellaria composed of separate lateral follicles. Parasites of European fishes.
C. michaelis Monticelli, 1892 (fig. 237)

2 (1) With thirty-one to thirty-four medial and one hundred to one hundred and ten peripheral locules; vitellaria forming continuous mass, not of individual follicles, lateral, on both sides of body. Parasites of North American fishes.
C. occidentalis Nickerson, 1899

KEY TO THE SPECIES OF THE GENUS LOBATOSTOMA ECKMANN, 1932 (VI:86)

K. I. Skrjabin

1 (2) Thirty-six to forty-two peripheral locules on

disc; sixteen to nineteen transverse, medial locules in each row. L. ringens (Linton, 1907) (fig. 242)

2 (1) Thirty-two peripheral locules on disc; transverse medial locules, fifteen per row.

3 (4) Disc about one-third to one-fourth length of body; ovary and testis posterior to disc; vitellaria extending from level of middle of disc to point near posterior end of body.
L. kemostoma (MacCallum and MacCallum, 1913)

4 (3) Disc not less than half of body length; ovary and testis dorsal to disc; vitellaria originating near anterior edge of disc and extending to posterior end of intestinal ceca. L. pacificum Manter, 1940

KEY TO THE SPECIES OF THE GENUS LOPHOTASPIS LOOSS, 1900 (VI:95)

K. I. Skrjabin

1 (2) Total number of sucking locules on disc, thirty-eight: twenty peripheral and eighteen medial; genital pore posterior to pharynx. Parasites of oysters.
L. margaritiferae (Shipley and Hornell, 1904)

2 (1) Total number of locules on disc exceeding fifty.

3 (4) Total number of locules, one hundred and twenty: sixty peripheral and sixty medial; genital pore directly anterior to disc. Parasites of marine gastropods. L. macdonaldi (Monticelli, 1892)

4 (3) Total number of locules on disc, less than one hundred; genital pore posterior to edge of mouth. Parasites of turtles.

5 (6) Total number of locules on disc, seventy-seven: forty-one peripheral and thirty-six medial.
L. vallei (Stossich, 1899) (fig. 241)

6 (5) Total number of locules, less than seventy.

7 (8) Total number of locules on disc, fifty-four: thirty peripheral and twenty-four medial.
L. orientalis Faust and Tang, 1936

8 (7) Total number of locules on disc, sixty-five: thirty-five peripheral and thirty medial.
L. interiora Ward and Hopkins, 1931

KEY TO THE GENERA OF THE FAMILY STICHOCOTYLIDAE FAUST AND TANG, 1936 (VI:128)

K. I. Skrjabin

1 (2) Single row of sucker present along ventral surface; suckers at considerable distance from one another; suckers simple, lacking transverse partitions; with two testes.
Stichocotyle Cunningham, 1884 (fig. 244)

2 (1) Single row of suckers present along ventral surface; each sucker with transverse partition; space between suckers also partitioned; testis single.
Multicalyx (Faust and Tang, 1936) (fig. 245)

LITERATURE ON THE TREMATODES OF THE SUBCLASS ASPIDOGASTREA FAUST AND TANG, 1936 (VI:147)

Bykhovskaya, I. E. and B. E. Bykhovsky. 1934. On the morphology and systematics of Aspidogaster limacoides Diesing, Zeitschr. für Parasitenkunde, 7(2): (In German).

Bykhovskaya (Pavlovskaya), I. E. and B. E. Bykhovsky. 1940. The parasite fauna of fishes of the Akhtarinskye estuaries (Sea of Azov, delta of the River Kuban). Parazitologichesky Sbornik Zoologicheskogo Instituta Akad. Nauk SSSR. 8:131-161.

Layman, E. M. 1949. Course in diseases of fishes. Pischepromizdat, Moskva. 305 pp.

Markevich, A. P. 1950. Fundamentals of parasitology. Kiev.

Popov, N. P. 1926. On the fauna of parasitic worms of the Don River basin. Parasitic worms of bream (Abramis brama). Russky Gidrobiological Zhurnal, Saratov. 5(3-4):64-72.

Skrjabin, K. I. 1927. The Fourth Russian Helminthological Expedition in the Don district (Novocherkassk). Deyatelnosti 28-y Gelmintologicheskoy Expeditsii v SSSR. pp. 32-40.

Skrjabin, K. I. and R. Ed. Schulz. 1940. Fundamentals of general helminthology. Selkhozgiz, Moskva. 470 pp.

KEY TO THE FAMILIES OF THE SUPERFAMILY HETEROPHYOIDEA FAUST, 1929 (VI:228)

F. N. Morozov

1 (4) Testes distal from posterior end of body, separated from posterior end by loops of uterus.

2 (3) Testes and ovary in middle third of body; vitellaria predominantly in anterior half of body; body not attenuated anteriorly, broad posteriorly. Parasites of fishes.   Cryptogonimidae Ciurea, 1933

3 (2) Testes in third fourth of body; vitellaria mainly in anterior half of body; anterior portion of body attenuated. Parasites of birds and mammals.
                Galactosomatidae Morosov, 1950

4 (1) Testes in posterior fourth of body; uterus usually not extending beyond testes; body subdivided into two parts: thin, muscular anterior portion, ventrally concave; posterior portion oval or circular in cross-section. Parasites of birds and mammals.
                Heterophyidae Odhner, 1914

KEY TO THE SUBFAMILIES OF THE FAMILY HETEROPHYIDAE ODHNER, 1914 (VI:229-230)

F. N. Morozov

1 (10) Oral sucker simple, lacking spines and appendages.

2 (9) Ventral and genital suckers joining genital sinus.

3 (4) Genital sinus displaced laterally.
                Metagoniminae Ciurea, 1924

4 (3) Genital sinus medial.

5 (8) Genital sucker of one papilla.

6 (7) Genital papilla smaller than and anterior to ventral sucker; body oval, flattened; uterus short, forming three transverse branches.
                Euryhelminae Morosov, 1952

7 (6) Papilla of genital sucker larger than and posterior to ventral sucker; uterus well-developed.
                Cryptocotylinae Ciurea, 1924

8 (5) Genital sucker of two anterior papillae.
                Apophallinae Ciurea, 1924

9 (2) Ventral sucker well-developed, not included in genital sinus; genital sucker large, armed with chitinous spines, joined to genital sinus.
                Heterophyinae Ciurea, 1924

10 (1) Oral sucker with one or two crowns of spines, usually equipped with anterior and posterior appendages; genital sucker in form of one or two reniform papillae anterior to ventral sucker, or genital sucker reduced.   Centrocestinae Looss, 1899

KEY TO THE GENERA OF THE SUBFAMILY HETEROPHYINAE CIUREA, 1924 (VI:230)

F. N. Morozov

1 (4) Testes tandem; uterus extending to posterior edge of posterior testis.

2 (3) Genital sucker armed with comb-like chitinous plates.
    Heterophyopsis Tubangui and Africa, 1938 (fig. 246)

3 (2) Genital sucker armed with simple, small chitinous spines.
        Pseudoheterophyes Yamaguti, 1939 (fig. 247)

4 (1) Testes symmetrical, posterior to rest of gonads.   Heterophyes Cobbold, 1866 (fig. 248)

KEY TO THE SPECIES OF THE GENUS HETEROPHYES COBBOLD, 1866 (VI:232)

F. N. Morozov

1 (4) Less than thirty spines on genital sucker.

2 (3) Intestinal ceca terminating at level of anterior portion of testes.   H. aequalis Looss, 1902

3 (2) Intestinal ceca extending beyond testes.
                H. dispar Looss, 1902

4 (1) Not less than fifty spines on genital sucker.

5 (8) Not more than sixty spines on genital sucker.

6 (7) Sixty spines on genital sucker; diameter of ventral sucker not exceeding 2.5 times diameter of oral sucker.   H. nocens Onji and Nishio, 1915

7 (6) Fifty spines on genital sucker; diameter of ventral sucker more than three times diameter of oral sucker.
                H. katsuradai Ozaki and Asada, 1926

8 (5) Not less than sixty-two spines on genital sucker; intestinal ceca extending beyond testes.
                H. heterophyes (Siebold, 1852) (fig. 248)

KEY TO THE GENERA OF THE SUBFAMILY METAGONIMINAE CIUREA, 1924 (VI:252)

F. N. Morozov

1 (4) Testes asymmetrical; left testis oval; right testis spherical, smaller than left.
2 (3) Vitellaria not extending anteriorly beyond posterior edge of ventral sucker.
        Metagonimus Katsurada, 1912 (fig. 249)
3 (2) Vitellaria extending anteriorly to level of pharynx.   Metagonimoides Price, 1931 (fig. 250)
4 (1) Testes spherical, symmetrical, near posterior end of body.
5 (6) Ventral sucker longitudinally elongate with narrow, longitudinally oriented aperture; seminal vesicle flask-shaped, bipartite or tripartite.
        Dexiogonimus Witenberg, 1929 (fig. 251)
6 (5) Ventral sucker round; seminal vesicle spherical, joined to ejaculator.
        Diorchitrema Witenberg, 1929 (fig. 252)

KEY TO THE SPECIES OF THE GENUS METAGONIMUS KATSURADA, 1912 (VI:259)

F. N. Morozov

1 (4) Transverse vitelline duct anterior to seminal receptacle.
2 (3) Eggs: 0.023-0.028 x 0.013-0.018 mm.
        M. yokogawai (Katsurada, 1912) (fig. 249)
3 (2) Eggs: 0.030-0.035 x 0.018-0.020 mm.
        M. takanaschi Suzuki, 1929
4 (1) Transverse vitelline duct posterior to seminal receptacle; eggs: 0.023 x 0.013 mm.
        M. minutus Katzuta, 1932

KEY TO THE GENERA OF THE SUBFAMILY CRYPTOCOTYLINAE CIUREA, 1924 (VI:283)

F. N. Morozov

1 (2) Eggs oval; vitellaria not reaching intestinal bifurcation.   Cryptocotyle Lühe, 1899 (fig. 253)
2 (1) Eggs distorted; vitellaria extending to intestinal bifurcation.   Ciureana Skrjabin, 1923 (fig. 254)

KEY TO THE SPECIES OF THE GENUS CRYPTOCOTYLE LÜHE, 1899 (VI:283)

F. N. Morozov

1 (4) Vitellaria extending anteriorly to mid-point between ventral sucker and intestinal bifurcation.
2 (3) Body oval; testes symmetrical; eggs: 0.034-0.038 x 0.016-0.020 mm.
        C. cancavum (Creplin, 1825) (fig. 253)
3 (2) Body usually elongate; testes oblique; eggs: 0.040-0.050 x 0.018-0.025 mm.
        C. lingua (Creplin, 1825)
4 (1) Vitellaria extending to level of anterior edge

of ventral sucker; genital sinus small, about 0.05 mm.   C. jejuna (Nicoll, 1907)

KEY TO THE SPECIES OF THE GENUS CIUREANA SKRJABIN, 1923 (VI:298)

F. N. Morozov

1 (2) Body pentagonal; testes and ovary entire; eggs: 0.038 x 0.015 mm.
        C. quinqueangularis Skrjabin, 1923 (fig. 254)
2 (1) Body egg-shaped; testes and ovary sharply lobed; eggs: 0.040 x 0.020 mm.
        C. cryptocotyloides Issaitschikoff, 1923

KEY TO THE GENERA OF THE SUBFAMILY APOPHALLINAE CIUREA, 1924 (VI:305)

F. N. Morozov

1 (4) Vitellaria extending anteriorly to level of intestinal bifurcation, confluent anterior to ventral sucker.
2 (3) Testes slightly oblique, separated from posterior end by vitelline follicles; ventral sucker at posterior border of first third of body; prepharynx lacking.
    Rossicotrema Skrjabin and Lindtrop, 1919 (fig. 255)
3 (2) Testes symmetrical, near posterior end of body; ventral sucker nearly equatorial; prepharynx present.   Pricetrema Ciurea, 1933 (fig. 256)
4 (1) Vitellaria not extending anteriorly to level of intestinal bifurcation.
        Apophallus Lühe, 1909 (fig. 257)

KEY TO THE SPECIES OF THE GENUS APOPHALLUS LÜHE, 1909 (VI:308)

F. N. Morozov

1 (10) Vitellaria not extending anteriorly beyond level of ventral sucker.
2 (7) Vitellaria not confluent posterior to testes.
3 (6) Vitellaria extending beyond testes.
4 (5) Intestinal bifurcation equatorial.
        A. imperator Lystor, 1940
5 (4) Intestinal bifurcation at end of first third of body.
        A. muhlingi (Jägerskiöld, 1899) (fig. 257)
6 (3) Vitellaria not extending beyond testes; intestinal bifurcation at two-fifths of body length from anterior end.
        A. bacolloti (Balozet and Callot, 1939)
7 (2) Vitellaria confluent posterior to testes.
8 (9) Intestinal bifurcation nearly equatorial.
        A. americanus Van Cleave and Mueller, 1932
9 (8) Intestinal bifurcation at one-fifth of body length from anterior end.   A. crami Price, 1931
10 (1) Vitellaria extending slightly anterior to ventral sucker.
        A. brevis Ransom, 1920

KEY TO THE SPECIES OF THE GENUS ROSSICOTREMA SKRJABIN AND LINDTROP, 1919 (VI:324)

F. N. Morozov

1 (2) Vitellaria lateral, disjunct at level of transverse vitelline duct, forming two groups on each side of body; testes sub-equal.
R. donicum Skrjabin and Lindtrop, 1919 (fig. 255)
2 (1) Vitellaria continuous; transverse diameter of left testis two times larger than diameter of right testis.   R. venustus Ransom, 1920

KEY TO THE SPECIES OF THE GENUS EURYHELMIS POCHE, 1925 (VI:338)

F. N. Morozov

1 (2) Vitellaria anteriorly extending to level of pharynx, two testes present.
E. squamula (Rudolphi, 1819) (fig. 258)
2 (1) Vitellaria extending anteriorly to intestinal bifurcation; single testis, the right, present.
E. monorchis Ameel, 1938

KEY TO THE GENERA OF THE SUBFAMILY CENTROCESTINAE LOOSS, 1899 (VI:345)

F. N. Morozov

1 (8) Oral sucker with single crown of spines.
2 (7) Two testes present.
3 (6) Testes symmetrical.
4 (5) Triangular dorsal papilla directed anteriorly and blind conical appendage directed posteriorly present on oral sucker.
Parascocotyle Stunkard and Haviland, 1924 (fig. 259)
5 (4) Dorsal papilla and blind appendage lacking.
Pygidiopsis Looss, 1907 (fig. 260)
6 (3) Testes tandem.
Caimanicola Freitas and Lent, 1938 (fig. 261)
7 (2) Single testis present.
Pygidiopsoides Martin, 1951 (fig. 262)
8 (1) Oral sucker with two crowns of spines.
9 (10) Small blind appendage present on oral sucker; vitellaria and uterus anterior to ventral sucker extending into medial field.
Ascocotyle Looss, 1899 (fig. 263)
10 (9) Blind appendage on oral sucker absent; vitellaria and uterus not extending into medial field anterior to ventral sucker.
Centrocestus Looss, 1899 (fig. 264)

KEY TO THE SPECIES OF THE GENUS CENTROCESTUS LOOSS, 1899 (VI:346)

F. N. Morozov

1 (4) Intestinal ceca not extending beyond level of posterior edge of ovary; not more than thirty-six peri-oral spines present.

2 (3) Intestinal ceca extending only to level of ventral sucker; excretory bladder V-shaped.
C. cuspidatus (Looss, 1896) (fig. 264)
3 (2) Intestinal ceca reaching level of posterior edge of ovary; excretory bladder X-shaped.
C. formosanus (Nishigori, 1924)
4 (1) Intestinal ceca extending to posterior end of body; with forty-four peri-oral spines.
C. armatus (Tanabe, 1922)

KEY TO THE SPECIES OF THE GENUS ASCOCOTYLE LOOSS, 1899 (VI:357)

F. N. Morozov

1 (10) Intestinal ceca posteriorly not extending to level of testes.
2 (9) Not more than thirty-six peri-oral spines present.
3 (4) Thirty-six peri-oral spines present.
A. filippei Travassos, 1938
4 (3) Thirty-two peri-oral spines present.
5 (8) Uterus not extending beyond testes.
6 (7) Vitellaria extending from level of posterior edge of ventral sucker to posterior end of body.
A. puertoricensis Price, 1932
7 (6) Vitellaria originating anterior to genital pore, passing posteriorly to level of posterior edge of seminal receptacle.
A. coleostoma (Looss, 1896) (fig. 263)
8 (5) Uterus extending beyond testes.
A. tenuicollis Price, 1935
9 (2) Seventy-two peri-oral spines present.
A. megalocephala Price, 1932
10 (1) Intestinal ceca extending posteriorly to level of testes.   A. mcintoshi Price, 1936

KEY TO THE SPECIES OF THE GENUS PARASCOCOTYLE STUNKARD AND HAVILAND, 1924 (VI:371)

F. N. Morozov

1 (8) Intestinal ceca extending only to level of ventral sucker.
2 (7) Not less than sixteen peri-oral spines present.
3 (6) Conical appendage on oral sucker short, terminating mid-way between mouth and pharynx.
4 (5) Dorsal triangular appendage present on oral sucker; peri-oral spines: 0.018-0.020 mm. long.
P. longeniformes (Chandler, 1941)
5 (4) Dorsal appendage round; peri-oral spines 0.008-0.012 mm. long.   P. nana (Ransom, 1920)
6 (3) Conical appendage of oral sucker extending to level of pharynx.
P. minuta (Looss, 1899) (fig. 259)
7 (2) Not more than twelve peri-oral spines present.   P. pithecophagicola (Faust, 1920)
8 (1) Intestinal ceca extending to or beyond level of ovary.
9 (12) Vitellaria compact.

10 (11) Conical appendage of oral sucker terminating near pharynx. P. ascolonga Witenberg, 1929

11 (10) Conical appendage terminating mid-way between mouth and pharynx.
P. italica (Alessandrini, 1906)

12 (9) Vitellaria follicular.

13 (20) Bilobed genital sucker lacking.

14 (17) Two papillae present, anterior to genital pore.

15 (16) Vitellaria of nine to twelve follicles; perioral spines: 0.024-0.027 mm. long.
P. arnoldi (Travassos, 1928)

16 (15) Vitellaria of six to eight follicles; peri-oral spines: 0.018-0.020 mm. long.
P. longa (Ransom, 1920)

17 (14) One muscular papilla present, anterior to genital pore.

18 (19) Triangular, dorsal papilla present on oral sucker; two rows of peri-oral spines present, each row with 14 spines. P. angeloi (Travassos, 1928)

19 (18) Dorsal papilla on oral sucker lacking, nineteen to twenty-two peri-oral spines present.
P. sinoecum Ciurea, 1933

20 (13) Large bilobed genital sucker present, anterior to genital pore. P. angrense (Travassos, 1916)

KEY TO THE SPECIES OF THE GENUS
PYGIDIOPSIS LOOSS, 1907 (VI:397)

F. N. Morozov

1 (6) Prepharynx longer than esophagus.

2 (5) Loops of uterus not extending beyond level of ventral sucker.

3 (4) Oral sucker two times smaller than ventral sucker, equipped with saccular posterior appendage.
P. pindoramensis Travassos, 1929

4 (3) Oral sucker equal in size to ventral, equipped with posterior conical appendage.
P. phalacocoracis Yamaguti, 1939

5 (2) Loops of uterus extending anteriorly beyond level of intestinal bifurcation; oral sucker without appendage. P. macrostomum Travassos, 1928

6 (1) Prepharynx shorter than esophagus.

7 (8) Oral sucker without appendage; loops of uterus extending to level of anterior edge of ventral sucker; vitellaria composed of five to seven follicles.
P. genata Looss, 1907 (fig. 260)

8 (7) Oral sucker with small posterior appendage; vitellaria extending anteriorly to level of anterior edge of ovary. P. summa Onji and Nishio, 1924

KEY TO THE GENERA OF THE SUBFAMILY
GALACTOSOMATINAE CIUREA,
1924 (VI:413)

F. N. Morozov

1 (6) Body elongate, more or less fusiform.

2 (5) Body not subdivided by constriction into two sections.

3 (4) Ovary and seminal receptacle anterior to testes. Galactosomum Looss, 1899 (fig. 265)

4 (3) Ovary and seminal receptacle between anterior and posterior testis.
Sobolephya Morosov, 1950 (fig. 266)

5 (2) Body subdivided by constriction into two sections. Cercarioides Witenberg, 1929 (fig. 267)

6 (1) Body more or less pyriform.

7 (8) Vitellaria in posterior third of body, not extending anterior to posterior edge of terminal testis.
Stictodora Looss, 1899 (fig. 268)

8 (7) Vitellaria partially superimposed upon testes.
Parastictodora Martin, 1950 (fig. 269)

KEY TO THE SPECIES OF THE GENUS
GALACTOSOMUM LOOSS, 1899 (VI:414)

F. N. Morozov

1 (18) Anterior part of body not sharply expanded.

2 (13) Intestinal bifurcation in anterior fourth of body.

3 (6) Both testes in posterior-most fourth of body.

4 (5) Genital pore in anterior portion of second third of body.
G. lacteum (Jāgerskiöld, 1896) (fig. 265)

5 (4) Genital pore equatorial.
G. phalacocoracis Yamaguti, 1939

6 (3) Testes in third fourth of body.

7 (10) Esophagus well-developed.

8 (9) Genital pore at posterior end of anterior-most fourth of body. G. puffii Yamaguti, 1941

9 (8) Genital pore equatorial.
G. erinaceus (Poirier, 1886)

10 (7) Esophagus reduced.

11 (12) Vitellaria lateral.
G. spinoctum (Braun, 1901)

12 (11) Vitellaria intercecal.
G. humbergari Park, 1936

13 (2) Intestinal bifurcation in second fourth of body.

14 (17) Genital pore in anterior region of second third of body.

15 (16) Vitellaria not extending anterior to posterior edge of terminal testis. G. darbii Price, 1934

16 (15) Vitellaria extending anteriorly to midpoint of anterior testis. G. anguillarum (Tubangui, 1933)

17 (14) Genital pore equatorial; vitellaria confluent both posterior to testes and at level of anterior testis.
G. johnstoni Price, 1934

18 (1) Body sharply expanded anteriorly; vitellaria lateral, extending from posterior end of body to level of anterior testis.

G. cochleariforme (Rudolphi, 1819)

KEY TO THE SPECIES OF THE GENUS
CERCARIOIDES WITENBERG, 1929 (VI:437)

F. N. Morozov

1 (2) Anterior portion of body covered with fine

spines; anterior half of posterior part of body covered with short, thick spines; esophagus and prepharynx lacking.
C. aharoni Witenberg, 1929 (fig. 267)
2 (1) Anterior portion of body covered with short, thick spines; posterior portion of body covered with small, thin spines; prepharynx and esophagus present.
C. baylisi Nasmi, 1930

KEY TO THE SPECIES OF THE GENUS STICTODORA LOOSS, 1899 (VI:442)

F. N. Morozov

1 (4) Ventral sucker lacking.
2 (3) Six to ten rows of triangular chitinous plates present on genital sucker.
S. sawakinensis Looss, 1899 (fig. 268)
3 (2) Twenty-five to twenty-eight rows of thin spines present on genital sucker.
S. guerreroi Garcia and Refuerso, 1936
4 (1) Muscular ventral sucker present.
5 (8) Testes oblique; vitellaria lateral.
6 (7) Two cushion-shaped swellings armed with fine spines present on ventral sucker.
S. japonicum Yamaguti, 1934
7 (6) Appendages on ventral sucker lacking.
S. mergi Yamaguti, 1939
8 (5) Testes lateral, symmetrical; vitellaria intercecal posterior to testes.   S. lari Yamaguti, 1939

KEY TO THE GENERA OF THE SUBFAMILY KNIPOWITSCHETREMATINAE MOROSOV, 1950 (VI:460)

F. N. Morozov

1 (4) Vitellaria extending anteriorly to level of genital sucker; testes oblique.
2 (3) Esophagus lacking; oral sucker not exceeding twice diameter of ventral sucker.
Ponticotrema Issaitschikoff, 1927 (fig. 270)
3 (2) Esophagus present; oral sucker not less than three times diameter of ventral sucker.
Tauridiana Issaitschikoff, 1925 (fig. 271)
4 (1) Vitellaria extending anteriorly only to level of posterior edge of terminal testis; testes tandem.
Knipowitschetrema Issaitschikoff, 1927 (fig. 272)

KEY TO THE GENERA OF THE SUBFAMILY HAPLORCHINAE LOOSS, 1899 (VI:476)

F. N. Morozov

1 (4) Intestinal ceca thin; seminal receptacle anterior to testis.
2 (3) Seminal vesicle long, bipartite, walls of anterior portion equipped with chitinous fibers.
Procerovum Onji and Nishio, 1924 (fig. 273)
3 (2) Seminal vesicle composed of two globular portions, walls without chitinous fibers.
Haplorchis Looss, 1899 (fig. 274)

4 (1) Intestinal ceca saccular, broad, short; seminal receptacle posterior to testis, seminal vesicle simple.   Euhaplorchis Martin, 1950 (fig. 275)

KEY TO THE SPECIES OF THE GENUS HAPLORCHIS LOOSS, 1899 (VI:476-477)

F. N. Morozov

1 (6) Anterior portion of ventral sucker armed with spines; intestinal ceca extending to posterior end of body.
2 (3) Spines large, numbering eleven to twelve, 0.02 mm. long.   H. taichui (Nishigori, 1924)
3 (2) Spines small, numerous.
4 (5) Spines limited to anterior portion of ventral sucker.   H. yokogawai (Katzuta, 1932)
5 (4) Spines in continuous crown, surrounding genital pore.   H. milvi Gohar, 1934
6 (1) Anterior edge of ventral sucker not armed with spines, but with special hooks equipped with one to several lateral branches; intestinal ceca extending posteriorly to anterior edge of testis.
H. pumilio (Looss, 1896) (fig. 274)
Note: H. vanissima Africa, 1938 and H. pleurolophocerca (Sonsino, 1896) omitted from key.

KEY TO THE SUBFAMILIES OF THE FAMILY CRYPTOGONIMIDAE CIUREA, 1933 (VI:508)

F. N. Morozov

1 (8) Gonads remote from posterior end of body.
2 (7) Ovary slightly lobed, or consisting of several parts. Parasites of fresh-water fishes.
3 (4) Oral sucker considerably smaller than ventral; many testes present in posterior third of body; vitellaria extending to posterior end of body.
Polyorchitrematinae Srivastava, 1939
4 (3) Oral sucker considerably larger than ventral.
5 (6) Two testes present; vitellaria in anterior or middle thirds of body.
Haplorchoidinae Morosov, 1952
6 (5) Single testis present.
Cryptogoniminae Ward, 1917
7 (2) Ovary multilobed, occasionally with two distinct parts, nearly equatorial. Parasites of marine fishes.   Siphoderinae Manter, 1934
8 (1) Gonads in posterior half of body.
Acetodextrinae Morosov, 1952

KEY TO THE TRIBES OF THE SUBFAMILY CRYPTOGONIMINAE WARD, 1917 (VI:509)

F. N. Morozov

1 (2) Uterus forming single longitudinal loop in posterior half of body, skirting testes; oral sucker without spines.
Cryptogonimea Morosov, 1952
2 (1) Uterus passing between testes, forming

several loops posterior to testes; oral sucker armed with single row of chitinous spines.

Neochasmea Morosov, 1952

KEY TO THE GENERA OF THE TRIBE CRYPTOGONIMEA MOROSOV, 1950 (VI:509)

F. N. Morozov

1 (2) Body elongate; intestinal ceca reaching anterior boundary of terminal third of body; vitellaria in middle third of body; ovary anterior to testes.

Cryptogonimus Osborn, 1910 (fig. 276)

2 (1) Body vase-shaped; intestinal ceca short, terminating nearly equatorially; vitellaria in anterior third of body; ovary at level of testes; genital sucker rudimentary.

Caecincola Marshal and Gilbert, 1905 (fig. 277)

KEY TO THE SPECIES OF THE GENUS CRYPTOGONIMUS OSBORN, 1903 (VI:510)

F. N. Morozov

1 (2) Oral sucker funnel-shaped; testes oblique, widely separated.   C. chili Osborn, 1903 (fig. 276)

2 (1) Oral sucker not funnel-shaped; testes symmetrical, adjacent.   C. diaphanus (Stafford, 1905)

KEY TO THE GENERA OF THE TRIBE NEOCHASMEA MOROSOV, 1952 (VI:517)

F. N. Morozov

1 (2) Loops of uterus not extending anterior to testes; ovary consisting of separate follicles; genital pore anterior to genital sucker.

Neochasmus Van Cleave and Mueller, 1932 (fig. 278)

2 (1) Loops of uterus extending anterior to testes and ovary; ovary entire, irregularly triangular, or curved; genital pore posterior to genital sucker.

Allocanthochasmus Van Cleave and Mueller, 1932 (fig. 279)

KEY TO THE TRIBES OF THE SUBFAMILY SIPHODERINAE MANTER, 1934 (VI:530)

F. N. Morozov

1 (4) Vitellaria occupying restricted area in anterior or middle thirds of body; uterus extending beyond testes.

2 (3) Vitellaria mainly in middle third of body.

Paracryptogonimea Morosov, 1952

3 (2) Vitellaria mainly in anterior third of body.

Siphoderea Morosov, 1952

4 (1) Vitellaria extending from level of pharynx to posterior region of body; uterus not extending beyond testes.   Iheringotremea Morosov, 1952

KEY TO THE GENERA OF THE TRIBE

SIPHODEREA MOROSOV, 1952 (VI:530-531)

F. N. Morozov

1 (8) Two testes present.

2 (5) Body round or oval; anterior portion of body narrower than posterior.

3 (4) Seminal vesicle relatively small, not extending posteriorly beyond level of ovary.

Metadena Linton, 1910 (fig. 280)

4 (3) Seminal vesicle very large, passing posteriorly beyond level of testes.

Exorchis Kobayashi, 1918 (fig. 281)

5 (2) Body pyriform, greatly broadened anteriorly, attenuated posteriorly.

6 (7) Esophagus absent; intestinal ceca reaching posterior end of body.

Siphoderina Manter, 1934 (fig. 282)

7 (6) Esophagus present; intestinal ceca extending for half body length.   Centrovarium Stafford, 1904

8 (1) Eight testes present.

Siphodera Linton, 1910 (fig. 284)

KEY TO THE SPECIES OF THE GENUS METADENA LINTON, 1910 (VI:543)

F. N. Morozov

1 (6) Vitelline follicles forming ribbon, bisecting body at level of ventral sucker.

2 (5) Diameter of ventral sucker not greater than one-fourth diameter of oral sucker.

3 (4) Ovary multilobed, anterior to testes.

M. globosa (Linton, 1910)

4 (3) Ovary with not more than seven lobes; at level of testes.   M. adglobosa (Linton, 1910)

5 (2) Diameter of ventral sucker not less than one-half diameter of oral sucker.

M. pagrosomi Yamaguti, 1938

6 (1) Vitellaria in two groups, lateral at level of ventral sucker. M. crassulata Linton, 1910 (fig. 280)

Note: M. microvatus Tubangui, 1938 omitted from key.

KEY TO THE GENERA OF THE TRIBE PARACRYPTOGONIMEA MOROSOV, 1952 (VI:555)

F. N. Morozov

1 (4) Testes not symmetrical.

2 (3) Testes oblique; vitellaria lateral in middle third of body, not extending anteriorly beyond level of ventral sucker.

Paracryptogonimus Yamaguti, 1934 (fig. 285)

3 (2) Testes tandem, medial; vitellaria extending anteriorly beyond genital pore, confluent medially anterior to genital pore.

Biovarium Yamaguti, 1934 (fig. 286)

4 (1) Testes symmetrical, lateral.

Siphoderoides Manter, 1940 (fig. 287)

KEY TO THE GENERA OF THE SUBFAMILY ACETODEXTRINAE MOROSOV, 1952 (VI:580)

F. N. Morozov

1 (2) Body oval; ventral sucker slightly dextral; vitellaria extending from middle of body to posterior end.   Acetodextra Pearse, 1924 (fig. 288)

2 (1) Body pyriform; ventral sucker medial; vitellaria compact, at level of anterior region of testes and ends of intestinal ceca.

Pseudexorchis Yamaguti, 1938

KEY TO THE SUBFAMILIES OF THE FAMILY MICROPHALLIDAE TRAVASSOS, 1920 (VI:621)

M. M. Belopolskaya

1 (2) Cirrus sac lacking; seminal vesicle and prostatic glands free in parenchyma.

Microphallinae Ward, 1901

2 (1) Cirrus sac present; seminal vesicle and prostatic glands enclosed within cirrus sac.

Maritrematinae Lal, 1939

LITERATURE ON THE TREMATODES OF THE SUPERFAMILY HETEROPHYOIDEA FAUST, 1929 (VI:601)

Ass, M. Ya. 1939. The rule of Fuhrmann (phylogenetic relationships of parasites and their hosts). Trudy Leningradskogo Obschestva Estestvoispytateley. 67(4):8-54.

Afanasiev, V. P. 1941. The parasite fauna of commercial mammals of the Komandorskie Islands. Uchenye Zapiski Leningradskogo Gosudarstvennogo Universiteta, 74, seriya biologicheskikh nauk. No. 18:93-117.

Bobrinsky, N. A. 1944. Guide to the mammals of the U.S.S.R.

Borisov, G. P. 1939. On the helminth fauna of dogs of the city of Voroshilovsk-Kavkazsky. Priroda. No. 1:84-85.

Buturlin, S. A. 1935. Complete guide to the birds of the U.S.S.R. Vols. 1, 2, 3.

Bykhovsky, B. E. 1937. Ontogeny and phylogenetic inter-relationships of parasitic flatworms. Izvestiya Akad. Nauk SSSR, seriya biologicheskaya. No. 4:245-275.

Vlasenko, P. V. 1931. On the fauna of parasitic worms of fishes of the Black Sea. Trudy Karadagskoy Biologicheskoy Stantsii, Simferopol. No. 4:88-136.

Gamtsemlidze, S. Ya. 1941. On the fauna of parasitic worms of mammals of Georgia. Trudy Tbilisskogo Gosudarstvennogo Universiteta. 21:123-187.

Demidova, A. Ya. 1937. Helminth fauna of dogs of Azerbaydzhan. Sbornik Rabot po Gelmintologii, Posvyaschenny Akademiku K. I. Skrjabinu. pp. 123-125.

Dogiel, V. A. 1932. Parasitic diseases of fishes. Selkhozgiz, Moskva-Leningrad. 151 pp.

Dogiel, V. A. 1947. Course in general parasitology. Second Ed. Uchpedgiz. 371 pp.

Efimov, A. V. 1938. Investigations of the parasitic worm fauna of domestic animals of the Ukrainian S.S.R. Zbirnik Prats Zoologichnogo Muzeyu Akad. Nauk Ukr. RSR (21-22). Trudy Institutu Zoologii ta Biologii. 19:177-186. (In Ukrainian).

Zmeev, G. Ya. 1932. Infestations of fishes of the Amur River estuary with metacercariae of Metagonimus yokogawai Katsurada, 1912. Parazitologichesky Sbornik Zoologicheskogo Instituta Akad. Nauk SSSR. 3:253-259.

Zmeev, G. Ya. 1936. Trematodes and tapeworms of fishes of the Amur River. Parazitologichesky Sbornik Zoologicheskogo Instituta Akad. Nauk SSSR. 6:408-435.

Ivanov, A. S. 1946. On the helminth fauna of cyprinid fishes of the Volga delta. Sbornik Rabot po Gelmintologii, Posvyaschenny Akademiku K. I. Skrjabinu. pp. 121-125.

Isaychikov, I. M. 1923. Ciureana cryptocotyloides nov. sp., a new trematode from birds, and its position in the systematics of the family Heterophyidea. Trudy Gosudarstvennogo Instituta Experimentalnoy Veterinarii. 1(1):155-158.

Isaychikov, I. M. 1924. On the fauna of parasitic worms of domestic carnivores of the Crimea, I. Parasitic worms of dogs. Uchenye Trudy Sibirskogo Veterinarnogo Instituta. No. 6:47-105.

Isaychikov, I. M. 1927. On the fauna of parasitic worms of domestic carnivores of the Crimea, II. Parasitic worms of cats. Trudy Sibirskogo Veterinarnogo Instituta. No. 9:132-170.

Isaychikov, I. M. 1927z. A new trematode from the family Heterophyidae (from materials of the Black Sea-Azov Scientific-Commercial Expedition of Prof. Knipovich, 1922-1924). Sbornik v Chest Prof. N. M. Knipovicha, 1885-1925. Moskva. pp. 261-269.

Isaychikov, I. M. 1928. On the knowledge of parasitic worms of several groups of vertebrates of the Russian Arctic, A. Trematodes. Trudy Morskogo Nauchnogo Instituta. 3(2):5-79.

Lindgolm, V. A. 1937. The soft-bodies or molluscs: Mollusca. Fauna SSSR. 1:387-415.

Lysenko, T. D. 1938. On heredity and variability. Agrobiologiya.

Malevitska, M. O. 1938. On the presence of Metagonimus yokogawai Katsurada in the territory of the Ukrainian SSR. Zbirnik Prats Zoologichnogo Muzeyu Akad. Nauk Ukr. RSR (21-22), Trudy Institutu Zoologii ta Biologii. 19:187-192. (In Ukrainian).

Markowski, S. 1933. Cryptocotyle cancavum (Creplin) in the body cavity of Singhathus tyfle. Arkhiv Gidrobiologii, Suvalki. 7:18-20.

Mordvilko, A. 1908. On the origin of the phenomenon of intermediate hosts in animal parasites. Izvestiya Imperatorskoy Akad. Nauk. pp. 359-362.

Mordvilko, A. 1908. Origin of the phenomenon of intermediate hosts in animal parasites. Ezhegodnik Zoologicheskogo Muzeya Imperatorskoy Akad. Nauk. 13(1-2):129-222.

Morozov, F. N. 1950. Phylogenetic relationships of trematodes of the superfamily

Heterophyoidea. Doklady Akad. Nauk SSSR. 74(3):645-648.

Pavlovsky, E. N. 1937. Class Trematoda. *In:* Manual of zoology. I. Invertebrates. Moskva-Leningrad. pp. 461-501.

Pavlovsky, E. N. 1946. Manual on human parasitology. Izdatelstvo Akad. Nauk SSSR, Moskva-Leningrad. 521 pp.

Pavlovsky, E. N. 1947. Parasitology of the Far East. Medgiz. pp. 333-337.

Petrov, A. M. 1927. Work of the Helminthological Laboratory for the period 1917-1927. Vestnik Sovremennoy Veterinarii. 3(8):235.

Petrov, A. M. 1928. On parasitic worms of domestic carnivores of the U.S.S.R. Trudy 3-go Vserossiskogo Sezda Zoologov, Anatomov, i Gistologov. pp. 149-151.

Petrov, A. M. 1931. Helminth infestations in dogs, and their sanitary and economic significance. Selkhozgiz, Moskva-Leningrad. 192 pp.

Petrov, A. M. 1941. Helminth diseases of fur-bearing animals. Mezhdunarodnaya Kniga, Moskva. 228 pp.

Petryayev, P. A. and I. D. Starkov. 1934. Diseases and parasites of fur-bearing animals. Vneshtorgizdat, Moskva-Leningrad. pp. 133-211.

Popov, N. P. 1926. Parasitic worms of domestic carnivores of Armenia. Trudy Tropicheskogo Instituta Armenii. 1:12-17.

Prendel, A. R. 1937. Summary of the helminth fauna of cats of Odessa. Sbornik Rabot po Gelmintologii, Posvyaschenny Akademiku K. I. Skrjabin. pp. 542-546.

Severtsov, A. N. 1939. Morphological laws of evolution. Izdatelstvo Akad. Nauk SSSR, Moskva-Leningrad. 610 pp.

Skrjabin, K. I. 1919. The First Don-Azov Helminthological Expedition. Izvestiya Donskogo Veterinarnogo Instituta. 1(1):1-10.

Skrjabin, K. I. 1923. Works on the study of parasitic worms of carnivores, II-IV. Trudy Gosudarstvennogo Instituta Experimentalnoy Veterinarii. 1(1):67-71.

Skrjabin, K. I. 1923a. Parasitic worms of dogs of the Don district. Nauchnye Izvestiya Smolenskogo Gosudarstvennogo Universiteta. 1:56-59.

Skrjabin, K. I. 1927. The First Russian Helminthological Expedition on the north shores of the Sea of Azov. Deyatelnost 28-y Gelmintologicheskoy Expeditsii SSSR. Moskva. pp. 7-14.

Skrjabin, K. I. 1927a. The Second Russian Helminthological Expedition on the north shores of the Sea of Azov. Deyatelnost 28-y Gelmintologicheskoy Expeditsii SSSR. Moskva. pp. 14-26.

Skrjabin, K. I. 1927b. The Third Russian Helminthological Expedition into the Don River delta. Deyatelnost 28-y Gelmintologichskoy Expeditsii SSSR. Moskva. pp. 26-32.

Skrjabin, K. I. 1927c. The Fourth Russian Helminthological Expedition into the Don district (near Novocherkassk). Deyatelnost 28-y Gelmintologicheskoy Expeditsii SSSR. pp. 32-40.

Skrjabin, K. I. 1934. Short course in the parasitology of domestic animals. Selkhozgiz, Moskva.

Skrjabin, K. I., *et al.* 1934. Veterinary parasitology and infectious diseases of domestic animals. Selkhozgiz, Moskva.

Skrjabin, K. I. and R. Ed. Schulz. 1940. Fundamentals of general helminthology. Selkhozgiz, Moskva-Leningard. 470 pp.

Skrjabin, K. I. 1941. On the revision of the systematics of the nematodes of the families, Acuariidae and Ancyracanthidae. Doklady Akad. Nauk SSSR. 30(5):470-473.

Skrjabin, K. I. 1942. Paths of phylogenetic evolution of the nematodes of the family Pseudalidae, parasites of the auditory apparatus, circulatory system, and respiratory organs of marine mammals. Doklady Akad. Nauk SSSR. 37(1):41-46.

Skrjabin, K. I. 1945. On the revision of the systematics of trematodes of the family Opisthorchidae. Doklady Akad. Nauk SSSR. 49(2):155-156.

Skrjabin, K. I. 1946. The building of Soviet helminthology. Izdatelstvo Akad. Nauk SSSR, Moskva-Leningrad. 211 pp.

Skrjabin, K. I. 1947. Trematodes of animals and man. Izdatelstvo Akad. Nauk SSSR, Moskva-Leningrad. Vol. I, 515 pp.

Skrjabin, K. I. 1948. Trematodes of animals and man. Izdatelstvo Akad. Nauk SSSR, Moskva-Leningrad. Vol. II, 600 pp.

Skrjabin, K. I. 1949. Trematodes of animals and man. Izdatelstvo Akad. Nauk SSSR, Moskva-Leningrad. Vol. III, 623 pp.

Skrjabin, K. I. 1924. Kidney trematodes of Russian birds. Centrbl. Bakt., Abt. I. 62:80-90. (In German).

Skrjabin, K. I. 1924. On the characteristics of worm invasion of dogs and cats of the Don district. Berl. tier ärztl. Wschr. No. 20:257-259. (In German).

Skrjabin, K. I. and G. T. Lindtrop. 1919. Intestinal trematodes in dogs of the Don district. Izvestiya Donskogo Veterinarnogo Instituta. 1(1):30-43.

Skrjabin, K. I., V. P. Podyapolskaya, and R. Ed. S. Schulz. 1929. Brief summary of the activities of the 60th Union Helminthological Expedition into the Far East. Russky Zhurnal Tropicheskoy Meditsiny. 7(1):113-130.

Skrjabin, K. I. and R. Ed. S. Schulz. 1936. Trematodes-Trematoda. Zhivotny Mir SSSR. 1:592-595.

Skrjabin, K. I. and R. Ed. S. Schulz. 1937. Helminthiases of long-horned cattle and their young. Selkhozgiz, Moskva. 723 pp.

Spassky, A. A. 1951. Anoplocephalid tapeworms of domestic and wild animals. *In:* Spassky, A. A., Fundamentals of cestodology. Moskva. Vol. I, 735 pp.

Sushkin, B. P. and D. E. Beling. 1923. Guide to the fresh-water and marine fishes of European Russia. 115 pp.

Timiryazev, K. A. 1949. Selected works. 3:359-410.

KEY TO THE GENERA OF THE SUBFAMILY MICROPHALLINAE WARD, 1901 (VI:621)

M. M. Belopolskaya

1 (8) Ventral sucker of usual type.
2 (3) Intestinal ceca terminating considerable distance from seminal vesicle; occasionally with one cecum rudimentary, or with only one cecum present.
  Microphallus Ward, 1901 (fig. 290)
3 (2) Intestinal ceca reaching seminal vesicle or extending beyond.
4 (5) Special sensory organ present, muscular, saccular, containing chitinous plate, communicating with and sinistral to genital cavity.
  Spiculotrema Belopolskaia, 1949 (fig. 291)
5 (4) Special sensory organ lacking.
6 (7) Genital cavity of complex construction, with four thimble-shaped pockets; male papilla small.
  Levinseniella Stiles and Hassall, 1901 (fig. 292)
7 (6) Genital cavity simple, nearly filled by large male papilla. Spelotrema Jägerskiöld, 1901 (fig. 293)
8 (1) Posterior half of ventral sucker with spines, covered with cuticle; ejaculatory duct opening into ventral sucker.
  Endocotyle Belopolskaia, 1952 (fig. 294)

KEY TO THE GENERA OF THE SUBFAMILY MARITREMATINAE LAL, 1939 (VI:689)

M. M. Belopolskaya

1 (12) Single ventral sucker present.
2 (5) Loops of uterus extending anterior to ventral sucker.
3 (4) Two loops of uterus extending anteriorly, parallel to sides of body to level of pharynx.
  Maritreminoides Rankin, 1939 (fig. 295)
4 (3) One loop of uterus passing between seminal vesicle and ceca.
  Numeniotrema Belopolskaia, 1952 (fig. 296)
5 (2) Loops of uterus not extending anterior to ventral sucker.
6 (7) Vitellaria forming U-shaped figure, parallel to posterior edges of body.
  Maritrema Nicoll, 1907 (fig. 297)
7 (6) Vitellaria otherwise.
8 (11) Vitellaria lateral, never merging medially.
9 (10) Vitellaria anterior to intestinal ceca, near lateral edges of body; cirrus sac enclosing sucker, equipped terminally with chitinous outgrowths.
  Microphalloides Yoshida, 1938 (fig. 298)
10 (9) Vitellaria posterior to intestinal ceca, origi-nating posterior to intestinal ceca, passing parallel to lateral edges of body, and terminating at level of testes; cirrus sac of usual type, anterior to ventral sucker.
  Pseudospelotrema Yamaguti, 1939 (fig. 299)
11 (8) Vitellaria merging medially, forming loop between testes, giving off two small branches of follicles laterally anterior to testes.
  Pseudomaritrema Belopolskaia, 1952 (fig. 300)
12 (1) Two ventral suckers present.
13 (14) Intestinal ceca not extending beyond ventral suckers; genital pore dextral to suckers; genital cavity with two cornate structures.
  Gynaecotyla Yamaguti, 1939 (fig. 301)
14 (13) Intestinal ceca extending beyond ventral suckers, skirting suckers posteriorly, thence directing medially; genital pore sinistral to suckers.
  Diacetabulum Belopolskaia, 1952 (fig. 302)

LITERATURE ON THE TREMATODES OF THE FAMILY MICROPHALLIDAE TRAVASSOS, 1920 (VI:754)

Afanasiev, V. P. 1941. The parasite fauna of commercial mammals of the Komandorskie Islands. Uchenye Zapiski Leningradskogo Gosudarstvennogo Universiteta, 74, seriya biologicheskikh nauk. No. 18:93-117.
Belopolskaya, M. M. 1949. The life cycle of Spelotrema pygmaeum, a parasite of birds. Doklady Akad. Nauk SSSR, novaya seriya. 66(1):133-135.
Belopolskaya, M. M. 1949. The "sensory organ" in the trematode, Spiculotrema litoralis nov. gen., nov. sp. (family Microphallidae Travassos, 1921). Doklady Akad. Nauk SSSR, novaya seriya. 67(1):205-208.
Ginetsinskaya, T. A. 1949. The parasite fauna of anatids of the Volga delta. Uchenye Zapiski Leningradskogo Universiteta, No. 101, seriya biologicheskikh nauk. No. 19:81-109.
Markov, G. S. 1941. Parasitic worms of birds of a nameless bay of Novaya Zemlya. Doklady Akad. Nauk SSSR, novaya seriya. 30(16):573-576.
Sinitsyn, D. F. 1911. Parthenogenetic generation of trematodes and its offspring in molluscs of the Black Sea. Zapiski Imperatorskoy Akad. Nauk. 30(5):1-127.

LIST OF SUPPLEMENTARY ILLUSTRATIONS

Galactosomatidae Morosov, 1950
  Adleriella minutissima (Witenberg, 1929) (fig. 829)
Cryptogonimidae Ciurea, 1933
  Iheringtrema iheringi Travassos, 1947 (fig. 830)
  Polyorchitrema piscicola Srivastava, 1939 (fig. 831)

PART VII

KEY TO THE GENERA OF THE FAMILY CEPHALOPORIDAE TRAVASSOS, 1934 (VII:10)

K. I. Skrjabin

1 (2) Genital pore dorsal to oral sucker; posterior sucker considerably larger than oral sucker; vitellaria consisting of separate follicles, extending beyond posterior limits of gonads. Intestinal parasites of fishes.

Plectognathotrema Layman, 1930 (fig. 303)

2 (1) Genital pore lateral, at level of pharynx, ventral sucker slightly larger than oral.

3 (4) Vitellaria consisting of indistinct mass of fused follicles, in anterior half of body, reaching only to anterior limits of testes. Parasites in oviducts of fishes.   Cephaloporus Yamaguti, 1934 (fig. 304)

4 (3) Vitellaria in distinct follicles, located in posterior half of body, posterior to testes. Intestinal parasites of birds.

Khalilloossia Hilmy, 1948 (fig. 305)

LITERATURE ON THE TREMATODES OF THE FAMILY CEPHALOPORIDAE TRAVASSOS, 1934 (VII:18)

Layman, È. M. 1930. Parasitic worms of fishes of Peter the Great Bay. Izvestiya Tikhookeanskogo Nauchno-Promyslovoy Stantsii. 3(6):1-120.

KEY TO THE SUBFAMILIES OF THE FAMILY MONODHELMIDAE (DOLLFUS, 1937) (VII:21)

K. I. Skrjabin

1 (2) Cirrus sac and genital sucker well-developed; metraterm present.

Mehratrematinae Srivastava, 1939

2 (1) Cirrus sac, genital sucker, and metraterm lacking.   Monodhelminae Srivastava, 1939

KEY TO THE SPECIES OF THE GENUS MEHRATREMA SRIVASTAVA, 1939 (VII:23)

K. I. Skrjabin

1 (2) Intestinal ceca extending to posterior end of body; posterior limit of vitellaria not, by considerable distance, reaching blind ends of intestinal ceca; vitelline follicles pyriform.

M. dollfusi Srivastava, 1939 (fig. 306)

2 (1) Intestinal ceca not extending to posterior end of body; posterior limit of vitellaria passing beyond blind ends of intestinal ceca; vitelline follicles spherical.   M. polynemusinis Chauhan, 1943

KEY TO THE SUBFAMILIES OF THE FAMILY DICROCOELIIDAE ODHNER, 1911 from Travassos (1944) (VII:36-37)

a) Cirrus sac with twisted seminal vesicle; genital pore medial; cuticle with conical papillae, or with scales; seminal receptacle present. Parasites of liver and pancreas.   Dicrocoeliinae Looss, 1899

b) Cirrus sac with saccular seminal vesicle; genital pore sub-medial; cuticle with conical papillae or with scales; seminal receptacle lacking. Parasites of liver.   Infidinae Travassos, 1944

c) Cirrus sac with saccular seminal vesicle; genital pore medial; cuticle with scales; seminal receptacle present. Parasites of small intestine.

Mesocoeliinae

KEY TO THE SPECIES OF THE GENUS DICROCOELIUM DUJARDIN, 1845 from Sudarikov and Ryzhikov (1951) (VII:40)

1 (16) Parasites of mammals.

2 (3) Testes medial; anterior boundary of vitellaria not reaching, by considerable distance, level of ovary. Parasites of ruminants.   D. hospes Looss, 1907

3 (2) Testes with different position.

4 (9) Testes symmetrical.

5 (6) Testes entire; ovary nearly equal in size to testes; intestinal ceca reaching posterior region of body; uterus inter-cecal. Parasites of insectivores.

D. soricis (Diesing, 1858)

6 (5) Testes with indented borders, or lobed.

7 (8) Suckers, very small, not exceeding 0.1 mm. in diameter; anterior limit of vitellaria not reaching level of testes; cirrus sac descending to level of middle of ventral sucker. Parasites of monkeys.

D. macaci Kobayashi, 1915

8 (7) Suckers greater than 0.3 mm. in diameter; anterior limit of vitellaria reaching level of each testis; cirrus sac not extending to level of anterior edge of ventral sucker. Parasites of deer.

D. orientalis Sudarikov and Ryjikov, 1951

9 (4) Testes oblique.

10 (13) Small trematodes with body not exceeding 3 mm.; vitelline fields short, with anterior limits not reaching level of ovary.

11 (12) Testes relatively large, indented along lateral edge; ovary considerably smaller than testes; ventral sucker larger than oral. Parasites of Todaria cynocephala (Africa).   D. rileyi Macy, 1931

12 (11) Testes small; ovary of nearly same size as testes; suckers nearly equal in size; posterior border of vitellaria at level of ends of intestinal ceca. Parasites of Chiroptera.   D. lasiuri McIntosh, 1933

13 (10) Trematodes of medium size; body more than 3 mm.; anterior border of vitelline fields reaching level of ovary.

14 (15) Suckers sub-equal in size; testes of different shapes (posterior testis lobed); longitudinal extent of vitelline field about one-seventh of body length. Parasites of monkeys.

D. colobosicola Sandground, 1929

15 (14) Ventral sucker larger than oral; testes more or less similar in shape; longitudinal extent of vitelline fields about one-fifth of body length. Parasites of ungulates and rodents, rarely of predators and primates (cosmopolitan distribution).

D. lanceatum Stiles and Hassall, 1896 (fig. 307)

16 (1) Parasites of birds.

17 (18) Oral sucker larger than ventral. Parasites of Gallinaceae.   D. macrostomum Odhner, 1911

18 (17) Oral sucker equal to or smaller than ventral.

19 (20) Eggs smaller than 0.040 mm. Parasites of diurnal predators.   D. albicolle (Rudolphi, 1819)

20 (19) Eggs larger than 0.040 mm. Parasites of magpies.   D. panduriforme Railliet, 1900

KEY TO THE SPECIES OF THE GENUS ATHESMIA LOOSS, 1899 (VII:95)

K. I. Skrjabin and V. G. Evranova

1 (2) Ovary in anterior half of body.

A. heterolecithodes (Braun, 1899) (fig. 308)

2 (1) Ovary equatorial or in posterior half of body.

3 (4) Ovary larger than testes.

A. pricei McIntosh, 1937

4 (3) Testes larger than ovary.

5 (6) Testes and ovary nearly entire.

A. parkeri Vigueras, 1942

6 (5) Testes deeply lobed, or branched.

7 (8) Parasites of mammals (monkeys).

A. foxi Goldberger and Crane, 1911

8 (7) Parasites of birds.

9 (10) Oral sucker considerably larger than ventral; testes oblique.   A. rudecta (Braun, 1901)

10 (9) Oral sucker slightly larger than ventral; testes tandem.   A. wehri McIntosh, 1937

KEY TO THE SPECIES OF THE GENUS BRACHYDISTOMUM TRAVASSOS, 1944 (VII:109)

K. I. Skrjabin and V. G. Evranova

1 (2) Ovary and testes nearly equal in size; testes adjacent; anterior testis posterior to ventral sucker; testes considerably smaller than ventral sucker; cirrus sac short, not reaching anterior edge of ventral sucker.   B. microscelis (Yamaguti, 1933) (fig. 309)

2 (1) Ovary considerably smaller than testes; testes separated by distinct space; anterior testis dorsal to ventral sucker; testes and ventral sucker equal in size; cirrus sac reaching anterior testis.

B. salebrosum (Braun, 1901)

KEY TO THE SPECIES OF THE GENUS BRODENIA GEDOELST, 1913 (VII:211)

K. I. Skrjabin and V. G. Evranova

1 (2) Fifteen tooth-like projections present on each extremity of expanded portion of body. Parasites of Cercocebus sp.   B. serrata Gedoelst, 1913 (fig. 310)

2 (1) Seven to eight tooth-like projections present on each extremity of expanded portion of body. Parasites of baboons (Papio maimon).

B. laciniata (Blainville, 1820)

KEY TO THE SUBGENERA OF THE GENUS EURYTREMA LOOSS, 1907 from Bhalerao (1936) (VII:288)

1 (2) Ovary larger than testes.

Skrjabinus Bhalerao, 1936

2 (1) Ovary smaller than testes.

3 (4) Genital pore posterior to intestinal bifurcation.

Pancreaticum Bhalerao, 1936

4 (3) Genital pore anterior to intestinal bifurcation.

5 (6) Uterus occupying considerably more than half of body area.   Lubens Travassos, 1919

6 (5) Uterus occupying only about half of body area.

7 (8) Vitellaria consisting of small number of follicles.   Concinnum Bhalerao, 1936

8 (7) Vitellaria occupying more than one-third of body length.   Conspicuum Bhalerao, 1936

KEY TO THE SPECIES OF THE GENUS EURYTREMA LOOSS, 1907 (VII:290)

K. I. Skrjabin and V. G. Evranova

1 (2) Pancreatic parasites of dogs.

E. rebelle Railliet, 1924

2 (1) Parasites of other mammals.

3 (4) Efferent duct of Laurer's canal obliterated; body covered with spines. Parasites of bile ducts of zebu.   E. dajii Bhalerao, 1924

4 (3) Laurer's canal with free efferent duct. Parasites of pancreas or bile ducts.

5 (8) Suckers nearly equal in size. Pancreatic parasites.

6 (7) Body 5-6 mm. long; uterus not forming dense loops anterior to ventral sucker. Parasites of ruminants.   E. coelomaticum (Giard and Billet, 1892)

7 (6) Body 11-12 mm. long; uterus forming thick tangle of loops anterior to ventral sucker. Parasites of sheep.   E. ovis Tubangui, 1925

8 (5) Suckers not equal in size.

9 (12) Oral sucker larger than ventral.

10 (11) Vitellaria each consisting of ten to twelve groups of follicles.

E. pancreaticum (Janson, 1889) (fig. 311)

11 (10) Vitelline follicles not forming distinct groups.   E. tonkinense Gaillard and Ngu, 1941

12 (9) Ventral sucker larger than oral.

13 (14) Genital pore posterior to intestinal bifurcation.   E. satoi Kobayashi, 1915

14 (13) Genital pore anterior to intestinal bifurcation.

15 (16) Vitellaria weakly developed, posterior to ovary.   E. vulpis Stunkard, 1947

16 (15) Vitellaria well-developed, originating at
level of ventral sucker.

$\qquad$ E. alveyi Martin and Gee, 1949

Note: E. parvum Senoo, 1907 omitted from key.

KEY TO THE SPECIES OF THE GENUS
INFIDUM TRAVASSOS, 1916 modified from
Ruiz and Leão (1943) (VII:581)

K. I. Skrjabin and V. G. Evranova

1 (2) Vitellaria extending anteriorly to level of genital pore, or beyond.

$\qquad$ I. infidum (Faria, 1910) (fig. 312)

2 (1) Vitellaria extending anteriorly only to level of
anterior edge of ventral sucker.

3 (4) Distance from ends of intestinal ceca to level
of vitelline zone considerably shorter than length of
vitellaria. $\qquad$ I. luckeri McIntosh, 1939

4 (3) Distance from ends of intestinal ceca to level
of vitelline zone nearly equal to length of vitellaria.

5 (6) Vitellaria reaching only to equatorial line.

$\qquad$ I. similis Travassos, 1916

6 (5) Vitellaria extending both posterior and ante-
ior to equatorial line.

$\qquad$ I. intermedium Ruiz and Leão, 1943

LITERATURE ON THE TREMATODES OF THE
FAMILY DICROCOELIIDAE ODHNER, 1911
(VII:591-594)

Aleynikova, M. M. and M. M. Mendelevich. 1938.
On the study of dicrocoeliasis of rabbits of the Tatar
and neighboring republics. Uchenye Zapiski Kazanskogo Gosudarstvennogo Zooveterinarnogo Instituta.
49(2):134-141.

Badanin, N. V. 1935. Investigation of the qualitative and quantitative composition of the parasite fauna
of a camel, using the method of complete helminthological dissections. Trudy Turkmenskogo Selskokhozyaystvennogo Instituta. 1(1):3-14.

Vereschagin, M. N. 1926. On the fauna of parasitic
worms of goats of Turkestan. Trudy Gosudarstvennogo
Instituta Experimentalnoy Veterinarii. 2(2):3-15.

Vsevolodov, B. P. 1937. Pathological-anatomical
changes of the pancreas in eurytrematodiasis. Sbornik
Rabot po Gelmintologii, Posvyaschenny Prof. K. I.
Skrjabinu. pp. 758-762.

Vsevolodov, B. P. 1950. Outline on the patho-
morphology of the parasitic diseases of Alectoris
graeca. Izvestiya Akad. Nauk Kazakhsk. SSR, 75,
seriya parazitologicheskaya. No. 8:246-254.

Gaibov, A. D. 1937. On the study of the fauna of
parasitic worms of horses of Azerbaydzhan. Sbornik
Rabot po Gelmintologii, Posvyaschenny Prof. K. I.
Skrjabinu. pp. 178-179.

Gushanskaya, L. Kh. 1952. On the helminth fauna
of wild gallinaceous birds of the U.S.S.R. Trudy Gelminthologicheskoy Laboratorii Akad. Nauk SSSR. 6:
175-222.

Demidova, A. I. 1935. The helminth fauna of dogs
of Azerbaydzhan. Arch. f. Schiffs-u. Tropenhyg.
39(10):412-416. (In German).

Ivanitsky, S. V. 1927. On the trematode fauna of
vertebrates of the Ukraine. Veterinarne Dilo. 5(42):
36-42.

Isaychikov, I. M. 1919. New representatives of
trematodes of the genus Lyperosomum. Izvestiya
Donskogo Veterinarnogo Instituta. 1(1):1-15.

Isaychikov, I. M. 1920. A new representative of
the genus Eurytrema Looss. Izvestiya Donskogo Veterinarnogo Instituta. 1(2):1-11.

Isaychikov, I. M. 1929. A new trematode of the
genus Plagiorchis (Lühe, 1899) from sandpipers.
Trudy Sibirskogo Veterinarnogo Instituta. No. 10:
285-288.

Kalantaryan, E. V. 1924. On the fauna of parasitic
worms of rodents of Armenia. Trudy Tropicheskogo
Instituta Armenii. 1:18-31.

Kasimov, G. B. 1948. A new species of trematode,
Corriga skrjabini n. sp., in Caucasus mountain turkeys
of Azerbaydzhan. Doklady Akad. Nauk Azerbaydzh.
SSR. 4(4):174-177.

Kazimov, G. B. 1952. Skrjabinus popovi n. sp., a
new trematode from the Caucasus mountain turkey.
Trudy Gelmintologicheskoy Laboratorii Akad. Nauk
SSSR. 6:232-234.

Kleynbok, M. T. 1949. Patho-morphology of the
pancreas in eurytrematodiasis of domestic animals.
Trudy Alma-Atinskogo Veterinarno-Zootekhnicheskogo
Instituta. 6:341-355.

Linstov, O. 1885. Roundworms, trematodes and
acanthocephalans from materials collected on the travels of A. P. Fedchenko in Turkestan. Izvestiya Imperatorskoy Obschestva Lyubiteley Estestvoznaniya,
Antropologii i Etnografii. 34(3); 40 pp.

Layman, E. M. 1922. On the characteristics of a
new representative of Lyperosomum. Arten. Zentralbl.
Bakt. Parasite u. Infekt. 56(23-24):568-572. (In German).

Layman, E. M. 1923. Lyperosomum fringillae n.
sp., a new liver parasite of birds. Arkhiv Nauchnoy i
Praktichnoy Veterinarii. 1(1):54-55.

Layman, E. M. 1926. Trematodes of bile ducts of
the liver of birds of Russia. Raboty Parazitologicheskoy Laboratorii I Moskovskogo Gosudarstvennogo
Universiteta pod Redaktsii K. I. Skrjabina. pp. 59-72.

Oliger, I. M. 1950. The parasite fauna of game
birds of the forested zone (Polesie) of the European
part of the R. S. F. S. R. Avtoreferat dissertatsii.

Oshmarin, P. G. 1947. Description of two new
species of trematodes from the liver of birds, with
reference to the analysis of their phylogenetic relationships. Trudy Gorkovskogo Gosudarstvennogo Pedagogicheskogo Instituta. 12:33-47.

Panova, L. G. 1927. Helminthology in Kazakhstan.
Sbornik Rabot po Gelmintologii, Posvyaschenny Prof.
K. I. Skrjabinu. pp. 121-137.

Petrov, A. M. 1930. On the fauna of parasitic
worms of domestic carnivores of the North Dvina
Province. Raboty 32-y i 38-y Soyuznykh Gelminto-
logichekikh Expeditsy g. Vyatka. pp. 56-67.

Petrov, A. M. and E. S. Shakhovtseva. 1926. On the fauna of parasitic worms of sheep of Turkestan. Trudy Gosudarstvennogo Instituta Experimentalnoy Veterinarii. 4(1):78-88.

Petrov, A. M. and A. A. Skvortsov. 1929. The discovery of dicrocoeliosis of the liver of man in the Nizhenovgoradskaya (Nizhny Novgorod) Province. Rabota Corok Pervoy Soyuznoy Gelminthologicheskoy Expeditsii. pp. 43-45.

Podyapolskaya, V. P. 1927. On the helminthiases of man in the U.S.S.R. Sbornik Rabot po Gelmintologii, Posvyaschenny Prof. K. I. Skrjabinu. pp. 155-179.

Potekhina, L. F. 1948. A new trematode of birds, Brachylecithum platynosomoides. Trudy Gelmintologicheskoy Laboratorii Akad. Nauk SSSR. 1:156-157.

Pukhov, V. I., E. E. Krivoshta, and P. A. Velichkin. 1937. On the biology of Dicrocoelium lanceatum. Sbornik Rabot po Gelmintologii, Posvyaschenny Prof. K. I. Skrjabinu. pp. 547-549.

Rayevskaya, Z. A. and N. V. Badanin. 1933. Helminth infestations of camels and their control. Selkhozgiz, Moskva-Lenigrad. 116 pp.

Semenov, V. D. 1927. Trematodes of birds of the western U.S.S.R. Sbornik Rabot po Gelmintologii, Posvyaschenny Prof. K. I. Skrjabinu. pp. 221-271.

Skvortsov, A. A. 1934. Investigations on the morphology, biology of the egg, and life cycle of Dicrocoelium lanceatum. Meditsinskaya Parazitologiya i Parazitarnye Bolezni. 3(3):240-253.

Skvortsov, A. A. 1936. The biology of the agent of dicrocoeliasis of domestic animals. Doklady VASKhNIL. No. 1:35-40.

Skrjabin, K. I. 1911. The discovery of Dicrocoelium lanceatum in the liver of a horse. Vestnik Obschestvennoy Veterinarii. 23(13):701-702.

Skrjabin, K. I. 1911. On the dependence between the pathological-anatomical picture of liver infection and the species of parasite in distomatiasis. Uchenye Zapiski Kazanskogo Veterinarnogo Instituta. 28(2):225-227.

Skrjabin, K. I. 1913. Bird trematodes of Russian Turkestan. Zool. Jahrb. Abt. Syst., 35(3):351. (In German).

Skrjabin, K. I. 1913. Lyperosomum filiforme n. sp. Materials on the systematics of the genus Lyperosomum Looss, 1899. Zhurnal Nauchnoy i Praktichnoy Veterinarnoy Meditsiny. 7(2):274-292.

Skrjabin, K. I. 1916. Parasitic trematodes and nematodes collected by Prof. V. A. Dogiel and I. I. Sokolov in British East Africa and Uganda. Nauchnye Rezultaty Zoologicheskoy Expeditsii Prof. V. A. Dogielya i I. I. Sokolova v Britanskuyu Vostochnuyu Afriku i Ugandu v 1914 Godu. Petrograd. 1(14):1-157.

Skrjabin, K. I. 1920. Helminthological notes. Izvestiya Donskogo Veterinarnogo Instituta. 2(2):1-7.

Skrjabin, K. I. 1920. Trematodes of snakes of Paraguay. Izvestiya Donskogo Veterinarnogo Instituta. 1(2):6-11.

Skrjabin, K. I. 1923. Helminth infestations of sheep in the light of present knowledge. Sherstyanoye Delo. Nos. 10-12:100-109.

Skrjabin, K. I. 1924. Parasitic worms of swine and their pathogenic significance. Trudy Sibirskogo Veterinarnogo Instituta. 6:133-134.

Skrjabin, K. I. 1931. Worm infestations of sheep and their significance in the economy of sheep production. Second Ed. Moskva-Leningrad. 168 pp.

Skrjabin, K. I. 1932. The prevention by treatment of helminthiases of sheep according to the practise in the Soviet Union. Bull. Off. Inter. des Epizoot. 6(1):155-171. (In French).

Skrjabin, K. I. 1944. Analysis of the generic components of the three trematode families: Opisthorchidae, Dicrocoeliidae, and Echinostomatidae. Doklady Akad. Nauk SSSR. 44(7):328-330.

Skrjabin, K. I. and B. G. Massino. 1925. Trematodes of birds of the Moscow district. Zentralbl. Bakt. Abt. 2, 64(5):453-462. (In German).

Skrjabin, K. I. and I. M. Isaychikov. 1927. Four new species of the family Dicrocoeliidae from the liver of birds. Ann. Trop. Med. Parasit. 21(3):303-308. (In English).

Skrjabin, K. I. and R. Ed. S. Schulz. 1928. On the analysis of the helminth fauna of the population of Central Asia. Raboty 35-y Soyuznoy Gelmintologicheskoy Expeditsii v Srednyuy Aziyu. pp. 52-70.

Skrjabin, K. I. and A. M. Udintsev. 1930. Two new trematodes from the bile ducts of birds from Armenia. Journ. Parasit. 16(4):213-219. (In English).

Skrjabin, K. I. and R. Ed. S. Schulz, A. I. Metelkin, and P. P. Popov. 1934. Veterinary parasitology and infectious diseases of domestic animals. Moskva-Leningrad. 600 pp.

Skrjabin, K. I. and R. Ed. S. Schulz. 1937. Helminthiases of long-horned cattle and their young. Selkhozgiz, Moskva. 723 pp.

Soloviev, P. F. 1911. A new species of the genus Dicrocoelium Dujardin, 1845 and an investigation of the systematics and phylogeny of Fasciolidae from birds. Izvestiya Varshavskogo Universiteta. Pt. 2, art. 12:1-23.

Sudarikov, V. E. and K. M. Ryzhikov. 1951. On the helminth fauna of ungulates of Pribaykalye (the Baikal region.) Trudy Gelmintologicheskoy Laboratorii Akad. Nauk SSSR. 5:53-58.

Tarasov, V. 1932. On the differential diagnosis of real and false dicrocoeliasis. Meditsinskaya Parazitologiya i Parazitologicheskye Bolezni. 1:50-52.

Strom, Zh. K. 1927. On hepatic pseudo-distomatiase. Vestnik Mikrobiologii i Epidemiologii. 6(4):433-438.

Strom, Zh. K. 1928. A new species of trematodes, Oswaldoia pawlowski n. sp. from birds. Zool. Anz. 77(7/8):184-189. (In German).

Strom, Zh. K. 1935. On the trematode fauna of Tadzhikistan. In: Materials on the parasitology and fauna of southern Tadzhikistan. Trudy Tadzhikskoy Komplexnoy Expeditsii. No. 10:219-254.

Strom, Zh. K. 1940. On the trematode fauna of wild animals of Kirgizia. Parazitologichesky Sbornik Zoologicheskogo Instituta Akad. Nauk SSSR. 8:189-224.

Strom, Zh. K. 1940. Notes on the systematics of Dicrocoeliinae (Trematoda). Parazitologichesky Sborni Zoologicheskogo Instituta Akad. Nauk SSSR. 8:176-188.

Strom, Zh. K. and V. A. Sondak. 1935. New and little known trematodes of the families Plagiorchidae and Dicrocoeliidae (from materials of the Talyshskaya Expedition, 1934). Parasites, transmitting agents, and poisonous animals. Sbornik Rabot po Gelmintologii, Posvyaschenny 25-let Nauchnoy Deyatelnosti Prof. E. N. Pavlovskogo. Izdatelstvo Veterinarnogo Instituta Experimentalnoy Meditsiny. pp. 348-359.

Schulz, R. Ed. S. 1931. Parasitic worms of hares and rabbits, and the diseases caused by them. Selkhozgiz, Moskva. 238 pp.

Scherbakova, E. Ya. 1942. On the study of the helminth fauna of rodents of Armenia. Izvestiya Armyanskogo Filiala Akad. Nauk SSSR. 1-2:159-172.

Scherbovich, I. A. 1946. Trematodes of birds of the Far East. Sbornik Rabot po Gelmintologii, Posvyaschenny Akademiku K. I. Skrjabinu. pp. 296-300.

KEY TO THE SUBFAMILIES OF THE FAMILY GORGODERIDAE LOOSS, 1901 (VII:630)

S. V. Pigulevsky

1 (4) Muscular pharynx present.
2 (3) More than two testes present.
   Anaporrhutinae Looss, 1901
3 (2) Not more than two testes present.
   Plesiorchinae Pigulevsky, 1952
4 (1) Muscular pharynx lacking.
5 (6) More than two testes present.
   Gorgoderinae Looss, 1901
6 (5) Not more than two testes present.
   Phyllodistomatinae Pigulevsky, 1952

KEY TO THE GENERA OF THE SUBFAMILY GORGODERINAE LOOSS, 1901 (VII:631)

S. V. Pigulevsky

1 (2) Nine to forty testes present.
   Gorgotrema Dayal, 1938 (fig. 313)
2 (1) Not more than nine testes present.
   Gorgodera Looss, 1899 (fig. 314)

KEY TO THE SUBGENERA OF THE GENUS GORGODERA LOOSS, 1899 (VII:632)

S. V. Pigulevsky

1 (8) Testes clearly separated into right and left groups.
2 (5) Ovary, vitellaria, testes closely adjacent.
3 (4) Ventral sucker protruding beyond surface of body.   Antodera Pigulevsky, 1952
4 (3) Ventral sucker not protruding beyond body surface.   Extremodera Pigulevsky, 1952
5 (2) Ovary, vitellaria, and testes not closely adjacent.
6 (7) Groups of testes symmetrical.
   Mediodera Pigulevsky, 1952
7 (6) Groups of testes not symmetrical, but displaced obliquely.   Postodera Pigulevsky, 1952

8 (1) Testes not clearly separated into right and left groups; right and left groups confluent.
   Gorgodera (Looss, 1899) (fig. 314)

KEY TO THE SPECIES OF THE SUBGENUS GORGODERA (Looss, 1899) PIGULEVSKY, 1952 (VII:633)

S. V. Pigulevsky

1 (4) Ventral sucker two times larger than oral.
2 (3) Ovary lobed.   G. (G.) japonica Yamaguti, 1936
3 (2) Ovary entire, oval.
   G. (G.) microovata Fuhrmann, 1924
4 (1) Ventral sucker less than two times larger than oral.
5 (6) Both groups of testes diffuse.
   G. (G.) cygnoides (Zeder, 1800) (fig. 314)
6 (5) Both groups of testes compactly distributed.
   G. (G.) cygnoides var. asiatica (Skarbilovitsch, 1950)

KEY TO THE SPECIES OF THE SUBGENUS ANTODERA PIGULEVSKY, 1952 (VII:649)

S. V. Pigulevsky

1 (2) Not more than six vitelline follicles present; eggs small.   G. (A.) amplicava Looss, 1899
2 (1) More than six vitelline follicles present; eggs large.   G. (A.) circava Guberlet, 1920

KEY TO THE SPECIES OF THE SUBGENUS MEDIODERA PIGULEVSKY, 1952 (VII:671)

S. V. Pigulevsky

1 (8) Ovary larger than testes.
2 (5) Testes posterior to middle third of body.
3 (4) Testes and ovary entire.
   G. (M.) asymmetrica Fuhrmann, 1924
4 (3) Testes and ovary lobed.
   G. (M.) pagenstecheri Sinitsin, 1905
5 (2) Testes in middle third of body.
6 (7) Middle part of body greatly expanded; posterior end of body tapered; ovary equatorial.
   G. (M.) asiatica Pigulevsky, 1945
7 (6) Middle part of body narrow; posterior end bluntly rounded; ovary not equatorial, in anterior third of body.   G. (M.) media Strom, 1940
8 (1) Ovary not larger than testes.
   G. (M.) pawlowskyi Pigulevsky, 1952

KEY TO THE SPECIES OF THE SUBGENUS POSTODERA PIGULEVSKY, 1952 (VII:696)

S. V. Pigulevsky

1 (2) Ventral sucker two times larger than oral.
   G. (P.) varsoviensis Sinitsin, 1905
2 (1) Ventral sucker less than two times larger than oral.

3 (4) Vitellaria in clusters.
                    G. (P.) dollfusi Pigulevsky, 1945
4 (3) Vitellaria not in clusters, digitiform.
                    G. (P.) loossi (Sinitsin, 1905)

KEY TO THE GENERA OF THE SUBFAMILY ANAPORRHUTINAE LOOSS, 1901 (VII:717)

S. V. Pigulevsky

1 (4) Testes extra-cecal.
2 (3) Vitellaria inter-cecal.
            Petalodistomum Johnston, 1913 (fig. 315)
3 (2) Vitellaria extra-cecal.
            Probolitrema Looss, 1902 (fig. 316)
4 (1) Testes and vitellaria superimposed on intestinal ceca.   Anaporrhutum Ofenheim, 1900 (fig. 317)

KEY TO THE SUBGENERA OF THE GENUS PETALODISTOMUM JOHNSTON, 1913 (VII:723)

S. V. Pigulevsky

1 (2) Intestinal ceca tubular, elongate, sinuous, sometimes having small lateral diverticula; testes small.   Staphlorchis (Travassos, 1923)
2 (1) Intestinal ceca always with large, lateral diverticula; testes medium-sized or large.
            Petalodistomum (Johnston, 1913) (fig. 315)

KEY TO THE SPECIES OF THE SUBGENUS PETALODISTOMUM PIGULEVSKY, 1952 (VII:724)

S. V. Pigulevsky

1 (2) Not more than three testes present on each side; vitellaria not branched.
            P. (P.) polycladum S. Johnston, 1913 (fig. 315)
2 (1) More than three testes present on each side; vitellaria branched.   P. (P.) yorkei (Nagaty, 1930)

KEY TO THE SPECIES OF THE SUBGENUS STAPHYLORCHIS (TRAVASSOS, 1923) (VII:728)

S. V. Pigulevsky

1 (2) Twenty to fifty testes present; intestinal ceca sinuous, tubular, lacking lateral diverticula.
            P. (S.) cymatodes S. Johnston, 1913
2 (1) Not more than twenty testes present; intestinal ceca with small lateral diverticula.
            P. (S.) largus (Lühe, 1906)

KEY TO THE SUBGENERA OF THE GENUS PROBOLITREMA LOOSS, 1902 (VII:737)

S. V. Pigulevsky

1 (2) Vitellaria branched, extra-cecal; testes extra-cecal.   Probolitrema (Looss, 1902) (fig. 316)

2 (1) Vitellaria not branched, partially superimposed on ceca; testes extending inter-cecally.
            Reduxotrema Pigulevsky, 1952

KEY TO THE SPECIES OF THE SUBGENUS PROBOLITREMA PIGULEVSKY, 1952 (VII:737)

S. V. Pigulevsky

1 (4) Seminal receptacle larger than ovary.
2 (3) Ventral sucker larger than oral; ovary oval.
            P. (P.) richiardii (Lopez, 1888) (fig. 316)
3 (2) Ventral sucker equal in size to oral; ovary lobed.   P. (P.) capense Looss, 1902
4 (1) Seminal receptacle and ovary of same size.
5 (6) Genital pores near intestinal bifurcation.
            P. (P.) californiense Stunkard, 1935
6 (5) Genital pores far from intestinal bifurcation.
            P. (P.) antarcticus Woolcock, 1935

KEY TO THE SPECIES OF THE SUBGENUS REDUXOTREMA PIGULEVSKY, 1952 (VII:744)

S. V. Pigulevsky

1 (4) Seminal receptacle smaller than ventral sucker.
2 (3) Ovary entire, oval.
            P. (R.) phillippi Woolcock, 1935
3 (4) Ovary trilobed.
            P. (R.) rotundatum T. Johnston, 1934
4 (1) Seminal receptacle larger than ventral sucker.
            P. (R.) clelandi T. Johnston, 1934

LITERATURE ON THE TREMATODES OF THE FAMILY GORGODERIDAE (SUBFAMILIES GORGODERINAE AND ANAPORRHUTINAE) (VII:755)

Bykhovsky, B. E. 1933. Trematodes of amphibians of the Kiev district. Zoolog. Anzeiger. 102:44-58. (In German).

Bykhovsky, B. E. 1935. Parasitic worms of amphibians of Kulyab. Trudy Tadzhikskoy Bazy Akad. Nauk SSSR, Zoologiya i Parazitologiya. 5:135-149.

Dogiel, V. A. 1947. Course in general parasitology. Second Ed. Uchpedgiz. 371 pp.

Dubinina, M. N. 1950. Ecological investigations on the parasite fauna of lake frog (Rana ridibunda Pall.) of the Volga delta. Parazitologichesky Sbornik Zoologicheskogo Instituta Akad. Nauk SSSR. 12:300-350.

Zhadin, V. I. 1921. Trematodes of amphibians and unionids in the vicinity of the city of Murom. Raboty Okskoy Biologicheskoy Stantsii. 1(2-3):63-89.

Zmeev, G. Ya. 1936. Trematodes and tapeworms of fishes of the Amur River. Parazitologichesky Sbornik Zoologicheskogo Instituta Akad. Nauk SSSR. 6:408-435.

Zmeev, G. Ya. and B. E. Bykhovsky. 1939. Parasites of amphibians of the Gissarkskaya valley. Trudy Tadzhikskoy Bazy Akad. Nauk SSSR. No. 11:127-143.

Isaychikov, I. M. 1923. On the knowledge of the helminth fauna of amphibians of Russia. Centralbl. für Bakt. Parasit. Abt. II, 59(1/4). (In German).

Isaychikov, I. M. and N. P. Zakharov. 1929. On the fauna of parasitic worms of Rana esculenta of the Don district. Russky Gidrobiologichsky Zhurnal. 8(1-3):49-54.

Mazurmovich, B. N. 1947. On the knowledge of the helminth fauna of tail-less amphibians. Kievsky Derzhavny Universitet im. T. G. Shevchenko, IV. Naukova Sessiya. Tezi Dopovidey. Biologiya. pp. 6-11. (In Ukrainian).

Mazurmovich, B. N. 1950. Parasitic worms of the amphibians in the vicinity of Kiev; their interrelationships with their hosts and with the external environment. Avtoreferat dissertatsii, Zoologichesky Institut Akad. Nauk SSSR.

Pigulevsky, S. V. 1938. On the revision of the parasites of the genus Lecithaster Lühe, 1901. Livro Jubilar Prof. Travassos. 3:391-397. (In German).

Pigulevsky, S. V. 1944-1945. Two new species of the genus Gorgodera. Annales de Parasitologie humaine et comparée, Paris. 20(5-6):284-287. (In French).

Sinitsyn, D. F. 1905. Materials on the natural history of trematodes. Distomes of fishes and frogs in the vicinity of Warsaw. Izvestiya Varshavskogo Universiteta, Varshava. 210 pp.

Skarbilovich, T. S. 1950. On the knowledge of the helminth fauna of amphibians and reptiles of southern Kirgizia. Trudy Gelmintologicheskoy Laboratorii Akad. Nauk SSSR. 4:108-132.

Skrjabin, K. I. 1926. Scientific results of helminthological research in Armenia. Trudy Tropicheskogo Instituta Armenii. 1:9-11.

Skrjabin, K. I. 1927. The Fourth Russian Helminthological Expedition into the Don district (Novocherkassk). Deyatelnosti 28-y Gelmintologicheskoy Expeditsii v SSSR. pp. 32-40.

Skrjabin, K. I. and R. Ed. S. Schulz. 1940. Fundamentals of general helminthology. Selkhozgiz, Moskva. 470 pp.

Timofeev, N. E. 1900. Trematodes of amphibians and reptiles in the vicinity of Kharkov. Trudy Obschestva Ispytateley Prirody pri Kharkovskom Universitete. 34:137-166.

Strom, Zh. K. 1940. On the trematode fauna of wild animals of Kirgizia. Parazitologichesky Sbornik Zoologicheskogo Instituta Akad. Nauk SSSR. 8:189-224.

LIST OF SUPPLEMENTARY ILLUSTRATIONS

PART VIII

KEY TO THE FAMILIES OF THE SUBORDER NOTOCOTYLATA SKRJABIN AND SCHULZ, 1933 (VIII:8)

K. I. Skrjabin

1 (2) Intestinal ceca united posteriorly forming arch; posterior end of body with dorsal indentation, the cavity of Johnstone with nine tubular diverticula, each with broad muscular appendix; genital pore at level of oral sucker; vitellaria posterior to testes. Intestinal parasites of mammals.

Rhabdiopoeidae Poche, 1925

2 (1) Intestinal ceca usually not uniting (exception: Hippocrepinae; Notocotylidae); posterior diverticula lacking; vitellaria either wholly or partially anterior to testes.

3 (4) Seminal receptacle present; genital pore medial near posterior end of body. Parasites in respiratory organs of mammals.
                    Opisthotrematidae Poche, 1925
4 (3) Seminal receptacle lacking. Parasites of digestive organs of mammals, birds, and reptiles.
5 (6) Cephalic collar present; seminal vesicle external to cirrus sac; ovary dextral; genital pore sinistral.   Pronocephalidae Looss, 1902
6 (5) Cephalic collar lacking.
7 (8) Genital pores in posterior half of body.
                    Nudacotylidae Skrjabin, 1953
8 (7) Genital pores in anterior half of body, medial or sub-medial; seminal vesicle either wholly or only partially within cirrus sac. Notocotylidae Lühe, 1909

KEY TO THE SUBFAMILIES OF THE FAMILY NOTOCOTYLIDAE LÜHE, 1909 (VIII:9)

K. I. Skrjabin

1 (2) Special rib-shaped structures present on ventral surface of body. Parasites of cetaceans and pinnipeds.   Ogmogasterinae Kossack, 1911
2 (1) Rib-shaped structures on ventral surface lacking.
3 (6) Genital pores medial.
4 (5) Intestinal ceca uniting posteriorly, forming unpaired trunk. Parasites of rodents.
                    Hippocrepinae Mehra, 1932
5 (4) Intestinal ceca not uniting posteriorly. Parasites of birds and rodents.
                    Notocotylinae Kossack, 1911
6 (3) Genital pores ventro-lateral, in anterior half of body. Parasites of ruminants.
                    Ogmocotylinae Skrjabin and Schulz, 1933

KEY TO THE GENERA OF THE SUBFAMILY NOTOCOTYLINAE KOSSACK, 1911 (VIII:18)

K. I. Skrjabin

1 (2) Vitellaria passing beyond posterior border of testes, reaching posterior end of body; lateral rows of ventral glands lacking, weakly developed medial row of glands present, opening into cylindrical keel.
          Hofmonostomum Harwood, 1939 (fig. 318)
2 (1) Vitellaria not passing beyond level of posterior border of testes.
3 (6) Ventral glands absent.
4 (5) Three ventral cylindrical keels present.
          Tristriata Belopolskaia, 1953 (fig. 319)
5 (4) Ventral keels lacking.
          Paramonostomum Lühe, 1909 (fig. 323)
6 (3) Ventral glands present.
7 (8) Five rows of well-developed glands present ventrally.
          Quinqueserialis (Skvorzov, 1934) (fig. 320)
8 (7) Ventral glands in three rows.
9 (10) Ventral glands relatively weakly developed, not protruding; glands of medial row sometimes

opening on surface of single, elongate, cylindrical keel.   Catatropis Odhner, 1905 (fig. 321)
10 (9) Ventral glands well-developed, protruding; keel lacking.   Notocotylus Diesing, 1839 (fig. 322)

KEY TO THE SPECIES OF THE GENUS NOTOCOTYLUS DIESING, 1839 (VIII:19)

K. I. Skrjabin

1 (28) Genital pore posterior to intestinal bifurcation.
2 (9) Number of ventral glands not exceeding twelve in each row.
3 (4) Five ventral glands in each row.
                    N. skrjabini Ablassov, 1953
4 (3) Nine to twelve ventral glands present in each row.
5 (6) Length of metraterm equal to length of cirrus sac.   N. porzanae Harwood, 1939
6 (5) Length of metraterm less than length of cirrus sac.
7 (8) Length of metraterm reaching two-thirds length of cirrus sac.   N. seineti Fuhrmann, 1919
8 (7) Length of metraterm reaching one-half length of cirrus sac. N. thienemanni Szidat and Szidat, 1933
9 (2) Number of ventral glands exceeding twelve in each row.
10 (13) Not less than twenty-one ventral glands in each row.
11 (12) Eggs: 0.015 mm. in length, 0.003 mm. width. Parasites of swans (Japan).
                    N. parviovatus Yamaguti, 1934
12 (11) Eggs: 0.018-0.024 mm. in length. Parasites of rails (Europe).   N. ralli Baylis, 1936
13 (10) Thirteen to seventeen ventral glands in each row.
14 (17) Anterior limit of vitellaria not reaching middle of body by considerable distance.
15 (16) Cirrus sac extending posteriorly for about one-third length of body; not more than 15 ventral glands in central row.
          N. attenuatus (Rudolphi, 1809) (fig. 322) and
                    N. linearis (Rudolphi, 1819)
16 (15) Cirrus sac extending posteriorly for about three-eights of body length; not less than 16 ventral glands in central row.
                    N. indicus Lal, 1935
17 (14) Anterior limit of vitellaria reaching middle of body, or passing beyond.
18 (23) Length of metraterm one-half length of cirrus sac.
19 (20) Intestinal ceca equipped with small diverticula.   N. urbanensis (Cort, 1914)
20 (19) Intestinal ceca without diverticula.
21 (22) Dimensions of simple, entire ovary: 0.19 x 0.16 mm.   N. dafilae Harwood, 1939
22 (21) Dimension of lobed ovary: 0.28 mm. in diameter.   N. magniovatus Yamaguti, 1934
23 (18) Length of metraterm exceeding one-half length of cirrus sac.

24 (25) Length of metraterm reaching two-thirds length of cirrus sac. N. noyeri Joyeux, 1922

25 (24) Length of metraterm reaching three-fourths length of cirrus sac.

26 (27) Eggs: 0.021-0.025 mm. (length) x 0.014-0.017 mm. (width). N. stagnicolae Herber, 1942

27 (26) Eggs: 0.018-0.020 mm. (length) x 0.0137-0.0145 mm. (width). N. intestinalis Tubangui, 1932

28 (1) Genital pore anterior to, or at level of intestinal bifurcation.

29 (32) Genital pore anterior to intestinal bifurcation.

30 (31) Body 3.5 mm. long, 1.1 mm. wide; twelve to fourteen glands in each row. N. aegyptiacus Odhner, 1905

31 (30) Body 1.6-1.8 mm. long, 0.43-0.56 mm. wide; thirteen ventral glands in central row, ten in lateral rows. N. naviformis Tubangui, 1932

32 (29) Genital pore at level of intestinal bifurcation.

33 (40) Cirrus sac not reaching level of mid-body.

34 (35) Six to eight ventral glands in each row. N. gibbus (Mehlis, 1846)

35 (34) Not less than ten ventral glands in each row.

36 (37) Ten ventral glands in each row; length of metraterm two-thirds length of cirrus sac. N. regis Harwood, 1939

37 (36) Fifteen to seventeen ventral glands in each row.

38 (39) Seventeen ventral glands in lateral rows, fifteen in medial row; ovary deeply lobed, reaching 0.3-0.31 mm. N. babai Bhalerao, 1935

39 (38) Sixteen ventral glands in each row; ovary in form of hour-glass, reaching 0.22 x 0.17 mm. N. micropalmae Harwood, 1939

40 (33) Cirrus sac reaching mid-body or extending beyond this level.

41 (42) Length of metraterm not exceeding one-third length of cirrus sac. N. lucknowensis (Lal, 1935)

42 (41) Length of metraterm exceeding one-third length of cirrus sac.

43 (44) Length of metraterm equaling two-thirds length of cirrus sac. N. chionis Baylis, 1920

44 (43) Length of metraterm equaling three-fourths length of cirrus sac. N. tachyeretis Duthoit, 1931

Note: N. imbricatus (Looss, 1894) U. Szidat, 1935 omitted from key.

KEY TO THE SPECIES OF THE GENUS CATATROPIS ODHNER, 1905 (VIII:101)

K. I. Skrjabin

1 (2) Body relatively short, broad; medio-ventral keel lacking. C. gallinulae Johnstone, 1928

2 (1) Body rectangular; medio-ventral keel present.

3 (8) Genital pore anterior to intestinal bifurcation.

4 (5) Cirrus sac reaching beyond posterior boundary of anterior third of body; oblique folds of uterus reaching cirrus sac. C. pricei Harwood, 1939

5 (4) Cirrus sac not reaching to posterior end of anterior third of body; seminal vesicle almost entirely external to cirrus sac.

6 (7) Metraterm longer than cirrus sac. C. harwoodi Bullock, 1952

7 (6) Metraterm equal in length to cirrus sac. C. indicus Srivastava, 1935

8 (3) Genital pore posterior to intestinal bifurcation.

9 (10) Cirrus sac extending beyond level of midpoint of body; anterior vitelline follicles reaching level of middle folds of uterus. C. liara Kossack, 1911

10 (9) Cirrus sac not reaching level of mid-point of body.

11 (12) Metraterm equal in length to cirrus sac. C. filamentis Barker, 1915

12 (11) Metraterm shorter than cirrus sac.

13 (14) Number of ventral glands ten to eleven in each lateral row. C. pacifera Noble, 1933

14 (13) More than eleven ventral glands in each lateral row.

15 (16) Fifteen to seventeen ventral glands in each lateral row; vitellaria originating at midpoint of body. C. hisikui Yamaguti, 1939

16 (15) Twelve to seventeen ventral glands in right row; thirteen to eighteen in left row; vitellaria not reaching mid-point of body. C. cygni Yamaguti, 1939

17 (18) Lateral rows of ventral glands situated in zone of uterus. C. orientalis Harshe, 1932

18 (17) Lateral rows of ventral glands situated in zone of testes and vitellaria.

19 (20) Length of cirrus sac exceeding one-third of body; length of esophagus less than one-half diameter of oral sucker. C. verrucosa (Fröhlich, 1789) (fig. 321)

20 (19) Length of cirrus sac less than one-third body length; length of esophagus greater than one-half diameter of oral sucker. C. charadrii Skrjabin, 1915

KEY TO THE SPECIES OF THE GENUS PARAMONOSTOMUM LÜHE, 1909 (VIII:143)

K. I. Skrjabin

1 (8) Genital pore anterior to intestinal bifurcation.

2 (5) Loops of uterus few, not more than six to eight.

3 (4) Vitellaria reaching mid-point of body. P. alveatum (Mehlis, 1846) (fig. 323)

4 (3) Vitellaria extending for two-thirds of body. P. pseudalveatum Price, 1931

5 (2) Loops of uterus many, more than fifteen.

6 (7) Genital pore near base of oral sucker; intestinal ceca with small diverticular at anterior end. P. querquedulum Lal, 1936

7 (6) Genital pore posterior to oral sucker; intestinal ceca without diverticula. P. casarcum Lal, 1936

8 (1) Genital pore posterior to intestinal bifurcation.

9 (10) Body length nearly equal to width; body reaching 0.5 mm. in length.
P. parvum Stunkard and Dunhue, 1931

10 (4) Length of body considerably exceeding width.

11 (12) Intestinal ceca with small external and internal diverticula.   P. echinum Harrah, 1922

12 (11) Intestinal ceca without diverticula.

13 (16) Vitellaria reaching level of posterior limit of cirrus sac.

14 (15) Ovary deeply lobed, reaching 0.33 x 0.35 mm.; body length 3.2 mm.; testes 0.5-0.52 x 0.21 mm.
P. ionorne Travassos, 1921

15 (14) Ovary slightly lobed, 0.06-0.1 mm. in diameter; body length 0.5-0.9 mm.; testes 0.10-0.16 x 0.06-0.12 mm.   P. brantae Bullock, 1952

16 (13) Vitellaria not reaching posterior limit of cirrus sac.

17 (18) Metraterm and cirrus sac of equal length.
P. microstomum Moghe, 1932

18 (17) Metraterm shorter than cirrus sac.

19 (20) Cirrus covered with tubercles.
P. bucephalae Yamaguti, 1935

20 (19) Cirrus smooth, without tubercles.
P. elongatum Yamaguti, 1934

KEY TO THE SPECIES OF THE GENUS QUINQUESERIALIS (SKVORZOV, 1934) (VIII:168)

K. I. Skrjabin

1 (2) Vitelline follicles in two rows, lateral to both lateral rows of ventral glands.
Q. hassali (McIntosh and McIntosh, 1934)

2 (1) Vitelline follicles in single row, dorsal to lateral rows of ventral glands.

3 (4) Vitellaria not reaching posterior limit of cirrus sac.
Q. quinqueserialis (Barker and Laughlin, 1911) (fig. 320)

4 (3) Vitellaria extending anteriorly beyond posterior limit of cirrus sac.
Q. wolgensis Skvorzov, 1934

KEY TO THE SPECIES OF THE GENUS HIPPOCREPIS TRAVASSOS, 1922 (VIII:181)

K. I. Skrjabin

1 (2) Testes symmetrical. Parasites of Hydrochoerus capybara.
H. hippocrepis (Diesing, 1850) (fig. 324)

2 (1) Testes oblique. Parasites of Myopotamus coypus. H. fulleborni Travassos and Vögelsang, 1930

KEY TO THE SPECIES OF THE GENUS OGMOGASTER JÄGERSKIÖLD, 1891 (VIII:200)

K. I. Skrjabin

1 (2) Intestinal ceca each with five lateral knee-like protruberances; vitellaria anteriorly not reaching posterior limit of cirrus sac, in large separate follicles, medial and anterior to testes. Parasites of cetaceans and pinnipeds.
O. antarcticus Johnston, 1931

2 (1) Intestinal ceca considerably less sinuous; vitellaria follicular, lateral, in space anterior to testes and posterior to cirrus sac. Parasites of cetaceans.
O. plicatus (Creplin, 1829) (fig. 325)

KEY TO THE GENERA OF THE FAMILY NUDACOTYLIDAE SKRJABIN, 1953 (VIII:213)

K. I. Skrjabin

1 (2) Ovary between or posterior to testes.
Nudacotyle Barker, 1916 (fig. 326)

2 (1) Ovary anterior to testes.
Neocotyle Travassos, 1922 (fig. 327)

KEY TO THE SPECIES OF THE GENUS NUDACOTYLE BARKER, 1916 (VIII:213)

K. I. Skrjabin

1 (2) Posterior limit of cirrus sac posterior to testis; testis on same side as sac.
N. valdevaginatus Travassos, 1922

2 (1) Posterior limit of cirrus sac anterior to, or at same level as associated testis.

3 (4) Genital pores in posterior third of body.
N. novicia Barker, 1916 (fig. 326)

4 (3) Genital pores in posterior fourth of body.
N. tertius Travassos, 1939

KEY TO THE GENERA OF THE FAMILY OPISTHOTREMATIDAE POCHE, 1925 (VIII:228)

K. I. Skrjabin

1 (4) Testes extra-cecal.

2 (3) Intestinal ceca relatively broad, ends directed externally. Parasites of dugongs.
Opisthotrema Fischer, 1883 (fig. 328)

3 (2) Intestinal ceca relatively thin, ends directed medially. Parasites of manatees.
Cochleotrema Travassos and Vögelsang, 1931 (fig. 329)

4 (1) Testes intercecal at posterior end. Parasites of dugongs.   Pulmonicola Poche, 1925 (fig. 330)

LITERATURE ON THE TREMATODES OF THE SUBORDER NOTOCOTYLATA SKRJABIN AND SCHULZ, 1933 (VIII:243)

Ablasov, N. A. 1953. A new trematode of ducks, Notocotylus skrjabini n. sp. Sbornik Rabot po Gelmintologii, Posvyaschenny 75-letiyu Akademika K. I. Skrjabina. pp. 15-16.

Ginetsinskaya, T. A. 1952. Parasites of rails and grebes of the Astrakhan Preserve. Trudy

Leningradskogo Obschestva Estestvoispytateley. 71(4):53-72.

Gorshkov, I. P. 1937. On the knowledge of the helminth fauna of domestic geese of the Omsk and Chelyabinsk districts. Sbornik Rabot po Gelmintologii, Posvyaschenny Akademiku K. I. Skrjabinu. pp. 191-202.

Dubinina, M. N. 1948. The parasite fauna of the wild gray-lag goose (Anser anser L.). Parazitologichesky Sbornik Zoologicheskogo Instituta Akad. Nauk SSSR. 10:165-188.

Sinitsyn, D. F. 1896. Worm endoparasites of birds in the vicinity of Warsaw. Izvestiya Varshavskogo Universiteta. No. 2:1-22.

Skvortsov, A. A. 1934. On the study of the helminth fauna of the water rat, Arvicola terrestris L. Vestnik Mikrobiologii, Epidemiologii, i Parazitologii, Saratov. 13(4):317-326.

Skrjabin, K. I. 1915. Trematodes of birds of the Urals. Ezhegodnik Zoologicheskogo Muzeya Akad. Nauk. 20(3):395-417.

Skrjabin, K. I. 1916. On the knowledge of the helminth fauna of domestic animals of Turkestan. Dissertatsiya, Yuriev.

Skrjabin, K. I. and N. P. Zakharov. 1919. Results of the initial investigation of the helminth fauna of the Don district. Trudy Obschestva Veterinarnykh Vrachey Donskoy Oblasti. No. 1:1-25.

Skrjabin, K. I. 1923. Trematodes of poultry. Trudy Gosudarstvennogo Instituta Experimentalnoy Veterinarii. 1(2):193-256.

Skrjabin, K. I. 1926. The activities of twenty-eight Helminthological Expeditions in the U.S.S.R. (1919-1925). Izdatelstvo Gosudarstvennogo Instituta Experimentalnoy Veterinarii. pp. 1-296.

Skrjabin, K. I. and R. Ed. S. Schulz. 1931. Trematodology. Selkhozgiz, Moskva. 47 pp.

Skrjabin, K. I. 1946. The building of Soviet helminthology. Izdatelstvo Akad. Nauk SSSR, Moskva-Leningrad. 211 pp.

Skrjabin, K. I. and R. Ed. S. Schulz. 1935. Controlling helminthiases in birds. Trudy Moskovskogo Veterinarnogo Instituta. 1:3-23.

Skrjabin, K. I. and R. Ed. S. Schulz. 1940. Fundamentals of general helminthology. Selkhozgiz, Moskva. 470 pp.

KEY TO THE GENERA OF THE SUBFAMILY PHYLLODISTOMATINAE PIGULEVSKY, 1952 (VIII:254)

S. V. Pigulevsky

1 (8) Body pyriform or lanceolate, flattened in cross section.
2 (5) Testes, ovaries and vitellaria diffusely oriented between ventral sucker and posterior end of body.
3 (4) Loops of uterus extending anteriorly to oral sucker.   Dendrorchis Travassos, 1926 (fig. 331)

4 (3) Loops of uterus not reaching oral sucker.
      Phyllodistomum Braun, 1899 (fig. 332)
5 (2) Testes, ovary, vitellaria restricted to compact area near ventral sucker.
6 (7) Body covered with fine spines and transverse furrows; intestinal ceca uniting posteriorly; seminal receptacle lacking. Xystretum Linton, 1910 (fig. 333)
7 (6) Body unarmed and without transverse furrows; intestinal ceca ending blindly; seminal receptacle present.   Phyllochorus Dayal, 1938 (fig. 334)
8 (1) Body attenuated, lanceolate, oval in cross section, not flattened.
      Gorgoderina Looss, 1902 (fig. 335)

KEY TO THE SPECIES OF THE GENUS PHYLLODISTOMUM BRAUN, 1899 from Lewis (1935) (VIII:257)

1 (2) Body spade-shaped, posterior portion clearly delimited from anterior part.
    A (B) Ovary lateral to and near vitellaria.
    a (b) Testes closely adjacent, symmetrical.
    Uterine loops few, intercecal.
    With small posterior cavity.
1 (2) Testes large, round.   spatula
2 (1) Testes small, slightly lobed.   spatulaeforme
    b (a) Testes oblique.
    Uterus with many loops, extra-cecal; with posterior cavity.
    Testes deeply lobed, far apart from each other.
                                              patellare
    Testes closely adjacent.   fausti
    B (A) Ovary posterior to vitellaria.
    a (b) Testes oblique.
1 (2) Uterus with many loops, usually extra-cecal.
    Testes deeply lobed, adjacent; with posterior cavity.
    Posterior region with several grooves.
                                            superbum
    External edge with grooves.   megalorchis
    Testes not adjacent; without posterior cavity.
                                             carolina
    With posterior groove.   simile
    Testes far apart, not distinguishable.
    Uterus with numerous extra-cecal loops.
                                            staffordi
    Posterior lateral papillae ordinary.   lacustri
    Oral sucker larger than ventral.   pearsei
    Ventral sucker very large; posterior region lacking groove.   angulatum
    Eggs relatively numerous; vitellaria large, regular; with posterior cavity.   folium (fig. 332)
    b (a) Testes more or less medial, tandem, near posterior end.   americanum
2 (1) Body not spade-shaped; anterior portion not sharply delimited from posterior.
    A (B) Testes regularly lobed.
    Vitellaria slightly lobed; lacking posterior cavity.
                                           conostomum

Genital pores directly anterior to ventral sucker.   elongatum

B (A) Testes irregularly lobed; vitellaria deeply lobed.

1 (2) Ovary posterior to vitellaria; vitellaria deeply lobed.   acceptum

2 (1) Ovary lateral, adjacent to vitellaria; uterus weakly developed; vitellaria with shallow lobes.   linguale

C Testes symmetrical; ovary opposite to anterior testis; with posterior cavity.   marinum

KEY TO THE SPECIES OF THE GENUS PHYLLODISTOMUM BRAUN, 1899 from Bhalerao (1937) (VIII:258)

1. Posterior portion of body discoid, delimited from comparatively narrow anterior portion.   2
   Posterior portion of body not discoid, not distinct from anterior portion.   9
2. Testes symmetrical or slightly oblique.   3
   Testes distinctly oblique.   6
3. Testes in posterior half of discoidal part of body.   P. hunteri (Arnold, 1934)
   Testes in middle of discoidal portion of body.   P. lacustri (Loewen, 1929)
   Testes in anterior half of discoidal portion of body.   4
4. Ovary entire; testes symmetrical.   P. spatula (Odhner, 1902)
   Ovary lobed; testes slightly oblique.   5
5. Vitellaria at level of ovary.   P. spatulaeforme (Odhner, 1902)
   Vitellaria slightly anterior to ovary.   P. staffordi Pearse, 1924
6. Vitellaria at level of ovary.   P. patellare (Sturges, 1897)
   Vitellaria anterior to ovary.   7
7. Testes nearly tandem.   P. lohrenzi (Loewen, 1935)
   Testes oblique.   8
8. Anterior portion of body distinctly delimited from posterior portion.   P. simile Nybelin, 1926
   Anterior portion of body not distinctly delimited from posterior portion.   P. carolini Holl, 1929
9. Posterior portion of body attenuated.   10
   Posterior portion of body leaf-shaped.   13
10. Testes entire; genital pores far anterior to ventral sucker.   P. marinum Layman, 1930
    Testes lobed; genital pores near ventral sucker.   11
11. Oral and ventral suckers nearly equal in size.   P. elongatum Nybelin, 1926
    Ventral sucker nearly 1.5 times size of oral sucker.   12
12. Anterior testis near ventral sucker.   P. shandrai Bhalerao, 1937
    Anterior testis far posterior to ventral sucker.   P. kajika (Ozaki, 1926)
13. Anterior testis slightly oblique and posterior to ovary.   P. conostomum (Olsson, 1876)

Anterior testis at level of ovary.   14
Both testes posterior to ovary.   P. americanum Osborn, 1903
14. Testes nearly symmetrical.   P. angulatum Linstow, 1907
    Testes distinctly oblique.   15
15. Oral sucker larger than ventral.   16
    Oral sucker smaller than or equal to ventral sucker.   17
16. Vitellaria nearly digitiform.   P. mogurndae Yamaguti, 1934
    Vitellaria slightly lobed.   17
17. Anterior portion of body tapering gradually into posterior.   18
    Anterior portion of body strongly constricted in comparison with posterior.   20
18. Vitellaria nearly digitiform.   P. acceptum Looss, 1901
    Vitellaria slightly lobed or entire.   19
19. Suckers of equal size.   P. unicum Odhner, 1902
    Ventral sucker larger than oval.   P. linguale Odhner, 1902
20. Gonads large, nearly tandem, inter-cecal, posterior to ventral sucker.   21
    Gonads small, not tandem, inter-cecal, posterior to ventral sucker.   22
21. Intestinal ceca reaching posterior end of body.   P. megalorchis Nybelin, 1926
    Intestinal ceca not reaching posterior end of body.   P. parasiluri Yamaguti, 1934
22. Testes closely adjacent.   P. fausti Pearse, 1924
    Testes separated by loops of uterus.   23
23. Suckers subequal.   P. pseudofolium Nybelin, 1926
    Ventral sucker larger than oral.   24
24. Posterior portion of body folded.   25
    Posterior portion of body not folded.   P. folium (Olfers, 1816) (fig. 332)
25. Loops of uterus inter-cecal.   P. macrobrachicola Yamaguti, 1934
    Loops of uterus partially extra-cecal.   P. superbum Stafford, 1904

KEY TO THE SUBGENERA OF THE GENUS PHYLLODISTOMUM BRAUN, 1899 (VIII:262)

S. V. Pigulevsky

1 (4) Body pyriform.
2 (3) Vitellaria either branched or in clusters.   Catoptroides (Odhner, 1902)
3 (2) Vitellaria entire or weakly lobed.   Phyllodistomum (Braun, 1899) (fig. 332)
4 (1) Body attenuated, lanceolate.
5 (6) Vitellaria deeply lobed.   Vitellarinus (Zmeev, 1936)
6 (5) Vitellaria round or oval.   Microlecithus (Ozaki, 1926)

KEY TO THE SPECIES OF THE SUBGENUS PHYLLODISTOMUM (BRAUN, 1899) (VIII:263)

S. V. Pigulevsky

1 (18) Vitellaria entire, oval.
2 (9) Posterior portion of body greatly expanded.
3 (6) Anterior portion of body constricted and attenuated.
4 (5) Vitellaria transversely elongate.
$\qquad$ P. (P.) simile Nybelin, 1926
5 (4) Vitellaria longitudinally elongate.
$\qquad$ P. (P.) megalorchis Nybelin, 1926
6 (3) Anterior portion of body not strongly constricted, short and broad.
7 (8) Posterior testis far from posterior end of body. $\qquad$ P. (P.) lohrenzi (Loewen, 1935)
8 (7) Posterior testis near posterior end of body.
$\qquad$ P. (P.) wiskowskyi Pigulevsky, 1953
9 (2) Posterior part of body not expanded, relatively narrow.
10 (17) Testes lobed.
11 (14) Posterior testis far from posterior end of body.
12 (13) Intestinal ceca short.
$\qquad$ P. (P.) fausti Pearse, 1924
13 (12) Intestinal ceca long.
$\qquad$ P. (P.) unicum Odhner, 1902
14 (11) Posterior testis near posterior end of body.
15 (16) Vitellaria transversely elongate.
$\qquad$ P. (P.) folium (Olfers, 1816) (fig. 332)
16 (15) Vitellaria obliquely or longitudinally elongate. $\qquad$ P. (P.) angulatum Linstow, 1907
17 (10) Testes entire, round.
$\qquad$ P. (P.) lesteri Wu, 1938
18 (1) Vitellaria weakly lobed.
19 (24) Ventral sucker larger than oral.
20 (23) Testes with large lobes.
21 (22) Anterior portion of body sharply delimited from posterior portion.
$\qquad$ P. (P.) superbum Stafford, 1904
22 (21) Anterior portion of body not sharply delimited from posterior portion.
$\qquad$ P. (P.) dogieli Pigulevsky, 1953
23 (20) Testes with small lobes.
$\qquad$ P. (P.) bychowskii Pigulevsky, 1953
24 (19) Ventral sucker equal in size to oral.
25 (28) Posterior testis far from posterior end of body.
26 (27) Ovary, vitellaria, testis close together.
$\qquad$ P. (P.) pearsei Holl, 1929
27 (26) Ovary, vitellaria, testes dispersed spatially.
$\qquad$ P. (P.) pseudaspii Achmerow, 1941
28 (25) Posterior testis near posterior end of body.
$\qquad$ P. (P.) pseudofolium Nybelin, 1926

KEY TO THE SPECIES OF THE SUBGENUS CATOPTROIDES (ODHNER, 1902) (VIII:344)

S. V. Pigulevsky

1 (18) Vitellaria branched.

2 (17) Intestinal ceca long, terminating near posterior end of body.
3 (10) Ventral sucker smaller than, or equal to oral sucker.
4 (7) Ovary larger than testes.
5 (6) Ovary and testes entire; loops of uterus not extending external to intestinal ceca.
$\qquad$ P. (C.) carangis Manter, 1947
6 (5) Ovary and testes lobed; loops of uterus extending extra-cecally.
$\qquad$ P. (C.) mogurndae Yamaguti, 1934
7 (4) Ovary smaller than testes.
8 (9) Branches of vitellaria thin.
$\qquad$ P. (C.) pawlovskii (Zmeev, 1936)
9 (8) Branches of vitellaria broad.
$\qquad$ P. (C.) acceptum Looss, 1901
10 (3) Ventral sucker larger than oral.
11 (14) Posterior testis near ends of intestinal ceca.
12 (13) Ovary, testes, vitellaria close together.
$\qquad$ P. (C.) parasiluri Yamaguti, 1934
13 (12) Ovary, testes, vitellaria spatially dispersed.
$\qquad$ P. (C.) hunteri (Arnold, 1934)
14 (11) Posterior testis far anterior to ends of intestinal ceca.
15 (16) Testes considerably larger than ovary, longitudinally elongate.
$\qquad$ P. (C.) petruschewskii Pigulevsky, 1953
16 (15) Testes equal to or slightly larger than ovary, not longitudinally elongate, imperfectly round.
$\qquad$ P. (C.) linguale Odhner, 1902
17 (2) Intestinal ceca short, terminating far anterior to posterior end of body.
$\qquad$ P. (C.) singulare Lynch, 1936
18 (1) Vitellaria in cluster-like lobes.
19 (34) Ventral sucker smaller or equal in size to oral sucker.
20 (31) Ovary, vitellaria, testes close together, posterior to ventral sucker, far from posterior end of body.
21 (24) Genital pores near intestinal bifurcation.
22 (23) Intestinal ceca long, terminating near posterior end of body. P. (C.) patellare (Sturges, 1896)
23 (22) Intestinal ceca short, terminating far anterior to posterior end of body.
$\qquad$ P. (C.) brevicaecum Steen, 1938
24 (21) Genital pores midway between level of intestinal bifurcation and anterior edge of ventral sucker.
25 (28) Ovary lateral to, or anterior to vitellaria.
26 (27) Testes and ovary large.
$\qquad$ P. (C.) spatula (Odhner, 1902)
27 (26) Testes and ovary small.
$\qquad$ P. (C.) spatulaeforme (Odhner, 1902)
28 (25) Ovary posterior to vitellaria.
29 (30) Testes and ovary large.
$\qquad$ P. (C.) lacustri (Loewen, 1929)
30 (29) Testes and ovary small.
$\qquad$ P. (C.) staffordi Pearse, 1924
31 (20) Ovary, vitellaria and testes spatially dispersed.

32 (33) Testes larger than ovary.
               P. (C.) zachwatkini Pigulevsky, 1953
33 (32) Testes smaller than ovary.
               P. (C.) caudatum Steelman, 1938
34 (19) Ventral sucker larger than oral.
35 (43) Vitellaria transversely elongate.
36 (39) Ovary elongate, oval, elongation parallel to
vitellaria; excretory bladder without lateral branches.
37 (38) Seminal vesicle large, long.
               P. (C.) massino Pigulevsky, 1953
38 (37) Seminal vesicle small.
               P. (C.) levisi Srivastava, 1938
39 (36) Ovary rounded, slightly lobed.
40 (41) Loops of uterus extending extra-cecally.
               P. (C.) carolini Holl, 1929
41 (40) Loops of uterus not extending extra-cecally.
          P. (C.) macrobrachicola Yamaguti, 1934
42 (36) Excretory bladder with three lateral
branches.   P. (C.) singhiai Gupta, 1951
43 (35) Vitellaria not transversely elongate, round.
44 (45) Ovary entire, oval.
               P. (C.) sinense Wu, 1937
45 (44) Ovary lobed.
               P. (C.) stromi Pigulevsky, 1953

KEY TO THE SPECIES OF THE SUBGENUS
MICROLECITHUS (OZAKI, 1926) (VIII:425)

S. V. Pigulevsky

1 (8) Posterior portion of body sharply attenuated,
tapered.
2 (5) Testes slightly lobed; ovary small.
3 (4) Ventral sucker equatorial; vitellaria egg-
shaped.   P. (M.) baueri Pigulevsky, 1953
4 (3) Ventral sucker in anterior third of body; vitellaria oval.   P. (M.) marinum Layman, 1930
5 (2) Testes deeply lobed; ovary large.
6 (7) Ovary and anterior testis symmetrical.
               P. (M.) shandrai Bhalerao, 1937
7 (6) Ovary anterior to anterior testis.
               P. (M.) kajika (Ozaki, 1926)
8 (1) Posterior portion of body not attenuated.
9 (10) Testes symmetrical, far from posterior end
of body.   P. (M.) almorii Pande, 1937
10 (9) Testes oblique, near posterior end of body.
               P. (M.) solidum Rankin, 1937

KEY TO THE SPECIES OF THE SUBGENUS
VITELLARINUS (ZMEEV, 1936) (VIII:440)

S. V. Pigulevsky

1 (8) Posterior portion of body greatly attenuated.
2 (5) Ventral sucker smaller than oral.
3 (4) Ovary at level of anterior testis.
               P. (V.) orientale Achmerow, 1941
4 (3) Ovary anterior to anterior testis.
               P. (V.) markevitschi Pigulevsky, 1953
5 (2) Ventral sucker equal or larger than oral.
6 (7) Vitellaria in clusters.

6 (7) Vitellaria in clusters.
               P. (V.) conostomum Nybelin, 1926
7 (6) Vitellaria not in clusters, rather either deeply
lobed or digitiform.   P. (V.) elongatum Nybelin, 1926
8 (1) Posterior portion of body not attenuated.
9 (10) Testes oblique.
               P. (V.) skrjabini Pigulevsky, 1953
10 (9) Testes tandem, medial.
               P. (V.) americanum Osborn, 1903

KEY TO THE SUBGENERA OF THE GENUS
GORGODERINA LOOSS, 1902 (VIII:473)

S. V. Pigulevsky

1 (2) Vitellaria far posterior to ventral sucker.
          Gorgoderina (Looss, 1902) (fig. 335)
2 (1) Vitellaria directly posterior to ventral
sucker.   Gorgorimma Pigulevsky, 1952

KEY TO THE SPECIES OF THE SUBGENUS
GORGODERINA (LOOSS, 1902) PIGULEVSKY,
1952 (VIII:473)

S. V. Pigulevsky

1 (14) Ventral sucker protruding from body surface.
2 (13) Testes not bead-like.
3 (6) Body attenuated, narrow.
4 (5) Ovary and anterior testis near vitellaria.
               G. (G.) orientalis Strom, 1940
5 (4) Ovary and anterior testis far from vitellaria.
               G. (G.) tanneri Olsen, 1937
6 (3) Body not attenuated, relatively broad.
7 (10) Ventral sucker 2.5 times larger than oral.
8 (9) Vitellaria entire.
               G. (G.) attenuata (Stafford, 1902)
9 (8) Vitellaria lobed.   G. (G.) aurora Ingles, 1936
10 (7) Ventral sucker not 2.5 times larger than
oral.
11 (12) Ovary, anterior testis, vitellaria closely
adjacent.   G. (G.) intermedia Holl, 1928
12 (11) Ovary, anterior testis, vitellaria spatially
dispersed.   G. (G.) vitelliloba (Olsson, 1876)
13 (2) Testes bead-like, lobed.
               G. (G.) skarbilovitschi Pigulevsky, 1953
14 (1) Ventral sucker not protruding beyond surface
of body.
15 (22) Loops of uterus expanded near genital
pores.
16 (19) Vitellaria always in clusters.
17 (18) Ovary with central globular inclusion composed of large cells; Mehlis' gland small.
          G. (G.) multilobata Ingles and Langston, 1933
18 (17) Ovary without globular inclusion; Mehlis'
gland large.   G. (G.) skrjabini Pigulevsky, 1953
19 (16) Vitellaria in cluster-like lobes.
20 (21) Genital pores at level of intestinal bifurcation.   G. (G.) bilobata Rankin, 1937
21 (20) Genital pores posterior to intestinal bifurcation.   G. (G.) simplex (Looss, 1899) (fig. 335)

22 (15) Loops of uterus narrow near genital pores.
23 (26) Seminal vesicle running parallel to long axis of body.
24 (25) Vitellaria deeply lobed.
    G. (G.) translucida (Stafford, 1902)
25 (24) Vitellaria slightly lobed.
    G. (G.) megalorchis Bravo-Hollis, 1948
26 (23) Seminal vesicle transverse to long axis of body. G. (G.) capensis Joyeux and Baer, 1934

KEY TO THE SPECIES OF THE SUBGENUS GORGORIMMA PIGULEVSKY, 1952 (VIII:533)

S. V. Pigulevsky

1 (8) Vitellaria deeply lobed.
2 (5) Vitellaria distinctly separated.
3 (4) Testes greatly elongate, deeply lobed.
    G. (G.) schistorchis Steelman, 1938
4 (3) Testes slightly elongate, entire.
    G. (G.) tenua Rankin, 1937
5 (2) Vitellaria closely adjacent, merging.
6 (7) Testes and ovary of equal size.
    G. (G.) diaster Lutz, 1926
7 (6) Testes larger than ovary.
    G. (G.) permagna Lutz, 1926
8 (1) Vitellaria oval.
9 (12) Ovary equal in size to testes.
10 (11) Vitellaria entire.
    G. (G.) cedroi Travassos, 1924
11 (10) Vitellaria not entire; slightly lobed.
    G. (G.) cryptorchis Travassos, 1924
12 (9) Ovary smaller than testes.
13 (14) Ventral sucker larger than oral.
    G. (G.) carli Baer, 1930
14 (13) Ventral sucker smaller than oral.
    G. (G.) parvicava Travassos, 1920

KEY TO THE SPECIES OF THE GENUS XYSTRETUM LINTON, 1910 (VIII:554)

S. V. Pigulevsky

1 (2) Cuticle with spines and transverse furrows.
    X. solidum Linton, 1910 (fig. 333)
2 (1) Cuticle without spines or furrows.
    X. pulchrum (Travassos, 1920)

LITERATURE ON THE TREMATODES OF THE FAMILY GORGODERIDAE (SUBFAMILIES PHYLLODISTOMATINAE AND PLESIOCHORINAE) (VIII:607-610)

Akhmerov, A. K. 1941. Trematodes, tapeworms and acanthocephalids of fishes of the Amur River. Avtoreferat dissertatsii.

Barysheva, A. F. 1949. Parasite fauna of fishes of Lake Ladoga. Uchenye Zapiski Leningradskogo Gosudarstvennogo Universiteta, 101, seriya biologicheskikh nauk. No. 19:5-11.

Bauer, O. N. 1946. The parasite fauna of cisco from various bodies of water in the U.S.S.R. Trudy Leningradskogo Obschestva Estestvoispytateley. 19(4):7-21.

Bauer, O. N. 1948. Parasites of fishes of the Yenisei River. Izvestiya Vsesoyuznogo Nauchno-Issledovatelskogo Instituta Ozernogo i Rechnogo Rybnogo Khozyaystva. 27:97-156.

Bauer, O. N. 1948. Parasites of fishes of the Lena River. Izvestiya Vsesoyuznogo Nauchno-Issledovatelskogo Instituta Ozernogo i Rechnogo Rybnogo Khozyaystva. 27:157-174.

Bauer, O. N. 1950. The parasite fauna of whitefish of the U.S.S.R.; its zoogeography, and commercial significance. Trudy Barabinskogo Otdeleniya Vsesoyuznogo Nauchno-Issledovatelskogo Instituta Ozernogo i Rechnogo Rybnogo Khozyaystva. 4:56-76.

Bykova, E. V. 1939. On the knowledge of the parasite fauna of commercial fishes of Lake Charkhal. Uchenye Zapiski Leningradskogo Universiteta, 43, seriya biologicheskikh nauk. No. 11:33-43.

Bykhovskaya, I. E. 1949. The parasite fauna of perch (Perca fluviatilis L.) and its variability under the influence of several ecological factors. Izvestiya Akad. Nauk SSSR, seriya biologicheskaya. No. 3:316-339.

Bykhovskaya (Pavlovskaya), I. E. and B. E. Bykhovsky. 1940. The parasite fauna of the Akhtarinske estuaries (Sea of Azov, delta of the River Kuban). Parazitologichesky Sbornik Zoologicheskogo Instituta Akad. Nauk SSSR. 8:131-161.

Bykhovsky, B. E. 1929. Trematodes of fishes in the vicinity of the city of Kostroma. Materials on the study of the trematode fauna of the fishes of the Volga River. Trudy Leningradskogo Obschestva Estestvoispytateley. 59(1):13-27.

Bykhovsky, B. E. 1936. Parasitological research on the Barabinskie lakes, I. The parasite fauna of fishes. Parazitologichesky Sbornik Zoologicheskogo Instituta Akad. Nauk SSSR. 6:437-482.

Volkova, M. M. 1941. The parasite fauna of fishes of the Ob River basin. Uchenye Zapiski Leningradskogo Universiteta 74, seriya biologicheskikh nauk. No. 18:20-36.

Gvozdev, E. V. 1950. Materials on the parasite fauna of fishes of Lake Markakul. Izvestiya Akad. Nauk Kazakhsk. SSR, seriya parazitologicheskaya. No. 8:208-225.

Gnedina, M. P. and N. V. Savina. 1930. On the fauna of parasitic worms of fishes of the North Dvina River basin. Rabota 32-y i 38-y Soyuznikh Gelmintologicheskikh Expeditsy v 1926/1927 gg. pp. 87-106.

Dogiel, V. A. 1933. Problems of research on the parasite fauna of fishes. Trudy Leningradskogo Obschestva Estestvoispytateley. 62(3):247-268.

Dogiel, V. A. 1935. The immediate problems of ecological parasitology. Trudy Petergofskogo Biologicheskogo Instituta, No. 15. No. 2:31-45.

Dogiel, V. A. 1947. Course in general parasitology. Second Ed. Uchpedgiz. 371 pp.

Dogiel, V. A. and A. Kh. Akhmerov. 1946. The

parasite fauna of Amur River fishes and its zoogeographical significance. Trudy Yubileynoy Nauchnoy Sessii Leningradskogo Gosudarstvennogo Universiteta, 1814-1944. Sektsiya biologicheskikh nauk. pp. 171-173.

Dogiel, V. A. and B. E. Bykhovsky. 1934. The parasite fauna of fishes of the Aral Sea. Parazitologichesky Sbornik Zoologicheskogo Instituta Akad. Nauk SSSR. 4:241-346.

Dogiel, V. A. and B. E. Bykhovsky. 1939. Parasites of fishes of the Caspian Sea. Trudy Komissii po Komplexnomu Izucheniyu Kaspyskogo Morya Akad. Nauk SSSR. No. 7:1-149.

Dogiel, V. A. and G. K. Petrushevsky. 1933. Parasite fauna of fishes of the Neva Gulf. Trudy Leningradskogo Obschestva Estestvoispytateley. 62(3): 366-434.

Dogiel, V. A. and G. K. Petrushevsky. 1935. Experiments in ecological research on the parasite fauna of White Sea salmon. In: Voprosy Ekologii i Biotsenologii. Sbornik Statey. Biomedgiz, Leningrad. pp. 137-169.

Dubinin, V. B. 1936. Research on the parasite fauna of grayling in different periods of their life. Uchenye Zapiski Leningradskogo Gosudarstvennogo Universiteta, 7, seriya biologicheskaya. No. 3:31-48.

Dubinina, M. N. 1950. Ecological research on the parasite fauna of the lake frog (Rana ridibunda Pall.) of the Volga delta. Parazitologichesky Sbornik Zoologicheskogo Instituta Akad. Nauk SSSR. No. 12:300-350.

Zhadin, V. I. 1921. Trematodes of amphibians and unionids in the vicinity of the city of Murom. Rabota Okskoy Biologicheskoy Stantsii. 1(2-3):63-89.

Zakhvatkin, V. A. 1936. On the fauna of parasitic worms of Siberian fishes. Uchenye Zapiski Permskogo Gosudarstvennogo Universiteta. 2(3):175-199.

Zakhvatkin, V. A. 1936. The parasite fauna of fishes of the Kama River, Art. I. Uchenye Zapiski Permskogo Gosudarstvennogo Universiteta. 2(3): 175-199.

Zakhvatkin, V. A. 1946. The parasite fauna of fishes of the mountain stream Uzyan. Uchenye Zapiski Molotovskogo Gosudarstvennogo Universiteta. 4(2):71-77.

Zakhvatkin, V. A. 1951. Parasites of fishes of bodies of water in the Transcarpathian district. Nauchkovi Zapiski Prirodoznavchogo Muzeyu Institut Agrobiologii Akad. Nauk Ukr. RSR. 1:119-149. (In Ukrainian).

Zakhvatkin, V. A. and N. S. Azheganova. 1940. Parasites of fishes of lakes of the Ilmensky Preserve in the Urals. Uchenye Zapiski Molotovskogo Gosudarstvennogo Universiteta. 4(1):3-31.

Zmeev, G. A. 1936. Trematodes and tapeworms of fishes of the Amur River. Parazitologichesky Sbornik Zoologicheskogo Instituta Akad. Nauk SSSR. 6:408-435.

Zmeev, G. A. and B. E. Bykhovsky. 1939. Parasites of amphibians of the Gissarskaya valley. Trudy Tadzhikskoy Bazy Akad. Nauk SSSR. No. 11:127-143.

Ivanitsky, S. V. 1927. On the trematode fauna of vertebrates of the Ukraine. Veterinarnoye Delo. 5(42):36-42; No. 8(45):23-24.

Ivanitsky, S. V. 1928. On the trematode fauna of vertebrates of the Ukraine. Veterinarnoye Delo. No. 2(51):30-48.

Isaychikov, I. M. 1923. On the knowledge of the helminth fauna of amphibians of Russia. Centralblatt für Bakteriologie, Parasitenkunde, und Infektionskrankheiten, II. 59(1-4):19-26.

Isaychikov, I. M. 1928. On the knowledge of the parasitic worms of several groups of vertebrates of the Russian Arctic, A. Trematodes. Trudy Morskogo Nauchnogo Instituta. 3(2):5-79.

Isaychikov, I. M. and N. P. Zakharov. 1929. On the fauna of parasitic worms of Rana esculenta of the Don district. Russky Gidrobiologichesky Zhurnal. 8(1-3):49-54.

Lavrov, S. D. 1908. Results of the research on the fauna of parasitic worms of the Volga River and flood plains near Saratov. Raboty Volzhskoy Biologicheskoy Stantsii. 3(3):1-86.

Lavrov, S. D. 1949. Seasonal and age variability in the parasite fauna of the pike-perch. Avtoreferat dissertatsii, Saratovskogo Gosudarstvennogo Universiteta.

Layman, E. M. 1930. Parasitic worms of fishes of Peter the Great Bay. Izvestiya Tikhookeanskoy Nauchno-Promyslovoy Stantsii. 3(6):1-120.

Layman, E. M. 1934. Fish diseases caused by parasitic worms (Helminthiases of fishes). Snabtekhizdat, Moskva-Leningrad. 135 pp.

Layman, E. M. 1949. Course in diseases of fishes. Pischepromizdat, Moskva. 305 pp.

Mazurmovich, B. N. 1947. On the knowledge of the parasite fauna of tail-less amphibians. Kievsky Derzhavny Universitet im. T. G. Shevchenko Naukova Sessiya. Tezisy Kopovidey. Biologiya. pp. 6-11.

Mazurmovich, B. N. 1950. Parasitic worms of amphibians in the vicinity of Kiev; their interrelationships with hosts and with the external environment. Avtoreferat dissertatsii, Zoologichesky Institut Akad. Nauk SSSR.

Malevitska, M. O. 1936. Trematodes (Trematoda) of pond carp fingerlings of several fish culture ponds of the Ukrainian S.S.R. Zbirnik Prats Zoologichnogo Muzeyu Akad. Nauk Ukr. SSR (18). Trudy Institut Zoologii ta Biologii. 13:29-51. (In Ukrainian).

Markevich, A. P. 1934. Parasitic diseases of fishes and their control. Koiz, Leningrad. 100 pp.

Markevich, A. P. 1937. Materials on the research of the parasite fauna of fishes of Lake Yuskovo (Leningrad district). Naukovi Zapiski Kievskogo Derzhavnogo Universitetu. 3(4):363-379. (In Ukrainian).

Markevich, A. P. 1949. Helminth fauna of fishes of the Dnieper River in the vicinity of Kanev. Naukovi Zapiski Kievskogo Derzhavnogo Universitetu. 8(6): 1-12. (In Ukrainian).

Mosevich, M. V. 1948. On the parasite fauna of fishes of lakes of the Ob-Irtysh basin. Izvestiya Vsesoyuznogo Nauchno-Issledovatelskogo Instituta

Ozernogo i Rechnogo Rybnogo Khozyaystva. 27: 177-185.

Osmanov, S. U. 1940. Materials on the parasite fauna of fishes of the Black Sea. Uchenye Zapiski Leningradskogo Pedagogicheskogo Instituta, Kafedra Zoologii i Darvinizma. 30:187-265.

Petrov, A. M. 1930. On the fauna of parasitic worms of domestic carnivores of the North Dvina Province. Raboty 32-y i 38-y Soyuznykh Gelmintologichskikh Expeditsy, Vyatka, pp. 31-40.

Petrushevsky, G. A. 1940. Materials on the parasitology of fishes of Karelia, II. Parasites of fishes of Lake Onega. Uchenye Zapiski Leningradskogo Gosudarstvennogo Pedagogicheskogo Instituta, Kafedra Zoologii i Darvinizma. 30:133-186.

Petrushevsky, G. K. and O. N. Bauer. 1948. Zoogeography of parasites of fishes of Siberia. Izvestiya Vsesoyuznogo Nauchno-Issledovatelskogo Instituta Ozernogo i Rechnogo Rybnogo Khozyaystva. 27:217-231.

Petrushevsky, G. K. and I. E. Bykhovskaya (Pavlovskaya). 1935. Materials on the parasitology of fishes of Karelia, I. Parasites of fishes of lakes in the vicinity of Konchozero. Trudy Borodinskoy Biologicheskoy Stantsii. 8(1):15-77.

Petrushevsky, G. K., M. V. Mosevich, and I. G. Schupakov. 1948. The parasite fauna of fishes of the Ob and Irtysh Rivers. Izvestiya Vsesoyuznogo Nauchno-Issledovatelskogo Instituta Ozernogo i Rechnogo Rybnogo Khozyaystva. 27:67-96.

Popov, N. P. 1926. On the fauna of parasitic worms of the Don River basin. Parasitic worms of the bream (Abramis brama). Russky Gidrobiologichesky Zhurnal, Saratov. 5(3-4):64-72.

Sinitsyn, D. F. 1905. Materials on the natural history of trematodes. Distomes of fishes and frogs in the vicinity of Warsaw. Izvestiya Varshavskogo Universiteta, Varshava. pp. 1-210.

Skrjabin, K. I. 1926. Scientific results of helminthological research in Armenia. Trudy Tropicheskogo Instituta Armenii. 1:9-11.

Skrjabin, K. I. 1928. The organization of the 35th Union Helminthological Expedition into Central Asia and its missions. Rabota 35-y Soyuznoy Gelmintologicheskoy Expeditsii v Srednyuy Aziyu, Moskva.

Skrjabin, K. I. 1946. The building of Soviet helminthology. Izdatelstvo Akad. Nauk SSSR, Moskva-Leningrad. 211 pp.

Skrjabin, K. I. 1947. Trematodes of animals and man. Izdatelstvo Akad. Nauk SSSR, Moskva-Leningrad. Vol. I, 515 pp.

Skrjabin, K. I. and R. Ed. S. Schulz. 1940. Fundamentals of general helminthology. Selkhozgiz, Moskva. 470 pp.

Suvorov, E. K. 1931. Diseases of fishes. Selkhozgiz, Moskva. 112 pp.

Stsiborskaya, T. V. 1947. The parasite fauna of several fishes of the Pechora River. In: Material on the knowledge of the flora and fauna of the U.S.S.R. Izdatelstvo Moskovskogo Obschestva Ispytateley Prirody, novaya seriya, Otdel zoologii. No. 6:209-216.

Timofeev, N. E. 1900. Trematodes of amphibians and reptiles in the vicinity of Kharkov. Trudy Obschestva Ispytateley Prirody pri Kharkovskom Universitete. 34:137-166.

Titova, S. D. 1946. Parasites of fishes of the Tom River basin. Trudy Tomskogo Gosudarstvennogo Universiteta. 97:137-150.

Titova, S. D. 1947. The parasite fauna of salmonid fishes of the Ob River basin. Uchenye Zapiski Tomskogo Gosudarstvennogo Universiteta. No. 6:76-83.

Shmidt, P. Yu. 1936. Migrations of fishes. OGIZ. 327 pp.

Strom, Zh. K. 1940. On the trematode fauna of wild animals of Kirgizia. Parazitologichesky Sbornik Zoologicheskogo Instituta Akad. Nauk SSSR. 8:189-224.

Shulman, S. S. 1949. Parasites of fishes of the Latvian S.S.R. Avtoreferat dissertatsii.

LIST OF SUPPLEMENTARY ILLUSTRATIONS

Notocotylidae Lühe, 1909
  Ogmocotyle pygargi Skrjabin and Schulz, 1933 (fig. 859)
Rhabdiopoeidae Poche, 1925
  Rhabdiopoeus taylori S. Johnston, 1913 (fig. 860)
Gorgoderidae Looss, 1901
  Plesiochorus cymbiformis (Rudolphi, 1819) (fig. 861)

PART IX

KEY TO THE GENERA OF THE FAMILY OPISTHOLEBETIDAE FUKUI, 1929 (IX:9)

K. I. Skrjabin

1 (4) Ventral sucker at posterior end of body; vitelline follicles lacking posterior to ventral sucker.

2 (3) Testes at posterior end; loops of uterus lacking posterior to testes.

       Opistholebes Nicoll, 1915 (fig. 336)

3 (2) Testes equatorial; loops of uterus present posterior to testes.

  Choanomyzus Manter and Crowcroft, 1950 (fig. 337)

4 (1) Ventral sucker not at posterior end of body; vitelline follicles present posterior to ventral sucker.

5 (6) Testes symmetrical.

       Heterolebes Ozaki, 1935 (fig. 338)

6 (5) Testes oblique.

       Maculifer Nicoll, 1915 (fig. 339)

KEY TO THE SPECIES OF THE GENUS
OPISTHOLEBES NICOLL, 1915 (IX:10)

K. I. Skrjabin

1 (4) Ventral sucker surrounded by glandular disc.
2 (3) Testes rounded, partially dorsal to ventral
sucker.   O. cotylophorus Ozaki, 1935
3 (2) Testes transversely oval, entirely anterior to
ventral sucker.   O. adcotylophorus Manter, 1947
4 (1) Glandular disc around ventral sucker absent.
5 (6) Intestinal ceca not reaching ventral sucker;
testes rounded.   O. elongatus Ozaki, 1937
6 (5) Intestinal ceca extending to middle of ventral
sucker; testes reniform.
                    O. amplicoelus Nicoll, 1915 (fig. 336)

KEY TO THE SPECIES OF THE GENUS
MACULIFER NICOLL, 1915 (IX:35)

K. I. Skrjabin

1 (2) Testes oblique; cirrus sac not extending to
ventral sucker.   M. japonicus Layman, 1930
2 (1) Testes tandem; cirrus sac reaching ventral
sucker.
3 (4) Loops of uterus not descending between ovary
and testes.   M. subaequiporus Nicoll, 1915 (fig. 339)
4 (3) Loops of uterus descending between ovary and
anterior testis.
5 (6) Testes lobed, especially posterior testis; eggs
numerous.   M. ictaluri (Pearse, 1924)
6 (5) Testes entire, unlobed; eggs few.
                    M. chandleri Harwood, 1935

LITERATURE ON THE TREMATODES OF THE
FAMILY OPISTHOLEBETIDAE FUKUI, 1929
(IX:43)

Layman, E. M. 1930. Parasitic worms of fishes
of Peter the Great Bay. Izvestiya Tikhookeanskoy
Nauchno-Promyslovoy Stantsii. 3(6):1-120.
Skrjabin, K. I. 1949. Trematodes of animals and
man. Izdatelstvo Akad. Nauk SSSR, Moskva-
Leningrad. Vol. III, 623 pp.
Shulman-Albova, R. E. 1952. Parasites of fishes
of the White Sea, in the vicinity of the village of
Gridino, I. Monogenetic and digenetic trematodes.
Uchenye Zapiski Karelo-Finskogo Gosudarstvennogo
Universiteta. 4(2):78-97.

KEY TO THE SUBFAMILIES OF THE FAMILY
ACANTHOCOLPIDAE LÜHE, 1909 (IX:49)

K. I. Skrjabin

1 (2) Oral sucker armed with rows of large spines.
                    Stephanostomatinae Skrjabin, 1954
2 (1) Oral sucker lacking chitinous armament.
3 (4) Many testes present in two ventral and two
dorsal rows in posterior half of body.
                    Pleorchiinae Caballero, 1952

4 (3) Two testes present.
                    Acanthocolpinae Lühe, 1906

KEY TO THE GENERA OF THE SUBFAMILY
ACANTHOCOLPINAE LÜHE, 1906 (IX:50)

K. I. Skrjabin

1 (6) Cirrus sac and metraterm long.
2 (3) Testes and ovary adjacent.
                    Acanthocolpus Lühe, 1906 (fig. 340)
3 (2) Testes and ovary separated by distinct space.
4 (5) Cirrus sac with external and internal seminal
vesicles.
    Paratormopsolus Dubinina and Bychovsky, 1954
                                        (fig. 341)
5 (4) Cirrus sac without external seminal vesicle.
                    Tormopsolus Poche, 1925 (fig. 342)
6 (1) Cirrus sac and metraterm short.
7 (8) Testes oblique.
                    Acanthopsolus Odhner, 1905 (fig. 343)
8 (7) Testes tandem.
9 (10 Prepharynx rudimentary.
                    Skrjabinopsolus Ivanov, 1935 (fig. 344)
10 (9) Prepharynx well-developed.
11 (12) Vitellaria reaching level of pharynx.
                    Lepidauchen Nicoll, 1913 (fig. 345)
12 (11) Vitellaria reaching level of ventral sucker.
                    Pseudolepidapedon Yamaguti, 1938 (fig. 346)

KEY TO THE SPECIES OF THE GENUS
ACANTHOCOLPUS LÜHE, 1906 (IX:51)

K. I. Skrjabin

1 (4) Ventral sucker considerably larger than oral;
cirrus sac short.
2 (3) Genital pore at level of anterior edge of ventral sucker.   A. liodorus Lühe, 1906 (fig. 340)
3 (2) Genital sinus traversing antero-medial wall
of ventral sucker, opening at middle of sucker.
                    A. indicus Srivastava, 1939
4 (1) Ventral and oral suckers sub-equal; cirrus
sac extremely elongate; genital pore at level of anterior edge of ventral sucker.
                    A. orientalis Srivastava, 1939

KEY TO THE SPECIES OF THE GENUS
ACANTHOPSOLUS ODHNER, 1905 from Caballero
(1952) (IX:60)

1 (2) Vitellaria of numerous follicles, extra-and
inter-cecal.   A. oculatus (Levinson, 1881) (fig. 343)
2 (1) Vitellaria of few follicles, mainly extra-cecal;
inter-cecal space nearly free of vitellaria.
                    A. anarrhicae Nicoll, 1909

KEY TO THE SPECIES OF THE GENUS
LEPIDAUCHEN Nicoll, 1913 (IX:67)

K. I. Skrjabin

1 (2) Pharynx pyriform; cirrus sac short; vitelline follicles reaching pharynx.

L. stenostoma Nicoll, 1913 (fig. 345)

2 (1) Pharynx cylindrical; cirrus sac elongate; vitelline follicles extending to intestinal bifurcation.

L. hysterospina Manter, 1931

KEY TO THE SPECIES OF THE GENUS PSEUDOLEPIDAPEDON YAMAGUTI, 1938 (IX:71)

K. I. Skrjabin

1 (2) Vitellaria originating at level of pharynx; ovary dextral.   P. balistis Manter, 1940

2 (1) Vitellaria originating posterior to pharynx; ovary medial.

3 (4) Vitellaria originating posterior to ventral sucker.   P. paralichthydis Yamaguti, 1938 (fig. 346)

4 (3) Vitellaria originating at level of middle of ventral sucker.   P. kobayashii Yamaguti, 1938

KEY TO THE SPECIES OF THE GENUS SKRJABINOPSOLUS IVANOV, 1935 from Osmanov (1940) (IX:80)

1 (2) Prepharynx absent; posterior border of uterus extending to level of anterior testis.

S. acipenseris Ivanov, 1935 (fig. 344)

2 (1) Prepharynx present; uterus extending to posterior end of body.   S. skrjabini Osmanov, 1940

KEY TO THE SPECIES OF THE GENUS TORMOPSOLUS POCHE, 1925 (IX:87)

K. I. Skrjabin

1 (2) Ovary adjacent to anterior testis.

T. lintoni Caballero, 1952

2 (1) Ovary separated from anterior testis by loops of uterus.

3 (4) Oral sucker smaller than pharynx; bursa and metraterm short.

T. osculatus (Looss, 1901) (fig. 342)

4 (3) Oral sucker larger than pharynx; bursa and metraterm long.   T. orientalis Yamaguti, 1934

KEY TO THE SPECIES OF THE GENUS PLEORCHIS RAILLIET, 1896 modified from Caballero (1952) (IX:97)

K. I. Skrjabin

1 (6) Intestinal ceca equipped with small lateral diverticula.

2 (5) Less than one hundred testes present.

3 (4) About sixty testes present; testes in two dorsal and two ventral rows; prepharynx and esophagus long.   P. americanus Lühe, 1906

4 (3) Forty-four to forty-eight testes present; testes in two dorsal and two ventral rows; prepharynx

long; esophagus very short.

P. sciaenae Yamaguti, 1938

5 (2) One hundred and four to one hundred and eight testes present; testes in two dorsal rows with twenty-six to twenty-seven pairs of testes in each row; prepharynx very long and narrow; esophagus very short.

P. californiensis Manter and Van Cleave, 1951

6 (1) Intestinal ceca without lateral diverticula; twenty-four testes present; testes in two longitudinal rows; prepharynx short; esophagus absent.

P. polyorchis (Stossich, 1888) (fig. 347)

KEY TO THE GENERA OF THE SUBFAMILY STEPHANOSTOMATINAE SKRJABIN, 1954 (IX:107)

K. I. Skrjabin

1 (2) With single testis.

Monorchistephanostomum Vigueras, 1942 (fig. 348)

2 (1) With two testes.

3 (4) Spines surrounding oral sucker, forming one, two or three rows.

Stephanostomum Looss, 1899 (fig. 349)

4 (3) Spines of oral sucker interrupted ventrally.

5 (6) Spines of oral sucker interrupted dorsally; ventral sucker large.

Manteria Caballero, 1950 (fig. 350)

6 (5) Spines of oral sucker not interrupted dorsally; ventral sucker small.

Dihemistephanus Looss, 1901 (fig. 351)

LITERATURE ON THE TREMATODES OF THE FAMILY ACANTHOCOLPIDAE LÜHE, 1909 (IX:221)

Ivanov, A. S. and I. I. Murygin. 1937. Materials on the helminth fauna of fishes of the lower Volga. Parasitic worms of acipenserids. Yubilarny Sbornik, Posvyaschenny Akademiku K. I. Skrjabin. pp. 253-268.

Osmanov, S. U. 1940. Materials on the parasite fauna of fishes of the Black Sea. Uchenye Zapiski Leningradskogo Pedagogicheskogo Instituta, Kafedra Zoologii i Darvinizma. 30:187-267.

KEY TO THE SUBFAMILES OF THE FAMILY HEMIURIDAE LÜHE, 1901 (IX:245)

K. I. Skrjabin and L. Kh. Gushanskaya

1 (2) Anal appendage present; two vitellaria present, entire or slightly lobed.

Hemiurinae Looss, 1899

2 (1) Anal appendage absent; vitellaria single, entire or slightly lobed or separated into two equal parts. Aphanurinae Skrjabin and Guschanskaja, 1954

KEY TO THE GENERA OF THE SUBFAMILY HEMIURINAE LOOSS, 1899 (IX:246)

K. I. Skrjabin and L. Kh. Gushanskaya

1 (4) Cuticle annulated; anal appendage well-developed.
2 (3) Seminal vesicle bipartite.
             Hemiuris Rudolphi, 1809 (fig. 352)
3 (2) Seminal vesicle not subdivided, large with thick muscular walls.
       Parahemiuris Vaz and Pereira, 1930 (fig. 353)
4 (1) Cuticle covered with scales; anal appendage very small; seminal vesicle undivided, thick-walled.
             Anahemiuris Manter, 1947 (fig. 354)
5 (4) Cuticle serrate; serrate surface scaly posterior to ventral sucker; seminal vesicle bipartite.
       Glomericirrus Yamaguti, 1937 (fig. 355)

KEY TO THE SUBGENERA OF THE GENUS HEMIURIS RUDOLPHI, 1809 (IX:251)

K. I. Skrjabin and L. Kh. Gushanskaya

1 (2) Oral sucker smaller than ventral; annulations of cuticle not extending to posterior end of body; anal appendage long. Hemiuris (Rudolphi, 1809) (fig. 352)
2 (1) Oral sucker larger than ventral; annulations of cuticle extending nearly to posterior end of body; anal appendage short.
       Metahemiuris Skrjabin and Guschanskaja, 1954

KEY TO THE GENERA OF THE SUBFAMILY APHANURINAE SKRJABIN AND GUSCHANSKAJA, 1954 (IX:32)

K. I. Skrjabin and L. Kh. Gushanskaya

1 (2) Cuticle annulated; testes posterior to seminal vesicle; vitellaria single, entire or weakly indented.
             Aphanurus Looss, 1907 (fig. 356)
2 (1) Cuticle not annulated, with small spines; testes at same level as seminal vesicle; vitellaria single, equally bipartite.
       Chauhanurus Skrjabin and Guschanskaja, 1954
                                                (fig. 357)

LITERATURE ON THE TREMATODES OF THE FAMILY HEMIURIDAE LÜHE, 1901 (IX:334)

Bykhovsky, B. E. 1949. The parasitic worms. *In:* Fresh-water life of the U.S.S.R. Pod Redaktsii Prof. Zhadina. Zoologichesky Institut Akad. Nauk SSSR. 2:69-110.

Volkova, M. M. 1941. The parasite fauna of fishes of the Ob River basin. Uchenye Zapiski Leningradskogo Gosudarstvennogo Universiteta 74, seriya biologicheskikh nauk. No. 18:20-36.

Gubanov, N. M. 1952. Helminth fauna of commercial animals of the Sea of Okhotsk and the Pacific Ocean. Avtoreferat dissertatsii, Kiev.

Dixon, B. I. 1905. On the question of feeding in migrating black-spined herring (Clupea kessleri Gr.) of the Central Volga. Vestnik Rybprom. No. 5.

Dogiel, V. A. 1936. Parasites of cod from Mogilnoye Lake. Uchenye Zapiski Leningradskogo Gosudarstvennogo Universiteta, No. 3, seriya biologicheskikh nauk. No. 7:125-133.

Zernov, S. A. 1913. On the question of the study of life in the Black Sea. Zapiski Imperatorskoy Akad. Nauk. 32(1):

Ivanov, A. S. 1940. Materials on the helminth fauna of fishes of the lower Volga. Parasitic worms of salmonids, clupeids, esocids, and silurids. Trudy Astrakhanskogo Gosudarstvennogo Meditsinskogo Instituta. 7:10-27.

Isaychikov, I. M. 1928. On the knowledge of the parasitic worms of several groups of vertebrates of the Russian Arctic, A. Trematodes. Trudy Morskogo Nauchnogo Instituta. 3(2):5-79.

Isaychikov, I. M. 1933. On the knowledge of the parasitic worms of several groups of vertebrates of the Russian Arctic, II. Trudy Gosudarstvennogo Okeanograficheskogo Instituta. 3(1):3-44.

Koval, V. P. 1950. Digenetic trematodes of fishes of the lower Dnieper. Trudy Biologo-Gruntoznavchogo Fakulteta Kievskogo Derzhavnogo Universitetu. No. 5:187-207.

Koval, V. P. 1952. Digenetic trematodes of fishes of the Dnieper River. Avtoreferat dissertatsii, Kiev.

Kutikova, L. A. 1950. The influence of the food regime of the host on the parasite fauna of fishes (based on the example of the parasite fauna of the Arctic cod and other gadid fishes). Vestnik Leningradskogo Gosudarstvennogo Universiteta. 5(2):134-141.

Lavrov, S. D. 1908. Results of research on the fauna of parasitic worms of the Volga River and of flood plains near Saratov. Raboty Volzhskoy Biologicheskoy Stantsii. 3(3):1-86.

Levashov, M. M. 1921. On the parasites of the migratory herring, Caspialosa kessleri (Grimm). Raboty Volzhskoy Biologicheskoy Stantsii. 6(2):89.

Layman, E. M. 1930. Parasitic worms of fishes of Peter the Great Bay. Izvestiya Tikhookeanskoy Nauchno-Promyslovoy Stantsii. 3(6):1-120.

Layman, E. M. 1949. Course in the diseases of fishes. Pischepromizdat, Moskva. 309 pp.

Markevich, A. P. 1951. The parasite fauna of fresh-water fishes of the Ukrainian S.S.R. Izdatelstvo Akad. Nauk Ukr. S.S.R., Kiev. 376 pp.

Osmanov, S. U. 1940. Materials on the parasite fauna of fishes of the Black Sea. Uchenye Zapiski Leningradskogo Pedagogicheskogo Instituta, Kafedra Zoologii i Darvinizma. 30:187-267.

Pigulevsky, S. V. 1938. On the revision of the parasites of the genus Lecithaster Lühe, 1901. Livro Jubilar Prof. Travassos. 3:391-397. (In German).

Savina, N. V. 1927. On the knowledge of the parasitic worms of fishes of Murmansk. Sbornik Rabot po Gelmintologii, Posvyaschenny Prof. K. I.Skrjabinu. pp. 216-220.

Ulyanin, V. N. 1872. Materials on the fauna of the Black Sea. Izvestiya Moskovskogo Obschestva Lyubiteley Estestvoznaniya, Antropologii, i Etnografii. 9(1):77-137.

Chernyshenko, A. S. 1949. New helminths of fishes from the Black Sea. Trudy Odesskogo Gosudarstvennogo Universiteta. Sbornik Biologicheskogo Fakulteta, 4(5). 5:79-91.

Chubrik, G. K. 1952. Encysted cercariae from Nautica clausa Brod. and Sow. Doklady Akad. Nauk SSSR. 86(6):1233-1236.

Shulman, R. E. 1950. The parasite fauna of commercial fishes of the White Sea. Tezisy dissertatsii. Trudy Gelmintologicheskoy Laboratorii Akad. Nauk SSSR. 4:275-278.

Shulman, S. S. and R. E. Shulman-Albova. 1953. Parasites of fishes of the White Sea. Izdatelstvo Akad. Nauk SSSR, Moskva-Leningrad. 198 pp.

KEY TO THE SUBFAMILIES OF THE FAMILY DINURIDAE SKRJABIN AND GUSCHANSKAJA, 1954 (IX:343)

K. I. Skrjabin and L. Kh. Gushanskaya

1 (4) Anal appendage present.
2 (3) Body elongate; vitellaria sinuous, tubular, medial (exception: Pseudostomachicola), posterior to ovary, not extending far posteriorly; pars prostatica compact.   Dinurinae Looss, 1907
3 (2) Body attenuated anteriorly, expanded posteriorly; sinuous, tubular, vitellaria extra-cecal; pars prostatica of two separate components joined by narrow duct.

Mecoderinae Skrjabin and Guschanskaja, 1954
4 (1) Anal appendage absent; vitellaria composed of exceptionally long, thin, sinuous tubules, filling body from ovary to posterior end; testes anterior to ventral sucker.   Prosorchinae Yamaguti, 1934

KEY TO THE GENERA OF THE SUBFAMILY DINURINAE LOOSS, 1907 (IX:344)

K. I. Skrjabin and L. Kh. Gushanskaya

1 (4) Seminal vesicle tripartite.
2 (3) Length of anal appendage equaling or exceeding body length; prostatic cells present along entire (or nearly entire) extent of pars prostatica.
       Dinurus Looss, 1907 (fig. 358)
3 (2) Anal appendage always shorter than body length; pars prostatica short; prostatic cells enclosing portion connecting with hermaphroditic bursa.
       Ectenurus Looss, 1907 (fig. 359)
4 (1) Seminal vesicle not subdivided.
5 (14) Cuticle smooth, not annulated.
6 (11) Anal appendage considerably shorter than body.
7 (8) Prostatic cells enclosing pars prostatica for entire or greater part of its length; loops of uterus

descending into anal appendage.
       Tubulovesicula Yamaguti, 1934 (fig. 360)
8 (7) Prostatic cells surrounding small portion of pars prostatica adjacent to hermaphroditic bursa; loops of uterus not extending into anal appendage.
9 (10) Distal part of uterus expanded, forming special organ (vesicula uterina); organ with narrow duct uniting with terminal end of pars prostatica, forming hermaphroditic canal.

Uterovesiculurus Skrjabin and Guschanskaja, 1954 (fig. 361)
10 (9) Vesicula uterina absent.
       Erilepturus Woolcock, 1935 (fig. 362)
11 (6) Anal appendage considerably longer than body.
12 (13) Tubular vitellaria confluent medially.
       Stomachicola Yamaguti, 1934 (fig. 363)
13 (12) Vitellaria lateral, both dextral and sinistral.
Pseudostomachicola Skrjabin and Guschanskaja, 1954 (fig. 364)
14 (5) Cuticle transversely annulated.
15 (18) Seminal receptacle present.
16 (17) Seminal vesicle oval, united to hermaphroditic bursa by very long duct, far posterior to ventral sucker; pars prostatica and hermaphroditic duct small; vitellaria of separate, unequal, narrow, elongate tubules.   Clupenurus Srivastava, 1935 (fig. 365)
17 (16) Vitellaria of two independent portions of sinuous tubules; seminal vesicle cylindrical with thick muscular wall, far posterior to ventral sucker, directly anterior to testes; prostatic cells present along entire length (or nearly entire length) of pars prostatica.   Lecithocladium Lühe, 1901 (fig. 366)
18 (15) Seminal receptacle absent.
19 (20) Seminal vesicle tubular, not extending posteriorly beyond ventral sucker; ventral sucker nearly four times larger than oral, pedunculate; prostatic cells lacking or rudimentary.
       Magnacetabulum Yamaguti, 1934 (fig. 367)
20 (19) Seminal vesicle saccular, extending from middle of ventral sucker to testes; prostatic cells enclosing portion of pars prostatica adjacent to hermaphroditic bursa; ventral sucker nearly two times larger than oral.
       Parectenurus Manter, 1947 (fig. 368)

KEY TO THE GENERA OF THE SUBFAMILY PROSORCHINAE YAMAGUTI, 1934 (IX:495)

K. I. Skrjabin and L. Kh. Gushanskaya

1 (2) Short esophagus equipped with basal diverticulum; testes anterior to ventral sucker; Laurer's canal long, terminating in vesicle without external pore.
       Prosorchis Yamaguti, 1934 (fig. 369)
2 (1) Esophagus and diverticulum absent; anterior testis anterior to ventral sucker; posterior testis at same level as ventral sucker or slightly anterior; Laurer's canal short, opening to exterior, lacking terminal vesicle.
       Prosorchiopsis (Dollfus, 1947) (fig. 370)

LITERATURE ON THE TREMATODES OF THE FAMILY DINURIDAE SKRJABIN AND GUSCHANSKAJA, 1954 (IX:504)

Vlasenko, P. V. 1931. On the fauna of parasitic worms of fishes of the Black Sea. Trudy Karadagskoy Biologicheskoy Stantsii. No. 4:118-134.

Zernov, S. A. 1913. On the question of the study of the life of the Black Sea. Zapiski Imperatorskoy Akad. Nauk. 32(1):

Layman, E. M. 1930. Parasitic worms of fishes of Peter the Great Bay. Izvestiya Tikhookeanskoy Nauchno-Promyslovoy Stantsii. 3(6):1-120.

Osmanov, S. U. 1940. Materials on the parasite fauna of fishes of the Black Sea. Uchenye Zapiski Leningradskogo Pedagogicheskogo Universiteta, Kafedra Zoologii i Darvinizma. 30:187-267.

KEY TO THE SUBFAMILIES OF THE FAMILY LECITHASTERIDAE SKRJABIN AND GUSCHANSKAJA, 1954 (IX:510)

K. I. Skrjabin and L. Kh. Gushanskaya

1 (10) Anal appendage absent.
2 (9) Stellate vitellaria composed of elongate lobes, united at base.
3 (4) Ovary and vitellaria anterior to testes; vitellaria composed of twelve radially disposed elongate lobes.
    Macradenininae Skrjabin and Guschanskaja, 1954
4 (3) Ovary and vitellaria posterior to testes; vitellaria composed of seven lobes.
5 (6) Hermaphroditic bursa absent.
    Johniophyllinae Skrjabin and Guschanskaja, 1954
6 (5) Hermaphroditic bursa present.
7 (8) Proximal end of hermaphroditic duct enclosed within large muscular hermaphroditic bursa; distal portion of duct excluded; eggs with filament at one pole. Parasites of submembranous regions of liver of marine fishes.
    Hypohepaticolinae Skrjabin and Guschanskaja, 1954
8 (7) Entire hermaphroditic duct enclosed within muscular hermaphroditic bursa; eggs without filaments. Intestinal parasites of marine fishes.
    Lecithasterinae Odhner, 1905
9 (2) Vitellaria composed of large, round, separate follicles, not basally united, not forming stellate configuration.
    Lecithophyllinae Skrjabin and Guschanskaja, 1954
10 (1) Anal appendage present; vitellaria stellate, composed of seven elongate lobes; hermaphroditic duct enclosed in bursa; seminal vesicle with very thick walls, anterior to ventral sucker.
    Musculovesiculinae Skrjabin and Guschanskaja, 1954

KEY TO THE GENERA OF THE SUBFAMILY LECITHASTERINAE ODHNER, 1905 (IX:511)

K. I. Skrjabin and L. Kh. Gushanskaya

1 (2) Vitellaria composed of seven elongate main lobes, branching dichotomously, forming numerous appendices.   Macradena Linton, 1910 (fig. 371)
2 (1) Vitellaria stellate, composed of seven elongate unbranched lobes.
3 (6) Ovary lobed.
4 (5) Ovary quadri-lobed, directly posterior to testes; pars prostatica long; seminal vesicle dorsal to ventral sucker; uterine loops extending posteriorly beyond complex of female genitalia, nearly reaching posterior end of body.
    Lecithaster Lühe, 1901 (fig. 372)
5 (4) Ovary trilobed, far posterior to testes, in posterior part of body; cylindrical seminal vesicle at some distance from posterior edge of ventral sucker; uterine loops terminating anterior to ovary, not passing posterior to complex of female genitalia.
    Trifoliovarium Yamaguti, 1934 (fig. 373)
6 (3) Ovary entire.
7 (8) Seminal receptacle absent; pars prostatica short; seminal vesicle anterior to ventral sucker.
    Hysterolecitha Linton, 1910 (fig. 374)
8 (7) Seminal receptacle present.
9 (10) Pars prostatica long, extending posteriorly beyond ventral sucker; seminal vesicle posterior to ventral sucker; seminal receptacle posterior to ovary.   Dichadena Linton, 1910 (fig. 375)
10 (9) Pars prostatica anterior to ventral sucker; seminal vesicle slightly superimposed on anterior edge of ventral sucker; seminal receptacle anterior to ovary.   Brachadena Linton, 1910 (fig. 376)

KEY TO THE GENERA OF THE SUBFAMILY LECITHOPHYLLINAE SKRJABIN AND GUSCHANSKAJA, 1954 (IX:607)

K. I. Skrjabin and L. Kh. Gushanskaya

1 (4) Genital pore at level of or anterior to intestinal bifurcation; ventral sucker pre-equatorial; seminal vesicle oval; uterine seminal receptacle absent.
2 (3) Eggs large, 0.056-0.065 mm. long.
    Lecithophyllum Odhner, 1905 (fig. 377)
3 (2) Eggs small, 0.025-0.038 mm. long.
    Aponurus Looss, 1907 (fig. 378)
4 (1) Genital pore at considerable distance posterior to intestinal bifurcation; ventral sucker equatorial; seminal vesicle tubular, sinuous; uterine seminal receptacle present.
    Hysterolecithoides Yamaguti, 1934 (fig. 379)

LITERATURE ON THE TREMATODES OF THE FAMILY LECITHASTERIDAE SKRJABIN AND GUSCHANSKAJA, 1954 (IX:650-651)

Belous, E. V. 1953. Parasitic worms of freshwater vertebrates of the Primorye region. Avtoreferat dissertatsii.

Bauer, O. N. 1948. Parasites of fishes of the Lena River. Izvestiya Vsesoyuznogo Nauchno-Issledovatel-

skogo Instituta Ozernogo i Rechnogo Rybnogo Khozyaystva. 27:157-174.

Vlasenko, P. V. 1931. On the fauna of parasitic
worms of fishes of the Black Sea. Trudy Karadagskoy
Biologicheskoy Stantsii, Simferopol. No. 4:88-136.

Dogiel, V. A. 1947. Course in general parasitology. Second Ed. Uchpedgiz. 371 pp.

Dogiel, V. A. and G. K. Petrushevsky. 1935. Experiment in ecological research on the parasite fauna
of the White Sea salmon. In: Voprosy Ekologii i
Biotsenologii. Sbornik Statey. Biomedgiz, Leningrad.
pp. 137-169.

Zmeev, G. Ya. 1932. Infestations of fishes of the
Amur River Estuary with metacercariae of Metagonimus yokogawai Katsurada, 1913. Parazitologichesky
Sbornik Zoologicheskogo Instituta Akad. Nauk SSSR.
3:253-259.

Isaychikov, I. M. 1927. On the fauna of parasitic
worms of fishes of the family Mullidae. Trudy
Sibirskogo Veterinarnogo Instituta. 9:6-11.

Isaychikov, I. M. 1928. On the knowledge of the
parastic worms of several groups of vertebrates of
the Russian Arctic, A. Trematodes. Trudy Morskogo
Nauchnogo Instituta. 3(2):3-44.

Isaychikov, I. M. 1933. On the knowledge of the
parasitic worms of several groups of vertebrates of
the Russian Arctic, II. Trudy Gosudarstvennogo
Okeanograficheskogo Instituta. 3(1):3-44.

Koval, V. P. 1952. Digenetic trematodes of fishes
of the Dnieper River. Avtoreferat dissertatsii.

Layman, E. M. 1930. Parasitic worms of fishes
of Peter the Great Bay. Izvestiya Tikhookeanskoy
Nauchno-Promyslovoy Stantsii. 3(6):1-120.

Layman, E. M. 1937. Parasitic worms of pink
salmon from the Amur River. Sbornik Rabot po Gelmintologii, Posvyaschenny Akademiku K. K. Skrjabinu.
pp. 359-362.

Layman, E. M. 1949. Course in the diseases of
fishes. Pischepromizdat, Moskva. 305 pp.

Osmanov, S. U. 1940. Materials on the parasite
fauna of fishes of the Black Sea. Uchenye Zapiski
Leningradskogo Pedagogicheskogo Instituta. Kafedra
Zoologii i Darvinizma. 30:187-267.

Petrushevsky, G. K. and O. N. Bauer. 1948. Zoo-
geography of parasites of fishes of Siberia. Izvestiya
Vsesoyuznogo Nauchno-Issledovatelskogo Ozernogo i
Rechnogo Rybnogo Khozyaystva. 27:217-231.

Pigulevsky, S. V. 1938. On the revision of the parasites of the genus Lecithaster Lühe, 1901. Livro
Jubilar Prof. Travassos. 3:391-397. (In German).

Sinitsyn, D. F. Materials on the natural history of
trematodes. Distomes of fishes and frogs in the vicinity of Warsaw. Izvestiya Varshavskogo Universita,
Varshava. pp. 1-210.

Sinitsyn, D. F. 1911. Parthenogenic generation of
trematodes and its offspring in molluscs of the Black
Sea. Mem. Acad. Imp. Sc. St. Petersb. Ser. 8, 30:1-
127. (In French).

Shulman, S. S. and R. E. Shulman-Albova. 1953.
Parasites of fishes of the White Sea. Izdatelstvo
Akad. Nauk SSSR, Moskva-Leningrad. 198 pp.

LIST OF SUPPLEMENTARY ILLUSTRATIONS

PART X

KEY TO THE SUBFAMILIES OF THE FAMILY PRONOCEPHALIDAE LOOSS, 1902 (X:13-14)

K. I. Skrjabin

1 (2) Testes broken into separate fragments forming lateral chain on each side of body.
                    Charaxicephalinae Price, 1931
2 (1) Two testes present, not fragmented.
3 (4) Testes medial, tandem.
                    Teloporinae Stunkard, 1934
4 (3) Testes symmetrical or slightly oblique.
5 (6) Testes anterior to ovary; vitellaria posterior
to testes.   Neopronocephalinae Mehra, 1932
6 (5) Testes posterior to ovary.
7 (8) Excretory bladder joined to so-called "vestibular apparatus" or secondary ectodermal excretory

bladder.   Choanophorinae Caballero, 1942
8 (7) Vestibular apparatus of excretory system
lacking.   Pronocephalinae Looss, 1899

KEY TO THE GENERA OF THE SUBFAMILY PRONOCEPHALINAE LOOSS, 1899 (X:14)

K. I. Skrjabin

1 (2) Longitudinal rows of grouped cuticular glands
present along ventral surface of body.
2 (1) Cuticular glands lacking.
3 (4) Intestinal ceca passing external to testes;
testes oblique. Pronocephalus Looss, 1899 (fig. 380)
4 (3) Intestinal ceca superimposed upon or medial
to testes.

5 (8) Intestinal ceca superimposed upon testes, testes extending extra- and inter-cecally.

6 (7) Genital pore medial.

Medioporus Oguro, 1936 (fig. 381)

7 (6) Genital pore to one side of medial line.

Ruicephalus Skrjabin, 1955 (fig. 382)

8 (5) Intestinal ceca skirting testes medially.

9 (14) Intestinal ceca forming symmetrical, snake-like curves, approaching and departing from medial line.

10 (11) Sinuous ceca lacking lateral diverticula.

Astrorchis Poche, 1925 (fig. 383)

11 (10) Sinuous ceca with lateral diverticula.

12 (13) Shoulder collar ring-shaped, not interrupted dorsally, forming cavity ventrally with two sub-lateral protrusions.

Pyelosomum Looss, 1899 (fig. 384)

13 (12) Shoulder collar rudimentary, not forming dorsal protrusion. Barisomum Linton, 1910 (fig. 385)

14 (9) Intestinal ceca straight.

15 (16) Posterior end of body blunt, equipped with two small lateral conical appendages; pars prostatica in cirrus sac separated from cirrus by sharp contriction. Cricocephalus Looss, 1899 (fig. 386)

16 (15) Posterior end of body lacking lateral appendages.

17 (18) Branches of excretory bladder united by transverse anastomoses; shoulder collar crossing cylindrical dorsal surface of body, forming ventrally two lobes with straight, internal borders.

Epibathra Looss, 1902 (fig. 387)

18 (17) Branches of excretory bladder lacking lateral anastomeses.

19 (22) Shoulder collar composed of two lateral lobes bending ventrally, or continuous, not forming cylinder on dorsal side.

20 (21) Genital pore anterior to intestinal bifurcation. Renigonius Mehra, 1939 (fig. 388)

21 (20) Genital pore posterior to intestinal bifurcation. Pleurogonius Looss, 1901 (fig. 389)

22 (19) Shoulder collar crossing dorsal surface of body, forming sharply protruberant ring-shaped dorsal cylinder.

23 (24) Testes sharply lobed; main collecting excretory vessels not anastomosing. Parasites of marine iguanids. Iguanacola Gilbert, 1938 (fig. 390)

24 (23) Testes entire or slightly lobed; main excretory vessels not anastomosing. Parasites of marine turtles. Glyphicephalus Looss, 1901 (fig. 391)

Note: Myosaccus Gilbert, 1938 omitted from key.

KEY TO THE SPECIES OF THE GENUS
GLYPHICEPHALUS LOOSS, 1901 (X:61)

K. I. Skrjabin

1 (2) Funnel-shaped cavity of efferent excretory vessels equipped internally with twenty-four longitudinal ribs; vitellaria extending from anterior border of testes to posterior end of seminal vesicle.

G. solidus Looss, 1901 (fig. 391)

2 (1) Funnel-shaped cavity of efferent excretory vessels equipped internally with twelve longitudinal ribs; vitellaria extending from anterior border of testes to point slightly anterior to middle of body.

G. lobatus Looss, 1901

KEY TO THE SPECIES OF THE GENUS
MEDIOPORUS OGURO, 1936 (X:77)

K. I. Skrjabin

1 (2) Ovary deeply lobed; shoulder collar forming ventrally, two large rounded lobes, not merging medially; intestinal bifurcation considerably posterior to lateral lobes of collar; testes not adjacent medially.

M. cheloniae Oguro, 1936 (fig. 381)

2 (1) Ovary entire; internal borders of lateral lobes of shoulder collar uniting ventrally along medial line; intestinal bifurcation at level of lateral lobes of collar; testes adjacent medially.

M. macrophallus Oguro, 1936

KEY TO THE SPECIES OF THE GENUS
PYELOSOMUM LOOSS, 1899 (X:111)

K. I. Skrjabin

1 (2) Parasites of urinary bladders of turtles; intestinal ceca with four deep medial bends.

P. cochlear Looss, 1899 (fig. 384)

2 (1) Intestinal parasites of turtles; intestinal ceca bending medially six times.

3 (4) Testes at posterior end of body; body reaching 3.86 mm. in length, 1.2 mm. in width.

P. posterorchis Oguro, 1936

4 (3) Testes slightly anterior to posterior end of body; body reaching 7 mm. in length, 2.5 mm. in width. P. longicaecum Luhman, 1935

KEY TO THE GENERA OF THE SUBFAMILY
CHARAXICEPHALINAE PRICE, 1931 (X:122)

K. I. Skrjabin

1 (2) Testes originating posterior to anterior end of vitellaria, in horseshoe configuration, forming arch in posterior end of body.

Diaschistorchis Johnston, 1913 (fig. 392)

2 (1) Testes originating anterior to anterior end of vitellaria, not in horseshoe configuration.

3 (4) Testes inter-cecal.

Charaxicephalus Looss, 1901 (fig. 393)

4 (3) Testes extra-cecal.

Desmogonius Stephens, 1911 (fig. 394)

KEY TO THE SPECIES OF THE GENUS
DIASCHISTORCHIS JOHNSTON, 1913 (X:133)

K. I. Skrjabin

1 (2) Cirrus sac equatorial; testes in two longitu-

dinal rows, not uniting medially in posterior part of body.   D. lateralis Oguro, 1936

2 (1) Cirrus sac in anterior third of body; testes merging in posterior part of body, forming horseshoe configuration.

3 (6) Vitellaria originating at level of genital pore, or slightly posterior.

4 (5) Testes consisting of fourteen to fifteen separate fragments; vitellaria extending anteriorly beyond level of genital pore.

D. takahashii Fukui and Ogata, 1936

5 (4) Testes consisting of sixteen to eighteen separate fragments; vitellaria originating slightly posterior to level of genital pore.

D. gastricus Mehra, 1932

6 (3) Vitellaria originating at considerable distance posterior to genital pore.

D. pandus (Braun, 1901) (fig. 392)

KEY TO THE GENERA OF THE SUBFAMILY CHOANOPHORINAE CABALLERO, 1942 (X:156)

K. I. Skrjabin

1 (2) Vestibular apparatus simple, single; testes tandem.   Cetiosaccus Gilbert, 1938 (fig. 395)

2 (1) Vestibular apparatus forked; testes symmetrical.

3 (4) "Cuticular copulatory bursa" present.
Choanophorus Caballero, 1942 (fig. 396)

4 (3) "Cuticular copulatory bursa" lacking.
Macravestibulum Mackin, 1930 (fig. 397)

KEY TO THE SPECIES OF THE GENUS MACRAVESTIBULUM MACKIN, 1930 (X:164)

K. I. Skrjabin

1 (2) Three pores present at distal end of cirrus: one for seminal ejaculatory duct, two for supplementary ducts leading from vesicles, equipped with thin muscular fibers.

M. kepneri Jones, Mounts, and Wolcott, 1945

2 (1) Supplementary pores on cirrus lacking.

3 (4) Metraterm short, narrow; walls of excretory trunks equipped with numerous short, lobed protrusions.   M. obtusicaudum Mackin, 1930 (fig. 397)

4 (3) Metraterm large, strongly muscular; walls of excretory trunks smooth, unbranched.

M. eversum Hsü, 1937

KEY TO THE SPECIES OF THE GENUS NEOPRONOCEPHALUS MEHRA, 1932 (X:176)

K. I. Skrjabin

1 (4) Body exceeding 2.0 mm. in length; excretory pore dorsal.

2 (3) Cirrus sac reaching 0.59-0.62 mm. in length; cephalic collar triangular; intestinal bifurcation 0.6-

0.8 mm. from anterior end.

N. triangularis Mehra, 1932 (fig. 398)

3 (2) Cirrus sac reaching 0.4-0.52 mm. in length; cephalic collar not entirely separated from body; intestinal bifurcation 0.46-0.5 mm. from anterior end.

N. gangeticus Mehra, 1932

4 (1) Body length not exceeding 1.5 mm.; excretory pore ventral; cirrus sac reaching 0.25-0.27 mm. in length.   N. mehri Chatterji, 1936

LITERATURE ON THE TREMATODES OF THE FAMILY PRONOCEPHALIDAE LOOSS, 1902 (X:194)

Skvortsov, A. A. 1934. On the study of the helminth fauna of the water rat, Arvicola terrestris L. Vestnik Mikrobiologii, Epidemiologii, i Parazitologii, Saratov. 13(4):317-326.

SUPPLEMENTARY LITERATURE ON THE TREMATODES OF THE FAMILY NOTOCOTYLIDAE LÜHE, (X:210)

Belopolskaya, M. M. 1952. Parasites of marine water-fowl. Uchenye Zapiski Leningradskogo Gosudarstvennogo Universiteta, 141, seriya biologicheskikh nauk. No. 28:127-180.

Skrjabin, K. I. 1953. Trematodes of animals and man. Izdatelstvo Akad. Nauk SSSR, Moskva-Leningrad. Vol. VIII, 618 pp.

Skrjabin, K. I. and R. Ed. S. Schulz. 1933. A new trematode, Ogmocotyle pygari n. g., n. sp. from Capreolus pygarus bedfordi. Thomas. Zool. Anz. 102(9-10):267-270. (In German).

Chubrik, G. K. 1954. On the life cycle of the trematode, Parapronocephalum symmetricum Belopolskaya, 1952. Doklady Akad. Nauk SSSR. 97(3):565-567.

KEY TO THE SUBFAMILIES OF THE FAMILY MEGASOLENIDAE SKRJABIN, 1942 (X:217)

K. I. Skrjabin

1 (2) Two pairs of lymph vessels present. Parasites of marine fishes.   Megasoleninae Manter, 1935

2 (1) Lymph vessels lacking. Parasites of freshwater fishes.   Carassotrematinae Skrjabin, 1942

KEY TO THE GENERA OF THE SUBFAMILY MEGASOLENINAE MANTER, 1935 (X:218)

K. I. Skrjabin

1 (2) Two testes present; body smooth, lacking spines; pigmented eye-spots present posterior to oral sucker.   Megasolena Linton, 1910 (fig. 399)

2 (1) Testis single; anterior section of body armed with spines; eye spots lacking.

Hapladena Linton, 1910 (fig. 400)

KEY TO THE SPECIES OF THE GENUS HAPLADENA LINTON, 1910 (X:226)

K. I. Skrjabin

1 (2) Posterior end of body tapered; aperture of ventral sucker in form of longitudinal crevice; genital pore at level of mid-point of pharynx.
H. leptotelea Manter, 1947

2 (1) Body oval without sharply tapered posterior part; aperture of ventral sucker circular.

3 (4) Hermaphroditic bursa not extending beyond posterior edge of ventral sucker; vitellaria originating at level of posterior half of ventral sucker.
H. ovalis (Linton, 1910)

4 (3) Hermaphroditic bursa extending far posterior to edge of ventral sucker; vitellaria originating from anterior edge of ventral sucker.
H. varia Linton, 1910 (fig. 400)

LITERATURE ON THE TREMATODES OF THE FAMILY MEGASOLENIDAE SKRJABIN, 1942 (X:239)

Skrjabin, K. I. 1942. The creation of a new family of trematodes, Megasolenidae fam. nov. Doklady Akad. Nauk SSSR. 34(4-5):158-160.

KEY TO THE FAMILIES OF THE SUPERFAMILY MICROPHALLOIDEA MOROSOV, 1955 (X:245)

F. N. Morozov

1 (2) Branches of excretory bladder broad, passing anteriorly to level of pharynx; esophagus short.
Gymnophallidae Morosov, 1955

2 (1) Branches of excretory bladder short, narrow; esophagus long.   Microphallidae Travassos, 1920

KEY TO THE SUPERFAMILIES OF THE SUBORDER HETEROPHYATA MOROSOV, 1955 (X:247)

F. N. Morozov

1 (4) Seminal receptacle present; cirrus sac lacking.

2 (3) More or less developed genital sinus and genital sucker present; cercariae symmetrical.
Heterophyoidea Faust, 1929

3 (2) Genital sinus and sucker lacking; cercariae asymmetrical.   Opisthorchoidea Faust, 1929

4 (1) Seminal receptacle lacking; cirrus sac present or absent.   Microphalloidea Morosov, 1955

LITERATURE ON THE TREMATODES OF THE SUBORDER HETEROPHYATA MOROSOV, 1955 (X:247)

Belopolskaya, M. M. 1952. Trematodes of the family Microphallidae Travassos, 1920. In: Skrjabin, K. I., Trematodes of animals and man. Izdatelstvo Akad. Nauk SSSR, Moskva-Leningrad. 6:617-756.

Morozov, F. N. 1952. Trematodes of the superfamily Heterophyoidea Faust, 1929. In: Skrjabin, K. I., Trematodes of animals and man. Izdatelstvo Akad. Nauk SSSR, Moskva-Leningrad. 6:151-615.

Skrjabin, K. I. and A. M. Petrov. 1950. Trematodes of the superfamily Opisthorchoidea Faust, 1929. In: Skrjabin, K. I., Trematodes of animals and man. Izdatelstvo Akad. Nauk SSSR, Moskva-Leningrad. 4:81-328.

KEY TO THE SUBFAMILIES OF THE FAMILY ACANTHOSTOMATIDAE POCHE, 1925 (X:251)

F. N. Morozov

1 (4) Vitellaria primarily in anterior half of body; genital sucker absent.

2 (3) Vitellaria anterior to ovary lateral.
Anisocoeliinae Price, 1940

3 (2) Vitellaria along medial line of body in two groups: one anterior, one posterior to ovary.
Isocoeliinae Price, 1940

4 (1) Vitellaria lateral, in posterior half of body; genital sinus and genital sucker present.

5 (8) Vitellaria extending posteriorly far beyond posterior testis.

6 (7) Very small peri-oral spines present.
Brientrematinae Dollfus, 1950

7 (6) Peri-oral spines lacking.
Oesophagicolinae Yamaguti, 1933

8 (5) Vitellaria not extending beyond testes.
Acanthostomatinae Nicoll, 1914

KEY TO THE GENERA OF THE SUBFAMILY ACANTHOSTOMATINAE NICOLL, 1914 (X:252)

F. N. Morozov

1 (2) Intestinal ceca terminating blindly.
Acanthostomum Looss, 1899 (fig. 401)

2 (1) Intestinal ceca opening externally by anal pores.   Atrophecoecum Bhalerao, 1940 (fig. 402)

KEY TO THE SPECIES OF THE GENUS ATROPHECOECUM BHALERAO, 1940 (X:279)

F. N. Morosov

1 (4) Intestinal ceca of equal width.

2 (3) Vitellaria of large compact follicles.
A. minimum (Stunkard, 1938)

3 (2) Vitellaria of small numerous follicles.
A. diploporum (Stunkard, 1931)

4 (1) Right intestinal cecum five times narrower than left.   A. burminis (Bhalerao, 1926) (fig. 402)

KEY TO THE GENERA OF THE SUBFAMILY ANISOCOELINAE PRICE, 1940 (X:286)

F. N. Morozov

1 (2) Oral sucker two times larger than ventral; ventral sucker near boundary of first and second fourths of body; testes very small.
        Anisocoelium Lühe, 1900 (fig. 403)
2 (1) Oral and ventral suckers of equal size; ventral sucker near oral sucker, at point one-twentieth of body length from anterior end; testes large.
        Anisocladium Looss, 1902 (fig. 404)

KEY TO THE GENERA OF THE SUBFAMILY BRIENTREMATINAE DOLLFUS, 1950 (X:296)

F. N. Morozov

1 (2) Body oval; vitellaria not merging posterior to testes, composed of large follicles.
        Brientrema Dollfus, 1950 (fig. 405)
2 (1) Body elongate, nearly equal in width throughout; vitellaria composed of small follicles, merging posterior to testes.
        Gymnatrema Morosov, 1955 (fig. 406)

KEY TO THE SPECIES OF THE GENUS BRIENTREMA DOLLFUS, 1950 (X:296)

F. N. Morozov

1 (2) Esophagus and prepharynx lacking.
        B. pelecani Dollfus, 1950 (fig. 405)
2 (1) Esophagus and prepharynx present.
        B. malapteruri Dollfus, 1950

KEY TO THE GENERA OF THE SUBFAMILY ISOCOELIINAE PRICE, 1940 (X:304)

F. N. Morozov

1 (2) Ovary and vitellaria medial.
        Isocoelium Ozaki, 1927 (fig. 407)
2 (1) Ovary and vitellaria to one side of medial line.   Paraisocoelium Ozaki, 1932

LITERATURE ON THE TREMATODES OF THE FAMILY ACANTHOSTOMATIDAE POCHE, 1925 (X:312)

Markevich, A. P. 1951. The parasite fauna of the fresh-water fishes of the Ukrainian S.S.R. Izdatelstvo Akad. Nauk Ukr. SSR, Kiev. 376 pp.
Osmanov, S. U. 1940. Materials on the parasite fauna of fishes of the Black Sea. Uchenye Zapiski Leningradskogo Gosudarstvennogo Pedagogicheskogo Instituta, Kafedra Zoologii i Darvinizma. 30:187-267.
Pogoreltseva, T. P. 1952. New trematodes from fishes of the Black Sea. Trudy Karadagskoy Biologicheskoy Stantsii. No. 12:34-35.

Skrjabin, K. I. 1950. Trematodes of animals and man. Izdatelstvo Akad. Nauk SSSR, Moskva-Leningrad. 4:265-269.

KEY TO THE GENERA OF THE FAMILY GYMNOPHALLIDAE MOROSOV, 1955 (X:316)

F. N. Morozov

1 (2) Vitellaria near ventral sucker, medial.
        Gymnophallus Odhner, 1900 (fig. 409)
2 (1) Vitellaria diffuse over all of body, with exception of medial region.
        Gymnophalloides Fujita, 1925 (fig. 410)

LITERATURE ON THE TREMATODES OF THE FAMILY GYMNOPHALLIDAE MOROSOV, 1955 (X:334)

Isaychikov, I. M. 1924. Individual variations in Gymnophallus choledochus Odhner, 1900. Compte Rendus des Séances de la Société de Biologie, 91:11-87. (In French).
Skrjabin, K. I. and R. Ed. S. Schulz. 1937. Helminthiases of long-horned cattle and their young. Selkhozgiz, Moskva. 723 pp.

KEY TO THE SUBFAMILIES OF THE FAMILY LECITHOCHIRIIDAE SKRJABIN AND GUSCHANSKAJA, 1954 (X:359)

K. I. Skrjabin and L. Kh. Gushanskaya

1 (2) Hermaphroditic bursa present.
                Lecithochiriinae Lühe, 1901
2 (1) Hermaphroditic bursa absent.
    Brachyphallinae Skrjabin and Guschanskaja, 1955

KEY TO THE TRIBES OF THE SUBFAMILY LECITHOCHIRIINAE LÜHE, 1901 (X:361)

K. I. Skrjabin and L. Kh. Gushanskaya

1 (2) Hermaphroditic duct lacking; ejaculatory duct and metraterm opening independently into hermaphroditic bursa.
    Separogermiductea Skrjabin and Guschanskaja, 1955
2 (1) Ejaculatory duct and metraterm united, forming hermaphroditic duct.
3 (4) Clearly developed prostatic vesicle present within hermaphroditic bursa.
        Lecithochiriea Skrjabin and Guschanskaja, 1955
4 (3) Prostatic vesicle within hermaphroditic bursa lacking.
        Ceratotremea Skrjabin and Guschanskaja, 1955

KEY TO THE GENERA OF THE TRIBE CERATOTREMEA SKRJABIN AND GUSCHANSKAJA, 1955 (X:434)

K. I. Skrjabin and L. Kh. Gushanskaya

1 (2) Genital pore at level of pharynx; testes inter-cecal; lip-like bipartite appendage absent at anterior end of body.   Dissosaccus Manter, 1947 (fig. 411)

2 (1) Genital pore posterior to intestinal bifurcation; testes partially extra-cecal; lip-like, bipartite appendage present at anterior end of body.
Ceratotrema Jones, 1933 (fig. 412)

KEY TO THE SPECIES OF THE GENUS DISSOSACCUS MANTER, 1947 (X:441)

K. I. Skrjabin and L. Kh. Gushanskaya

1 (2) Genital atrium present; genital pore near posterior part of pharynx; seminal vesicle consisting of two saccular parts, united by long, narrow duct; posterior part of vesicle passing beyond ventral sucker; vitellaria slightly lobed.
D. laevis (Linton, 1898) (fig. 411)

2 (1) Genital atrium absent; seminal vesicle composed of three saccular parts of equal size; long narrow duct absent.

3 (4) Seminal vesicle anterior to ventral sucker; genital pore just posterior to intestinal bifurcation; vitellaria of small, thick lobes.
D. polynemus (Chauhan, 1945)

4 (3) Seminal vesicle passing beyond anterior edge of ventral sucker.

5 (6) Genital pore beneath oral sucker; lobes of vitellaria longer than wide.   D. gravidus (Looss, 1907)

6 (5) Genital pore at level of posterior part of pharynx; vitellaria composed of broad, round lobes.
D. medius (Acena, 1941)

KEY TO THE TRIBES OF THE SUBFAMILY BRACHYPHALLINAE SKRJABIN AND GUSCHANSKAJA, 1955 (X:468)

K. I. Skrjabin and L. Kh. Gushanskaya

1 (2) Prostatic vesicle present, at base of hermaphroditic duct.
Plerurea Skrjabin and Guschanskaja, 1955

2 (1) Prostatic vesicle at base of hermaphroditic duct lacking.
Brachyphallea Skrjabin and Guschanskaja, 1955

KEY TO THE GENERA OF THE TRIBE BRACHYPHALLEA SKRJABIN AND GUSCHANSKAJA, 1955 (X:468)

K. I. Skrjabin and L. Kh. Gushanskaya

1 (2) Pars prostatica long, S-shaped, surrounded by numerous prostatic cells; ventral sucker two times larger than oral; eggs bean-shaped.
Synaptobothrium Linstow, 1904

2 (1) Pars prostatica weakly developed, surrounded by small number of prostatic cells; suckers nearly equal in size; eggs oval, symmetrical, not bean-shaped.   Brachyphallus Odhner, 1905 (fig. 413)

KEY TO THE SPECIES OF THE GENUS BRACHYPHALLUS ODHNER, 1905 (X:470)

K. I. Skrjabin and L. Kh. Gushanskaya

1 (6) Ventral sucker larger than oral.

2 (3) Hermaphroditic duct surrounded by small number of glandular cells; vitellaria composed of digitiform lobes with width exceeding length; eggs: 0.012-0.015 x 0.007-0.008 mm.
B. parvus (Manter, 1947)

3 (2) Glandular cells not surrounding hermaphroditic duct; vitellaria with digitiform lobes with length exceeding width; eggs: 0.019-0.021 x 0.011-0.013 mm.   B. musculus (Looss, 1907)

4 (5) Genital atrium present; seminal receptacle small; cuticle smooth; vitellaria of broad, short lobes; eggs: 0.015 x 0.01 mm.
B. acutus (Chauhan, 1945)

5 (4) Genital atrium and seminal receptacle lacking; cuticle sharply furrowed transversely; vitellaria compact, slightly lobed; eggs: 0.011-0.029 x 0.009-0.019 mm.   B. amuriensis Babaskin, 1928

6 (1) Suckers nearly equal in size; cuticle annulated; pre-acetabular cavity in form of broad fissure; seminal receptacle very large; vitellaria composed of round lobes.
B. crenatus (Rudolphi, 1802) (fig. 413)

KEY TO THE GENERA OF THE TRIBE PLERUREA SKRJABIN AND GUSCHANSKAJA, 1955 (X:500)

K. I. Skrjabin and L. Kh. Gushanskaya

1 (6) Cuticle without transverse rows of scales.

2 (3) External prostatic cells lacking; short genital atrium present; vitellaria entire, partially or entirely in anal appendage.   Lethadena Manter, 1947 (fig. 414)

3 (2) External prostatic cells present; genital atrium absent; vitellaria not descending into anal appendage.

4 (5) External prostatic cells well-developed; seminal vesicle posterior to ventral sucker; seminal receptacle rudimentary; ovary entire; vitellaria composed of short broad lobes.
Adinosoma Manter, 1947 (fig. 415)

5 (4) External prostatic cells weakly developed; seminal vesicle extending only to anterior edge of ventral sucker; seminal receptacle large; ovary lobed; vitellaria of digitiform lobes.
Plerurus Looss, 1907 (fig. 416)

6 (1) Cuticle covered with transverse rows of scales; prostatic vesicle and hermaphroditic vesicle present; posterior part of seminal vesicle posterior to ventral sucker.   Dinosoma Manter, 1934 (fig. 417)

KEY TO THE SPECIES OF THE GENUS ADINOSOMA MANTER, 1947 (X:509)

K. I. Skrjabin and L. Kh. Gushanskaya

1 (2) Seminal vesicle bipartite: anterior part superimposed on right edge of ventral sucker, posterior part at right angles to anterior part, along posterior edge of ventral sucker; genital pore near posterior edge of ventral sucker; sucker ratio 2:5; eggs: 0.022-0.025 x 0.008-0.011 mm.

        A. robusta (Manter, 1934) (fig. 415)

2 (1) Seminal vesicle tripartite, reaching anterior edge of ventral sucker.

3 (4) Prostatic vesicle bipartite; esophagus oval; genital pore near pharynx; sucker ratio (oral to ventral) 1:2.5-2.8.   A. microstoma (Chandler, 1935)

4 (3) Prostatic vesicle simple; esophagus elongate.

5 (6) Genital pore posterior to intestinal bifurcation; ventral sucker 2-2.4 times larger than oral; eggs: 0.021-0.025 x 0.012-0.014 mm.

        A. exodica (McFarlane, 1936)

6 (5) Genital pore near posterior end of pharynx; ventral sucker three to four times larger than oral; eggs: 0.015-0.018 x 0.009-0.010.

        A. japonica (Yamaguti, 1938)

KEY TO THE SPECIES OF THE GENUS DINOSOMA MANTER, 1934 (X:525)

K. I. Skrjabin and L. Kh. Gushanskaya

1 (6) Loops of uterus descending into anal appendage, reaching ends of intestinal ceca, or passing beyond.

2 (5) Vitellaria compact, slightly lobed.

3 (4) Seminal receptacle approximately 0.060-0.080 mm. long; eggs elongate, oval 0.035-0.045 mm.

        D. manteri Yamaguti, 1938

4 (3) Seminal receptacle lacking; eggs elongate, curved, 0.033-0.035 x 0.013-0.014 mm.

        D. synaphobranchi Yamaguti, 1938

5 (2) Vitellaria with short, thick lobes; seminal receptacle rudimentary; eggs: 0.023-0.027 x 0.013-0.014 mm.   D. rubra Manter, 1934 (fig. 417)

6 (1) Loops of uterus not reaching ends of intestinal ceca, not descending into anal appendage.

7 (8) Vitellaria with broad lobes; testes posterior to ventral sucker, symmetrical; seminal receptacle present; eggs: 0.033-0.036 x 0.009-0.012 mm.

        D. apogonis Yamaguti, 1938

8 (7) Vitellaria compact, slightly lobed; seminal receptacle lacking.

9 (10) Testes transversely oval, posterior to ventral sucker, slightly oblique; eggs: 0.024-0.032 x 0.012-0.015 mm.   D. tortum Yamaguti, 1938

10 (9) Testes nearly round, tandem, posterior to ventral sucker; eggs slightly curved: 0.027-0.033 x 0.015-0.018 mm.   D. hynnodi Yamaguti, 1938

LITERATURE ON THE TREMATODES OF THE FAMILY LECITHOCHIRIIDAE SKRJABIN AND GUSCHANSKAJA, 1954 (X:553)

Belous, E. V. 1953. Parasitic worms of fresh-water vertebrates of the Primorye region. Avtoreferat dissertatsii.

Vlasenko, P. V. 1931. On the fauna of parasitic worms of fishes of the Black Sea. Trudy Karadagskoy Biologicheskoy Stantsii, Simferopol. No. 4:88-136.

Bykhovsky, B. E. The parasitic worms. In: Fresh-water life of the U.S.S.R. Pod Redaktsii Prof. Zhadina. Zoologichesky Institut Akad. Nauk SSSR. pp. 69-100.

Dogiel, V. A. 1947. Course in general parasitology. Second Ed. Uchpedgiz. 371 pp.

Zmeev, G. Ya. 1932. Infestations of fishes of the Amur estuary with metacercariae of Metagonimus yokogawai Katsurada, 1913. Parazitologichesky Sbornik Zoologicheskogo Instituta Akad. Nauk SSSR. 3:253-259.

Layman, E. M. 1930. Parasitic worms of fishes of Peter the Great Bay. Izvestiya Tikhookeanskoy Nauchno-Promyslovoy Stantsii. 3(6):1-120.

Layman, E. M. 1937. Parasitic worms of pink salmon from the Amur River. Sbornik Rabot po Gelmintologii, Posvyaschenny K. I. Skrjabinu. pp. 359-362.

Osmanov, S. U. 1940. Materials on the parasite fauna of fishes of the Black Sea. Uchenye Zapiski Leningradskogo Gosudarstvennogo Pedagogicheskogo Instituta, Kafedra Zoologii i Darvinizma. 30:187-267.

Petrushevsky, G. K. and O. N. Bauer 1948. Zoogeography of parasites of fishes of Siberia. Izvestiya Vsesoyuznogo Nauchno-Issledovatelskogo Instituta Ozernogo i Rechnogo Rybnogo Khozyaystva. 27:217-231.

Pigulevsky, S. V. 1938. On the revision of the parasites of the genus Lecithaster Lühe 1901. Livro Jubilar. Prof. Travassos. 3:391-397. (In German).

Skrjabin, K. I. and L. Kh. Gushanskaya 1954. The sub-order Hemiurata (Markewitsch, 1951) Skrjabin and Guschanskaja, 1954. In: Skrjabin, K. I., Trematodes of animals and man. Izdatelstvo Akad. Nauk SSSR, Moskva-Leningrad. 9:227-653.

Chulkova, V. N. 1939. On the parasite fauna of fishes in the vicinity of the city of Batum. Uchenye Zapiski Leningradskogo Universiteta, No. 43, seriya biologicheskikh nauk. No. 11:21-32.

Shulman, R. E. 1950. The parasite fauna of commercial fishes of the White Sea. Tezisy dissertatsii. Trudy Gelmintologicheskoy Laboratorii Akad. Nauk SSSR. 4:275-278.

Shulman, S. S. and R. E. Shulman-Albova 1953. Parasites of fishes of the White Sea. Izdatelstvo Akad. Nauk SSSR, Moskva-Leningrad. 198 pp.

KEY TO THE SPECIES OF THE GENUS BATHYCOTYLE DARR, 1902 (X:559)

K. I. Skrjabin and L. Kh. Gushanskaya

1 (2) Body 24.0 mm. long; eggs: 0.033-0.036 mm. (length) x 0.014-0.015 mm. (width). Parasites of Coryphaena hippurus (Japan).

        B. coryphaenae Yamaguti, 1938

2 (1) Body 8-10 mm. long; eggs: 0.028 mm. (length)
x 0.013 mm. (width). Parasites of mackeral (East
Africa and Indonesia).
                    B. branchialis Darr, 1902 (fig. 418)

LITERATURE ON THE TREMATODES OF THE FAMILY ELYTROPHALLIDAE SKRJABIN AND GUSCHANSKAJA, 1954 (X:577)

Markevich, A. P. 1951. The parasite fauna of
fresh-water fishes of the Ukrainian S. S. R. Izdatelstvo Akad. Nauk Ukr. SSR, Kiev. 376 pp.

KEY TO THE SUBFAMILIES OF THE FAMILY HAPLOSPLANCHNIDAE POCHE, 1925 (X:582)

K. I. Skrjabin and L. Kh. Gushanskaya

1 (2) Ventral sucker muscular, cylindrical, pedunculate; single vitellaria weakly developed; single long
vas deferens functioning as seminal vesicle.
Haplosplanchninae Skrjabin and Guschanskaja, 1955
2 (1) Ventral sucker muscular, lacking peduncle;
vitellaria well-developed, forming two lateral groups
of follicles; seminal vesicle well-developed.
Schikhobalotrematinae Skrjabin and Guschanskaja,
                                                    1955

KEY TO THE SPECIES OF THE GENUS HAPLOSPLANCHNUS LOOSS, 1902 (X:584)

K. I. Skrjabin and L. Kh. Gushanskaya

1 (2) Posterior end of body sharply curved ventrally; posterior third of body not containing genital
elements.   H. caudatus (Srivastava, 1939)
2 (1) Posterior end of body straight, conical; posterior third of body containing testis.
3 (4) Genital pore on protruding conical papilla;
posterior end of intestine descending into posterior
half of body.   H. purii Srivastava, 1939
4 (3) Genital pore in cavity between ventral and
oral sucker; posterior end of intestine not descending
into posterior half of body.
          H. pachysomus (Eysenhardt, 1829) (fig. 419)

KEY TO THE SPECIES OF THE GENUS SCHIKHOBALOTREMA SKRJABIN AND GUSCHANSKAJA, 1955 (X:592)

K. I. Skrjabin and L. Kh. Gushanskaya

1 (12) Ventral sucker larger than oral; genital pore
medial, near posterior end of pharynx.
2 (11) Ventral sucker in anterior half of body.
3 (10) Ovary entire.
4 (5) Length of ventral sucker exceeding width;
width of ventral sucker 1.5-2 times larger than width
of oral sucker; large, bulbous atrium present; spherical seminal receptacle near dorsal edge of ovary.
                    S. acuta (Linton, 1910) (fig. 420)

5 (4) Ventral sucker slightly larger than oral,
round or transversely oval; genital atrium lacking;
seminal receptacle long, narrow, extending far posterior to ovary.   S. obtusa (Linton, 1910)
6 (9) Prostatic vesicle present.
7 (8) Sucker ratio 2:3; genital atrium well-
developed; seminal receptacle anterior or posterior
to ovary; vitellaria composed of large follicles.
                    S. pomacentri (Manter, 1947)
8 (7) Ventral sucker slightly larger than oral;
sucker ratio 1:0.85-1.04; genital atrium absent; seminal receptacle dorsal to and slightly posterior to
ovary; vitellaria not follicular, resembling amorphous
mass.   S. girellae (Manter and Van Cleave, 1951)
9 (6) Prostatic vesicle lacking; genital atrium present; oval seminal receptacle posterior to testis; vitellaria consisting of large follicles.
                    S. adacuta (Manter, 1947)
10 (3) Ovary three or four lobed, directly posterior
to ventral sucker; ventral sucker oval, 1.5 times
larger than oral; oval seminal receptacle posterior
to ovary.   S. sparisomae (Manter, 1947)
11 (2) Ventral sucker slightly posterior to middle
of body; ventral sucker 1.5 times larger than oral;
small seminal receptacle posterior to ovary.
                    S. brachyura (Manter, 1947)
12 (1) Ventral sucker smaller than oral; genital
pore medial, about half-way between suckers; testis
triangular; ovary tri-lobed; uterus between Mehlis'
gland and ventral sucker.   S. kyphosi (Manter, 1947)

LITERATURE ON THE TREMATODES OF THE FAMILY HAPLOSPLANCHNIDAE POCHE, 1925 (X:616)

Vlasenko, P. V. 1931. On the fauna of parasitic
worms of fishes of the Black Sea. Trudy Karadagskoy
Biologicheskoy Stantsii, Simferopol. No. 4:88-136.
Markevich, A. P. 1951. The parasite fauna of
fresh-water fishes of the Ukrainian S. S. R. Izda-
telstvo Akad. Nauk Ukr. SSR, Kiev. 376 pp.
Osmanov, S. U. 1940. Materials on the parasite
fauna of fishes of the Black Sea. Uchenye Zapiski
Leningradskogo Gosudarstvennogo Pedagogicheskogo
Instituta, Kafedra Zoologii i Darvinizma. 30:187-267.

KEY TO THE SPECIES OF THE GENUS ISOPARORCHIS SOUTHWELL, 1913 (X:622)

K. I. Skrjabin and L. Kh. Gushanskaya

1 (2) Genital atrium present; cuticle dense, 0.04
mm. thick; ovary 2.3 mm. long in parasite with body
length of 13 mm.
          I. trisimilitubis Southwell, 1913 (fig. 421)
2 (1) Genital atrium absent; cuticle very thin,
transparent; ovary 6.9 mm. long in parasite with
body length of 25-30 mm.   I. tandani Johnston, 1927

LITERATURE ON THE TREMATODES OF THE FAMILY ISOPARORCHIDAE POCHE, 1925 (X:634)

Belous, G. V. 1953. Parasitic worms of fresh-water vertebrates of the Primorye region. Avtoreferat dissertatsii.

Bykhovsky, B. E. 1949. The parasitic worms. *In:* Fresh-water life of the U. S. S. R. Pod Redaktsii Prof. Zhadina, Zoologichesky Institut Akad. Nauk. SSSR. 2:69-110.

Layman, E. M. 1930. Parasitic worms of fishes of Peter the Great Bay. Izvestiya Tikhookeanskoy Nauchno-Promyslovoy Stantsii. 3(6):1-120.

Markevich, A. P. 1951. The parasite fauna of fresh-water fishes of the Ukrainian S. S. R. Izdatelstvo Akad. Nauk. Ukr. SSR, Kiev. 376 pp.

Shulman, S. S. 1954. On specificity of parasites of fishes. Zoologichesky Zhurnal. 33(1):14-25.

LITERATURE ON THE TREMATODES OF THE FAMILY LAMPRITREMATIDAE SKRJABIN AND GUSCHANSKAJA, 1954 (X:643)

Markevich, A. P. 1951. The parasite fauna of fresh-water fishes of the Ukrainian S. S. R. Izdatelstvo Akad. Nauk Ukr. SSR, Kiev. 376 pp.

LIST OF SUPPLEMENTARY ILLUSTRATIONS

Pronocephalidae Looss, 1902
  Adenogaster serialis Looss, 1901 (fig. 867)
  Myosaccus amblyrhynchi Gilbert, 1938 (fig. 868)
  Teloporia aspidonectes (MacCallum, 1917) (fig. 869)
  Parapronocephalum symmetricum Belopolskaia, 1952 (fig. 870)
Megasolenidae Skrjabin, 1942
  Carassotrema koreanum Park, 1938 (fig. 871)
Lecithochiriidae Skrjabin and Guschanskaja, 1954
  Lecithochirium rufoviride (Rudolphi, 1819) (fig. 873)
  Separogermiductus inimici (Yamaguti, 1934) (fig. 874)
  Synaptobothrium caudiporum (Rudolphi, 1819) (fig. 875)
Elytrophallidae Skrjabin and Guschanskaja, 1954
  Elytrophallus mexicanus Manter, 1940 (fig. 876)
Lampritrematidae Yamaguti, 1940
  Lampritrema nipponicum Yamaguti, 1940 (fig. 877)

PART XI

KEY TO THE SUBFAMILIES OF THE FAMILY DIDYMOZOIDAE MONTICELLI, 1888 (XI:20)

K. I. Skrjabin

1 (2) Body of uniform width; intestinal ceca straight, extending to posterior end of body, uniting posteriorly to form arch; two suckers present; hermaphroditic.   Philopinninae Skrjabin, 1955

2 (1) Body not of uniform width; intestinal ceca not uniting.

3 (6) Posterior portion of body elongate.

4 (5) Posterior portion of body thread-shaped or leaf-shaped; hermaphroditic.
            Nematobothriinae Ishii, 1935

5 (4) Posterior portion of body thread-shaped; gonochoristic.   Gonapodasmiinae Ishii, 1935

6 (3) Posterior portion of body expanded.

7 (8) Posterior portion of body cylindrical, fusiform, reniform, or semi-circular; hermaphroditic.
            Didymozoinae Ishii, 1935

8 (7) Posterior portion of body reniform, oval or spherical; gonochoristic.   Kollikeriinae Ishii, 1935

KEY TO THE GENERA OF THE SUBFAMILY DIDYMOZOINAE ISHII, 1935 (XI:20)

K. I. Skrjabin

1 (2) Posterior sections of parasites adherent ventrally, joined along posterior thirds; excretory bladder consisting of two canals, joined at both ends.
            Diplotrema Yamaguti, 1938

2 (1) Posterior ends of parasites not joined; excretory bladder single.

3 (4) Anterior end of body thin; posterior sharply flattened laterally, semi-circular.
            Platocystis Yamaguti, 1938 (fig. 423)

4 (3) Posterior end of body not flattened laterally.

5 (6) Posterior section of body broad, reniform, comma-shaped, or hemispherical.
            Didymocystis Ariola, 1902 (fig. 424)

6 (5) Posterior section of body fusiform or cylindrical.

7 (8) Anterior section of body originating at one end of posterior section.
            Didymozoon Taschenberg, 1879 (fig. 425)

8 (7) Anterior section of body originating at middle of posterior section.

9 (10) Long, thread-like appendage present on posterior end of body.
            Didymoproblema Ishii, 1935 (fig. 426)

10 (9) Thread-like appendage at posterior end of body lacking.

11 (12) Posterior region of posterior section consisting of many lobes.
            Lobatozoum Ishii, 1935 (fig. 427)

12 (11) Posterior section smooth, lacking lobes.
            Didymocylindrus Ishii, 1935 (fig. 428)

KEY TO THE SPECIES OF THE GENUS DIDYMOZOON Taschenberg, 1879 from Ishii (1935) (XI:21)

1 (2) Special four-cornered structure present at union of anterior and posterior sections of body.
D. pretiosum Ariola, 1902
2 (1) Four-cornered structure lacking.
3 (4) Posterior section of body long, thread-shaped.
D. taenioides Monticelli, 1888
4 (3) Posterior section of body not thread-shaped.
5 (10) Posterior section of body elongate, cylindrical.
6 (7) Cyst long, cylindrical.
D. fillicolle Ishii, 1935
7 (6) Cyst not cylindrical.
8 (9) Cyst fusiform, relatively short.
D. longicolle Ishii, 1935
9 (8) Cyst oval; trematodes in cysts spiral in position.
D. auxis Taschenberg, 1879
10 (5) Posterior section of body thick, with rounded posterior end.
11 (12) Neck sharply delimited from anterior and posterior sections of body.
D. sphyraenae Taschenberg, 1879
12 (11) Neck not delimited from rest of body.
D. tenuicolle (Rudolphi, 1819)
Note: A whole list of species omitted, due to lack of literature sources.

KEY TO THE GENERA OF THE SUBFAMILY GONAPODASMIINAE ISHII, 1935 (XI:120)

K. I. Skrjabin

1 (2) Testes medial, tandem, in anterior half of body; initial section of intestinal ceca surrounded by glandular cells.
Paragonapodasmius Yamaguti, 1938 (fig. 429)
2 (1) Testes symmetrical, lateral, in lateral zones of posterior half of body; initial trunk of intestinal ceca not surrounded by glandular cells.
Gonapodasmius Ishii, 1935 (fig. 430)

KEY TO THE SPECIES OF THE GENUS GONAPODASMIUS ISHII, 1935 (XI:123)

K. I. Skrjabin

1 (4) Ventral sucker lacking.
2 (3) Paired in gill apparatus of fishes, forming cysts.
G. haemuli (G. and W. MacCallum, 1916) (fig. 430)
3 (2) Paired in musculature of fishes, free, without cysts.
G. okushimai Ishii, 1935
4 (1) Ventral sucker present.
5 (6) Rudimentary ventral sucker (0.027 mm. in diameter) present; in mucous membrane of oral cavity of fishes.
G. cypseluri Yamaguti, 1940
6 (5) Ventral sucker well-developed (0.15-0.135 mm. in diameter); in gills of fishes.
G. pacificus Yamaguti, 1938

KEY TO THE GENERA OF THE SUBFAMILY KOLLIKERIINAE ISHII, 1935 (XI:140)

K. I. Skrjabin

1 (4) Ventral sucker present.
2 (3) Male with long uterus; lacking eggs.
Kollikeria Cobbold, 1860 (fig. 431)
3 (2) Male without uterus, with four pyriform testes.
Tricharrhen Poche, 1925
4 (1) Ventral sucker absent.
5 (6) Male with rudimentary female organs; female without traces of male sex organs.
Coeliotrema Yamaguti, 1938 (fig. 433)
6 (5) Male with rudimentary female organs; female with rudimentary male system.
Wedlia Cobbold, 1860 (fig. 434)

KEY TO THE SPECIES OF THE GENUS WEDLIA COBBOLD, 1860 (XI:152)

K. I. Skrjabin

1 (2) Pharynx lacking.   W. reniformis Ishii, 1935
2 (1) Pharynx present.
3 (4) Male cannot be separated from female without damage to latter; oral sucker 0.127 mm. in diameter; eggs: 0.017-0.019 mm. (length) x 0.010-0.012 mm. (width).   W. globosa Ishii, 1935
4 (3) Male easily separated from female.
5 (6) Male oral sucker 0.2-0.32 mm.; eggs: 0.023 mm. (length) x 0.017 mm. (width).
W. bipartita (Wedl, 1855) (fig. 434)
6 (5) Male oral sucker 0.024-0.1 x 0.018-0.088 mm.; eggs: 0.015-0.017 mm. (length) x 0.009-0.011 mm. (width).   W. orientalis Yamaguti, 1934

KEY TO THE GENERA OF THE SUBFAMILY NEMATOBOTHRIINAE ISHII, 1905 (XI:174)

K. I. Skrjabin

1 (2) Body thread-shaped; encysted in tissue of marine fishes.
Nematobothrium van Beneden, 1858 (fig. 435)
2 (1) Body ribbon-shaped; not encysting in tissue of host.
3 (4) Rudimentary ventral sucker present; ovary consisting of sinuous trunk and two opposed, lateral branches.
Metanematobothrium Yamaguti, 1938 (fig. 436)
4 (3) Ventral sucker absent or present; ovary thick, curving, tubular, not forming two branches.
Atalostrophion MacCallum, 1915 (fig. 437)

KEY TO THE SUBGENERA OF THE GENUS NEMATOBOTHRIUM (VAN BENEDEN, 1858) (XI:178)

K. I. Skrjabin

1 (2) Ventral sucker absent.
Nematobothrium (van Beneden, 1858) (fig. 435)

2 (1) Ventral sucker present.

Maclarenozoum Ishii, 1935

KEY TO THE SPECIES OF THE SUBGENUS NEMATOBOTHRIUM (VAN BENEDEN, 1858) modified from Ishii (1935) (XI:178)

K. I. Skrjabin

1 (2) Both individuals in cysts of equal size.

N. (N.) filarina van Beneden, 1858

2 (1) Individuals enclosed in cysts of different sizes.

3 (6) Oral sucker lacking.

4 (5) Intestines present.

N. (N.) scombri (Taschenberg, 1879)

5 (4) Intestines lacking.

N. (N.) pelamydis (Taschenberg, 1879)

6 (3) Oral sucker present.

7 (8) Testis single; body length reaching 9 mm.; neck thin.

N. (N.) sardae (G. and W. MacCallum, 1916)

8 (7) Two testes present.

9 (10) Body length reaching 23 mm.; maximum width 0.127 mm.   N. (N.) sabae (Ishii, 1935)

10 (9) Body length reaching 16.5 mm.; maximum width 1.4 mm.

N. (N.) faciale (Baylis, 1938) (fig. 435)

Note: Several species omitted, due to incomplete descriptions.

KEY TO THE SUBGENERA OF THE GENUS ATALOSTROPHION MAC CALLUM, 1915 (XI:235)

K. I. Skrjabin

1 (2) Ventral sucker absent.

Atalostrophion (MacCallum, 1915) (fig. 437)

2 (1) Ventral sucker present.

Maccallozoum Ishii, 1935

KEY TO THE SPECIES OF THE SUBGENUS ATALOSTROPHION (MAC CALLUM, 1915) (XI:235)

K. I. Skrjabin

1 (4) Pharynx lacking; ovary single, tubular.

2 (3) Body delicate, slender; uterus double.

A. (A.) sardae MacCallum, 1915 (fig. 437)

3 (2) Body muscular, not slender; uterus single.

A. (A.) promicrops MacCallum, 1915

4 (1) Pharynx present; two ovaries present, tubular.   A. (A.) biovarium Skrjabin, 1955

LITERATURE ON THE TREMATODES OF THE SUBORDER DIDYMOZOATA SKRJABIN AND SCHULZ, 1937 (XI:250)

Zernov, S. 1913. On the question of the study of life in the Black Sea. Zapiski Imperatorskoy Akad. Nauk, S. Peterburg. 32(1):

Skrjabin, K. I. and R. Ed. S. Schulz. 1937. Helminthiases of long-horned cattle and their young. Selkhozgiz, Moskva. 723 pp.

KEY TO THE SUBFAMILIES OF THE FAMILY MONORCHIDAE ODHNER, 1911 (XI:265)

A. A. Sobolev

1 (2) Genital pore lateral, usually sinistral.

Asymphylodorinae Szidat, 1943

2 (1) Genital pore, usually anterior to ventral sucker, medial, never lateral.

3 (4) Terminal portion of female system represented by organ of Looss; metraterm entering organ laterally at limit of spinose portion.

Monorchinae Odhner, 1911

4 (3) Organ of Looss absent.

Monorcheidinae Odhner, 1905

KEY TO THE GENERA OF THE SUBFAMILY MONORCHINAE ODHNER, 1911 (XI:266)

A. A. Sobolev

1 (18) Eggs without filaments.

2 (12) Testis single.

3 (17) Vitellaria anterior to testes or at same level.

4 (5) Testis at posterior end of body; intestinal ceca terminating at posterior end of testis.

Postmonorchis Hopkins, 1941 (fig. 438)

5 (4) Testis in middle region of body, medial or sinistral; excretory bladder Y-shaped or tubular.

6 (7) Excretory bladder distinctly Y-shaped, basal trunk and lateral branches nearly equal in length, broad.   Monorchis Looss, 1902 (fig. 439)

7 (6) Excretory bladder tubular, if Y-shaped, narrow, lateral branches shorter than basal trunk.

8 (9) Spines of genital atrium, distal portion of organ of Looss, and cirrus differing in shape and size.   Genolopa Linton, 1910 (fig. 440)

9 (8) Armament of distal section of genital system not as above.

10 (11) Oral sucker smaller than ventral; metraterm at junction with organ of Looss equipped with muscular sphincter.

Paraproctotrema Yamaguti, 1934 (fig. 441)

11 (10) Oral sucker larger than ventral; muscular sphincter of metraterm lacking.

Proctotrema Odhner, 1911 (fig. 442)

12 (2) Two testes present.

13 (14) Vitellaria lateral to pharynx, anterior to level of ventral sucker.

Achoerus Wlasenko, 1931 (fig. 443)

14 (13) Vitellaria partially anterior to ventral sucker, partially lateral.

15 (16) Testes nearly round.

Physochoerus Poche, 1925

16 (15) Testes longitudinally elongate; length more than two times greater than width.

Paramonorcheides Yamaguti, 1938 (fig. 445)

17 (3) Vitellaria posterior to testis.
Telolecithus Lloyd and Guberlet, 1932 (fig. 446)
18 (1) Eggs with filaments.
Hurleytrema Srivastava, 1939 (fig. 447)

KEY TO THE SPECIES OF THE GENUS
MONORCHIS LOOSS, 1902 (XI:267)

A. A. Sobolev

1 (4) Vitellaria lateral to pharynx, wholly extra-cecal.
2 (3) Posterior end of bursa of cirrus extending slightly beyond ventral sucker.
M. parvus Looss, 1902
3 (2) Posterior end of bursa of cirrus extending far beyond ventral sucker.
M. monorchis (Stossich, 1890) (fig. 439)
4 (1) Vitellaria lateral to ventral sucker; partially extra-cecal.   M. latus Manter, 1942

KEY TO THE SPECIES OF THE GENUS
GENOLOPA LINTON, 1910 (XI:279)

A. A. Sobolev

1 (4) Intestinal ceca not reaching posterior end of body, terminating approximately at boundary of the second and third thirds of body, or, at most, at boundary of third and fourth fourths of body.
2 (3) Oral sucker smaller than ventral.
G. cacuminata Nicoll, 1915
3 (2) Oral sucker considerably larger than ventral.
G. plectorhynchi (Yamaguti, 1934)
4 (1) Intestinal ceca reaching posterior end of body.
5 (6) Ovary lobed.   G. trifolifer Nicoll, 1915
6 (5) Ovary entire.
7 (8) Esophagus long, exceeding length of pharynx; vitellaria anteriorly reaching level of ventral sucker, extending posteriorly beyond testis.
G. pisodontophidis (Yamaguti, 1938)
8 (7) Esophagus short, not exceeding length of pharynx; vitellaria anteriorly not reaching level of ventral sucker, posteriorly not extending beyond testis.   G. ampullacea Linton, 1910 (fig. 440)

KEY TO THE SPECIES OF THE GENUS
HURLEYTREMA SRIVASTAVA, 1939 (XI:294-297)

A. A. Sovolev

1 (4) Vitellaria anterior to testis.
2 (3) Intestinal ceca terminating anterior to testis.
H. eucinostomi Manter, 1942
3 (2) Intestinal ceca extending for considerable distance beyond testis.   H. chaetodoni Manter, 1942
4 (1) Vitellaria both anterior to and posterior to testis.   H. ovocaudatum Srivastava, 1939 (fig. 447)

KEY TO THE SPECIES OF THE GENUS
PARAMONORCHEIDES YAMAGUTI, 1938 (XI:306)

A. A. Sobolev

1 (2) Testes posterior to ventral sucker.
P. awatati Yamaguti, 1938 (fig. 445)
2 (1) Testes lateral to ventral sucker, anterior ends passing considerably beyond ventral sucker.
P. sirembonis Yamaguti, 1938

KEY TO THE SPECIES OF THE GENUS
PARAPROCTOTREMA YAMAGUTI, 1934 (XI:313)

A. A. Sobolev

1 (2) Intestinal ceca passing slightly beyond level of ventral sucker, not reaching by far, level of testis.
P. brevicaecum Manter, 1942
2 (1) Intestinal ceca either reaching level of testis or extending beyond.
3 (4) Proximal end of organ of Looss un-armed.
P. fusiforme Yamaguti, 1934 (fig. 441)
4 (3) Proximal end of organ of Looss armed.
P. elongatum (Manter, 1934)

KEY TO THE SPECIES OF THE GENUS
PROCTOTREMA ODHNER, 1911 modified from
Nagaty (1948) (XI:328)

A. A. Sobolev

1 (8) Intestinal ceca terminating equatorially or sub-equatorially.
2 (5) Ovary clearly three or four-lobed.
3 (4) Eggs oval.   P. macrorchis Yamaguti, 1934
4 (3) Eggs elongate.   P. parvum Manter, 1942
5 (2) Ovary entire or slightly lobed.
6 (7) Eggs oval.   P. truncatum (Linton, 1910)
7 (6) Eggs elongate.   P. costaricae Manter, 1940
8 (1) Intestinal ceca extending beyond mid-point of body.
9 (12) Suckers of equal size, or oral sucker slightly larger.
10 (11) Body 0.19-0.63 mm. long, oval.
P. minuta (Manter, 1931)
11 (10) Body 0.86-1.135 mm. long, elongate.
P. malasi Nagaty, 1948
12 (9) Oral sucker considerably larger than ventral.
13 (16) Eggs elongate.
14 (15) Ovary distinctly lobed; oral sucker less than two times larger in diameter than ventral.
P. bacilliovatum Odhner, 1911 (fig. 442)
15 (14) Ovary slightly lobed or entire; diameter of oral sucker more than two times larger than ventral.
P. longovatum (Hopkins, 1941)
16 (13) Eggs not elongate.
17 (18) Loops of uterus extending anterior to ventral sucker.   P. odhneri Srivastava, 1939
18 (17) Loops of uterus not passing anteriorly beyond level of ovary, not reaching level of ventral sucker by considerable distance.
P. lintoni Manter, 1931

19 (20) Posterior vitelline follicles lateral to testis.
P. longicaecum Manter, 1940
20 (19) Posterior vitelline follicles anterior to testis.
P. beauforti (Hopkins, 1941)

KEY TO THE SPECIES OF THE GENUS TELOLECITHUS LLOYD AND GUBERLET, 1932 (XI:355)

A. A. Sobolev

1 (2) Esophagus short, shorter than pharynx, testis not passing into posterior third of body.
T. pugetensis Lloyd and Guberlet, 1932 (fig. 446)
2 (1) Esophagus considerably longer than pharynx; testis entirely in posterior third of body, almost reaching posterior end of body.
T. tropicus Manter, 1940

KEY TO THE GENERA OF THE SUBFAMILY MONORCHEIDINAE ODHNER, 1905 (XI:363)

A. A. Sobolev

1 (2) Vitelline follicles not passing into region posterior to testes.
Monorcheides Odhner, 1905 (fig. 448)
2 (1) Vitelline follicles passing into region posterior to testes.
Diplomonorchis Hopkins, 1941 (fig. 449)

KEY TO THE SPECIES OF THE GENUS MONORCHEIDES ODHNER, 1905 (XI:363)

A. A. Sobolev

1 (6) Ovary anterior to testes.
2 (3) Vitellaria not extending anteriorly beyond anterior edge of ventral sucker.
M. cumingae Martin, 1940
3 (2) Vitellaria extending anteriorly beyond anterior edge of ventral sucker.
4 (5) Vitelline follicles present only anterior to vitelline reservoir, not extending posteriorly beyond level of anterior edge of ovary.
M. diplorchis Odhner, 1905 (fig. 448)
5 (4) Vitelline follicles present both anterior and posterior to vitelline reservoir, passing posteriorly beyond anterior edge of ovary, reaching middle of ovary.
M. soldatovi Issaitschikoff, 1928
6 (1) Ovary posterior to testes.
M. petrowi Layman, 1930

KEY TO THE SPECIES OF THE GENUS DIPLOMONORCHIS HOPKINS, 1941 (XI:373)

A. A. Sobolev

1 (2) Uterus extending anterior to ventral sucker.
D. leiostomi Hopkins, 1941 (fig. 449)
2 (1) Uterus not extending anterior to ventral sucker.
D. bivitellosus (Manter, 1940)

KEY TO THE GENERA OF THE SUBFAMILY ASYMPHYLODORINAE SZIDAT, 1943 (XI:378)

A. A. Sobolev

1 (2) Testes paired; intestinal ceca short, saccular; excretory bladder tubular.
Palaeorchis Szidat, 1943 (fig. 450)
2 (1) Testis single; intestinal ceca extending at most to posterior level of testis; excretory bladder saccular.
Asymphylodora Looss, 1899 (fig. 451)

KEY TO THE SPECIES OF THE GENUS ASYMPHYLODORA LOOSS, 1899 (XI:380)

A. A. Sobolev

1 (2) Genital pore dextral.
A. kedarai Srivastava, 1951
2 (1) Genital pore sinistral.
3 (8) Vitelline follicles extending posteriorly beyond testis.
4 (5) Esophagus very short; esophageal expansion passing into intestinal bifurcation, beginning immediately posterior to pharynx.
A. demeli Markowski, 1935
5 (4) Esophagus long, walls parallel at some points.
6 (7) Eggs very large, 0.066-0.074 mm. long, elongate.
A. imitans (Mühling, 1898)
7 (6) Eggs considerably smaller, 0.021-0.027 mm. long.
A. kubanicum Issaitschikoff, 1923
8 (3) Vitelline follicles not extending posterior to testis.
9 (10) Ovary dorsal to ventral sucker.
A. macracetabulum Belouss, 1954
10 (9) Ovary posterior to ventral sucker.
11 (12) Cirrus sac posteriorly reaching level of testis.
A. carpiae Szidat, 1943
12 (11) Cirrus sac posteriorly not reaching level of testis.
13 (18) Cirrus sac posteriorly not reaching level of ovary.
14 (15) Vitelline follicles posterior to level of ventral sucker.
A. atherinopsidis Annereaux, 1947
15 (14) Vitelline follicles lateral to ventral sucker, passing anteriorly.
16 (17) Loops of uterus posterior to ventral sucker, not reaching level of sucker.
A. indica Srivastava, 1936
17 (16) Loops of uterus passing anteriorly beyond ventral sucker.
A. macrostoma Ozaki, 1925
18 (13) Cirrus sac extending at least to level of anterior edge of ovary.
19 (22) Vitellaria not extending beyond anterior edge of testis, or at least, not beyond middle of testis.
20 (21) Cirrus sac very small, not reaching level of testis.
A. pontica Tschernyschenko, 1949
21 (20) Cirrus sac large, passing posteriorly beyond level of anterior edge of testis.
A. markewitschi Kulakowskaja, 1947

22 (19) Vitellaria lateral to testis, extending both anterior and posterior to testis.

23 (24) Eggs very small, 0.018 x 0.014 mm., rounded anteriorly and posteriorly.

A. exspinosa (Haussmann, 1897)

24 (23) Eggs usually considerably larger (0.030-0.045 x 0.016-0.021 mm.), when only slightly larger (0.022-0.027 x 0.012-0.013 mm.) with scarcely distinguishable appendix present at posterior end.

25 (26) Excretory bladder very small, length not exceeding width of posterior loop of uterus.

A. tincae (Modeer, 1790) (fig. 451)

26 (25) Excretory bladder long, passing beyond posterior edge of testis.   A. japonica Yamaguti, 1938

Note: A. ferruginosa (Linstow, 1877) and A. progenetica Serkova and Bychowsky, 1940 omitted from key.

KEY TO THE SPECIES OF THE GENUS PALAEORCHIS SZIDAT, 1943 (XI:443)

A. A. Sobolev

1 (2) Vitellaria in posterior half of body.

P. incognitus Szidat, 1943

2 (1) Vitellaria in anterior half of body.

3 (4) Ovary and testes in middle third of body.

P. diplorchis (Yamaguti, 1936) (fig. 450)

4 (3) Ovary and testes in posterior third of body.

5 (6) Genital pore anterior to ventral sucker; cirrus sac small, proximal end not passing posteriorly beyond region of vitellaria.   P. unicus Szidat, 1943

6 (5) Genital pore at level of middle of ventral sucker; cirrus sac very large, proximal end passing beyond region of vitellaria, reaching level of anterior edge of left testis.   P. skrjabini Kowal, 1950

LITERATURE ON THE TREMATODES OF THE FAMILY MONORCHIDAE ODHNER, 1911 (XI:461-462)

Borovitskaya, M. P. 1952. Comparison of the parasite fauna of commercial fishes from the Danube estuaries and the Danube River. Trudy Leningradskogo Obschestva Estestvoispytateley. 71(4):10-25.

Bykhovskaya (Pavlovskaya), I. E. and B. E. Bykhovsky. 1940. The parasite fauna of fishes of the Akhtarinskie estuaries (Sea of Azov, delta of the Kubana River). Parazitologichesky Sbornik Zoologicheskogo Instituta Akad. Nauk SSSR. 8:131-161.

Vlasenko, P. V. 1931. On the fauna of parasitic worms of fishes of the Black Sea. Trudy Karadagskoy Biologicheskoy Stantsii, Simferopol. No. 4:88-136.

Ivanitsky, S. V. 1928. On the trematode fauna of vertebrates of the Ukraine. Veterinarne Dilo. No. 2(51):30-48.

Isaychikov, I. M. 1926. On the knowledge of the parasitic worms of cyprinid fishes of the Kuban River. Trudy Gosudarstvennogo Instituta Experimentalnoy Veterinarii. 2(2):159-170.

Isaychikov, I. M. 1928. On the knowledge of the parasitic worms of several groups of vertebrates of the Russian Arctic, A. Trematodes. Trudy Morskogo Nauchnogo Instituta. 3(2):5-79.

Isaychikov, I. M. 1933. On the knowledge of the parasitic worms of several groups of vertebrates of the Russian Arctic, II. Trudy Gosudarstvennogo Okeanograficheskogo Instituta. 3(1):3-44.

Koval, V. P. 1949. Digenetic trematodes of the genus Paleorchis in fishes of the Dnieper River. Biol. Zbirnik, Kievskogo Derzhavnogo Universitetu. No. 4: (In Ukrainian).

Koval, V. P. 1950. Digenetic trematodes of fishes of the lower Dnieper. Trudy Biologo-Gruntoznavchego Fakultetu, Kievskogo Derzhavnogo Universitetu. No. 5:187-207.

Kulakivskaya, O. P. 1947. Asymphylodora markewitschi, a new species of digenetic trematode from fishes of the Dnieper River. Trudy Inst. Zool. Akad. Nauk Ukr. SSR. Zbirnik Prats Zoologii i Parazitologii. No. 1:152-154. (In Ukrainian).

Layman, E. M. 1930. Parasitic worms of fishes of Peter the Great Bay. Izvestiya Tikookeanskoy Nauchno-Promyslovoy Stantsii. 3(6):1-120.

Markevich, A. P. 1951. The parasite fauna of fresh-water fishes of the Ukrainian S. S. R. Izdatelstvo Akad. Nauk Ukr. SSR, Kiev. 376 pp.

Serkova, O. P. and B. E. Bykhovsky. 1940. Asymphylodora progenetica sp. n. and some information on its morphology and development. Parazitologichesky Sbornik Zoologicheskogo Instituta Akad. Nauk SSSR. 8:162-175.

Skarbilovich, T. S. 1948. The family Lecithodendriidae Odhner, 1911. In: Skrjabin, K. I., Trematodes of animals and man. Izdatelstvo Akad. Nauk SSSR, Moskva-Leningrad. 2:337-590.

Stolyarov, V. P. 1952. On the parasite fauna of fishes of the Rybinskoye reservoir. Trudy Leningradskogo Obschestva Estestvoispytateley. 71(4): 261-285.

Chernyshenko, A. S. 1949. New helminths of fishes of the Black Sea. Trudy Odeskogo Gosudarstvennogo Universiteta im. Mechnikova, 4(57). Sbornik Biologicheskogo Fakulteta. 5:79-91.

KEY TO THE SUBFAMILIES OF THE FAMILY HALIPEGIDAE POCHE, 1925 (XI:477)

K. I. Skrjabin and L. Kh. Gushanskaya

1 (2) Hermaphroditic bursa and seminal receptacle present; gonads aligned with two oval testes posterior to ventral sucker, oval ovary posterior to testes, vitellaria posterior to ovary; loops of uterus passing beyond boundary of vitellaria.

Derogenetinae Odhner, 1927

2 (1) Hermaphroditic bursa lacking.

3 (10) Two compact vitellaria present, lobed or entire.

4 (7) Gonads aligned with testes anterior, ovary posterior to testes, vitellaria posterior to ovary.

5 (6) Loops of uterus not passing beyond vitellaria;

vitellaria limited to posterior region of body; intestinal ceca not forming arch at posterior end of body.
Halipeginae Ejsmont, 1931

6 (5) Loops of uterus not passing beyond vitellaria; vitellaria limited to posterior region of body, posterior to intestinal arch.
Genarchinae Skrjabin and Guschanskaja, 1955

7 (4) Gonads with different alignment.

8 (9) Loops of uterus not passing beyond ovary or vitellaria; ovary entire, anterior to two compact vitellaria; testes at extreme end of body. Parasites of gills, digestive tract, and ovary of fishes.
Gonocercinae Skrjabin and Guschanskaja, 1955

9 (8) Loops of uterus passing beyond ovary; ovary limited to region posterior to other gonads; testes posterior to ventral sucker; stellate vitellaria considerably posterior to testes; lobed ovary terminal. Parasites of swim bladder of fishes.
Dictysarcinae Skrjabin and Guschanskaja, 1955

10 (3) Vitellaria single, entire, round, posterior to round ovary; two round testes posterior to ventral sucker, medial. Gastric and intestinal parasites of fishes.
Bunocotylinae Dollfus, 1950

KEY TO THE GENERA OF THE SUBFAMILY HALIPEGINAE EJSMONT, 1931 (XI:479)

K. I. Skrjabin and L. Kh. Gushanskaya

1 (4) Eggs with filament at one pole; ventral sucker equatorial.

2 (3) Genital pore posterior to pharynx; short esophagus present. Parasites of frogs (exceptionally of snakes and fishes).
Halipegus Looss, 1899 (fig. 452)

3 (2) Genital pore posterior to intestinal bifurcation; esophagus lacking. Parasites of fishes.
Genarchella Travassos, Artigas and Pereira, 1928 (fig. 453)

4 (1) Eggs lacking filaments. Parasites of fishes.

5 (6) Ventral sucker in posterior third of body; genital pore posterior to intestinal bifurcation; large prostatic vesicle present, surrounded by prostatic cells; genital cone present; short esophagus with egg-shaped diverticulum present; ovary oval.
Gonocercella Manter, 1940 (fig. 454)

6 (5) Ventral sucker in anterior third of body; genital pore on conical papilla directly posterior to oral sucker; prostatic vesicle and genital cone absent; short esophagus present, without diverticulum; ovary pyriform. Indoderogenes Srivastava, 1941 (fig. 455)

KEY TO THE GENERA OF THE SUBFAMILY DEROGENETINAE ODHNER, 1927 (XI:581)

K. I. Skrjabin and L. Kh. Gushanskaya

1 (6) Ventral sucker equatorial or post-equatorial; two vitellaria present.

2 (5) Hermaphroditic bursa not filled with prostatic cells; eggs without filaments.

3 (4) Testes directly posterior to ventral sucker, symmetrical, superimposed on intestinal ceca; ovary posterior to one testis; vitellaria symmetrical, superimposed on intestinal ceca, directly posterior to ovary; hermaphroditic bursa surrounding short hermaphroditic duct, ends of ejaculatory duct and metraterm; genital atrium present; loops of uterus extending beyond level of vitellaria.
Derogenes Lühe, 1900 (fig. 456)

4 (3) Testes symmetrical, far apart, extra-cecal, slightly posterior to ventral sucker; ovary medial, posterior to testes; vitellaria dextral to ovary, on one side of body, superimposed on intestinal ceca, oblique; hermaphroditic bursa surrounding hermaphroditic duct and genital atrium; loops of uterus not passing beyond level of vitellaria.
Leurodera Linton, 1910 (fig. 457)

5 (2) Hermaphroditic bursa filled with prostatic cells, surrounding ejaculatory duct, part of metraterm, and hermaphroditic duct with opening into genital atrium; testes nearly symmetrical, directly posterior to ventral sucker; ovary at posterior end of body; vitellaria posterior to ovary; loops of uterus not passing beyond level of vitellaria; eggs with single polar filament.
Vitellotrema Guberlet, 1928 (fig. 458)

6 (1) Ventral sucker pre-equatorial.

7 (8) Three vitellaria present; hermaphroditic bursa surrounding hermaphroditic duct, distal ends of ejaculatory canal and of metraterm; testes in middle region of body, tandem or slightly oblique; ovary posterior to testes in posterior third of body; vitellaria directly posterior to ovary.
Theletrum Linton, 1910 (fig. 459)

8 (7) Two vitellaria present.

9 (12) Hermaphroditic bursa surrounding hermaphroditic duct.

10 (11) Testes symmetrical, close together, posterior to ventral sucker; ovary medial, directly posterior to testes; vitellaria symmetrical, directly posterior to ovary; spherical seminal vesicle far anterior to ventral sucker; not more than forty eggs in uterus; end of egg opposite operculum attenuated into spike-like structure.
Derogenoides Nicoll, 1912 (fig. 460)

11 (10) Testes medial or slightly oblique, posterior to ventral sucker; ovary posterior to posterior testis; vitellaria posterior to ovary, tandem, medial (exception: G. lintoni); tubular, sinuous seminal vesicle extending to anterior edge of ventral sucker; many eggs in uterus, oval, without spike-like projection.
Genolinea Manter, 1925 (fig. 461)

12 (9) Hermaphroditic bursa surrounding hermaphroditic duct and hermaphroditic vesicle; vesicle surrounded by prostatic cells.

13 (14) Testes oblique, posterior to ventral sucker; ovary posterior to posterior testes, ventrally superimposed on left intestinal cecum; vitellaria oblique, dextral and partially posterior to ovary; tubular, sinuous seminal vesicle reaching anterior edge of ventral sucker. Parasterrhurus Manter, 1934 (fig. 462)

14 (13) Testes far posterior to ventral sucker in posterior half of body, tandem (rarely symmetrical); ovary nearly medial, posterior to testes; two vitellaria symmetrical, directly posterior to ovary; spherical seminal vesicle far posterior to ventral sucker.   Opisthadena Linton, 1910 (fig. 463)

KEY TO THE SPECIES OF THE GENUS GENOLINEA MANTER, 1925 (XI:614)

K. I. Skrjabin and L. Kh. Gushanskaya

1 (8) Esophagus lacking.
2 (3) Vitellaria symmetrical.
          G. lintoni Skrjabin and Guschanskaja, 1955
3 (2) Vitellaria tandem or slightly oblique.
4 (5) Fleshy lip present, fringing dorsal edge of oral aperture.
          G. bowersi (Leiper and Atkinson, 1914)
5 (4) Fleshy lip lacking.
6 (7) Anterior testis directly posterior to ventral sucker; posterior testis slightly oblique, posterior to anterior testis; vitellaria oblique; eggs: 0.032-0.035 x 0.022-0.024 mm.
          G. montereyensis Annereaux. 1947
7 (6) Testes considerably posterior to ventral sucker, widely separated; vitellaria tandem; eggs: 0.027-0.029 x 0.0195 mm.   G. anurus (Layman, 1930)
8 (1) Esophagus present.
9 (12) Seminal vesicle tubular, sinuous, extending to anterior edge of ventral sucker.
10 (11) Aperture of ventral sucker surrounded by sphincter.   G. robusta Lloyd, 1938
11 (10) Sphincter around aperture of ventral sucker lacking.   G. laticauda Manter, 1925 (fig. 461)
12 (9) Seminal vesicle extending beyond level of anterior edge of ventral sucker.
13 (14) Seminal vesicle large, S-shaped, reaching level of anterior testis; seminal receptacle dorsal to ovary.   G. aburame Yamaguti, 1934
14 (13) Seminal vesicle large, tubular, sinuous, passing beyond level of middle of ventral sucker; seminal receptacle between ovary and posterior testis.   G. manteri Lloyd, 1938

KEY TO THE SPECIES OF THE GENUS THELETRUM LINTON, 1910 (XI:657)

K. I. Skrjabin and L. Kh. Gushanskaya

1 (2) Ring-shaped elevation and group of round papilla present on ventral surface of body posterior to ventral sucker; esophagus two times longer than pharynx; testes pyriform, far posterior to ventral sucker at middle of body; seminal receptacle, almost equal in size to testes, directly posterior to testes; ovary and vitellaria far from testes in posterior end of body.   T. fustiforme Linton, 1910 (fig. 459)
2 (1) Ring-shaped elevation near ventral sucker lacking.
3 (4) Esophagus short, with small diverticulum;

testes spherical, oblique, mid-way between ventral sucker and ovary; seminal receptacle directly anterior to ovary; ovary and vitellaria at anterior part of posterior third of body; anterior pair of vitellaria symmetrical, united by constricted bridge; third vitellaria bi-lobed, posterior to anterior pair.
                    T. lissosomum Manter, 1940
4 (3) Esophagus in form of spherical diverticulum; testes round, oblique, pre-equatorial; large, spherical seminal receptacle partially anterior to and partially dorsal to ovary; ovary and vitellaria directly post-equatorial; anterior pair of vitellaria symmetrical; posterior vitellaria entire, oval.
                    T. gravidum Manter, 1940

KEY TO THE GENERA OF THE SUBFAMILY GENARCHINAE SKRJABIN AND GUSCHANSKAJA, 1955 (XI:677)

K. I. Skrjabin and L. Kh. Gushankaya

1 (4) Intestinal arch near posterior end of body; many eggs present in uterus; eggs with single polar filament; only vitellaria present posterior to intestinal arch.
2 (3) Esophageal diverticulum present (except in O. dasus); hermaphroditic duct long.
          Ophiocorchis Srivastava, 1933 (fig. 464)
3 (2) Esophageal diverticulum lacking; hermaphroditic duct short.   Genarches Looss, 1902 (fig. 465)
4 (1) Intestinal arch extending only to level of testes; few eggs present in uterus; eggs lacking filament, containing miracidia with black eye-spots; hermaphroditic duct in form of short swollen sinus; saccular seminal receptacle present; testes, ovary, and vitellaria present all posterior to intestinal arch.
Tangiopsis Skrjabin and Guschanskaja, 1955 (fig. 466)

KEY TO THE SPECIES OF THE GENUS GENARCHES LOOSS, 1902 (XI:678)

K. I. Skrjabin and L. Kh. Gushanskaya

1 (6) Uterus extending beyond border of intestinal arch, reaching posterior end of body.
2 (5) Vitellaria at posterior end of body, extending beyond posterior limit of uterus.
3 (4) Esophagus absent; body 2.3 mm. (length) x 0.5-0.8 mm. (width); diameter of ventral sucker 0.09-0.12 mm.; testes triangular.
                    G. ovocaudatus (Srivastava, 1933)
4 (3) Esophagus present; body 0.82 mm. (length) x 0.225 mm. (width); diameter of ventral sucker 0.2 mm.; testes round.   G. gigi (Yamaguti, 1939)
5 (2) Vitellaria not reaching posterior end of body; loops of uterus posterior to vitellaria.
                    G. mulleri (Levinson, 1881) (fig. 465)
6 (1) Uterus not passing beyond posterior boundary of intestinal arch.
7 (8) Ventral sucker greatly displaced towards posterior half of body; main mass of uterine loops

anterior to ventral sucker; genital pore anterior to esophagus, at level of pharynx.

G. piscicola (Srivastava, 1933)

8 (7) Ventral sucker nearly equatorial or slightly post-equatorial; loops of uterus equally anterior and posterior to ventral sucker.

9 (10) Genital pore directly posterior to intestinal bifurcation; testes usually oblique; vitellaria symmetrical; eggs: 0.046-0.050 x 0.025-0.026 mm.

G. goppo (Ozaki, 1925)

10 (9) Genital pore at level of posterior end of pharynx; testes symmetrical; vitellaria oblique; eggs: 0.069-0.078 x 0.033-0.035 mm.

G. anguillae (Yamaguti, 1938)

KEY TO THE SPECIES OF THE GENUS OPHIOCORCHIS SRIVASTAVA, 1933 (XI:696)

K. I. Skrjabin and L. Kh. Gushanskaya

1 (8) Esophageal diverticulum present.
2 (5) Testes asymmetrical.
3 (4) Dimensions of esophageal diverticulum 0.16 x 0.08 mm.; vitellaria lobed; egg filament: 0.05-0.06 mm. long.   O. lobatum Srivastava, 1933 (fig. 464)
4 (3) Dimensions of esophageal diverticulum 0.13 x 0.05 mm.; vitellaria entire; egg filament: 0.012 mm.

O. singularis Srivastava, 1933

5 (2) Testes with different arrangement.
6 (7) Testes superimposed on one another; genital pore directly posterior to oral sucker; hermaphroditic duct 0.16 mm. long; egg filament: 0.064-0.088 mm.   O. indicus Gupta, 1951
7 (6) Testes symmetrical; genital pore ventral to left intestinal cecum, 0.36 mm. from anterior end of body; hermaphroditic duct 0.09 mm. long; egg filament 0.018-0.45 mm. long.   O. faruquis Gupta, 1951
8 (1) Esophageal diverticulum lacking; genital pore posterior to intestinal bifurcation; testes symmetrical; hermaphroditic duct 0.08 mm. long; vitellaria compact; egg filament 0.021-0.04 mm. long.

O. dasus Gupta, 1951

KEY TO THE GENERA OF THE SUBFAMILY GONOCERCINAE SKRJABIN AND GUSCHANSKAJA, 1955 (XI:721)

K. I. Skrjabin and L. Kh. Gushanskaya

1 (2) Eggs with single, long polar filament; genital pore near pharynx.

Hemiperina Manter, 1934 (fig. 467)

2 (1) Eggs without filament; genital pore near oral sucker.   Gonocerca Manter, 1925 (fig. 468)

KEY TO THE SPECIES OF THE GENUS GONOCERCA MANTER, 1925 (XI:722)

K. I. Skrjabin and L. Kh. Gushanskaya

1 (4) Vitellaria entire; esophagus present.

2 (3) Short, broad genital atrium present; genital pore posterior to oral sucker; ventral sucker post-equatorial; body: 2.24-3.57 mm. Gastric parasites of fishes.   G. crassa Manter, 1934
3 (2) Genital atrium lacking; genital pore posterior to oral orifice; ventral sucker in posterior third of body; body 1.3-1.9 mm. Parasites of gills, rarely of stomachs of fishes.

G. phycidis Manter, 1925 (fig. 468)

4 (1) Vitellaria lobed; genital atrium lacking; ventral sucker post-equatorial.
5 (6) Esophagus present; body: 4 mm.; genital pore at level of pharynx. Parasites of esophagus and stomach of fishes.   G. kobayashi (Layman, 1930)
6 (5) Esophagus lacking; body 4.4-13 mm.; genital pore posterior to aperture of oral sucker. Parasites of ovaries of cod.

G. macroformis Wolfgang and Myers, 1954

KEY TO THE SPECIES OF THE GENUS HEMIPERINA MANTER, 1934 (XI:736)

K. I. Skrjabin and L. Kh. Gushanskaya

1 (2) Genital atrium present, short; testes round, oblique, posterior to ends of intestinal ceca; loops of uterus anterior to ovary.

H. nicolli Manter, 1934 (fig. 467)

2 (1) Genital atrium lacking; testes triangular, symmetrical, lateral, anterior to ends of intestinal ceca; loops of uterus forming compact mass both anterior and posterior to ovary.

H. manteri Crowcroft, 1947

LITERATURE ON THE TREMATODES OF THE FAMILY HALIPEGIDAE POCHE, 1925 (XI:743-744)

Bauer, O. N. and S. S. Shulman. 1948. On the question of the ecological classification of fish parasites. Izvestiya Vsesoyuznogo Nauchno-Issledovatelskogo Instituta Ozernogo i Rechnogo Rybnogo Khozyaystva. 27:239-243.

Belous, E. V. 1953. Parasitic worms of freshwater vertebrates of the Primorye region. Avtoreferat dissertatsii.

Bykhovsky, B. E. 1929. Distomum kessleri Grebnizki, 1872, its systematic position and its synonyms. Gidrobiologichesky Zhurnal, Saratov. 8:321-324.

Bykhovsky, B. E. 1949. The parasitic worms. In: Fresh-water life of the U. S. S. R. Pod Redaktsii Prof. Zhadina, Zoologichesky Institut Akad. Nauk SSSR. 2:69-110.

Vlasenko, P. V. 1929. On the systematics and diagnoses of the genus Halipegus Looss and the family Halipegidae Poche. Zool. Anz. 86(42):21-27. (In German).

Vlasenko, P. V. 1930. On the trematode fauna of amphibians and reptiles in the vicinity of Kharkov. Trudy Kharkivsko Tovaristva Doslidnikiv Prirodi. 53(1):49-57. (In Ukrainian).

Vlasenko, P. V. 1931. On the fauna of parasitic

worms of fishes of the Black Sea. Trudy Karadagskoy Biologicheskoy Stantsii, Simferopol. No. 4:88-
136.

Grebnitsky, N. A. 1873. Materials on the fauna of
worms of the Novorossysk region. Zapiski Novoros-
syskogo Obschestva Estestvoispytateley. 2(2):230-
272.

Dogiel, V. A. 1947. Course in general parasitology. Second Ed. Uchpedgiz. 371 pp.

Dogiel, V. A. and B. E. Bykhovsky 1939. Parasites
of fishes of the Caspian Sea. Trudy Komissii po
Komplexnomu Izucheniyu Kasypskogo Morya. Izdatelstvo Akad. Nauk SSSR. No. 7:1-149.

Dogiel, V. A. and G. S. Markov. 1937. Variations
in the parasite fauna with age of the char (Salvelinus
alpinus) of Novaya Zemlya. Trudy Leningradskogo
Obschestva Estestvoispytateley. 66(3):434-455.

Dogiel, V. A. and A. Rozova. 1931. The parasite
fauna of four-horned sculpin (Myoxocephalus quadricornis) in different regions of its distribution.
Uchenye Zapiski Leningradskogo Gosudarstvennogo
Universiteta 74, seriya biologicheskikh nauk. No.
18:4-19.

Dubinia, M. N. 1950. Ecological research on the
parasite fauna of lake frog (Rana ridibunda Pall.) of
the Volga delta. Parazitologichesky Sbornik Zoologicheskogo Instituta Akad. Nauk SSSR. 12:300-350.

Isaychikov, I. M. 1926. On the knowledge of the
helminth fauna of amphibians of Russia, I. Trudy
Sibirskogo Veterinarnogo Instituta. No. 7:61-159.

Isaychikov, I. M. 1928. On the knowledge of the
parasitic worms of several groups of vertebrates of
the Russian Arctic, A. Trematodes. Trudy Morskogo
Nauchnogo Instituta. 3(2):5-27.

Isaychikov, I. M. and N. P. Zakharov 1929. On the
fauna of parasitic worms of Rana esculenta of the
Don district. Russky Gidrobiologichesky Zhurnal.
8(1-3):49-54.

Isaychikov, I. M. 1933. On the knowledge of the
parasitic worms of several groups of vertebrates of
the Russian Arctic, II. Trudy Gosudarstvennogo
Okeanograficheskogo Instituta. 3(1):3-44.

Layman, E. M. 1930. Parasitic worms of fishes
of Peter the Great Bay. Izvestiya Tikhookeanskoy
Nauchno-Promyslovoy Stantsii. 3(6):1-120.

Markevich, A. P. 1951. The parasite fauna of
fresh-water fishes of the Ukrainian S. S. R. Izdatelstvo Akad. Nauk Ukr. SSR, Kiev. 376 pp.

Osmanov, S. U. 1940. Materials on the parasite
fauna of fishes of the Black Sea. Uchenye Zapiski
Leningradskogo Pedagogicheskogo Instituta, Kafedra
Zoologii i Darvinizma. 30:187-267.

Saidov, Yu. S. 1953. The helminth fauna of fishes
and piscivorous birds of Dagestan. Avtoreferat dissertatsii, Moskva.

Skrjabin, K. I. and L. Kh. Gushanskaya. 1954. The
sub-order Hemiurata (Markevitsch, 1951) Skrjabin
and Guschanskaja, 1954, Part I. In: Skrjabin, K. I.,
Trematodes of animals and man. Izdatelstvo Akad.
Nauk SSSR, Moskva-Leningrad. 9:227-653.

Skrjabin, K. I. and L. Kh. Gushanskaya. 1954. The
sub-order Hemiurata (Markevitsch, 1951) Skrjabin
and Guschankaja, 1954, Part. II. In: Skrjabin, K. I.,
Trematodes of animals and man. Izdatelstvo Akad.
Nauk SSSR, Moskva-Leningrad. 10:339-649.

Shulman, R. E. 1948. The parasite fauna of commercial fishes of the White Sea. Avtoreferat dissertatsii.

Shulman, R. E. 1950. The parasite fauna of com-
mercial fishes of the White Sea. Tezisy dissertatsii.
Trudy Gelmintologicheskoy Laboratorii Akad. Nauk
SSSR. 4:275-278.

Shulman, S. S. and R. E. Shulman-Albova. 1953.
Parasites of fishes of the White Sea. Izdatelstvo
Akad. Nauk SSSR, Moskva-Leningrad. 198 pp.

Shulman, S. S. 1954. On the specificity of parasites of fishes. Zoologichesky Zhurnal. 33(1):14-25.

LIST OF SUPPLEMENTARY ILLUSTRATIONS

PART XII

KEY TO THE SUBFAMILIES OF THE FAMILY HAPLOPORIDAE NICOLL, 1914 (XII:10)

K. I. Skrjabin

1 (2) Vitellaria rudimentary, usually globular, not follicular, more rarely subdivided into small number of follicles; uterus chiefly posterior to ventral sucker.   Haploporinae Looss, 1902
2 (1) Vitellaria well-developed, composed of elongate cord-shaped bodies, represented by two sinuous structures, or in few large fusiform fragments; uterus short, not passing posteriorly beyond level of ovary.   Waretrematinae Belouss, 1954

KEY TO THE GENERA OF THE SUBFAMILY HAPLOPORINAE LOOSS, 1902 (XII:11)

K. I. Skrjabin

1 (2) Intestinal ceca nearly reaching posterior end of body; uterus well-developed, filling whole posterior half of body, anteriorly reaching ventral sucker or level of pharynx; vitellaria composed of small number of separate follicles, between ventral sucker and testes.   Paralecithobothrys Freitas, 1948 (fig. 469)

2 (1) Intestinal ceca short, not passing beyond posterior edge of testes; uterus mainly occupying space posterior to ventral sucker.

3 (4) Vitellaria appearing single, compact, posterior to intestinal ceca.
Dicrogaster Looss, 1902 (fig. 470)

4 (3) Vitellaria clearly paired.

5 (6) Ovary and vitellaria at considerable distance posterior to ventral sucker and ends of intestinal ceca; long pre-pharynx present.
Wlassenkotrema Skrjabin, 1956 (fig. 471)

6 (5) Ovary and vitellaria not extending beyond level of ends of intestinal ceca.

7 (8) Vitellaria globular, close together, intercecal.   Haploporus Looss, 1902 (fig. 472)

8 (7) Vitellaria extra-cecal.

9 (10) Vitellaria compact, slightly lobed, at posterior limit of intestinal ceca.
Saccocoelium Looss, 1902 (fig. 473)

10 (9) Vitellaria follicular; follicles few, at midpoint of length of intestinal ceca.
Lecithobothrys Looss, 1902 (fig. 474)

KEY TO THE SPECIES OF THE GENUS HAPLOPORUS LOOSS, 1902 (XII:12)

K. I. Skrjabin

1 (2) Body 2.5-3.0 mm. (length) x 0.75-1.0 mm. (width); hermaphroditic bursa smaller than ventral sucker; eggs containing miracidium with pigmented eye-spots.   H. benedeni (Stossich, 1887) (fig. 472)

2 (1) Body 0.8-0.95 mm. (length) x 0.38 mm. (width); hermaphroditic bursa larger than ventral sucker; eggs containing miracidium without pigmented eye-spots.   H. lateralis Looss, 1902

KEY TO THE SPECIES OF THE GENUS DICROGASTER LOOSS, 1902 (XII:14)

K. I. Skrjabin

1 (2) Posterior end of body with tail-like constriction; testis in right half of body; eggs 0.035-0.040 x 0.023 mm.; miracidium without pigmented eye-spots.
D. contractus Looss, 1902

2 (1) Posterior end of body lacking tail-like constriction; testis nearly medial; eggs 0.053 x 0.025 mm.; miracidium with pigmented eye-spots.
D. perpusillus Looss, 1902 (fig. 470)

KEY TO THE SPECIES OF THE GENUS SACCOCOELIUM LOOSS, 1902 (XII:31)

K. I. Skrjabin

1 (2) Hermaphroditic bursa considerably larger than ventral sucker; pharynx 0.077 x 0.051 mm.
S. tensum Looss, 1902

2 (1) Hermaphroditic bursa and ventral sucker of equal size; pharynx 0.11 x 0.08 mm.
S. obesum Looss, 1902 (fig. 473)

KEY TO THE GENERA OF THE SUBFAMILY WARETREMATINAE BELOUSS, 1954 (XII:38-41)

K. I. Skrjabin

1 (2) Intestinal bifurcation posterior to ventral sucker; vitellaria of fusiform, elongate fragments; hermaphroditic bursa extending far beyond level of ventral sucker.
Waretrema Srivastava, 1939 (fig. 475)

2 (1) Intestinal bifurcation anterior to ventral sucker; cord-shaped vitellaria not in fragments; hermaphroditic bursa not passing beyond posterior edge of ventral sucker.
Skrjabinolecithum Belouss, 1954 (fig. 476)
Note: Chalcinotrema Freitas, 1947 omitted from key.

LITERATURE ON THE TREMATODES OF THE FAMILY HAPLOPORIDAE NICOLL, 1914 (XII:49)

Belous, E. V. 1954. On the systematics of trematodes of the family Haploporidae Nicoll, 1914. Trudy Gelmintologicheskoy Laboratorii Akad. Nauk SSSR. 7:277-281.

Vlasenko, P. V. 1931. On the fauna of parasitic worms of fishes of the Black Sea. Trudy Karadagskoy Biologicheskoy Stantsii, Simferopol. No. 4:88-136.

Markevich, A. P. 1951. The parasite fauna of fresh-water fishes of the Ukrainian S.S.R. Izdatelstvo Akad. Nauk Ukr. SSR, Kiev. 376 pp.

KEY TO THE SUBFAMILIES OF THE FAMILY ECHINOSTOMATIDAE DIETZ, 1909 from Skrjabin and Schulz (1938) (XII:55)

1 (2) Anal appendage absent.

2 (9) Cephalic collar with spines present.

3 (4) Oral sucker wholly reduced; pharynx only muscular organ in cephalic end. Liver parasites of birds.   Pegosomatinae Skrjabin and Schulz, 1938

4 (3) Oral sucker present. Parasites of digestive tracts, more rarely of fabrician bursa of birds and mammals.

5 (6) Cirrus sac extending beyond posterior edge of ventral sucker; single row of spines on cephalic collar; ventral cylinder of cephalic collar lacking; pars prostatica present.   Himasthlinae Odhner, 1911

6 (5) Cirrus sac not passing beyond posterior edge of ventral sucker.

7 (8) Cephalic spines forming single or double row, not interrupted dorsally; ventral cylinder of cephalic collar present; pars prostatica present or absent.
Echinostomatinae Odhner, 1911

8 (7) Cephalic spines in single row, interrupted dorsally; ventral cylinder of cephalic collar lacking; pars prostatica present.
Echinochasminae Odhner, 1911

9 (2) Cephalic collar with spines lacking or reduced.

10 (11) Canal of Mesaulus running from posterior edge of ventral sucker to posterior end of body, straight; ventral sucker sessile.
Cotylotretinae Skrjabin and Schulz, 1938

11 (10) Canal of Mesaulus absent; ventral sucker pedunculate. Parasites of beavers.
Stephanoproraoidinae Skrjabin and Schulz, 1938

12 (1) Constricted anal appendage present, more or less sharply delimited from body.

13 (14) Body subdivided into three sections: narrowly tapering anterior and posterior sections extending from leaf-shaped, expanded middle section; cephalic collar, weakly developed, with well-developed spines; ventral sucker in posterior half of body. Parasites of birds.
Chaunocephalinae Travassos, 1922

14 (13) Body subdivided into two sections: expanded leaf-shaped anterior part, and elongate anal appendage; cephalic collar lacking; corner spines present, lateral to flattened cephalic end; ventral sucker at boundary of anterior and posterior sections of body.
Sodalinae Skrjabin and Schulz, 1938

KEY TO THE SUBFAMILIES OF THE FAMILY ECHINOSTOMATIDAE DIETZ, 1909 from Skrjabin and Baschkirova (1956) (XII:85)

1 (20) Cephalic collar of typical echinostomatid construction.

2 (17) Anal appendage lacking.

3 (10) Cephalic collar well-developed, armed with spines laterally and along ventral angles.

4 (5) Oral sucker wholly reduced; pharynx only muscular organ at cephalic end. Liver parasites of birds.   Pegosomatinae Odhner, 1911

5 (4) Oral sucker present. Parasites of digestive tract (rarely of fabrician bursa and kidney) of birds and mammals.

6 (7) Cirrus sac passing beyond posterior edge of ventral sucker; single row of spines present on cephalic collar; ventral cylinder of cephalic collar lacking.   Himasthlinae Odhner, 1911

7 (6) Cirrus sac not extending beyond posterior edge of ventral sucker.

8 (9) Spines on cephalic collar in one or two rows, continuous, without dorsal interval; ventral cylinder of cephalic collar present.
Echinostomatinae Odhner, 1911

9 (8) Spines on cephalic collar in single row, dorsal interval present; ventral cylinder of cephalic collar lacking.   Echinochasminae Odhner, 1911

10 (3) Cephalic collar weakly developed; portion of spines reduced.

11 (16) Cephalic collar armed with spines at angles and border.

12 (13) Cephalic collar forming two cylinders lateral to large oral sucker; cephalic spines in double row, interrupted dorsally.
Microparyphiinae Mendheim, 1943

13 (12) Cephalic collar of different construction.

14 (15) Cephalic collar transversely oval; cephalic spines in double row, not interrupted dorsally. Intestinal parasites of birds.
Hypoderaeinae Skrjabin and Baschkirova, 1956

15 (14) Cephalic collar reniform; cephalic spines in single row, interrupted dorsally. Renal parasites of birds.
Nephroechinostomatinae Oschmarin and Belouss, 1951

16 (11) Cephalic collar lacking lateral spines.
Eurycephalinae Skrjabin and Baschkirova, 1956

17 (2) Constricted anal appendage present, more or less sharply delimited from rest of body.

18 (19) Body subdivided into three sections: leaf-shaped expanded middle portion, constricted cephalic portion and anal appendage; cephalic collar small, with well-developed spines; ventral sucker in posterior half of body. Chaunocephalinae Travassos, 1922

19 (18) Body sub-divided into two sections: leaf-shaped expanded anterior part and elongate anal appendage; cephalic collar lacking; lateral corner spines present on cephalic end of body; ventral sucker at border of anterior and posterior sections of body.
Sodalinae Skrjabin and Schulz, 1938

20 (1) Cephalic collar replaced by pro-adoral disc representing expanded anterior end of body. Parasites of crocodiles, more rarely of birds.
Allechinostomatinae Sudarikov, 1950

KEY TO THE GENERA OF THE SUBFAMILY ECHINOSTOMATINAE ODHNER, 1911 (XII:86)

K. I. Skrjabin and E. Ya. Bashkirova

1 (6) Parasites with long, thread-like body.

2 (3) Body sharply sub-divided into two sections: narrow, neck-like anterior section, 1.5-3 times longer than expanded posterior part of body; gonads and vitellaria in posterior section of body.
Longicollia Bychowskaja-Pawlowskaja, 1953
(fig. 477)

3 (2) Body not sub-divided into two sections.

4 (5) Suckers small; vitellaria not merging posterior to testes. Host: Anastomas lamelligerus.
Echinodollfusia Skrjabin and Baschkirova, 1956
(fig. 478)

5 (4) Ventral sucker well-developed; vitellaria merging posterior to testes. Host: Lutra brasiliensis.   Baschkirovitrema Skrjabin, 1944 (fig. 479)

6 (1) Body oblong or oval, not thread-like.

7 (10) Cephalic collar equipped with ventral and dorsal cavities.

8 (9) Cephalic collar possessing weakly developed dorsal cavity; cephalic spines forming single row, not interrupted dorsally.
Nephrostomum Dietz, 1909 (fig. 25)

9 (8) Cephalic collar with narrow, deep, dorsal

cavity; cephalic spines forming single row, interrupted dorsally.   Patagifer Dietz, 1909 (fig. 26)

10 (7) Cephalic collar equipped with ventral cavity only.

11 (26) Cephalic collar reniform, with well-developed ventral lobes, and double row of spines not interrupted dorsally.

12 (15) Uterus well-developed, with numerous eggs.

13 (14) Edges of posterior part of body serrate; each projection armed with spines.
          Prionosoma Dietz, 1909 (fig. 27)

14 (13) Edges of posterior part of body without serrate projections.
          Echinostoma Rudolphi, 1809 (fig. 29)

15 (12) Uterus weakly developed, with few eggs.

16 (17) Body thick, small; testes usually transversely elongate, oblique or symmetrical.
          Petasiger Dietz, 1909 (fig. 30)

17 (16) Body of medium or large size; testes usually longitudinally elongate, tandem or symmetrical.

18 (19) Testes round, symmetrical.
          Parallelotestis Belopolskaja, 1954 (fig. 480)

19 (18) Testes oblong, tandem.

20 (21) Body massive; testes deeply lobed.
          Paryphostomum Dietz, 1909 (fig. 31)

21 (20) Body thin, delicate; testes entire or slightly lobed.

22 (23) Vitellaria usually in posterior part of body.
          Euparyphium Dietz, 1909 (fig. 32)

23 (22) Vitellaria extending anteriorly nearly to level of ventral sucker or terminating slightly posterior to ventral sucker.

24 (25) Lateral spines of collar in single row.
Dietziella Skrjabin and Baschkirova, 1956 (fig. 481)

25 (24) Lateral spines of collar in double row.
          Echinoparyphium Dietz, 1909 (fig. 33)

26 (11) Cephalic collar halfmoon-shaped, with weakly developed ventral lobes; cephalic spines in single row, not interrupted dorsally.
          Drepanocephalus Dietz, 1909 (fig. 34)

Note: Ignavia Freitas, 1948 (fig. 482) and Molinella Hübner, 1939 (fig. 483) omitted from key.

KEY TO THE SPECIES OF THE GENUS EUPARYPHIUM DIETZ, 1909 (XII:386)

K. I. Skrjabin and E. Ya. Bashkirova

1 (10) Twenty-seven cephalic spines present.
2 (7) Cuticle armed.
3 (4) Anterior border of vitellaria at level of ventral sucker.   E. suinum Ciurea, 1921
4 (3) Anterior border of vitellaria at level of ovary.
5 (6) Testes entire; pre-pharynx lacking. Hosts: mammals.   E. melis (Schrank, 1788) (fig. 32)
6 (5) Testes slightly lobed; pre-pharynx present. Host: man.   E. jassyense Leon and Ciurea, 1922
7 (2) Cuticular armament lacking.
8 (9) Body small, up to 5 mm. long; testes long, sinuous.   E. capitaneum Dietz, 1909

9 (8) Body large, up to 14 mm. long; testes long, entire.   E. inerme Fuhrmann, 1904
10 (1) With different number of cephalic spines.
11 (14) Not more than forty-three cephalic spines present.
12 (13) Forty-one cephalic spines present.
          E. ochoterenai Cerecero, 1943
13 (12) Forty-three cephalic spines present.
          E. malayanum (Leiper, 1911)
14 (13) Forty-five cephalic spines present.
          E. murinum Tubangui, 1931
Note: E. longitestis Verma, 1936; E. stridulae (Reich, 1801); E. spiculator (Dujardin, 1845); E. ilocanum (Garrison, 1908) and E. guerreroi (Tubangui, 1931) omitted from key.

KEY TO THE SPECIES OF THE GENUS MOLINIELLA HÜBNER, 1931 (XII:440)

K. I. Skrjabin and E. Ya. Bashkirova

1 (2) Thirty-five spines on adoral disc. Parasites of Fulica atra (Europe).
          M. anceps (Molin, 1859) (fig. 483)
2 (1) Forty-five spines on adoral disc. Parasites of Parra africana (White Nile).
          M. nilotica (Odhner, 1911)

KEY TO THE SPECIES OF THE GENUS NEPHROSTOMUM DIETZ, 1909 from Mendheim (1943) (XII:451)

1 (4) Not more than forty spines present on cephalic collar.
2 (3) Thirty-two spines present on cephalic collar.
          N. australe (Johnston, 1928)
3 (2) Thirty-eight spines present on cephalic collar.
          N. limai Travassos, 1922
4 (1) More than forty-five spines present on cephalic collar.
5 (6) Forty-seven spines present on cephalic collar; dorsal cavity lacking.
          N. bicolanum Tubangui, 1933
6 (5) Forty-seven to fifty-one cephalic spines present; dorsal cavity present.
          N. ramosum (Sonsino, 1895) (fig. 25)

KEY TO THE SPECIES OF THE GENUS PARYPHOSTOMUM DIETZ, 1909 (XII:466)

K. I. Skrjabin and E. Ya. Bashkirova

1 (14) Twenty-seven cephalic spines present.
2 (5) Testes lobed, rosette-shaped.
3 (4) Testes deeply lobed; corner spines up to 0.16 mm. (Asia, W. Europe, USSR).
          P. radiatum (Dujardin, 1845) (fig. 31)
4 (3) Testes slightly lobed; corner spines up to 0.18 mm. (Germany).   P. carbonis Mendheim, 1940
5 (2) Testes differently shaped.
6 (7) Testes transversely elongate, multi-lobed.

Host: Phalacrocorax africanus (Africa).
P. lobulatum (Odhner, 1911)

7 (6) Testes longitudinally elongate.

8 (11) Testes compact, weakly lobed, triangular in outline.

9 (10) Cuticular armament lacking. Host: Anhinga anhinga (Brazil). P. fragosum (Dietz, 1909)

10 (9) Cuticular armament present. Host: Phalacrocorax melanoleucus (Australia).
P. tenuicollis (Johnston, 1917)

11 (8) Testes deeply lobed.

12 (13) Testes with five to seven lobes. Host: Catharista atrata (Germany).
P. segregatum Dietz, 1909

13 (12) Testes trilobed, cardiform. Hosts: Dendrocygna javanica and others (India, USSR).
P. testitrifolium Gogate, 1934

14 (1) More than twenty-seven cephalic spines present.

15 (16) Thirty-five cephalic spines present; body up to 19 mm. Host: snipe (India).
P. pentalobum Verma, 1936

16 (15) Thirty-seven cephalic spines present; body up to 11 mm. Hosts: Anas platyrhynchos and Anser indicus (India). P. novum Verma, 1936

KEY TO THE SPECIES OF THE GENUS PATAGIFER DIETZ, 1909 (XII:485)

K. I. Skrjabin and E. Ya. Bashkirova

1 (8) Width of cephalic collar less than width of anterior part of body.

2 (3) Vitellaria merging posterior to testes.
P. consimilis Dietz, 1909

3 (2) Vitellaria not merging posterior to testes.

4 (5) Testes entire.
P. parvispinosus Yamaguti, 1933

5 (4) Testes lobed.

6 (7) Three spines present on each angle of ventral lobes; maximal body width at level of ventral sucker.
P. acuminatus Johnston, 1917

7 (6) Five spines present on each angle of ventral lobes; maximal body width at level of testes.
P. skrjabini Hilmy, 1949

8 (1) Width of cephalic collar exceeding width of anterior part of body.

9 (12) Not more than sixty-two cephalic spines present.

10 (11) Fifty-two to sixty-two cephalic spines present; length of corner spines: 0.081-0.143 mm., lateral spines: 0.074-0.165 mm.
P. bilobus (Rudolphi, 1819) (fig. 26)

11 (10) Sixty to sixty-two cephalic spines present; length of corner spines 0.156 mm.; lateral 0.24-0.27 mm. P. wesley Verma, 1936

12 (9) Sixty-four cephalic spines present.
P. fraternus Johnston, 1917

KEY TO THE SPECIES OF THE SUBGENUS PETASIGER (DIETZ, 1909) (XII:504)

K. I. Skrjabin and E. Ya. Bashkirova

1 (12) Cephalic spines forming double row.

2 (7) Twenty-seven cephalic spines present.

3 (4) Vitellaria originating at level of anterior edge of ventral sucker. P. exaeretus Dietz, 1909 (fig. 30)

4 (3) Vitellaria originating at different level.

5 (6) Vitellaria originating posterior to middle of ventral sucker. P. hospitale (Mendheim, 1940)

6 (5) Vitellaria originating posterior to ventral sucker. P. phalacrocoracis (Yamaguti, 1939)

7 (2) Number of cephalic spines different.

8 (9) Twenty-four cephalic spines present.
P. coronatus Mendheim, 1940

9 (8) Nineteen to twenty-one cephalic spines present.

10 (11) Nineteen cephalic spines present; vitellaria originating near level of anterior edge of ventral sucker, merging both anterior and posterior to testes.
P. pungens (Linstow, 1894)

11 (10) Nineteen to twenty-one cephalic spines present; vitellaria originating anterior to ventral sucker, merging posterior to testes only.
P. brevicauda (Ishii, 1935)

12 (1) Cephalic spines forming single row.

13 (14) Twenty-five cephalic spines present.
P. aeratus Oschmarin, 1947

14 (13) Nineteen cephalic spines present.

15 (16) Vietllaria originating near intestinal bifurcation; maximal body width at level of ventral sucker.
P. megacanthum (Kotlan, 1922)

16 (15) Vitellaria originating at level of anterior edge of ventral sucker; maximal body width in zone of testes. P. lobatus Yamaguti, 1933

KEY TO THE SPECIES OF THE SUBGENUS NEOPETASIGER BASCHKIROVA, 1941 (XII:523)

K. I. Skrjabin and E. Ya. Bashkirova

1 (14) Cephalic spines forming single row.

2 (11) Testes oblique.

3 (4) Twenty-one cephalic spines present.
N. spasskyi Oschmarin, 1947

4 (5) Number of cephalic spines different.

5 (10) Nineteen cephalic spines present.

6 (7) Vitellaria merging anterior to ventral sucker.
N. grandivesicularis Ishii, 1935

7 (6) Vitellaria not merging anterior to ventral sucker.

8 (9) Cirrus sac anterior to ventral sucker.
N. nitidus Linton, 1928

9 (8) Cirrus sac sinistral to ventral sucker.
N. longicirratus Ku, 1938

10 (5) Twenty-three cephalic spines present.
N. minutissimus Gogate, 1934

11 (2) Testes symmetrical.

12 (13) Scales present along surface of anterior part of body; vitellaria not merging posterior to testes. N. neocomense Fuhrmann, 1927

13 (12) Scales along surface of anterior part of

body lacking; vitellaria merging posterior to
testes.   N. skrjabini Baschkirova, 1941
    14 (1) Cephalic spines forming double row; twenty-
seven spines present.
    15 (16) Cuticular spines present.
                        N. variospinosus (Odhner, 1911)
    16 (15) Cuticular spines lacking.
                        N. jubilarum Elperin, 1937
Note: P. novemedicum Lutz, 1928; P. wernicki Pont,
    1926; and P. magniovatum Stossich, 1898
    omitted from key.

KEY TO THE GENERA OF THE SUBFAMILY ALLECHINOSTOMATINAE SUDARIKOV, 1950 (XII:551)

K. I. Skrjabin and E. Ya. Bashkirova

    1 (2) Male genital pore opening on tip of genital
papilla; papilla protruding from bottom of genital
sinus.   Allechinostomum Odhner, 1911. (fig. 44)
    2 (1) Genital papilla lacking.
    3 (4) Ventral and dorsal sides of oral sucker armed
with spines.   Stephanoprora Odhner, 1902 (fig. 484)
    4 (3) Oral sucker not armed with spines.
        Sobolevistoma Sudarikov, 1950 (fig. 485)

KEY TO THE SPECIES OF THE GENUS ALLECHINOSTOMUM ODHNER, 1911 from Yeh (1954) (XII:552)

    1 (2) Cephalic crown with twenty spines; testes
deeply lobed, in anterior half of body.
                        A. renale Yeh, 1954
    2 (1) Cephalic crown with more than twenty spines;
testes smooth or slightly lobed, in posterior half of
body.
    3 (4) Cephalic crown with twenty-two spines; testes
slightly lobed.
        A. jacaretinga (Freitas and Lent, 1938)
    4 (3) Cephalic crown with twenty-four spines;
testes smooth.
    5 (6) Uterus with few loops.
        A. crocodili (Poirier, 1886) (fig. 44)
    6 (5) Uterus with many loops.
        A. famelicum Odhner, 1911
Note: Cephalic "crown" of Yeh = "pro-adoral disc"
    of Sudarikov.

KEY TO THE SPECIES OF THE GENUS CHAUNOCEPHALUS DIETZ, 1909 (XII:570)

K. I. Skrjabin and E. Ya. Bashkirova

    1 (4) Uroproct present.
    2 (3) Adoral disc with twenty-three to twenty-six
spines.   C. panduriformis Travassos, 1922
    3 (2) Adoral disc with twenty-seven spines.
        C. similiferox Verma, 1936
    4 (1) Uroproct absent.
    5 (6) Adoral disc with twenty-nine spines.
        C. schulzi Gnedina, 1941

    6 (5) Adoral disc with twenty-seven spines.
    7 (8) Corner spines 0.160-0.185 mm. long; periph-
eral spines 0.112-0.125 mm. long.
        C. ferox (Rudolphi, 1795) (fig. 49)
    8 (7) Corner spines 0.21-0.24 mm. long; peripheral
spines 0.130-0.135 mm. long.
        C. gerardi Gedoelst, 1913

KEY TO THE GENERA OF THE SUBFAMILY ECHINOCHASMINAE ODHNER, 1911 (XII:589)

K. I. Skrjabin and E. Ya. Bashkirova

    1 (2) Loops of uterus posterior to testes.
Saakotrema Skrjabin and Baschkirova, 1956 (fig. 486)
    2 (1) Loops of uterus anterior to testes.
    3 (4) Anterior border of vitellaria reaching only to
level of testes.   Mesorchis Dietz, 1909
    4 (3) Anterior border of vitellaria reaching level of
ventral sucker or pharynx.
    5 (6) Cephalic collar without fused ventral edge;
testes large, transversely elongate; anterior border
of vitellaria variable.
        Echinochasmus Dietz, 1909 (fig. 47)
    6 (5) Cephalic collar with fused ventral edge; testes
small, round; vitellaria reaching level of ventral
sucker.   Velamenophorus Mendheim, 1940 (fig. 487)

KEY TO THE SUBGENERA OF THE GENUS ECHINOCHASMUS DIETZ, 1909 (XII:596)

K. I. Skrjabin and E. Ya. Bashkirova

    1 (4) Vitellaria well-developed, merging anterior to
intestinal bifurcation.
    2 (3) Vitellaria originating at level of pharynx and
extending to posterior end of body. Parasites of
fabrician bursa (more rarely, intestines) of birds.
        Episthmium (Lühe, 1909)
    3 (2) Vitellaria originating at level of intestinal bi-
furcation. Intestinal parasites of mammals.
        Episthochasmus (Verma, 1935)
    4 (1) Vitellaria not merging anterior to intestinal
bifurcation.
    5 (6) Vitellaria originating at level of ventral
sucker, extending to posterior end of body. Intestinal
parasites of birds and mammals.
        Echinochasmus (Dietz, 1909) (fig. 47)
    6 (5) Vitellaria originating at level of testes, ex-
tending to posterior end of body. Intestinal parasites
of birds.   Monilifer (Dietz, 1909)

KEY TO THE SPECIES OF THE SUBGENUS EPISTHMIUM (LÜHE, 1909) (XII:669-670)

K. I. Skrjabin and E. Ya. Bashkirova

    1 (10) Parasites in fabrician bursa.
    2 (7) Cephalic collar well-developed, with rela-
tively large cephalic spines.
    3 (6) Twenty-four cephalic spines present.

4 (5) Cuticular spines covering entire body; testes slightly lobed; eggs 0.064-0.073 mm. long.
E. (E.) intermedium Skrjabin, 1919

5 (4) Cuticular spines covering only anterior half of body; testes entire; eggs 0.11-0.123 mm. long.
E. (E.) africanum (Stiles, 1901)

6 (3) Twenty to twenty-two cephalic spines present; cuticular spines covering entire body.
E. (E.) bursicola (Creplin, 1837)

7 (2) Cephalic collar weakly developed, with very small cephalic spines.

8 (9) Diameter of ventral sucker 0.34 mm., testes 0.5 mm. in diameter. Host: hen.
E. (E.) oscari Travassos, 1922

9 (8) Diameter of ventral sucker 0.64 mm.; testes 1.4 mm. in diameter. Hosts: Ardea cocoi, Euxenura maguari.   E. (E.) proximus (Travassos, 1922)

10 (1) Intestinal parasites.

11 (16) Twenty-four cephalic spines present.

12 (13) Cuticular armament covering entire body; testes large, of irregular shape, 0.64 mm. in diameter.   E. (E.) prostovitellatus Nicoll, 1914

13 (12) Cuticular armament extending only to level of testes; testes small, not exceeding 0.30 mm. in diameter.

14 (15) Ovary reniform, dextral. Parasites of Corvus splendens.   E. (E.) reniovarus Lal, 1939

15 (14) Ovary round, medial; anterior edge of ovary covered by posterior edge of ventral sucker. Parasites of Colymbus cristatus.
E. (E.) colymbi Schigin, 1956

16 (11) Twenty-two cephalic spines present; cuticular armament lacking; testes oblique, reaching 0.10 mm. in diameter.
E. (E.) skrjabini Oschmarin, 1947
Note: E. suspensus (Braun, 1901) omitted from key.

KEY TO THE SPECIES OF THE SUBGENUS EPISTHOCHASMUS VERMA, 1935 (XII:695)

K. I. Skrjabin and E. Ya. Bashkirova

1 (3) Parasites of mammals.

2 (4) Cephalic spines nearly equal in size; ventral and lateral spines in double alternating row; cirrus sac extending to middle of ventral sucker. Host: dog (India).   E. (E.) caninum Verma, 1935

3 (1) Parasites of birds.

4 (2) Cephalic spines unequal in size; three-corner ventral spines present on each lobe; cirrus sac reaching posterior edge of ventral sucker. Host: Corvus insolens (India).
E. (E.) corvus Bhalerao, 1926

KEY TO THE GENERA OF THE SUBFAMILY HIMASTHLINAE ODHNER, 1911 (XII:745)

K. I. Skrjabin and E. Ya. Bashkirova

1 (12) Eggs without filaments.
2 (7) Cephalic spines forming single row.

3 (4) Corner spines present, grouped; uterus with numerous eggs.   Himasthla Dietz, 1909 (fig. 37)

4 (3) Grouped ventral corner spines lacking; uterus with few eggs.

5 (6) Testes lobed; vitellaria extending anteriorly to level of testes.   Cleophora Dietz, 1909 (fig. 38)

6 (5) Testes entire; vitellaria extending to level of cirrus sac, occasionally only to level of testes.
Acanthoparyphium Dietz, 1909 (fig. 39)

7 (2) Cephalic spines in double row.

8 (11) Testes lobed or branched.

9 (10) Testes lobed; vitellaria anteriorly reaching cirrus sac. Artyfechinostomum Lane, 1915 (fig. 40)

10 (9) Testes branched; vitellaria anteriorly reaching ventral sucker.
Reptiliotrema Baschkirova, 1941 (fig. 41)

11 (8) Testes round; vitellaria anteriorly not extending beyond level of testes.
Pelmatostomum Dietz, 1909 (fig. 42)

12 (1) Eggs with filaments; vitellaria anteriorly reaching level of testes.
Aporchis Stossich, 1905 (fig. 43)

KEY TO THE SPECIES OF THE GENUS HIMASTHLA DIETZ, 1909 (XII:746)

K. I. Skrjabin and E. Ya. Bashkirova

1 (4) Not more than twenty-seven cephalic spines present.

2 (3) Twenty-seven cephalic spines present; anterior border of vitellaria reaching middle of cirrus sac.   H. incisa Linton, 1928

3 (2) Twenty-four cephalic spines present; anterior border of vitellaria at middle of body, not reaching posterior limit of cirrus sac.
H. harrisoni Johnston, 1914

4 (1) Number of cephalic spines different.

5 (20) Not more than thirty-one cephalic spines present.

6 (15) Twenty-nine cephalic spines present.

7 (8) Anterior border of vitellaria reaching level of posterior edge of ventral sucker.
H. multilecithosa Mendheim, 1940

8 (7) Anterior border of vitellaria not reaching ventral sucker.

9 (12) Vitellaria reaching posterior limit of cirrus sac.

10 (11) Two spines on each corner lobe of cephalic collar; testes large, oblong; eggs small.
H. militaris (Rudolphi, 1802)

11 (10) Four spines on each corner lobe of cephalic collar; testes small, oval; eggs large.
H. elongata (Mehlis, 1831)

12 (9) Vitellaria not extending to posterior limit of cirrus sac.

13 (14) Vitellaria originating slightly posterior to cirrus sac; ventral sucker large.
H. megacotyla Yamaguti, 1939

14 (13) Vitellaria originating at considerable distance posterior to cirrus sac; ventral sucker small.
H. leptosoma (Creplin, 1829)

15 (6) Thirty-one cephalic spines present.
16 (17) Testes lobed.
      H. quissentensis Miller and Northup, 1926
17 (16) Testes entire.
18 (19) Vitellaria originating at level of posterior
half of cirrus sac.   H. kusasigi Yamaguti, 1939
19 (18) Vitellaria originating at considerable distance posterior to cirrus sac. H. alincia Dietz, 1909
20 (5) More than thirty-one cephalic spines present.
21 (22) Thirty-two cephalic spines present; vitellaria originating at level of posterior limit of cirrus
sac. Parasites of man.   H. muhlensi Vogel, 1939
22 (21) Thirty-four to thirty-eight cephalic spines
present; vitellaria originating in posterior half of
body. Parasites of birds.
      H. rhigedana Dietz, 1909 (fig. 37)
Note: H. secunda Nicoll, 1906; H. ambigua Palombi,
    1934; and H. tensa Linton, 1940 omitted from
    key.

KEY TO THE SPECIES OF THE GENUS ACANTHOPARYPHIUM DIETZ, 1909 (XII:777)

K. I. Skrjabin and E. Ya. Bashkirova

1 (4) Vitellaria anteriorly extending to level of
posterior border of ventral sucker.
2 (3) Testes lobed. A. ochthodromi Tubangui, 1933
3 (2) Testes entire. A. melanittae Yamaguti, 1939
4 (1) Vitellaria extending to different level.
5 (10) Anterior border of vitellaria reaching level
of testes.
6 (7) Vitellaria reaching anterior level of testes.
      A. charadrii Yamaguti, 1939
7 (6) Vitellaria not reaching anterior level of
testes.
8 (9) Vitellaria extending anteriorly to posterior
level of anterior testis; loops of uterus extending
extra-cecally.   A. squatarole Yamaguti, 1934
9 (8) Vitellaria not extending to level of anterior
testis; loops of uterus restricted to intercecal area.
      A. marilae Yamaguti, 1934
10 (5) Vitellaria extending anteriorly beyond level
of testes, not reaching ventral sucker.
11 (12) Testes equatorial.
      A. spinulosum Johnston, 1917
12 (11) Testes in posterior portion of body.
13 (14) Ventral sucker at boundary of anterior and
middle thirds of body; sucker diameter 0.35 mm.
      A. kurogamo Yamaguti, 1939
14 (13) Ventral sucker equatorial, 0.24 mm. in diameter.   A. phoenicopteri (Lühe, 1898) (fig. 39)

KEY TO THE GENERA OF THE SUBFAMILY HYPODERAEINAE SKRJABIN AND BASCHKIROVA, 1956 (XII:823)

K. I. Skrjabin and E. Ya. Bashkirova

1 (2) Adoral disc transversely elongate; cirrus sac
small, anterior to ventral sucker.

Multispinotrema Skrjabin and Baschkirova, 1956
                 (fig. 488)
2 (1) Adoral disc weakly developed.
3 (4) Cirrus sac extending posteriorly beyond posterior edge of ventral sucker.
      Hypoderaeum Dietz, 1909 (fig. 35)
4 (3) Cirrus sac extending to middle of ventral
sucker. Skrjabinophora Baschkirova, 1941 (fig. 28)

KEY TO THE SPECIES OF THE GENUS HYPODERAEUM DIETZ, 1909 (XII:824)

K. I. Skrjabin and E. Ya. Bashkirova

1 (6) Not more than fifty-five cephalic spines present.
2 (5) Not less than forty-seven cephalic spines
present.
3 (4) Forty-nine cephalic spines present; vitellaria
merging posterior to testes; dimensions of suckers
in ratio of 1:5.   H. gnedini Baschkirova, 1941
4 (3) Forty-seven to fifty-three cephalic spines
present; vitellaria not merging posterior to testes;
dimensions of suckers in ratio of 1:4.
      H. conoideum (Bloch, 1782) (fig. 35)
5 (2) Forty-three cephalic spines present; vitellaria merging posterior to testes.
      H. vigi Baschkirova, 1941
6 (1) Seventy-two cephalic spines present; vitellaria merging posterior to testes.
      H. batanguensis (Tubangui, 1932)
Note: H. mainpuria Verma, 1926 omitted from key.

LITERATURE ON THE TREMATODES OF THE FAMILY ECHINOSTOMATIDAE DIETZ, 1909 (XII:917-919)

Bashkirova, E. Ya. 1939. Echinostomatids of
birds of the U.S.S.R. Dissertatsiya.
Bashkirova, E. Ya. 1941. Echinostomatids of
birds of the U.S.S.R. and a review of their life cycles.
Trudy Bashkirskoy Nauchno-Issledovatelskoy Veterinarnoy Stantsii. 3:243-300.
Bashkirova, E. Ya. 1946. Two new echinostomatids
from birds of Azerbaydzhan. Sbornik Rabot po Gelmintologii, Posvyaschenny Akademiku K. I. Skrjabinu.
pp. 42-46.
Belopolskaya, M. M. 1952. The parasite fauna of
marine water-fowl. Uchenye Zapiski Leningradskogo
Gosudarstvennogo Universiteta, No. 141, seriya biologicheskikh nauk. No. 28:127-180.
Belopolskaya, M. M. 1953. On the helminth fauna
of sandpipers of the U.S.S.R. Raboty po Gelmintologii k. 75-letiyu Akademika K. I. Skrjabina. pp. 47-
65.
Belopolskaya, M. M. 1954. The parasite fauna of
birds of the Sudzukhinsky Preserve (Primorye).
Uchenye Zapiski Leningradskogo Gosudarstvennogo
Universiteta, (172), seriya biologicheskikh nauk. No.
35:3-34.
Belous, E. V. 1953. Parasitic worms of

fresh-water vertebrates of the Primorye region.
Avtoreferat dissertatsii.

Burdelev, T. E. 1937. A new species of trematode,
Echinoparyphium syrdariense, from domestic hen.
Sbornik Rabot po Gelmintologii, Posvyaschenny 30-
let. Deyatel. Akademika K. I. Skrjabina. pp. 63-65.

Bykhovskaya-Pavlovskaya, I. E. 1953. The trematode fauna of birds of western Siberia and its dynamics. Parazitologichesky Sbornik Zoologicheskogo
Instituta Akad. Nauk SSSR. 15:5-116.

Bykhovskaya-Pavlovskaya, I. E. 1955. Trematodes of birds of the fauna of the U.S.S.R. Avtoreferat dissertatsii, Leningrad.

Gagarin, V. G. 1954. Materials on the helminth
fauna of game birds of the order Galliformes in the
territory of the Kirgiz S.S.R. Trudy Instituta Zoologii
i Parazitologii Kirgizskogo Filiala Akad. Nauk SSSR.
No. 2:83-113.

Ginetsinskaya, T. A. 1952. Interchange of parasitic worms in birds of the Volga delta. Uchenye
Zapiski Leningradskogo Gosudarstvennogo Universiteta, seriya biologicheskikh nauk. No. 28:181-187.

Ginetsinskaya, T. A. 1953. The helminth fauna of
migratory sandpipers of the Volga delta. Raboty po
Gelmintologii k 75-letiyu Akademika K. I. Skrjabina.
pp. 147-156.

Ginetsinskaya, T. A. and T. N. Kulik. 1952. De-
ciphering of the life cycle of the trematode, Patagifer
bilobus (Rud., 1819). Doklady Akad. Nauk SSSR.
85(5):1189-1191.

Ginetsinskaya, T. A. and D. V. Naumov. 1955. A
new representative of the rare genus of trematodes,
Cloephora Dietz (Trematoda: Echinostomatidae)
from a turn-stone. Trudy Zoologicheskogo Instituta
Akad. Nauk SSSR. 18:39-41.

Gnedina, M. P. and L. F. Potekhina. 1950. On the
trematode fauna of birds of the Kirgiz S.S.R. Trudy
Gelmintologicheskoy Laboratorii Akad. Nauk SSSR.
4:75-83.

Gorshkov, I. P. 1937. On the knowledge of the
helminth fauna of domestic geese of the Omsk and
Chelyabinsk districts. Sbornik Rabot po Gelmintologii, Posvyaschenny Akademiku K. I. Skrjabinu. pp.
191-202.

Gubanov, N. M. 1954. The helminth fauna of commercial animals of the Sea of Okhotsk and the Pacific
Ocean. Avtoreferat dissertatsii. Trudy Gelminthologicheskoy Laboratorii Akad. Nauk SSSR. 7:380-
381.

Gusev, A. V. 1951. On the parasite fauna of the
Ussurysky raccoon (Nyctereutes procyonoides Gray,
1834). Parazitologichesky Sbornik Zoologicheskogo
Instituta Akad. Nauk SSSR. 13:96-104.

Dotsenko, T. K. 1954. Parasitic worms of poultry
of the Primorye region, and the biology of Cheilospirura hamulosa. Avtoreferat dissertatsii. Trudy
Gelmintologicheskoy Laboratorii Akad. Nauk SSSR.
7:382-383.

Dubinin, V. E. 1938. Variations in the parasite
fauna of the glossy ibis (Plegadis falcinellus) brought
about with age and migration of the host. Trudy
Astrakhanskogo Gosudarstvennogo Zapovednika. No.
2:108-212.

Dubinin, V. B. 1952. The fauna of larvae of parasitic worms of vertebrate animals of the Volga River
delta. Parazitologichesky Sbornik Zoologicheskogo
Instituta Akad. Nauk SSSR. 14:213-265.

Dubinin, V. B. and M. N. Dubinina. 1940. The
parasite fauna of colonial birds of the Astrakhan
Preserve. Trudy Astrakhanskogo Gosudarstvennogo
Zapovednika. No. 3:190-298.

Dubinina, M. N. 1948. The parasite fauna of the
wild gray-lag goose (Anser anser). Parazitologichesky Sbornik Zoologicheskogo Instituta Akad. Nauk
SSSR. 10:165-188.

Zèlikman, E. A. 1954. Some littoral forms of the
northern part of Kandalakshsky Zaliv. Avtoreferat
dissertatsii.

Ivanitsky, S. V. 1927. On the trematode fauna of
vertebrates of the Ukraine. Veterinarnoye Delo. No.
2(51):30-48.

Isaychikov, I. M. 1924. A new representative of
avian trematodes of the genus Echinoparyphium
Dietz, 1909. Uchenye Zapiski Sibirskogo Veterinarnogo Instituta, Omsk. 6:5-17.

Isaychikov, I. M. 1927. A new trematode of the
genus Echinochasmus Dietz from the intestine of
birds. Sbornik Rabot po Gelmintologii, Posvyaschenny
Prof. K. I. Skrjabinu. pp. 78-83.

Kalantaryan, E. V. 1926. On the knowledge of the
trematodes of birds in the vicinity of the city of Erevan. Trudy Tropicheskogo Instituta Armenii. 1:74-
75.

Kopyrin, A. V. 1946. The helminth fauna of domestic geese of the southern region of the Omsk district. Sbornik Rabot po Gelmintologii, Posvyaschenny
Akademiku K. I. Skrjabinu. pp. 146-148.

Kulachkova, V. G. 1950. The parasite fauna of
gulls and terns of the Danube delta. Uchenye Leningradskogo Gosudarstvennogo Universiteta, 133,
seriya biologicheskikh nauk. No. 23:123-128.

Kurashvili, B. E. 1949. Two new helminths from
birds of Georgia, Pegosomum petrowi sp. nov. and
Ascaridia ketzkhovelii sp. nov. Sooscheniye Akad.
Nauk Gruz. SSR. 10(7):435-441.

Kurashvili, B. E. 1953. The helminth fauna of
game birds of Georgia. Raboty po Gelmintologii k
75-letiyu Akademiku K. I. Skrjabina. pp. 340-346.

Kurova, O. A. 1926. On the knowledge of the
trematodes of the family Echinostomatidae from
birds of Turkestan. Ezhegodnik Zoologicheskogo
Muzeya Akad. Nauk SSSR. 27(2-3):113.

Markevich, A. P. 1951. The parasite fauna of
fresh-water fishes of the Ukrainian S.S.R. Izdatelstvo
Akad. Nauk Ukr. SSR, Kiev. 376 pp.

Matevosyan, E. M. 1938. The helminth fauna of
wild birds of Bashkiria. Trudy Bashkirskoy Gelmintologicheskoy Expeditsii. pp. 372-391.

Miram, K. E. 1840. Concerning some new, not
yet described, intestinal worms. Byull. Imperatorskogo Obschestva Estestvoispytateley v Moskve. No.
11:139-163. (In German).

Nevostrueva, L. S. 1953. The life cycle of a new echinostomatid, Echinoparyphium petrowi nov. sp., from poultry. Raboty po Gelmintologii k 75-letiyu Akademiku K. I. Skrjabina. pp. 436-439.

Nevostrueva, L. S. 1953. On the study of the life cycle of Echinostoma miyagawai (Ishii, 1932), the agent of echinostomiasis of poultry. Doklady Akad. Nauk SSSR. 90(2):317-318.

Nevostrueva, L. S. 1954. Study on life cycles of the agents of echinostomiases in poultry. Avtoreferat dissertatsii.

Ovcharenko, D. A. 1955. Eurycephalus dogieli gen. nov., sp. nov., a new trematode from bittern. Doklady Akad. Nauk SSSR. 104(1):157-159.

Oshmarin, P. G. 1946. Parasitic worms of commercial animals of the Buryat-Mongolian A.S.S.R. Avtoreferat dissertatsii.

Oshmarin, P. G. 1952. Parasitic worms of mammals and birds of the Primorye region, and an attempt to characterize the helminthogeography of the region. Avtoreferat dissertatsii.

Oshmarin, P. G. 1950. On the helminth fauna of birds of the Far East (Kamchatka, Zemlya Koryakov, Kurile Islands, etc.). Trudy Gelmintologicheskoy Laboratorii Akad. Nauk SSSR. 3:166-179.

Oshmarin, P. G. and E. V. Belous. 1951. On the significance of location as a character of helminths in the construction of their systematics, based on an example of a new echinostomatid from the kidney of eagle. Doklady Akad. Nauk SSSR. 77(1):165-168.

Pavlovsky, E. N. 1946. Manual on the parasitology of man. Izdatelstvo Akad. Nauk SSSR, Moskva-Leningrad. 521 pp.

Palimpsestov, M. A. 1937. On the characteristics of the helminth fauna of domestic animals of the Mordovian Autotomy, the Kuybyshev and Orenburg districts. Sbornik Rabot po Gelmintologii, Posvyaschenny Prof. K. I. Skrjabinu. pp. 454-458.

Panova, L. G. 1927. Helminthology in Kazakhstan. Sbornik Rabot po Gelmintologii, Posvyaschenny Prof. K. I. Skrjabinu. pp. 121-137.

Petrov, A. M. 1926. On the fauna of parasitic worms of domestic and wild geese of the Don district. Trudy Gosudarstvennogo Instituta Experimentalnoy Veterinarii. 3(1):99-113.

Petrov, A. M. 1953. An epidemic and subsequent decimation by helminths of silver foxes. Raboty po Gelmintologii k 75-letiyu Akademika K. I. Skrjabina. pp. 489-506.

Prendel, A. R. 1937. Summary on the helminth fauna of cats of Odessa. Raboty po Gemintologii, Posvyaschenny Akademiku K. I. Skrjabinu. pp. 542-546.

Pukhov, V. I. 1939. On the fauna of parasitic worms of the coot (Fulica atra). Trudy Rostovskoy Oblastnoy Veterinarnoy Opytnoy Stantsii. No. 6:120-128.

Romanovich, M. I. 1915. Echinochasmus perfoliatus, a rare trematode from the intestine of a Petrograd dog. Vestnik Obschennoy Veterinarii. 27(12):458-461.

Saakova, E. O. 1952. The fauna of parasitic worms of birds of the Danube delta. Avtoreferat dissertatsii, Leningrad.

Semenov, V. D. 1927. Trematodes of birds of the western U.S.S.R. Sbornik Rabot po Gelmintologii, Posvyaschenny Akademiku K. I. Skrjabinu. pp. 221-271.

Skvortsov, A. A. 1934. On the study of the helminth fauna of the water rat, Arvicola terrestris L. Vestnik Mikrobiologii, Epidemiologii, i Parazitologii, Saratov. 13(4):317-326.

Skrjabin, K. I. 1913. Trematodes of birds from Russian Turkestan, Zool. Jahrb. Abt. Syst. 35(3):336-388. (In German).

Skrjabin, K. I. 1915. Trematodes of birds of the Urals. Ezhegodnik Zoologicheskogo Muzeya Akad. Nauk SSSR. 20(3):395-417.

Skrjabin, K. I. 1916. On the knowledge of the helminth fauna of domestic animals of Turkestan. Dissertatsiya, Yuriev.

Skrjabin, K. I. 1920. Helminthological notes. On the knowledge of the helminth fauna of Russia. Izvestiya Donskogo Veterinarnogo Instituta. 2(2):1-7.

Skrjabin, K. I. 1923. Trematodes of poultry. Trudy Gosudarstvennogo Instituta Experimentalnoy Veterinarii. 1(2):193-256.

Skrjabin, K. I. 1924. Works on the study of the parasitic worms of birds of Russia. Trudy Gosudarstvennogo Instituta Experimentalnoy Veterinarii. 2(1):149-157.

Skrjabin, K. I. 1932. Helminth infestations of pigeons. Selkhozgiz, Moskva-Leningrad. 124 pp.

Skrjabin, K. I. 1938. Echinostoma paraulum, a new parasite of man. Meditsinskaya Parazitologiya i Parazitarnye Bolezni. 7(1):129-138.

Skrjabin, K. I. 1944. Analysis of the generic components of three trematode families: Opisthorchidae, Dicrocoeliidae, and Echinostomatidae. Doklady Akad. Nauk SSSR. 44(7):328-330.

Skrjabin, K. I. 1947. Trematodes of animals and man. Izdatelstvo Akad. Nauk, Moskva-Leningrad. Vol. I, 515 pp.

Skrjabin, K. I. and G. T. Lindtrop. 1919. Intestinal trematodes of dogs of the Don district. Izvestiya Donskogo Veterinarnogo Instituta. 1(1):30-43.

Skrjabin, K. I., A. M. Petrov, and E. Ya. Bashkirova. 1947. Echinostomatids of domestic and game birds of the U.S.S.R. In: Skrjabin, K. I., Trematodes of animals and man. Izdatelstvo Akad. Nauk SSSR, Moskva-Leningrad. 1:392-488.

Smogorzhevskaya, L. A. 1956. Trematodes of piscivorous birds of the Dnieper River valley. Parazitologichesky Sbornik Zoologicheskogo Instituta Akad. Nauk SSSR. No. 16:244-263.

Soloviev, P. F. 1912. Parasitic worms of the birds of Turkestan. Ezhegodnik Zoologicheskogo Muzeya Imperatorskoy Akad. Nauk. 17(2):86-115.

Spassky, A. A., N. P. Romanova, and N. V. Naydenova. 1951. On the fauna of parasitic worms of the muskrat (Ondatra zibethica L.). Trudy Gelmintologicheskoy Laboratorii Akad. Nuak SSSR. 5:42-52.

Statirova, N. A. 1946. On the helminth fauna of the glossy ibis in Kazakhstan. Sbornik Rabot po Gelmintologii, Posvyaschenny Akademiku K. I. Skrjabinu. pp. 262-263.

Sudarikov, V. E. 1950. On the trematode fauna of vertebrates of the central Povolzhie district. Trudy Gelmintologicheskoy Laboratorii Akad. Nauk SSSR. 3:131-141.

Fedyushin, A. V. 1937. The helminth fauna of geese and ducks of western Sibiria, with reference to the problem of utilizing natural bodies of water for purposes of poultry production. Sbornik Rabot po Gelmintologii, Posvaschenny Akademiku K. I. Skrjabinu. pp. 167-177.

Chiaberashavili, E. A. 1954. Preliminary information on the study of the life cycles of several echinostomatids of birds. Soobscheniye Akad. Nauk Gruz. SSR. 15(5):287-293.

Shakhtakhtinskaya, Z. M. 1953. The helminth fauna of domestic and game water-fowl of the Azerbaydzhan S.S.R. Avtoreferat dissertatsii, Baku.

Shevchenko, N. N. 1954. On a new representative of the subfamily Nephroechinostomatinae Oshmarin and Belous, 1951, discovered in the Kharkov district. Trudy Nauchno-Issledovatelskogo Instituta Biologii Kharkovskogo Gosudarstvennogo Universiteta. 19: 119-121.

Shigin, A. A. 1955. The helminths of piscivorous birds of the Rybinskoye reservoir. Avtoreferat dissertatsii, Moskva.

Scherbovich, I. A. 1946. Trematodes of birds of the Far East. Sbornik Rabot po Gelmintologii, Posvyaschenny Akademiku K. I. Skrjabinu. pp. 296-300.

Schupakov, I. 1936. The parasite fauna of the Caspian seal. Uchenye Zapiski Leningradskogo Gosudarstvennogo Universiteta, No. 7, seriya biologicheskikh nauk. No. 3:134-143.

Elperina, M. A. 1937. A new species of trematode from Falco tinnunculus, Echinoparyphium jubilarum. Rukopis, Biblioteka, VIGIS, Moskva.

LIST OF SUPPLEMENTARY ILLUSTRATIONS

Echinostomatidae Dietz, 1909
    Eurycephalus dogieli Ovtscharenko, 1955 (fig. 882)
    Nephroechinostoma aquilae Oschmarin and Belouss, 1951 (fig. 883)

PART XIII

KEY TO THE FAMILIES OF THE SUPERFAMILY ZOOGONOIDEA SKRJABIN, 1957 (XIII:10)

K. I. Skrjabin

1 (2) Vitellaria compact, usually unpaired, closely adjacent to ovary.   Zoogonidae Odhner, 1911
2 (1) Vitellaria composed of longitudinal follicles, always paired, along both sides of body.
                    Steganodermatidae Dollfus, 1952

KEY TO THE GENERA OF THE SUBFAMILY ZOOGONINAE ODHNER, 1902 from Skrjabin (1957) (XIII:12)

1 (2) Oral sucker sharply delimited from body by deep groove; prepharynx present; intestinal ceca broad, extending to posterior end of body; testes posterior to ventral sucker; two accessory seminal receptacles present near metraterm.
                    Neozoogonus Arai, 1954 (fig. 489)
2 (1) Oral sucker not separated from body by deep groove; two accessory seminal receptacles lacking.
3 (6) Intestinal ceca short, not extending beyond level of ventral sucker; prepharynx lacking.
4 (5) Testes lateral to ventral sucker, at level of sucker; ovary posterior to testes.
                    Zoonogenus Nicoll, 1912 (fig. 490)
5 (4) Testes posterior to ventral sucker; ovary anterior to testes.
                    Diphterostomum Stossich, 1904 (fig. 491)
6 (3) Intestinal ceca passing beyond level of posterior edge of ventral sucker; prepharynx present or absent.
7 (8) Prepharynx very long; testes posterior to ventral sucker.   Zoogonus Looss, 1901 (fig. 492)
8 (7) Prepharynx very short or absent; testes at level of and lateral to ventral sucker.
                    Zoogonoides Odhner, 1902 (fig. 493)

LITERATURE ON THE TREMATODES OF THE FAMILY ZOOGONIDAE ODHNER, 1911 (XIII:61)

Vlasenko, P. V. 1931. On the fauna of parasitic worms of fishes of the Black Sea. Trudy Karadagskoy Biologicheskoy Stantsii, Simferopol. No. 4:88-136.

Isaychikov, I. M. 1926. On the knowledge of the parasitic worms of cyprinid fishes of the Kuban River. Trudy Gosudarstvennogo Instituta Experimentalnoy Veterinarii. 2(2):159-170.

Isaychikov, I. M. 1928. On the knowledge of the parasitic worms of several groups of vertebrates of the Russian Arctic, A. Trematodes. Trudy Morskogo Nauchnogo Instituta. 3(2):5-79.

Polyansky, Yu. I. 1955. Materials on the parasite fauna of fishes of the northern seas of the U.S.S.R. Parasites of fishes of the Barents Sea. Trudy Zoologicheskogo Instituta Akad. Nauk SSSR. 19:1-170.

Shulman, S. S. and R. E. Shulman-Albova. 1953. Parasites of fishes of the White Sea. Izdatelstvo Akad. Nauk SSSR, Moskva-Leningrad. 198 pp.

Shulman-Albova, R. E. 1952. Parasites of fishes of the White Sea in the vicinity of the village of Gridino, I. Monogenetic and digenetic trematodes. Uchenye Zapiski Karelo-Finskogo Gosudarstvennogo Universiteta. 4(3):78-97.

KEY TO THE GENERA OF THE FAMILY STEGANODERMATIDAE DOLLFUS, 1952 from Skrjabin (1957) (XIII:64-65)

1 (2) Intestinal ceca very short, not passing beyond level of ventral sucker; vitellaria grouped in anterior portion of body, not passing beyond level of ventral sucker; seminal vesicle bipartite; metraterm with sphincter.   Brachyenteron Manter, 1934 (fig. 494)

2 (1) Intestinal ceca extending beyond level of ventral sucker.

3 (8) Intestinal ceca reaching or nearly reaching posterior end of body.

4 (5) Intestinal ceca especially broad, contacting one another posterior to ventral sucker along medial line, extending posteriorly to posterior end of body; cuticle covered with spines; genital pore lateral; testes symmetrical, lateral, extra-cecal; vitellaria lateral, posterior to ventral sucker.
          Urinatrema Yamaguti, 1934 (fig. 495)

5 (4) Intestinal ceca thin, nearly reaching posterior end of body.

6 (7) Cuticle without spines; genital pore medial or slightly sinistral; testes tandem.
          Diplangus Linton, 1910 (fig. 496)

7 (6) Cuticle armed with spines; genital pore lateral; testes symmetrical.
          Manteroderma Skrjabin, 1957 (fig. 497)

8 (3) Intestinal ceca never reaching posterior end of body.

9 (10) Vitellaria concentrated in anterior portion of body, not extending beyond posterior edge of ventral sucker; genital pore in extreme lateral position.
          Deretrema Linton, 1910 (fig. 498)

10 (9) Vitellaria posterior to ventral sucker; genital pore slightly sinistral.

11 (12) Vitellaria rudimentary, consisting of two small stellate clusters, intercecal, near posterior ends of intestinal ceca, considerably posterior to ventral sucker.
          Lepidophyllum Odhner, 1902 (fig. 499)

12 (11) Vitellaria well-developed, consisting of several large follicles, twelve to fourteen on each side of body, originating at level of ventral sucker.
          Steganoderma Stafford, 1904 (fig. 500)

LITERATURE ON THE TREMATODES OF THE FAMILY STEGANODERMATIDAE DOLLFUS, 1952 (XIII:162)

Bazikalova, A. Ya. 1932. Materials on the parasitology of fishes of Murmansk. Sbornik Nauchno-

Promyslovykh Rabot na Murmane. Snabtekhizdat, Moskva. pp. 136-153.

Isaychikov, I. M. 1928. On the knowledge of the parasitic worms of several groups of vertebrates of the Russian Arctic, A. Trematodes. Trudy Morskogo Nauchnogo Instituta. 3(2):5-79.

Polyansky, Yu. I. 1955. Materials on the parasite fauna of fishes of the northern seas of the U.S.S.R. Parasites of fishes of the Barents Sea. Trudy Zoologicheskogo Instituta Akad. Nauk SSSR. 19:5-170.

Uspenskaya, A. V. 1952. Some information on the life cycle of Nordosttrema messjatzevi Issaitschikov. Doklady Akad. Nauk SSSR. 85(6):1419-1421.

Shulman-Albova, R. E. 1952. On the question of variability in the digenetic trematode of fishes, Podocotyle atomon (Rudolphi) Odhner. Uchenye Zapiski Leningradskogo Gosudarstvennogo Universiteta, No. 141, seriya biologicheskaya. 28:110-126.

KEY TO THE SUBFAMILIES OF THE FAMILY FELLODISTOMATIDAE NICOLL, 1913 (XIII:169)

K. I. Skrjabin and V. P. Koval

1 (10) Testes symmetrical or slightly oblique.

2 (9) Intestinal ceca terminating blindly.

3 (8) Oral and ventral suckers present.

4 (5) Ventral sucker four to five times larger than oral; loops of uterus in one side of body.
          Markevitschiellinae Skrjabin and Koval, 1957

5 (4) Ventral sucker 1.5-2 times larger than oral; loops of uterus in both right and left halves of body.

6 (7) Cuticle smooth.
          Fellodistomatinae Nicoll, 1909

7 (6) Cuticle covered with spines.
          Antorchinae Skrjabin and Koval, 1957

8 (3) With large fixatory disc instead of ventral sucker.   Discogasteroidinae Srivastava, 1939

9 (2) Intestinal ceca uniting in posterior region of body, forming arch.
          Pyriforminae Skrjabin and Koval, 1957

10 (1) Testes tandem or oblique.

11 (12) Testes lobed; latero-ventral out-growth of body present; eggs with polar filaments.
          Lissolomatinae Skrjabin and Koval, 1957

12 (11) Testes entire; without outgrowths from body; eggs without polar filaments.

13 (14) Single intestinal cecum.
          Haplocladinae Odhner, 1911

14 (13) Two intestinal ceca present.

15 (16) Spines present around oral sucker.
          Tergestinae Skrjabin and Koval, 1957

16 (15) Oral sucker unarmed.

17 (18) Cirrus sac with accessory sac; vitellaria tubular.   Ancylocoelinae Skrjabin and Koval, 1957

18 (17) Cirrus sac without sac; vitellaria follicular.
          Proctoecinae Skrjabin and Koval, 1957

KEY TO THE GENERA OF THE SUBFAMILY FELLODISTOMATINAE NICOLL, 1909 (XIII:171)

K. I. Skrjabin and V. P. Koval

1 (22) Eggs without spines.
2 (21) Testes entire; eggs without polar filaments.
3 (6) Genital atrium with diverticulum.
4 (5) Cirrus unarmed; testes posterior to ventral sucker.   Pseudosteringophorus Yamaguti, 1940 (fig. 501)
5 (4) Cirrus armed with spines; testes at level of ventral sucker. Megalomyzon Manter, 1947 (fig. 502)
6 (3) Genital atrium lacking diverticulum.
7 (18) Ventral sucker near midpoint of body.
8 (15) Ovary entire.
9 (10) Vitellaria reaching pharynx anteriorly, extending beyond level of center of ventral sucker posteriorly.   Bacciger Nicoll, 1914 (fig. 503)
10 (9) Posterior border of vitellaria posterior to ventral sucker.
11 (14) Vitellaria in two lateral groups, extending anterior and posterior to ventral sucker; circular fold around oral sucker lacking; esophagus absent.
12 (13) Vitellaria extending slightly anterior and posterior to ventral sucker. Liver parasites of fishes.   Fellodistomum Stafford, 1904 (fig. 504)
13 (12) Vitellaria extending from intestinal bifurcation to posterior end of body.   Pycnadena Linton, 1911 (fig. 505)
14 (11) Vitellaria posterior to ventral sucker, extending from level of testes to posterior end of body; circular body fold present around ventral sucker; esophagus short.   Pycnadenoides Yamaguti, 1938 (fig. 506)
15 (8) Ovary lobed.
16 (17) Vitellaria not extending beyond level of center of ventral sucker.   Rhodotrema Odhner, 1911 (fig. 507)
17 (16) Vitellaria extending from level of pharynx to posterior limit of testes.   Steringotrema Odhner, 1911 (fig. 508)
18 (7) Ventral sucker at end of first third of body.
19 (20) Vitellaria extending from level of posterior edge of ventral sucker to posterior level of testes; posterior end of cirrus sac touching anterior edge of ventral sucker.   Steringophorus Odhner, 1905 (fig. 509)
20 (19) Vitellaria originating posterior to ventral sucker, extending to posterior end of body, posterior to testes; cirrus sac entirely anterior to ventral sucker.   Lintonium Stunkard and Nigrelli, 1930 (fig. 510)
21 (2) Testes lobed; eggs with polar filaments.   Megenteron Manter, 1934 (fig. 511)
22 (1) Eggs with spines.   Benthotrema Manter, 1934 (fig. 512)

KEY TO THE SPECIES OF THE GENUS BACCIGER NICOLL, 1914 (XIII:192)

K. I. Skrjabin and V. P. Koval

1 (4) Vitellaria well-developed, lateral, extending from level of pharynx to level of ventral sucker.
2 (3) Genital pore medial, at level of intestinal bifurcation.   B. nicolli Palombi, 1934

3 (2) Genital pore slightly lateral, directly posterior to pharynx.   B. bacciger (Rudolphi, 1819) (fig. 503)
4 (1) Vitellaria in two small compact groups of follicles, lateral to ventral sucker.   B. harengulae Yamaguti, 1938

KEY TO THE SPECIES OF THE GENUS BENTHOTREMA MANTER, 1934 (XIII:205)

K. I. Skrjabin and V. P. Koval

1 (2) Egg with spines.   B. plenum Manter, 1934 (fig. 512)
2 (1) Egg without spines.
3 (4) Dimensions of suckers sub-equal; esophagus present.   B. haplognathi Yamaguti, 1938
4 (3) Oral sucker considerably larger than ventral sucker; esophagus lacking.   B. richardsoni Manter, 1954

KEY TO THE SPECIES OF THE GENUS LINTONIUM STUNKARD AND NIGRELLI, 1930 (XIII:214-215)

K. I. Skrjabin and V. P. Koval

1 (4) Ventral sucker in anterior half of body.
2 (3) Vitellaria originating at level of ovary; testes adjacent to intestinal ceca; uterus extending to posterior end of body. L. vibex (Linton, 1900) (fig. 510)
3 (2) Vitellaria originating at level of testes, or at level of posterior limit of testes; testes inter-cecal; uterus reaching posterior ends of intestinal ceca, not extending to posterior end of body.
L. consors (Lühe, 1906) and L. pulchrum (Johnston, 1913)
4 (1) Ventral sucker equatorial; testes adjacent to intestinal ceca. L. laymani Skrjabin and Koval, 1957

KEY TO THE SPECIES OF THE GENUS PYCNADENA LINTON, 1911 (XIII:241)

K. I. Skrjabin and V. P. Koval

1 (2) Genital pore at level of pharynx, nearly medial; vitellaria extending posteriorly beyond testes, merging medially.   P. lata (Linton, 1910) (fig. 505)
2 (1) Genital pore extremely lateral; vitellaria terminating at level of posterior limit of testes, not merging medially.   P. pyriforme Price, 1934

KEY TO THE SPECIES OF THE GENUS PYCNADENOIDES YAMAGUTI, 1938 (XIII:245)

K. I. Skrjabin and V. P. Koval

1 (2) Loops of uterus between ventral sucker and anterior testis; eggs: 0.075-0.09 x 0.048-0.057 mm.   P. pagrosomi Yamaguti, 1938 (fig. 506)
2 (1) Loops of uterus between ventral sucker and

posterior limit of testes; eggs: 0.061-0.071 x 0.042-0.046 mm.   P. calami Manter, 1947

KEY TO THE SPECIES OF THE GENUS RHODOTREMA ODHNER, 1911 (XIII:250)

K. I. Skrjabin and V. P. Koval

1 (8) Ovary lobed.

2 (7) Ovary tri-lobed; intestinal ceca not extending far beyond ventral sucker.

3 (6) Testes symmetrical; body pyriform or oval.

4 (5) Vitellaria not extending posterior to ventral sucker.   R. ovacutum (Lebour, 1908) (fig. 507)

5 (4) Vitellaria extending posterior to ventral sucker.   R. skrjabini Issaitschikoff, 1928

6 (3) Testes oblique; body fusiform.
          R. problematicum Issaitschikoff, 1928

7 (2) Ovary lobed; intestinal ceca extending significant distance posterior to ventral sucker.
R. quinquelobata Layman, 1930 and R. quadrilobata Basikalova, 1932

8 (1) Ovary entire.   R. lethrini Yamaguti, 1938

KEY TO THE SPECIES OF THE GENUS STERINGOPHORUS ODHNER, 1905 (XIII:274)

K. I. Skrjabin and V. P. Koval

1 (6) Ventral sucker considerably larger than oral.

2 (3) Vitellaria anteriorly extending to level of ventral sucker or to level of oral sucker; eggs large, 0.06-0.07 mm. long.
          S. furciger (Olsson, 1868) (fig. 509)

3 (2) Vitellaria anteriorly not reaching level of ventral sucker; eggs small, 0.030-0.034 mm. long.

4 (5) Vitellaria in two short lateral groups, between posterior edge of ventral sucker and posterior limit of testes.   S. profundus Manter, 1934

5 (4) Vitellaria in two short lateral groups, between posterior edge of ovary and posterior limit of testes.
          S. magnus Manter, 1934

6 (1) Ventral sucker equal to or smaller than oral sucker. Steringophorus sp. I. and sp. II Manter, 1934

KEY TO THE SPECIES OF THE GENUS STERINGOTREMA ODHNER, 1911 (XIII:295-296)

K. I. Skrjabin and V. P. Koval

1 (10) Ventral sucker larger than oral.

2 (7) Ventral sucker 1.5-2 times larger than oral.

3 (6) Vitellaria in two continuous lateral groups.

4 (5) Genital pore sinistral.
          S. cluthensis (Nicoll, 1909) (fig. 508)

5 (4) Genital pore medial.
          S. corpulenta (Linton, 1905)

6 (3) Vitellaria in two lateral groups, each group disrupted at level of ventral sucker, extending from level of pharynx to posterior ends of intestinal ceca.
          S. divergens (Rudolphi, 1809)

7 (2) Ventral sucker very large, 3 to 4 times larger than oral.

8 (9) Esophagus well-developed; anterior border of vitellaria anterior to ventral sucker.
          S. pagelli (Beneden, 1870)

9 (8) Esophagus present, weakly developed; anterior border of vitellaria at level of middle of ventral sucker.   S. rotundum Manter, 1954

10 (1) Oral sucker larger than ventral.
          S. ovata Price, 1934

KEY TO THE GENERA OF THE SUBFAMILY ANTORCHINAE SKRJABIN AND KOVAL, 1957 (XIII:314)

K. I. Skrjabin and V. P. Koval

1 (4) Ovary posterior to testes, posterior or dorsal to ventral sucker.

2 (3) Ovary entire; intestinal ceca short, not reaching ventral sucker. Antorchis Linton, 1911 (fig. 513)

3 (2) Ovary multi-lobed; intestinal ceca of medium length, passing beyond border of ventral sucker.
          Orientophorus Srivastava, 1935 (fig. 514)

4 (1) Ovary anterior to testes.

5 (6) Esophagus relatively long; intestinal ceca of medium length, passing posterior to ventral sucker; body without constriction.
          Parantorchis Yamaguti, 1934 (fig. 515)

6 (5) Esophagus absent; intestinal ceca short, limited to region anterior to ventral sucker; body subdivided into two parts by constriction.
Pseudodiscogasteroides Gupta, 1953 (fig. 516)

KEY TO THE SPECIES OF THE GENUS ORIENTOPHORUS SRIVASTAVA, 1935 (XIII:319)

K. I. Skrjabin and V. P. Koval

1 (2) Genital pore at level of intestinal bifurcation.
          O. brevichrus Srivastava, 1935 (fig. 514)

2 (1) Genital pore not at level of intestinal bifurcation.

3 (4) Genital pore anterior to intestinal bifurcation; cirrus sac between anterior edge of ventral sucker and posterior edge of pharynx.
          O. clupii Srivastava, 1935

4 (3) Genital pore posterior to intestinal bifurcation; cirrus sac between posterior limit of testes and intestinal bifurcation.

5 (6) Cirrus sac sinistrally skirting ventral sucker; esophagus present.   O. gangeticus Srivastava, 1935

6 (5) Cirrus sac dextrally skirting ventral sucker; esophagus lacking.   O. ilishii Srivastava, 1935
Note: O. sayori Yamaguti, 1942 omitted from key.

KEY TO THE SPECIES OF THE GENUS PSEUDODISCOGASTEROIDES GUPTA, 1953 (XIII:332)

K. I. Skrjabin and V. P. Koval

1 (2) Ovary anterior to right testis; uterus reaching posterior end of body.

P. caranxi (Srivastava, 1939)

2 (1) Ovary and right testis symmetrical, adjacent; uterus between excretory pore and ventral sucker.

P. indicum (Srivastava, 1939) (fig. 516)

KEY TO THE GENERA OF THE SUBFAMILY DISCOGASTEROIDINAE SRIVASTAVA, 1939 (XIII:339)

K. I. Skrjabin and V. P. Koval

1 (2) Esophagus very short; seminal vesicle large; vitellaria lateral to disc of Yamaguti.

Discogasteroides Strand, 1934

2 (1) Esophagus very long; seminal vesicle relatively small; vitellaria anterior to disc of Yamaguti.

Paradiscogaster Yamaguti, 1934 (fig. 517)

KEY TO THE SPECIES OF THE GENUS DISCOGASTEROIDES STRAND, 1934 (XIII:340)

K. I. Skrjabin and V. P. Koval

1 (2) Intestinal ceca of unequal lengths, left longer; seminal vesicle divided into three parts; cirrus sac sickle-shaped.   D. hawaiensis Hanson, 1955

2 (1) Intestinal ceca of equal lengths; seminal vesicle divided into two parts; cirrus sac not sickle-shaped.

3 (4) Intestinal ceca short, passing slightly into area of middle third of body; eggs: 0.048-0.057 mm. long.   D. ostracionis (Yamaguti, 1934) (fig. 518)

4 (3) Intestinal ceca reaching level of middle of body; eggs: 0.033-0.036 mm. long.

D. minor (Yamaguti, 1934)

KEY TO THE SPECIES OF THE GENUS PARADISCOGASTER YAMAGUTI, 1934 (XIII:348)

K. I. Skrjabin and V. P. Koval

1 (2) Body elongate, pyriform, with blunt cone at posterior end; eggs: 0.042-0.048 x 0.021-0.022 mm.

P. chaetodontis Yamaguti, 1938

2 (1) Body pyriform, without blunt cone at posterior end; eggs: 0.024-0.03 x 0.016-0.018 mm.

P. pyriformis Yamaguti, 1934 (fig. 517)

KEY TO THE SPECIES OF THE GENUS HAPLOCLADUS ODHNER, 1911 (XIII:356)

K. I. Skrjabin and V. P. Koval

1 (6) Testes in middle of posterior half of body or more posterior.

2 (3) Dimensions of oral sucker: 0.16-0.18 x 0.13-0.15 mm.; body length up to 2 mm.

H. minor Odhner, 1911

3 (2) Dimensions of oral sucker: 0.28-0.34 x 0.22-0.24 mm.; body length reaching 7 mm.

4 (5) Vitellaria extending to level of anterior testis.

H. typicus Odhner, 1911 (fig. 519)

5 (4) Vitellaria extending to level of posterior testis.   H. orientalis Srivastava, 1941

6 (1) Testes anterior to middle of posterior half of body.   H. filiformis (Rudolphi, 1819)

KEY TO THE GENERA OF THE SUBFAMILY LISSOLOMATINAE SKRJABIN AND KOVAL, 1957 (XIII:366)

K. I. Skrjabin and V. P. Koval

1 (2) Latero-ventral outgrowth of body walls lobed; eggs with short polar appendix.

Lomasoma Manter, 1935 (fig. 520)

2 (1) Latero-ventral outgrowth of body walls not lobed; eggs with single, long polar appendix; length of appendix equal to length of egg.

Lissoloma Manter, 1934 (fig. 521)

KEY TO THE SPECIES OF THE GENUS LOMASOMA MANTER, 1935 (XIII:371)

K. I. Skrjabin and V. P. Koval

1 (2) Posterior end of body truncate; cirrus sac relatively broad; genital atrium with two copulatory lobes; eggs: 0.026-0.031 mm.

L. wardi (Manter, 1934) (fig. 520)

2 (1) Body broadly rounded posteriorly; cirrus sac relatively narrow; genital atrium with single genital lobe; egg length different.

3 (4) Eggs without distinct polar appendices.

L. monolenei (Manter, 1934)

4 (3) Eggs with polar appendices; appendix in form of cap.   L. gracilis (Manter, 1934)

KEY TO THE GENERA OF THE SUBFAMILY PROCTOECINAE SKRJABIN AND KOVAL, 1957 (XIII:388)

K. I. Skrjabin and V. P. Koval

1 (8) Testes tandem; excretory bladder Y-shaped.

2 (7) Cirrus sac extending beyond posterior edge of ventral sucker.

3 (4) Seminal vesicle sinuous, tubular; genital pore lateral.   Proctoeces Odhner, 1911 (fig. 522)

4 (3) Seminal vesicle not sinuous; genital pore medial.

5 (6) Vitellaria lateral, forming uninterrupted row of follicles on each side of body.

Mesolecitha Linton, 1910 (fig. 523)

6 (5) Vitellaria lateral, in two groups on each side, anterior group lateral to esophagus and posterior group originating posterior to ventral sucker.

Gauhatiana Gupta, 1953 (fig. 524)

7 (2) Cirrus sac wholly anterior to ventral sucker or slightly overlapping.

Urorchis Ozaki, 1927 (fig. 525)

8 (1) Testes oblique; cirrus sac wholly anterior to ventral sucker; branches of excretory bladder parallel, leading to level of pharynx.

Symmetrovesicula Yamaguti, 1938 (fig. 526)

KEY TO THE SPECIES OF THE GENUS PROCTOECES ODHNER, 1911 (XIII:389)

K. I. Skrjabin and V. P. Koval

1 (6) Ovary entire.
2 (3) Vitellaria extending to anterior edge of anterior testis; egg: 0.032-0.037 x 0.015-0.019 mm.

P. magnorum Manter, 1940

3 (2) Posterior border of vitellaria posterior to level of anterior edge of anterior testis.
4 (5) Vitellaria extending to posterior edge of posterior testis, or extending further; eggs: 0.07-0.079 mm.; ventral sucker nearly twice size of oral.

P. maculatus (Looss, 1901) (fig. 522)

5 (4) Vitellaria reaching anterior edge of posterior testis; eggs: 0.046-0.053 mm.; dimensions of suckers in ratio of 1:1.4-1.6.   P. subtenue (Linton, 1907)
6 (1) Ovary trilobed.   P. major Yamaguti, 1934
Note: P. ostraea Fujita and Dollfus, 1925 (metacercaria) omitted from key.

KEY TO THE SPECIES OF THE GENUS URORCHIS OZAKI, 1927 (XIII:417)

K. I. Skrjabin and V. P. Koval

1 (2) Cirrus sac entirely anterior to ventral sucker; eggs: 0.063-0.072 x 0.038-0.042 mm.

U. goro Ozaki, 1927 (fig. 525)

2 (1) Cirrus sac extending posterior to middle of ventral sucker; eggs: 0.084-0.09 x 0.05-0.054 mm.

U. acheilognathi Yamaguti, 1934

KEY TO THE SPECIES OF THE GENUS TERGESTIA STOSSICH, 1899 from Manter (1954) (XIII:424-425)

1 (2) Ventral sucker smaller than oral.

T. agnostomi Manter, 1954

2 (1) Ventral sucker larger than oral.
3 (4) Ventral sucker slightly larger than oral.

T. laticollis (Rudolphi, 1819) (fig. 527)

4 (3) Ventral at least two times larger than oral.
5 (8) Vitellaria merging anterior to ovary.
6 (7) Posterior end of body sharply tapered; eggs: 0.017-0.019 x 0.009-0.010 mm.

T. acuta Manter, 1947

7 (6) Posterior end of body not sharply tapered; eggs: 0.021-0.027 x 0.014-0.018 mm.

T. acanthogobii Yamaguti, 1938

8 (5) Vitellaria not merging anterior to ovary.
9 (10) Length of pharynx two times less than width.

T. acanthocephala (Stossich, 1887)

10 (9) Length of pharynx more than two times greater than width.   T. pectinate (Linton, 1905)

LITERATURE ON THE TREMATODES OF THE FAMILY FELLODISTOMATIDAE NICOLL, 1913 (XIII:450)

Albova, R. E. 1952. Parasites of fishes of the White Sea in the vicinity of the village of Gridino, I. Monogenetic and digenetic trematodes. Ucheneye Zapiski Karelo-Finskogo Universiteta. 4(2):78-97.

Bazikalova, A. Ya. 1932. Materials on the parasitology of fishes of Murmansk. Sbornik Nauchno-Promyslovykh Rabot na Murmane. pp. 136-153.

Vlasenko, P. V. 1931. On the fauna of parasitic worms of fishes of the Black Sea. Trudy Karadagskoy Biologicheskoy Stantsii, Simferopol. No. 4:88-136.

Dogiel, V. A. and A. Rozova. 1941. The parasitic fauna of four-horned sculpin (Myoxocephalus quadricornis) in different regions of its distribution. Uchenye Zapiski Leningradskogo Gosudarstvennogo Universiteta, No. 74, seriya biologicheskikh nauk. No. 18:4-19.

Zhukov, E. V. 1953. Endoparasitic worms of fishes of the Sea of Japan and the Kurile shoal-waters. Dissertatsiya.

Isaychikov, I. M. 1928. On the knowledge of the parasitic worms of several groups of vertebrates of the Russian Arctic, A. Trematodes. Trudy Morskogo Nauchnogo Instituta. 3(2):5-79.

Koval, V. P. 1950. Digenetic trematodes of fishes of the lower Dnieper. Trudy Biologo-Gruntoznavchogo Fakultetu Kievskogo Derzhavnogo Universitetu. No. 5:187-205.

Layman, E. M. 1930. Parasitic worms of fishes of Peter the Great Bay. Izvestiya Tikhookeanskoy Nauchno-Promyslovoy Stantsii. 3(6):1-120.

Markevich, A. P. 1951. The parasite fauna of fresh-water fishes of the Ukrainian S. S. R. Izdatelstvo Akad. Nauk Ukr. SSR, Kiev. 376 pp.

Osmanov, S. U. 1940. Materials on the parasite fauna of fishes of the Black Sea. Uchenye Zapiski Leningradskogo Pedagogicheskogo Instituta, Kafedra Zoologii i Darvinizma. 30:187-267.

Polyansky, Yu. I. 1955. Materials on the parasite fauna of fishes of the northern seas of the U. S. S. R. Parasites of fishes of the Barents Sea. Trudy Zoologicheskogo Instituta Akad. Nauk SSSR. 19:1-170.

Reshetnikova, A. V. 1954. The parasite fauna of several commercial fishes of the Black Sea. Avtoreferat dissertatsii.

Shulman, S. S. and R. E. Shulman-Albova. 1953. Parasites of fishes of the White Sea. Izdatelstvo Akad. Nauk SSSR. 198 pp.

Chubrik, G. K. 1952. Life cycle of Rhodotrema quadrilobata Basikalova, 1932, intestinal parasites of flatfishes. Doklady Akad. Nauk SSSR. 83(6):981-983.

Chubrik, G. K. 1952. Larval stages of the trematode, Fellodistomum fellis Nicoll, 1909, from invertebrates of the Barents Sea. Zoologichesky Zhurnal. 31(5):653-658.

Chulkova, V. N. 1939. The parasite fauna of fishes in the vicinity of the city of Batum. Uchenye Zapiski Leningradskogo Gosudarstvennogo

Universiteta, No. 43, seriya biologicheskikh nauk.
No. 11:21-32.

KEY TO THE GENERA OF THE SUBFAMILY OCHETOSOMATINAE LEAO, 1945 modified from Byrd and Denton (1938) (XIII:464)

K. I. Skrjabin and D. N. Antipin

1 (12) Genital pore medial or slightly lateral, between ventral sucker and intestinal bifurcation.
  2 (11) Ovary directly posterior to ventral sucker.
    3 (10) Testes equatorial or slightly post-equatorial.
      4 (9) Body oval; uterus with few loops.
        5 (8) Vitellaria follicular; follicles distinct, mostly lateral to intestinal ceca.
          6 (7) Cirrus sac elongate, muscular; metraterm nearly half length of sac.
                  Lechriorchis Stafford, 1905 (fig. 528)
          7 (6) Cirrus sac of medium length, muscular; metraterm nearly equal to length of sac.
            Paralechriorchis Byrd and Denton, 1938 (fig. 529)
        8 (5) Vitellaria more or less branching, lateral, dorsal, and ventral to intestinal ceca.
                  Dasymetra Nicoll, 1911 (fig. 530)
      9 (4) Body spade-shaped, reaching greatest width posterior to testes; uterus with numerous loops posterior to ventral sucker.
                  Pneumatophilus Odhner, 1910 (fig. 531)
    10 (3) Testes in posterior fourth of body.
                  Zeugorchis Stafford, 1905 (fig. 532)
  11 (2) Ovary considerably posterior to ventral sucker.   Natriodera Mehra, 1937 (fig. 533)
12 (1) Genital pore lateral, not between ventral sucker and intestinal bifurcation.
  13 (14) Genital pore lateral, at level of intestinal bifurcation.   Ochetosoma Braun, 1901 (fig. 534)
  14 (13) Genital pore lateral, anterior to intestinal bifurcation, at level of pharynx or oral sucker.
                  Oudhia Gupta, 1953 (fig. 535)

KEY TO THE SPECIES OF THE GENUS LECHRIORCHIS STAFFORD, 1905 from Byrd and Denton (1938) (XIII:539)

1 (4) Intestinal ceca terminating anterior to testes.
  2 (3) Ventral sucker in anterior third of body.
                  L. propria (Nicoll, 1914)
  3 (2) Ventral sucker in middle third of body.
                  L. tygarti Talbot, 1933
4 (1) Intestinal ceca terminating posterior to testes.
  5 (6) Body large, reaching 7.6 mm. long; testes 1.26 mm. long; cirrus sac 2.12 mm. long.
                  L. abducens Byrd and Denton, 1938
  6 (5) Body length less than 7.0 mm.; cirrus sac less than 2.0 mm. long; testes less than 1.0 mm. long.
    7 (8) Suckers sub-equal.
                  L. megasorchis (Crow, 1913)
    8 (7) Ventral sucker considerably larger than oral.

9 (10) Ventral sucker in anterior third of body.
                  L. primus Stafford, 1905 (fig. 528)
10 (9) Ventral sucker in middle third of body.
                  L. plesientera Sumwalt, 1926

KEY TO THE SPECIES OF THE GENUS PARALECHRIORCHIS BYRD AND DENTON, 1938 (XIII:567)

K. I. Skrjabin and D. N. Antipin

1 (2) Intestinal ceca long, reaching posterior end of body.   P. bosci (Cobbold, 1859)
2 (1) Intestinal ceca short.
  3 (4) Intestinal ceca not reaching level of testes.
                  P. syntomentera (Sumwalt, 1926) (fig. 529)
  4 (3) Intestinal ceca reaching testes or passing beyond.   P. natricis (Hall and Allison, 1935)
Note: P. secundus (Canavan, 1937) and P. syntomenteroides Parker, 1941 omitted from key.

KEY TO THE SPECIES OF THE GENUS PNEUMATOPHILUS ODHNER, 1910 (XIII:581)

K. I. Skrjabin and D. N. Antipin

1 (2) Testes entire.   P. foliaformis Talbot, 1934
2 (1) Testes irregularly lobed.
  3 (4) Testes wider than long; intestinal ceca terminating near anterior limit of testes.
                  P. leidyi Byrd and Denton, 1937
  4 (3) Testes of equal length and width; intestinal ceca terminating posterior to anterior limit of testes.
                  P. variabilis (Leidy, 1856) (fig. 531)

KEY TO THE SPECIES OF THE GENUS ZEUGORCHIS STAFFORD, 1905 (XIII:590)

K. I. Skrjabin and D. N. Antipin

1 (2) Cirrus sac long; ovary large; vitellaria passing beyond central third of body.
                  Z. aequatus Stafford, 1905 (fig. 532)
2 (1) Cirrus sac short; ovary small; vitellaria restricted to central third of body.
                  Z. eurinus (Talbot, 1933)

KEY TO THE GENERA OF THE FAMILY HIRUDINELLIDAE DOLLFUS, 1932 (XIII:603)

K. I. Skrjabin and L. Kh. Gushanskaya

1 (2) Genital pore posterior to intestinal bifurcation; posterior ends of intestinal ceca uniting into one common trunk, opening into excretory bladder, forming uroproct; cuticle covered with fine spines.
Uroproctinella Skrjabin and Guschanskaja, 1956 (fig. 536)

2 (1) Genital pore near pharynx; intestinal ceca terminating blindly; uroproct lacking; cuticle aspinose.   Hirudinella (Garsin, 1730) (fig. 537)

LITERATURE ON THE TREMATODES OF THE FAMILY HIRUDINELLIDAE DOLLFUS, 1932 (XIII:645)

Skrjabin, K. I. and L. Kh. Gushanskaya. 1954. The sub-order Hemiurata (Markevitsch, 1951) Skrjabin and Guschanskaja, 1954, Part I. In: Skrjabin, K. I. Trematodes of animals and man. Izdatelstvo Akad. Nauk SSSR, Moskva-Leningrad. 9:227-653.

Skrjabin, K. I. and L. Kh. Gushanskaya. 1955. The sub-order Hemiurata (Markevitsch, 1951) Skrjabin and Guschanskaja, 1954, Part II. In: Skrjabin, K. I. Trematodes of animals and man. Izdatelstvo Akad. Nauk SSSR, Moskva-Leningrad. 10:339-649.

Skrjabin, K. I. and L. Kh. Gushanskaya. 1955. The sub-order Hemiurata (Markevitsch, 1951) Skrjabin and Guschanskaja, 1954, Part III. In: Skrjabin, K. I. Trematodes of animals and man. Izdatelstvo Akad. Nauk SSSR, Moskva-Leningrad. 11:465-748.

Skrjabin, K. I. and L. Kh. Gushanskaya. 1956. Systematics of the trematodes of the suborder Hemiurata (Markevitsch, 1951) Skrjabin and Gushanskaya, 1954. Trudy Gelmintologicheskoy Laboratorii Akad. Nauk SSSR. 8:144-158.

KEY TO THE SPECIES OF THE GENUS PTYCHOGONIMUS LÜHE, 1900 (XIII:648)

K. I. Skrjabin and L. Kh. Gushanskaya

1 (2) Vitellaria originating slightly anterior to ventral sucker; eggs: 0.042-0.096 x 0.027-0.063 mm. Parasites of sharks and rays.
          P. megastomus (Rudolphi, 1819) (fig. 538)
2 (1) Vitellaria originating at level of middle of ventral sucker; eggs: 0.056 x 0.035 mm. Parasites of percoid fishes.   P. fontanus Lyster, 1939

KEY TO THE GENERA OF THE SUBFAMILY SCLERODISTOMATINAE ODHNER, 1927 (XIII:660)

K. I. Skrjabin and L. Kh. Gushanskaya

1 (2) Genital pore posterior to intestinal bifurcation; hermaphroditic bursa absent; genital atrium present, filled with genital cone.
          Sclerodistomum Looss, 1912 (fig. 539)
2 (1) Genital pore directly posterior to oral sucker; hermaphroditic bursa present, enclosing hermaphroditic duct, terminal portions of ejaculatory duct and of metraterm; genital atrium lacking.
          Eurycoelum Brock, 1886

KEY TO THE SPECIES OF THE GENUS SCLERODISTOMUM LOOSS, 1912 (XIII:661)

K. I. Skrjabin and L. Kh. Gushanskaya

1 (2) Genital pore mid-way between intestinal bifurcation and ventral sucker; anterior portion of body expanded; body 13-15 mm. long.
          S. italicum (Stossich, 1893) (fig. 539)

2 (1) Genital pore directly posterior to intestinal bifurcation; body length not exceeding 10 mm.; anterior portion of body tapering.
3 (4) Testes directly posterior to ventral sucker, closely adjacent; ovary far from testes, medial or slightly dextral.   S. spheroidis Manter, 1947
4 (3) Testes oblique, separated by loops of uterus; ovary lateral, forming triangle with testes.
          S. diodontis Yamaguti, 1942

KEY TO THE SUBFAMILIES OF THE FAMILY SYNCOELIIDAE DOLLFUS, 1923 (XIII:680)

K. I. Skrjabin and L. Kh. Gushanskaya

1 (2) Hermaphroditic bursa present; anterior part of body cylindrical; posterior part expanded, leaf-shaped; entire posterior portion of body filled with branched follicular testes, ovary and vitellaria; posterior half of ceca with numerous, branching external, diverticula.
          Otiotrematinae Skrjabin and Guschanskaja, 1956
2 (1) Hermaphroditic bursa absent.
3 (4) Body not noticeably divided into anterior and posterior portions; testes of large follicles, in two longitudinal rows; ovary follicular; vitellaria of several large follicles; ceca without diverticula, uniting terminally.   Syncoeliinae Looss, 1899
4 (3) Body divided into narrow, anterior portion and expanded posterior portion; testes tubular, irregularly segmented; ovary follicular or globular; vitellaria tubular, more or less separated into elongate follicles; intestinal ceca without diverticula and not uniting.   Paronatrematinae Dollfus, 1950

KEY TO THE GENERA OF THE SUBFAMILY SYNCOELIINAE LOOSS, 1899 (XIII:681)

K. I. Skrjabin and L. Kh. Gushanskaya

1 (2) Cuticle covered with papillae; genital atrium large, with eversible copulatory organ; two vas deferens present; intestinal ceca extremely sinuous.
          Capiatestes Crowcroft, 1948 (fig. 541)
2 (1) Cuticle smooth, without papillae; glandular cells present under cuticle in parenchyma; single vas deferens present; genital atrium absent; intestinal ceca straight.   Syncoelium Looss, 1899 (fig. 542)

KEY TO THE SPECIES OF THE GENUS SYNCOELIUM LOOSS, 1899 (XIII:682)

K. I. Skrjabin and L. Kh. Gushanskaya

1 (2) Ventral sucker protruding, but not pedunculate; testes composed of eleven follicles; vitellaria of two to three pestle-like follicles; eggs: 0.03 x 0.021-0.022 mm.   S. ragazzii (Setti, 1897) (fig. 542)
2 (1) Ventral sucker pedunculate; testes composed of eighteen follicles; vitellaria of six to eight follicles; eggs: 0.04-0.05 x 0.03 mm.
          S. filiferum (Sars, 1885)

KEY TO THE SPECIES OF THE GENUS
PARONATREMA DOLLFUS, 1937 (XIII:715)

K. I. Skrjabin and L. Kh. Gushanskaya

1 (2) Body 17.5-19.8 mm. long; ovary spherical;
oral sucker with internal ring of forty-one to forty-
seven small accessory suckers; ventral sucker with
internal ring of twenty-nine to thirty-seven accessory
suckers.   P. mantae Manter, 1940
2 (1) Body 3.461-3.577 mm. long; ovary consisting
of groups of follicles; oral sucker lacking accessory
suckers; ventral sucker with internal ring of twenty-
seven small accessory suckers.
              P. vaginicola Dollfus, 1937 (fig. 543)

LITERATURE ON THE TREMATODES OF THE
FAMILY SYNCOELIIDAE DOLLFUS,
1923 (XIII:721)

Isaychikov, I. M. 1933. On the knowledge of the
parasitic worms of several groups of vertebrates of
the Russian Arctic, II. Trudy Gosudarstvennogo
Okeanograficheskogo Instituta. 3(1):3-44.
Skrjabin, K. I. and L. Kh. Gushanskaya. 1956.
Sytematics of the trematodes of the sub-order Hemiurata (Markevitsch, 1951) Skrjabin and Guschanskaja,
1954. Trudy Gelmintologicheskoy Laboratorii Akad.
Nauk SSSR. 8:144-158.

KEY TO THE SUBFAMILIES OF THE FAMILY
LECITHASTERIDAE SKRJABIN AND
GUSCHANSKAJA, 1954 (XIII:759)

K. I. Skrjabin and L. Kh. Gushanskaya

1 (10) Anal appendage lacking.
2 (9) Vitellaria stellate, consisting of elongate
lobes united at base.
3 (4) Ovary and vitellaria anterior to testes; vitellaria with twelve radially disposed elongate lobes.
    Macradenininae Skrjabin and Guschanskaja, 1954
4 (3) Ovary and vitellaria posterior to testes; vitellaria consisting of seven lobes.
5 (6) Hermaphroditic bursa lacking.
    Johniophyllinae Skrjabin and Guschanskaja, 1954
6 (5) Hermaphroditic bursa present.
7 (8) Proximal portion of hermaphroditic duct
enclosed in large, muscular hermaphroditic bursa,
distal portion external; eggs with single polar
filament at each pole. Liver parasites of marine
fishes.
    Hypohepaticolinae Skrjabin and Guschanskaja, 1954

8 (7) Entire hermaphroditic duct enclosed in muscular hermaphroditic bursa; eggs lacking filaments.
Intestinal parasites of marine fishes.
              Lecithasterinae Odhner, 1905
9 (2) Vitellaria consisting of separate, large, round
follicles, not basally joined to form stellate configuration; hermaphroditic duct enclosed within muscular
hermaphroditic bursa.
    Lecithophyllinae Skrjabin and Guschanskaja, 1954
10 (1) Anal appendage present; stellate vitellaria
with seven elongate lobes.
11 (12) Terminal portion of pars prostatica, prostatic vesicle, terminal portion of metraterm, and
hermaphroditic duct, enclosed in hermaphroditic
bursa; pre-oral accessory sucker present; muscular,
oval cylindrical structures present anteriorly along
lateral portions of body.
    Tricotyledoninae Skrjabin and Guschanskaja, 1956
12 (11) Hermaphroditic duct only enclosed within
hermaphroditic bursa; prostatic vesicle lacking; pre-
oral sucker and muscular cylinders lacking anteriorly. Musculovesiculinae Skrjabin and Guschanskaja,
1954.

SUPPLEMENTARY LITERATURE ON THE
TREMATODES OF THE SUBORDER HEMIURATA
(MARKEVITSCH, 1951) SKRJABIN AND
GUSCHANSKAJA, 1954 (XIII:779)

Polyansky, Yu. I. 1952. Two new species of di-
genetic trematodes from fishes of the North Atlantic.
Parazitologichesky Sbornik Zoologicheskogo Instituta
Akad. Nauk SSSR. 14:266-280.
Polyansky, Yu. I. 1955. Materials on the parasite
fauna of fishes of the northern seas of the U.S.S.R.
Parasites of fishes of the Barents Sea. Trudy Zoo-
logicheskogo Instituta Akad. Nauk SSSR. 19:1-170.

LIST OF SUPPLEMENTARY ILLUSTRATIONS

Fellodistomatidae Nicoll, 1913
    Ancylocoelium typicum Nicoll, 1912 (fig. 884)
    Markevitschiella nakazawai (Kobayashi, 1921)
        (fig. 885)
    Pyriforma macrorhamphosi Yamaguti, 1938
        (fig. 886)
    Yamagutia lateroporus Srivastava, 1939 (fig. 887)
Syncoeliidae Dollfus, 1923
    Otiotrema torosum Setti, 1897 (fig. 888)
Halipegidae Poche, 1925
    Mitrostoma nototheniae Manter, 1954 (fig. 889)
Lecithasteridae Skrjabin and Guschanskaja, 1954
    Tricotyledonia genypteri Fife, 1954 (fig. 890)

PART XIV

KEY TO THE SUBFAMILIES OF THE FAMILY TROGLOTREMATIDAE ODHNER, 1914 (XIV:8)

K. I. Skrjabin

1 (4) Body thick, broad. Parasites in cysts in birds and mammals.
2 (3) Testes posterior to ovary and ventral sucker.
Troglotrematinae Baer, 1931
3 (2) Testes anterior to ovary and ventral sucker.
Nephrotrematinae Baer, 1931
4 (1) Body small, pyriform, flat, not exceeding 1.1 mm. in length. Intestinal parasites of predatory mammals.
Nanophyetinae Wallace, 1935

KEY TO THE GENERA OF THE SUBFAMILY TROGLOTREMATINAE BAER, 1931 (XIV:8)

K. I. Skrjabin

1 (4) Uterus short, balled, occupying relatively small portion of body; genital pore posterior to ventral sucker; eggs large, 0.063-0.090 mm. Parasites of mammals.
2 (3) Cirrus sac present; uterus medial, posterior to ventral sucker; anal appendage present. Parasites of frontal sinuses of predators.
Troglotrema Odhner, 1914 (fig. 544)
3 (2) Cirrus sac lacking; uterus lateral (usually sinistral), lateral to ventral sucker; anal appendage lacking. Lung parasites of mammals.
Paragonimus Braun, 1899
4 (1) Uterus long, loops extending into both right and left halves of body; cirrus sac lacking; genital pore anterior to ventral sucker; when ventral sucker lacking, genital pore in anterior half of body; eggs small, 0.017-0.042 mm. Parasites of birds and mammals.
5 (6) Ventral sucker lacking; eggs 0.017 mm. long. Parasites under skin of birds.
Collyriclum Kossack, 1911
6 (5) Ventral sucker present; eggs greater than 0.020 mm. in length; not found under skin.
7 (8) Eggs 0.023-0.025 mm. long. Parasitic in cysts in stomachs of marine mammals (dolphins).
Pholeter Odhner, 1914 (fig. 545)
8 (7) Eggs 0.033-0.042 mm. long. Renal parasites of birds. Renicola Cohn, 1904

KEY TO THE SUBFAMILIES OF THE FAMILY TROGLOTREMATIDAE ODHNER, 1914 (XIV:10)

K. I. Skrjabin

1 (2) Testes posterior to ventral sucker; ovary anterior to testes; seminal receptacle very short. Parasites of frontal sinuses of mammals.
Troglotrematinae Baer, 1931

2 (1) Testes anterior to ventral sucker; ovary posterior to testes; seminal receptacle absent. Renal parasites of mammals.
Nephrotrematinae Baer, 1931

KEY TO THE GENERA OF THE SUBFAMILY NANOPHYETINAE WALLACE, 1935 from Wallace (1935) (XIV:35)

1 (4) Intestinal ceca not reaching posterior end of body.
2 (3) Cirrus sac present; intestinal ceca passing boundary of anterior limit of testes; body length not exceeding 0.8 mm.
Nanophyetus Chapin, 1927 (fig. 547)
3 (2) Cirrus sac absent; intestinal ceca not reaching level of anterior limit of testes; body less than 0.5 mm. long. Sellacotyle Wallace, 1935 (fig. 548)
4 (1) Intestinal ceca reaching posterior end of body; testes extra-cecal; structure of terminal apparatus of male genital system not clarified.
Macroorchis Ando, 1919

KEY TO THE SPECIES OF THE GENUS NANOPHYETUS CHAPIN, 1927 (XIV:37)

K. I. Skrjabin

1 (2) Eggs: 0.085 x 0.055 mm.; genital pore slightly posterior to ventral sucker; cirrus sac pyriform. Parasites of predatory mammals of N. America. N. salminicola (Chapin, 1926) (fig. 547)
2 (1) Eggs: 0.072 x 0.048 mm.; genital pore directly on posterior edge of ventral sucker; cirrus sac curved, flask-shaped. Parasites of man in Far East of USSR.
N. schikhobalowi Skrjabin and Podjapolskaja, 1931

LITERATURE ON THE TREMATODES OF THE FAMILY PHOLETERIDAE DOLLFUS, 1939 (XIV:66)

Delyamure, S. L. 1956. Helminth fauna of marine mammals, in light of their ecology and phylogeny. Izdatelstvo Akad. Nauk SSSR. 517 pp.

KEY TO THE SUBFAMILIES OF THE FAMILY PLAGIORCHIDAE LÜHE, 1901 from Mehra (1937) (XIV:82)

1 (2) Special copulatory organ armed with spines ("stachelsack" in German) present, in form of sac in genital atrium, capable of eversion along with cirrus.
Enodiotrematinae Baer, 1924
2 (1) Copulatory sac lacking.
3 (4) Eggs large, 0.059-0.095 mm. long, containing developed miracidia. Encyclometrinae Mehra, 1931

4 (3) Eggs small, 0.02-0.05 mm. long, not containing miracidia when laid.

5 (6) Testes at posterior end of body; uterus anterior to testes (exception: Rudolphiella).
Telorchiinae Looss, 1899

6 (5) Uterus extending beyond level of posterior limit of testes.

7 (8) Genital pore posterior to ventral sucker.
Opisthogoniminae Travassos, 1928

8 (7) Genital pore anterior to ventral sucker.

9 (14) Genital pore directly anterior to ventral sucker.

10 (11) Cirrus sac elongate, passing beyond ventral sucker for considerable distance; seminal vesicle sinuous; pars prostatica elongate.
Styphlotrematinae Baer, 1924

11 (10) Cirrus sac crescent-shaped, passing slightly beyond level of ventral sucker (exception: Astiotrema); seminal vesicle straight; pars prostatica short.

12 (13) Intestinal ceca short, passing slightly beyond posterior edge of ventral sucker; testes symmetrical.   Brachycoeliinae Looss, 1899

13 (12) Intestinal ceca long, nearly reaching posterior end of body (exception: Tremiorchis); testes oblique or tandem.   Lepodermatinae Looss, 1899

14 (9) Genital pore considerably anterior to ventral sucker.

15 (16) Ovary deeply lobed or follicular.
Prosthogoniminae Lühe, 1909

16 (15) Ovary entire.

17 (18) Genital pore at anterior end of body, or on dorsal side in region of oral sucker.
Cephalogoniminae Looss, 1899

18 (17) Genital pore posterior to oral sucker.

19 (20) Seminal receptacle very large; Laurer's canal lacking. Lung parasites of amphibians.
Pneumonoecesinae Mehra, 1937

20 (19) Seminal receptacle usually absent, very small when present; Laurer's canal present. Parasites of mouth, lungs, liver, gall bladder, intestines of snakes.   Reniferinae Pratt, 1902

KEY TO THE GENERA OF THE SUBFAMILY LEPODERMATINAE LOOSS, 1899 (XIV:83)

K. I. Skrjabin and D. N. Antipin

1 (10) Seminal receptacle present.

2 (3) Cirrus sac not crescent-shaped, extending far beyond ventral sucker.
Astiotrema Looss, 1899 (fig. 549)

3 (2) Cirrus sac crescent-shaped, passing slightly beyond posterior edge of ventral sucker.

4 (5) Testes nearly symmetrical.
Glypthelmins Stafford, 1905 (fig. 550)

5 (4) Testes differently arranged.

6 (7) Testes tandem.
Haplometrana Lucker, 1931 (fig. 551)

7 (6) Testes oblique.

8 (9) Intestinal ceca terminating at equator; cirrus unarmed.

9 (8) Intestinal ceca extending to posterior end of body; cirrus armed with small spines.
Neolepoderma Mehra, 1937

10 (1) Seminal receptacle absent.

11 (12) Testes nearly tandem; uterus passing ventral to testes. Lung parasites of amphibians.
Haplometra Looss, 1899 (fig. 552)

12 (11) Testes oblique; uterus between testes. Intestinal parasites of various vertebrates, most rarely of fishes.

13 (14) Cirrus not eversible; horns of excretory bladder very long.
Microderma Mehra, 1931 (fig. 553)

14 (13) Long, eversible cirrus present; excretory horns short.   Lepoderma Looss, 1899

KEY TO THE GENERA OF THE SUBFAMILY STYPHLOTREMATINAE BAER, 1924 (XIV:84)

K. I. Skrjabin and D. N. Antipin

1 (4) Testes symmetrical

2 (3) Esophagus short or lacking; intestinal ceca reaching posterior end of body.
Pachypsolus Looss, 1901

3 (2) Esophagus long; intestinal ceca terminating considerably distant from posterior end of body.
Styphlotrema Odhner, 1911 (fig. 579)

4 (1) Testes oblique, or tandem.

5 (8) Cirrus sac reaching posterior edge of ventral sucker, or extending slightly beyond.

6 (7) Genital pore medial, directly anterior to ventral sucker; vitellaria short, extending to anterior edge or to middle of anterior testis.
Styphlodora Looss, 1899 (fig. 575)

7 (6) Genital pore sub-medial, anterior to ventral sucker or in same zone as ventral sucker; vitellaria extending to posterior edge of posterior testis, or to ends of intestinal ceca.   Glossidium Looss, 1899

8 (5) Cirrus sac extending far beyond posterior edge of ventral sucker.

9 (10) Seminal receptacle absent.
Glossimetra Mehra, 1937 (fig. 576)

10 (9) Seminal receptacle present.

11 (12) Body tapering in anterior region; cirrus armed.   Spinometra Manter, 1931 (fig. 577)

12 (11) Body broad in anterior region; cirrus unarmed.   Glossidiella Travassos, 1928 (fig. 578)

KEY TO THE GENERA OF THE SUBFAMILY BRACHYCOELIINAE LOOSS, 1899 (XIV:85)

K. I. Skrjabin and D. N. Antipin

1 (2) Greater part of seminal vesicle external to cirrus sac.   Leptophallus Lühe, 1909

2 (1) Seminal vesicle within cirrus sac.

3 (4) Cirrus sac not extending beyond ventral sucker; metraterm weakly developed.
Brachycoelium Dujardin, 1845

4 (3) Cirrus sac passing beyond level of posterior

edge of ventral sucker; metraterm muscular, broad.
Cymatocarpus Looss, 1899

KEY TO THE GENERA OF THE SUBFAMILY RENIFERINAE PRATT, 1902 (XIV:86)

K. I. Skrjabin and D. N. Antipin

1 (2) Ventral sucker post-equatorial.
Dolichopera Nicoll, 1914 (fig. 554)
2 (1) Ventral sucker in anterior half of body.
3 (4) Metraterm very muscular, distant from cirrus sac.   Pseudorenifer Price, 1935
4 (3) Metraterm weakly developed, moderately muscular, usually along side of cirrus sac.
5 (8) Cirrus sac extending far beyond level of ventral sucker.
6 (7) Ventral sucker considerably larger than oral; intestinal ceca reaching posterior end of body.
Macrodera Looss, 1899 (synonym: Saphedera Looss, 1902)
7 (6) Ventral sucker smaller than oral; intestinal ceca not reaching posterior end of body.
Natriodera Mehra, 1937 (fig. 533)
8 (5) Cirrus sac not extending beyond posterior edge of ventral sucker, or only slightly beyond.
9 (20) Intestinal ceca reaching posterior part of body.
10 (13) Testes parallel.
11 (12) Seminal receptacle present; vitellaria weakly developed, lateral to pharynx, anterior to ventral sucker.   Stomatrema Guberlet, 1928 (fig. 555)
12 (11) Seminal receptacle absent; vitellaria elongate, reaching posterior end of body.
Bilorchis Mehra, 1937 (fig. 556)
13 (10) Testes oblique.
14 (15) Seminal receptacle absent.
Dasymetra Nicoll, 1911 (fig. 530)
15 (14) Seminal receptacle present.
16 (17) Cuticle armed with spines; esophagus relatively long.   Ptyasiorchis Mehra, 1937 (fig. 557)
17 (16) Cuticle smooth; esophagus short.
18 (19) Genital pore opening lateral to intestinal bifurcation; vitellaria originating at level of oral sucker.   Xenopharynx Nicoll, 1912 (fig. 558)
19 (18) Genital pore between intestinal bifurcation and ventral sucker; vitellaria originating directly posterior to intestinal bifurcation.
Ophiorchis Mehra, 1937
20 (9) Intestinal ceca not reaching posterior part of body.
21 (22) Intestinal ceca between testes, ends directed medially.
Lechriorchis Stafford, 1905 (fig. 528)
22 (21) Ceca not between testes, ends not directed medially.
23 (24) Testes in posterior part of body; uterus of single loop.   Zeugorchis Nicoll, 1906 (fig. 532)
24 (23) Testes in anterior part of body; uterus composed of numerous loops.
25 (26) Ovary mid-way between ventral sucker and

testes; vitellaria reaching posterior end of body.   Aptorchis Nicoll, 1914
26 (25) Ovary lateral to ventral sucker or nearer to ventral sucker than to anterior testis; vitellaria not reaching posterior end of body.
27 (28) Excretory bladder without lateral branches; testes slightly oblique; Laurer's canal ending blindly.
Platymetra Mehra, 1931
28 (27) Excretory bladder with lateral branches; testes parallel; Laurer's canal opening externally.
29 (30) Body considerably wider in posterior half, with rounded posterior end; genital pore not anterior to intestinal bifurcation.
Pneumatophilus Odhner, 1911 (fig. 531)
30 (29) Body elliptical, not expanded in posterior half; genital pore anterior to intestinal bifurcation.
Renifer Pratt, 1902

KEY TO THE GENERA OF THE SUBFAMILY ENCYCLOMETRINAE MEHRA, 1931 (XIV:87)

K. I. Skrjabin and D. N. Antipin

1 (2) Cirrus sac transversely oriented, anterior and adjacent to ventral sucker, sometimes partially covering anterior border of ventral sucker; eggs: 0.0748-0.095 x 0.030-0.057 mm.
Encyclometra Baylis and Cannon, 1924 (fig. 580)
2 (1) Cirrus sac sinistral and anterior to ventral sucker; eggs: 0.0444-0.059 mm.
Orthorchis Mödlinger, 1924

KEY TO THE GENERA OF THE SUBFAMILY ENODIOTREMATINAE BAER, 1924 (XIV:88)

K. I. Skrjabin and D. N. Antipin

1 (2) Body with special marginal, wing-like folds; esophagus very short; genital pore directly posterior to intestinal bifurcation, near anterior end of body; cirrus sac dextral to ventral sucker, with posterior limit extending slightly beyond center of ventral sucker.   Oistosomum Odhner, 1902 (fig. 583)
2 (1) Body lacking folds; esophagus moderately long; genital pore considerably posterior to anterior end of body; cirrus sac transversely oriented, anterior and adjacent to ventral sucker, with posterior part skirting ventral sucker dextrally.
Enodiotrema Looss, 1900 (fig. 581)

KEY TO THE GENERA OF THE SUBFAMILY PROSTHOGONIMINAE LÜHE, 1909 (XIV:89)

K. I. Skrjabin and D. N. Antipin

1 (2) Genital pore medial, posterior to and near pharynx; cirrus sac oval. Liver parasites of rodents.
Meiogonimus
2 (1) Genital pores near left edge of body, near oral sucker; cirrus sac narrow, cylindrical. Parasites in fabrician bursae and oviducts of birds.

3 (4) Male and female genital pores symmetrically adjacent; loops of uterus extending beyond intestinal ceca.   Prosthogonimus Lühe, 1899 (fig. 582)

4 (3) Male and female genital pores at considerable distance apart; loops of uterus inter-cecal.
          Schistogonimus Lühe, 1901 (fig. 584)

KEY TO THE GENERA OF THE SUBFAMILY TELORCHINAE LOOSS, 1899 (XIV:89)

K. I. Skrjabin and D. N. Antipin

1 (2) Loops of uterus extending slightly beyond level of testes, not reaching posterior end of body.
          Rudolphiella Travassos, 1924

2 (1) Uterus wholly anterior to testes.

3 (12) Vitellaria extending beyond level of testes.

4 (5) Genital pore sinistral, mid-way between ventral sucker and left edge of body.
          Telorchis Lühe, 1899

5 (4) Genital pore medial or sub-medial.

6 (7) Uterus well-developed, ascending and descending branches represented by numerous loops; cirrus sac passing beyond level of ovary.
          Cercolecithos Perkins, 1928

7 (6) Uterus comparatively short, loops not closely adjacent; cirrus sac not passing beyond level of ovary.

8 (9) Cirrus sac small, pyriform, not extending beyond level of ventral sucker.
          Opisthioglyphe Looss, 1899

9 (8) Cirrus sac elongate, extending beyond level of ventral sucker.

10 (11) Prepharynx short; testes tandem.
          Dolichosaccus Johnston, 1912

11 (10) Prepharynx long; testes symmetrical.
          Sigmapera Nicoll, 1918

12 (3) Vitellaria not extending beyond level of testes.

13 (14) Genital pore dorsal, near right or left edge of body.   Protenes Barker and Covey, 1911

14 (13) Genital pore medial or sub-medial.

15 (16) Genital pore medial, directly anterior to ventral sucker; cirrus sac and metraterm exceptionally long.   Cercorchis Lühe, 1900

16 (15) Genital pore slightly sinistral, slightly anterior to ventral sucker; cirrus sac and metraterm short.   Paracercorchis Mehra and Bokhari, 1932

KEY TO THE GENERA OF THE SUBFAMILY CEPHALOGONIMINAE LOOSS, 1899 (XIV:90)

K. I. Skrjabin and D. N. Antipin

1 (2) Excretory bladder with lateral branches; vitellaria well-developed; genital pore at extreme anterior end of body. Parasites of amphibians and reptiles.   Cephalogonimus Poirier, 1886 (fig. 165)

2 (1) Excretory bladder without lateral branches; vitellaria very small; genital pore dextral to oral sucker. Parasites of fishes.
          Emoleptalea Looss, 1900 (fig. 167)

KEY TO THE GENERA OF THE SUBFAMILY PLAGIORCHINAE PRATT, 1902 from Olsen (1937) (XIV:93)

1. Seminal receptacle lacking.   2
   Seminal receptacle present.   4

2. Excretory bladder short, saccular. Parasites of fishes.   Macroderoides Pearse, 1924 (fig. 559)
   Excretory bladder Y-shaped; not in fishes.   3

3. Uterus S-shaped, ascending and descending branches winding between ovary and anterior testes and between two testes; testes oblique. Intestinal parasites of vertebrates.   Plagiorchis Lühe, 1899
   Uterus not S-shaped, extending to posterior end of body, both branches in posterior region turning or remaining straight; uterine branches ventral to testes; testes nearly tandem. Lung parasites of amphibians.   Haplometra Looss, 1899 (fig. 552)

4. Cirrus sac very large, extending far posterior to ventral sucker, basal part of sac broad, terminal part narrow; seminal vesicle muscular, large, straight; ovary and testes entire, slightly lobed or lobed; genital pore anterior or posterior to intestinal bifurcation; excretory bladder Y-shaped, with long trunk.   Astiotrema Looss, 1900 (fig. 549)
   Cirrus sac small.   5

5. Intestinal ceca short, not passing into posterior third of body.   6
   Intestinal ceca long, extending nearly to posterior end of body.   7

6. Cirrus sac long, extending beyond posterior edge of ventral sucker to level of ovary; posterior testis posterior to blind ends of intestinal ceca.
          Tremiorchis Mehra and Negi, 1926 (fig. 560)
   Cirrus sac not reaching posterior edge of ventral sucker; genital pore anterior or posterior to intestinal bifurcation; testes not extending beyond ends of intestinal ceca.
          Haplometroides Odhner, 1911 (fig. 561)

7. Testes oblique or symmetrical, near ventral sucker; ovary near ventral sucker; uterus posterior to testes, forming numerous transverse loops between intestinal ceca, extending to posterior end of body; excretory bladder Y-shaped or flask-shaped with long trunk.   Glypthelmins Stafford, 1905 (fig. 550)
   Testes not parallel, far posterior to ventral sucker.   8

8. Vitellaria filling entire body posterior to intestinal bifurcation, excepting space occupied by ovary, testes, and uterus; uterus terminating at some distance from end of body; testes oblique, laterally widely separated in posterior portion of body; ovary very near to ventral sucker; cirrus sac small, transversely oriented, anterior to ventral sucker.
          Rudolphitrema Travassos, 1926 (fig. 562)
   Vitellaria originating far posterior to intestinal bifurcation, or even posterior to ventral sucker, not reaching posterior end of body.   9

9. Excretory bladder distinctly Y-shaped.   10
   Excretory bladder saccular or slightly bifurcated, in which case, very broad.   11

10. Esophagus absent; seminal vesicle twisted.
Microderma Mehra, 1931 (fig. 553)
Esophagus present; seminal vesicle straight.
Plagiorchoides Olsen, 1937 (fig. 563)
11. Seminal vesicle twisting, occupying basal third of cirrus sac; genital pore near intestinal bifurcation; excretory bladder very broad, occupying half of body width posterior to Mehlis' gland, sometimes slightly bifurcated.
Megacustis Bennett, 1935 (fig. 564)
Seminal vesicle straight, bipartite; genital pore near anterior edge of ventral sucker; excretory bladder saccular, not very wide.   12
12. Esophagus narrow, several times longer than total length of prepharynx and pharynx; both branches of uterus ventral to testes.
Haplometrana Lucker, 1931 (fig. 551)
Esophagus short, scarcely exceeding total length of pharynx and prepharynx; one or both branches of uterus passing between testes.   13
13. Oral sucker with one pair of papillae on antero-lateral edge; excretory bladder opening posteriorly into expanded muscular chamber; posterior end of body truncated.
Eustomos MacCallum, 1921 (fig. 565)
Oral sucker without papillae; excretory bladder opening directly to exterior through small pore; posterior end of body tapering, rounded.
Alloglossidium Simer, 1929 (fig. 566)

KEY TO THE SPECIES OF THE GENUS ALLOGLOSSIDIUM SIMER, 1929 from Van Cleave and Müller (1934) (XIV:347)

1 (2) Anterior follicles of vitellaria mid-way between pharynx and ventral sucker, or slightly anterior. Intestinal parasites of following fish genera: Schilbeodes, Ameiurus, Ictalurus, Ambloplites.
A. corti (Lamont, 1921) (fig. 566)
2 (1) Anterior follicles of vitellaria not extending anteriorly beyond ventral sucker. Intestinal parasites of Ameiurus.   A. geminus (Müller, 1930)

KEY TO THE SPECIES OF THE GENUS GLYPTHELMINS STAFFORD, 1905 from Olsen (1937) (XIV:413-414)

1 (4) Pharyngeal glands present in pharyngeal region.
2 (3) Vitelline follicles merging medially anterior to ventral sucker; pharynx larger than ventral sucker. Intestinal parasites of Rana (USA).
G. subtropica Harwood, 1932
3 (2) Vitelline follicles limited to edges of body, not merging medially; pharynx and ventral sucker of equal size. Intestinal parasites of Rana (USA).
G. quieta (Stafford, 1900) (fig. 550)
4 (1) Pharyngeal glands absent.
5 (6) Ovary noticeably larger than testes; testes oblique, separated by wide space; vitelline follicles in twelve to thirteen groups. Intestinal parasites of

Cystignathus ocelatus (Brazil).
G. repandum (Rudolphi, 1819)
6 (5) Ovary not larger than testes, nearly equal to testes in size; vitelline follicles not forming groups.
7 (8) Vitellaria extending from oral sucker to posterior limit of testes; testes large, spherical, symmetrical; eggs: 0.051 x 0.024 mm. Intestinal parasites of Rana aurora (USA).
G. californiensis (Cort, 1919)
8 (7) Vitellaria not extending anteriorly beyond level of intestinal bifurcation; eggs small.
9 (10) Uterus filling entire width of body posterior to ventral sucker; testes spherical, symmetrical. Intestinal parasite of Leptodactylus ocellatus (Brazil).
G. elegans Travassos, 1926
10 (9) Uterus not filling entire region posterior to ventral sucker, almost wholly contained between intestinal ceca, sometimes extending slightly extracecally.
11 (12) Esophagus long, thin; cirrus sac large, extending obliquely from genital pore dextral to ventral sucker, extending far posterior to ventral sucker. Intestinal parasites of Bufo boreas (USA).
G. shastai Ingles, 1936
12 (11) Esophagus short, wide; cirrus sac small or large, not extending far posterior to ventral sucker.
13 (14) Vitellaria extending from esophagus approximately to ends of intestinal ceca; branches of uterus distinctly separated in posterior region; testes widely separated by uterus; ovary at clearly distal from testes. Intestinal parasites of representatives of the genera: Cystignathus, Bufo, Certhophrys (Brazil).   G. linguatula (Rudolphi, 1819)
14 (13) Anterior border of vitellaria at level of ventral sucker; posterior branches of uterus not separated; ovary adjacent to testes or very near.
15 (16) Oral sucker, pharynx, ovary, and ventral sucker of approximately equal dimensions; cirrus sac very broad; ovary adjacent to posterior edge of ventral sucker. Intestinal parasites of Cystignathus ocellatus (Brazil).   G. parva Travassos, 1924
16 (15) Oral sucker noticeably larger than pharynx, ventral sucker, and ovary; cirrus sac slender; ovary at level of ventral sucker. Intestinal parasites of Rana vittigera (Philippine Islands).
G. staffordi Tubangui, 1928

KEY TO THE SPECIES OF THE GENUS HAPLOMETRANA LUCKER, 1931 (XIV:496)

K. I. Skrjabin and D. N. Antipin

1 (2) Testes medial, tandem, completely filling space between intestinal ceca and contacting them; ventral sucker with muscular sucking disc; disc dorsally modified to form conical protuberance; body width eight to ten times less than length; vitelline reservoir present in transverse vitelline duct; Laurer's canal leading directly from seminal receptacle; seminal vesicle composed of long chamber; vas efferens of posterior testis passing between

testis and seminal receptacle.
H. intestinalis Lucker, 1931 (fig. 551)
2 (1) Testes oblique, diameter considerably less than space between intestinal ceca; ventral sucker cup-shaped without conical tip; body width six to seven times less than length; vitelline reservoir absent; Laurer's canal leading from trunk of seminal receptacle; seminal vesicle composed of long posterior chamber and small spherical anterior chamber, separated by constriction; vas efferens of posterior testes passing between ovary and seminal receptacle.
H. utahensis Olsen, 1937

KEY TO THE SPECIES OF THE GENUS HAPLOMETROIDES ODHNER, 1911 from Olsen (1937) (XIV:510)

1 (2) Genital pore at level of anterior edge of ventral sucker; loops of uterus posterior to testes; oral sucker noticeably larger than ventral. Parasites of oral cavity of snakes.
H. buccicola Odhner, 1911 (fig. 561)
2 (1) Genital pore anterior to intestinal bifurcation; loops of uterus extending anterior to testes; suckers of same size. Intestinal parasites of tree frogs.
H. rappiae Szidat, 1932

KEY TO THE SPECIES OF THE GENUS MACRODEROIDES PEARSE, 1924 from Van Cleave and Müller (1934) (XIV:518)

1 (4) Body length not exceeding width by less than six times; anterior part of body noticeably flattened dorso-ventrally.
2 (3) Vitellaria not extending posteriorly beyond second testis. Parasites of fishes of the genera: Lepidosteus and Ameiurus.
M. spiniferus Pearse, 1924 (fig. 559)
3 (2) Vitellaria extending posteriorly beyond posterior testis, reaching posterior end of body. Intestinal parasites of fishes of the genera: Lepidosteus and Amia. M. parvus (Hunter, 1932)
4 (1) Body fusiform, length not more than five times greater than width, not flattened anteriorly.
5 (6) Prepharynx absent; maximal width occurring between suckers. Intestinal parasites of fishes of the genus Amia. M. typicus (Windfield, 1929)
6 (5) Prepharynx well-developed; maximal width occurring posterior to ventral sucker.
7 (8) Vitellaria originating at level of posterior edge of ventral sucker; testes oblique. Parasites of fishes of the genus Esox.
M. flavus Van Cleave and Müller, 1932
8 (7) Vitellaria originating at level of ovary; testes tandem. Parasites of fishes of the genus Pseudobagrus. M. asiaticus Belouss, 1958

KEY TO THE SPECIES OF THE GENUS MICRODERMA Mehra, 1931 from Olsen (1937) (XIV:541)

1 (2) Seminal vesicle large; vitelline follicles

grouped; intestinal parasites of Kachuga smithii (India). M. elinguis Mehra, 1931 (fig. 553)
2 (1) Seminal vesicle slender, vitelline follicles not grouped. Esophageal parasites of Cyclagras gigas (Brazil). M. luhei (Travassos, 1927)

KEY TO THE SPECIES OF THE GENUS PLAGIORCHOIDES OLSEN, 1937 (XIV:587)

K. I. Skrjabin and D. N. Antipin

1 (2) Ovary and testes lobed; cirrus tuberculate.
P. potamonides Tubangui, 1946
2 (1) Ovary and testes not lobed, smoothly entire, or with slightly wavy contours; cirrus not tuberculate, armed with small spines.
P. noblei (Park, 1936) (fig. 563)

KEY TO THE SPECIES OF THE GENUS TREMIORCHIS MEHRA AND NEGI, 1925 (XIV:600)

K. I. Skrjabin and D. N. Antipin

1 (2) Oral sucker smaller than ventral; anterior testis post-equatorial; ovary round; seminal receptacle reniform; vitelline follicles grouped. Intestinal parasites of Rana tigrina (India).
T. ranarum Mehra and Negi, 1925 (fig. 560)
2 (1) Oral sucker larger than ventral; anterior testis pre-equatorial; ovary pyriform; seminal receptacle long, twisting; vitelline follicles not grouped. Intestinal parasites of Varanus spp.
T. varanum Verma, 1930

LITERATURE ON THE TREMATODES OF THE SUBFAMILY PLAGIORCHINAE PRATT, 1902 (XIV:606-610)

Belopolskaya, M. M. 1952. The parasite fauna of marine water-fowl. Uchenye Zapiski Leningradskogo Gosudarstvennogo Instituta, No. 141, seriya biologicheskikh nauk. No. 28:126-180.
Belous, E. V. 1954. Parasitic worms of freshwater vertebrates of the Primorye region. Dissertatsiya.
Bykhovskaya-Pavlovskaya, I. E. 1956. Trematodes of birds of the fauna of the U. S. S. R. Dissertatsiya.
Vasiliev, A. E. 1939. The parasite fauna of muskrat. Trudy Karelskogo Gosudarstvennogo Pedagogicheskogo Instituta, seriya biologicheskaya. No. 1:93-100.
Witenberg, G. G. and V. P. Podyapolskaya. 1926. The Eleventh Union Helminthological Expedition into the Zabaykalye region. Deyatelnost 28 Gelmintologicheskikh Expeditsy v SSSR (1919-1924). pp. 144-152.
Dogiel, V. A. and Kh. Karolinskaya. 1936. The parasite fauna of swifts (Apus apus). Uchenye Zapiski Leningradskogo Gosudarstvennogo Universiteta, No. 7, seriya biologicheskaya. No. 3:49-79.
Dogiel, V. A. and N. Navtsevich. 1936. The

parasite fauna of the martin. Uchenye Zapiski Leningradskogo Gosudarstvennogo Universiteta, No. 7, seriya biologicheskaya. No. 3:80-113.

Dotsenko, T. K. 1954. Parasitic worms of poultry of the Primorye region, and the biology of Cheilospirura hamulosa. Avtoreferat dissertatsii. Trudy Gelmintologicheskoy Laboratorii Akad. Nauk SSSR. 7:382-383.

Dubinina (Gorbunova), M. N. 1937. The parasite fauna of the black-crowned night heron (Nycticorax nycticorax L.) and its variability in connection with migration of the host. Zoologichesky Zhurnal. 16(3):547-573.

Isaychikov, I. M. 1928. On the knowledge of the parasitic worms of several groups of vertebrates of the Russian Arctic, A. Trematodes. Trudy Morskogo Nauchnogo Instituta. 3(2):5-79.

Layman, E. M. 1930. Parasitic worms of fishes of Peter the Great Bay. Izvestiya Tikhookeanskoy Nauchno-Promyslovoy Stantsii. 3(6):1-120.

Massino, B. G. 1927. On the determination of species of the genus Plagiorchis Lühe, 1899. Sbornik Rabot po Gelmintologii, Posvyaschenny Prof. K. I. Skrjabinu. pp. 108-113.

Massino, B. G. Trematodes of the genus Plagiorchis Lühe, 1899, from birds of Russian. Zbl. Bakter., Parasitenk. u. Infekt. 78:125-142. (In German).

Morozov, Yu. F. 1956. On the knowledge of the helminth fauna of rodents and insectivores of the U. S. S. R. and an attempt in analyzing its ecological-geography. Dissertatsiya.

Orlov, I. V. and B. S. Moskalev. 1953. Dynamics of helminthiases in river beavers of the Voronezh Preserve. Trudy Voronezhskogo Gosudarstvennogo Zapovednika. No. 4:98-101.

Palimpsestov, M. A. 1929. A new species of trematode, Plagiorchis popovi n. sp. from the intestine of dogs. Rabota 74-y Soyuznoy Gelmintologicheskoy Expeditsii v Astrakhanskom Okruge Nizhno-Volzhskogo Kraya. pp. 48-52.

Panova, L. G. 1937. On the study of the trematode fauna of gulls of the Don district. Trudy Leningradskogo Gosudarstvennogo Veterinarnogo Instituta. 1(1):52-61.

Paskalskaya, M. Yu. 1954. Plagiorchiasis of hens. Life cycle of the agent, diagnosis, and epizootology of the disease. Avtoreferat dissertatsii.

Petrov, A. M. and P. N. Tikhonov. 1927. A new trematode, Plagiorchis massino nov. sp., from the intestine of domestic carnivores. Sbornik Rabot po Gelmintologii, Posvyaschenny Prof. K. I. Skrjabinu. pp. 150-154.

Pigulevsky, S. V. 1931. Parasitic worms of fishes of the Dnieper basin. Ezhegodnik Zoologicheskogo Muzeya Akad. Nauk SSSR. 32(4):425-452.

Pigulevsky, S. V. 1931. New species of trematodes from fishes of the Dnieper basin. Zoologischer Anzeiger. 96(1-2):9-18.

Plotnikov, N. N. 1933. On the parasitic flatworms of the cities, Tobolsk and Obdorsk, of the Ural district. Trudy Uralskogo Oblastnogo

Instituta Mikrobiologii i Epidemiologii. 1(1):28-41.

Sadovskaya, N. P. 1952. Parasitic worms of rodents and insectivores of the Primorye region. Avtoreferat dissertatsii. Trudy Gelmintologicheskoy Laboratorii Akad. Nauk SSSR. 7:388-390.

Semenov, V. D. 1927. Trematodes of birds of the western U. S. S. R. Sbornik Rabot po Gelmintologii, Posvyaschenny Prof. K. I. Skrjabinu. pp. 221-271.

Sinitsyn, D. F. 1905. Materials on the natural history of trematodes. Distomes of fishes and frogs in the vicinity of Warsaw. Varshava. 210 pp.

Sinitsyn, D. F. 1907. Observations on the metamorphoses of trematodes. Arch. Zool. Exp. et Gen. 7:21-37. (In French).

Sinitsyn, D. F. 1929. Unpublished drawings of Nanophyetus salmincola of the U. S. Department of Agriculture, Bureau of Animal Ind. Laboratory. Washington. (In English).

Skrjabin, K. I. 1920. Trematodes of snakes of Paraguay. Izvestiya Donskogo Veterinarnogo Instituta. 1(2):6-11.

Skrjabin, K. I. 1924. On the fauna of parasitic worms of pelicans of Turkestan. Trudy Gosudarstvennogo Instituta Experimentalnoy Veterinarii. 2(1):4-5.

Skrjabin, K. I. 1928. On the trematode fauna of birds of the Transbaikal region. Ann. Parasit. 6(1):80-87. (In French).

Skrjabin, K. I. and B. G. Massino. 1925. Trematodes of birds of the Moscow district. Zbl. Bakter., Parasitenk. u. Infekt., Abt. 2, 64:453-462. (In German).

Sobolev, A. A. 1946. Three new species of trematodes of marsh fowl. Sbornik Rabot po Gelmintologii, Posvyaschenny Akademiku K. I. Skrjabinu. pp. 247-251.

Solonitsyn, I. A. 1928. On the knowledge of the helminth fauna of birds of the Volzhsko-Kamsky region (Nematodes and trematodes). Uchenye Zapiski Kazanskogo Gosudarstvennogo Veterinarnogo Instituta. 38(1):75-99.

Sudarikov, V. E. 1950. On the trematode fauna of vertebrates of the central Povolzhie district. Trudy Gelmintologicheskoy Laboratorii Akad. Nauk SSSR. 3:131-141.

Fedyushin, A. V. 1949. A new species of trematode from domestic hen. Trudy Gelmintologicheskoy Laboratorii Akad. Nauk SSSR. 2:94-95.

Strom, Zh. K. 1924. A new trematode, Plagiorchis arcuatus, of poultry. Zool. Anz. 2(9-10):274-280. (In German).

Strom, Zh. K. 1928. Contributions on the systematics of the genus Xenopharynx Nicoll, 1912, and a description of a new species, X. amudariensis n. sp. Zool. Anz. 79:167-172. (In German).

Strom, Zh. K. 1935. On the trematode fauna of Tadzhikistan. In: Materials on the parasitology and fauna of southern Tadzhikistan. Trudy Komplexnoy Expeditsii. No. 10:219-254.

Strom, Zh. K. 1940. New species of trematodes of

the genus Plagiorchis Lühe, 1899. Parazitologichesky Sbornik Zoologicheskogo Instituta Akad. Nauk SSSR. 8:225-231.

Schulz, R. Ed. S. 1932. Trematodes of the genus Plagiorchis Lühe from rodents. Vestnik Microbiologii, Epidemiologii i Parazitologii. 2(1):53-60.

Schulz, R. Ed. S. and A. A. Skvortsov. 1931. Plagiorchis arvicolae n. sp. from water-rat. Zschr. f. Parasitenk. 3(4):765-774. (In German).

KEY TO THE GENERA OF THE SUBFAMILY LIOPHISTREMATINAE ARTIGAS, RUIZ AND LEÃO, 1942 (XIV:623)

K. I. Skrjabin and D. N. Antipin

1 (2) Genital pore posterior to ventral sucker, submedial.
　　Liophistrema Artigas, Ruiz and Leão, 1942 (fig. 567)
2 (1) Genital pore anterior to ventral sucker, posterior to intestinal bifurcation, extremely lateral.
　　　　　　　　　Bieria Leão, 1946 (fig. 568)

KEY TO THE FAMILIES OF THE SUPERFAMILY AZYGIOIDEA SKRJABIN AND GUSCHANSKAJA, 1956 (XIV:670)

K. I. Skrjabin and L. Kh. Gushanskaya

1 (4) Vitellaria follicular.
2 (3) Pars prostatica and seminal vesicle enclosed in cirrus sac; ejaculatory duct and metraterm opening into genital atrium; single ascending branch of uterus leading from ovary.   Azygiidae Odhner, 1911
3 (2) Long ejaculatory duct, pars prostatica and considerable portion of seminal vesicle, all enclosed in cirrus sac; long hermaphroditic duct external to sac; descending branch of uterus leading from ovary, reaching end of body, returning anteriorly as ascending branch.   Xenoperidae Poche, 1925
4 (1) Vitellaria differently constructed.
5 (6) Vitellaria compact, entire or rarely lobed; ejaculatory duct enclosed in cirrus sac, occasionally pars prostatica and seminal vesicle; pores of ejaculatory duct and metraterm open into genital atrium; atrium external to cirrus sac.
　　　Liocercidae Skrjabin and Guschanskaja, 1956
6 (5) Vitellaria tubular, lateral, extra-cecal; terminal segments of male and female genital ducts enclosed within cirrus sac, ducts opening into genital atrium.   Hirudinellidae Dollfus, 1932

KEY TO THE SUBFAMILIES OF THE FAMILY AZYGIIDAE ODHNER, 1911 (XIV:678)

K. I. Skrjabin and L. Kh. Gushanskaya

1 (2) Testes posterior to ovary; esophagus present.
　　　Azygiinae Skrjabin and Guschanskaja, 1956
2 (1) Testes anterior to ovary; esophagus lacking.
　　　　Leuceruthrinae Goldberger, 1911

KEY TO THE GENERA OF THE SUBFAMILY AZYGIINAE SKRJABIN AND GUSCHANSKAJA, 1956 (XIV:678)

K. I. Skrjabin and L. Kh. Gushanskaya

1 (2) Ventral sucker larger than oral; genital pore directly posterior to intestinal bifurcation; vitellaria not reaching level of ventral sucker; excretory trunks uniting in anterior portion of body.
　　　Otodistomum Stafford, 1904 (fig. 569)
2 (1) Ventral sucker smaller than oral; genital pore directly anterior to ventral sucker.
3 (4) Ventral sucker in anterior part of body; lateral excretory trunks not uniting in anterior part of body; vitellaria not reaching level of ventral sucker.
　　　Azygia Looss, 1899 (fig. 570)
4 (3) Ventral sucker post-equatorial; lateral excretory trunks uniting anteriorly near oral sucker; vitellaria anteriorly extending far beyond ventral sucker.   Proterometra Horsfall, 1933 (fig. 571)

LITERATURE ON THE TREMATODES OF THE FAMILY AZYGIIDAE ODHNER, 1911 (XIV:780-785)

Bauer, O. N. 1948. Parasites of fishes of the Lena River. Izvestiya Vsesoyuznogo Nauchno-Issledovatelskogo Instituta Ozernogo i Rechnogo Rybnogo Khozyaystva. 27:157-174.

Belozerova-Syplyakova, O. M. 1937. Variability of the position of the vitellaria in Azygia lucii (Müller, 1776). Sbornik Rabot po Gelmintologii, Posvyachenny Akademiku K. I. Skrjabinu. pp. 45-47.

Belous, E. V. 1954. Parasitic worms of freshwater vertebrates of the Primorye region. Dissertatsiya.

Berg, L. S. 1908. Scientific results of the Aral Expedition. No. 9:

Bogatova, Z. K. 1936. The parasite fauna of native fish and acclimatized white fish of Lake Turgoyak. Uchenye Zapiski Leningradskogo Gosudarstvennogo Universiteta, No. 7, seriya biologicheskaya. No. 3:144-155.

Bykhovskaya, I. E. 1936. Materials on the parasitology of fishes of Karelia, II. The parasite fauna of fishes of small bodies of water. Trudy Borodinskoy Biologicheskoy Stantsii. 8(2):123-138.

Bykhovskaya (Pavlovskaya), I. E. 1940. The influence of age on variability of the parasite fauna of perch. Parazitologichesky Sbornik Zoologicheskogo Instituta Akad. Nauk SSSR. 8:99-103.

Gorbunova, M. N. 1936. Variations in the parasite fauna with age of pike and roach. Uchenye Zapiski Leningradskogo Gosudarstvennogo Universiteta, No. 7, seriya biologicheskaya. No. 3:5-30.

Dobrokhotova, O. V. 1953. Parasites of fishes of Lake Zaysan, with reference to the reconstruction of the ichthyofauna. Avtoreferat dissertatsii, Alma-Ata.

Dogiel, V. A. and B. E. Bykhovsky. 1934. The parasite fauna of fishes of the Aral Sea. Parazitologichesky Sbornik Zoologicheskogo Instituta Akad. Nauk SSSR. 4:241-346.

Dubinin, V. B. 1948. The influence of increased salinity of the Maly Uzen River on the parasite fauna of the fish population. Zoologichesky Zhurnal. 27(4): 335-342.

Zmeev, G. Ya. 1932. Infestation of fishes of the Amur River estuary with metacercariae of Metagonimus yokogawai Katsurada, 1913. Parazitologichesky Sbornik Zoologicheskogo Instituta Akad. Nauk SSSR. 3:253-259.

Zmeev, G. Ya. 1936. Trematodes and tapeworms of fishes of the Amur River. Parazitologichesky Sbornik Zoologicheskogo Instituta Akad. Nauk SSSR. 6:408-435.

Zykov, V. P. 1903. Materials on the fauna of the Volga and the hydrofauna of the Saratov Province. Byulleten Obschestva Ispytateley Prirody. 17(1):1-148.

Ivanov, A. S. 1940. Materials on the helminth fauns of fishes of the lower Volga. Parasitic worms of salmonid, clupeid, esocid, and silurid fishes. Trudy Astrakhanskogo Gosudarstvennogo Meditsinskogo Instituta. 7:10-27.

Isaychikov, I. M. 1928. On the knowledge of the parasitic worms of several groups of vertebrates of the Russian Arctic, A. Trematodes. Trudy Morskogo Nauchnogo Instituta. 3(2):5-79.

Isaychikov, I. M. 1933. On the knowledge of the parasitic worms of several groups of vertebrates of the Russian Arctic, II. Trudy Gosudarstvennogo Okeanograficheskogo Instituta. 3(1):3-44.

Lavrov, S. 1908. Results of the research on the fauna of parasitic worms of the Volga River and flood plains near Saratov. Raboty Volzhskoy Biologicheskoy Stantsii. 3(3):1-86.

Layman, E. M. 1930. Parasitic worms of fishes of Peter the Great Bay. Izvestiya Tikhookeanskoy Nauchno-Promyslovoy Stantsii. 3(6):1-120.

Layman, E. M. 1949. Course in the diseases of fishes. Pischepromizdat, Moskva. 305 pp.

Markevich, A. P. 1951. The parasite fauna of fresh-water fishes of the Ukrainian S. S. R. Izdatelstvo Akad. Nauk Ukr. SSR, Kiev. 376 pp.

Petrushevsky, G. K. 1940. Materials on the parasitology of fishes of Karelia, II. Parasites of fishes of Lake Onega. Uchenye Zapiski Leningradskogo Pedagogicheskogo Instituta, Kafedra Zoologii i Darvinizma. 30:133-186.

Petrushevsky, G. K. and O. N. Bauer. 1948. Zoogeography of parasites of fishes of Siberia. Izvestiya Vsesoyuznogo Nauchno-Issledovatelskogo Instituta Ozernogo i Rechnogo Rybnogo Khozyaystva. 27:217-231.

Petrushevsky, G. K. and I. E. Bykhovskaya (Pavlovskaya). 1935. Materials on the parasitology of fishes of Karelia, I. Parasites of fishes of lakes in the vicinity of Konchozero. Trudy Borodinskoy Biologicheskoy Stantsii. 8(1):15-77.

Petrushevsky, G. K., M. V. Mosevich, and I. G. Schupakov. 1948. The parasite fauna of fishes of the Ob and Irtysh Rivers. Izvestiya Vsesoyuznogo Nauchno-Issledovatelskogo Instituta Ozernogo i Rechnogo Rybnogo Khozyaystva. 27:67-96.

Pigulevsky, S. V. 1931. A new species of trematode from the Dnieper basin. Zool. Anz. 96:9-18. (In German).

Saidov, Yu. S. 1953. The helminth fauna of fishes and piscivorous birds of Dagestan. Dissertatsiya, Moskva.

Sinitsyn, D. F. 1905. Materials on the natural history of trematodes. Distomes of fishes and frogs in the vicinity of Warsaw. Izvestiya Varshavskogo Universiteta. pp. 1-120.

Skrjabin, K. I. and L. Kh. Gushanskaya. 1954. The sub-order Hemiurata (Markevitsch, 1951) Skrjabin and Guschanskaja, 1954, Part I. In: Skrjabin, K. I. Trematodes of animals and man. Izdatelstvo Akad. Nauk SSSR, Moskva-Leningrad. 9:227-653.

Skrjabin, K. I. and L. Kh. Gushanskaya. 1955. The suborder Hemiurata (Markevitsch, 1951) Skrjabin and Guschanskaja, 1954, Part II. In: Skrjabin, K. I., Trematodes of animals and man. Izdatelstvo Akad. Nauk SSSR, Moskva-Leningrad. 10:339-649.

Skrjabin, K. I. and L. Kh. Gushanskaya. 1955. The suborder Hemiurata (Markevitsch, 1951) Skrjabin and Guschanskaja, 1954, Part III. In: Skrjabin, K. I. Trematodes of animals and man. Izdatelstvo Akad. Nauk SSSR, Moskva-Leningrad. 11:465-748.

Skrjabin, K. I. and L. Kh. Gushanskaya. 1956. Systematics of the trematodes of the suborder Hemiurata (Markevitsch, 1951) Skrjabin and Guschanskaja, 1954. Trudy Gelmintologicheskoy Laboratorii Akad. Nauk SSSR. 8:144-158.

Skrjabin, K. I. and L. Kh. Gushanskaya. 1958. Ontongeny and separate stages of development in representatives of the suborder Hemiurata. Trudy Gelmintologicheskoy Laboratorii Akad. Nauk SSSR. 9:280-293.

Stsiborskaya, T. V. 1947. The parasite fauna of several fishes of the Pechora River. In: Materials on the knowledge of the flora and fauna of the U. S. S. R. Izdatelstvo Moskovskogo Obschestva Ispytateley Prirody, novaya seriya, Otdel Zoologii. No. 6:209-216.

Tell, Kh. I. 1955. The parasite fauna of fishes of Lake Vyrtsyarv. Avtoreferat dissertatsii.

Shulman, S. S. 1954. Survey of the parasite fauna of acipenserids of the U. S. S. R. Trudy Leningradskogo Obschestva Estestvoispytateley. 72(4):190-254.

KEY TO THE SUBFAMILIES OF THE FAMILY LIOCERCIDAE SKRJABIN AND GUSCHANSKAJA, 1956 (XIV:792)

K. I. Skrjabin and L. Kh. Gushanskaya

1 (2) Uroproct present; excretory system asymmetrical; ejaculatory duct and metraterm enclosed in cirrus sac, not uniting, opening independently, not forming hermaphroditic duct; ovary posterior to testes.

Intuscirrinae Skrjabin and Guschanskaya, 1958

2 (1) Uroproct lacking; excretory system symmetrical.

3 (4) Ejaculatory duct or ejaculatory duct and pars prostatica enclosed in cirrus sac; ovary anterior to testes.   Liocercinae Ejsmont, 1931

4 (3) Seminal vesicle, ejaculatory duct and pars prostatica enclosed in cirrus sac; ovary posterior to testes.   Arnolinae Skrjabin and Guschanskaja, 1958

KEY TO THE GENERA OF THE SUBFAMILY LIOCERCINAE EJSMONT, 1931 (XIV:792)

K. I. Skrjabin and L. Kh. Gushanskaya

1 (2) Only ejaculatory duct enclosed in cirrus sac; ovary posterior to vitellaria, anterior to testes; eggs without filaments.   Liocerca Looss, 1902 (fig. 572)

2 (1) Pars prostatica and ejaculatory duct enclosed in cirrus sac; ovary anterior to both vitellaria and testes; eggs with long filament at one pole.
          Hemipera Nicoll, 1912 (fig. 573)

KEY TO THE SPECIES OF THE GENUS HEMIPERA NICOLL, 1912 (XIV:797)

1 (2) Ventral sucker slightly post-equatorial; cirrus sac elongate, sub-divided into anterior and posterior parts; Laurer's canal lacking.
          H. ovocaudata Nicoll, 1912 (fig. 573)

2 (1) Ventral sucker in posterior third of body; cirrus sac short; Laurer's canal present.
          H. sharpei J. Jones, 1933

KEY TO THE SPECIES OF THE GENUS ARNOLA STRAND, 1942 (XIV:804)

1 (2) Esophagus thick-walled, sometimes longer than pharynx; cirrus sac elongate, fusiform; posterior end of cirrus sac extending to anterior edge of ventral sucker; vitellaria elongate, oval, entire.
          A. infirmus (Linton, 1940)

2 (1) Esophagus very short; cirrus sac pyriform, far anterior to ventral sucker; vitellaria lobed.
          A. microcirrus (Vlassenko, 1931) (fig. 574)

SUPPLEMENTARY LITERATURE ON THE TREMATODES OF THE FAMILY MONORCHIDAE ODHNER, 1911 (XIV:929)

Sobolev, A. A. 1955. The family Monorchidae Odhner, 1911. In: Skrjabin, K. I., Trematodes of animals and man. Izdatelstvo Akad. Nauk SSSR, Moskva-Leningrad. 11:257-464.

LIST OF SUPPLEMENTARY ILLUSTRATIONS

Troglotrematidae Odhner, 1914
   Nephrotrema truncatum (Leuckart, 1842) (fig. 891)
Achillurbainiidae Dollfus, 1939
   Achillurbainia nouveli Dollfus, 1939 (fig. 892)
Nanophyetidae Dollfus, 1939
   Macroorchis spinulosus Goto and Ando, 1919 (fig. 893)
Plagiorchidae Lühe, 1901
   Allogyptus crenshawi Byrd, 1950 (fig. 894)
   Alloplagiorchis garricki Simer, 1929 (fig. 895)
   Paralepoderma cloacicola (Lühe, 1909) (fig. 896)
   Parastiotrema ottawanensis Miller, 1940 (fig. 897)
   Rauschiella tineri Babero, 1951 (fig. 898)
   Dolichoperoides macalpini (Nicoll, 1914) (fig. 899)
Azygiidae Odhner, 1911
   Leuceruthrus micropteri Marshall and Gilbert, 1905 (fig. 900)
Liocercidae Skrjabin and Guschanskaja, 1956
   Intuscirrus aspicotti Acena, 1947 (fig. 902)
Xenoperidae Poche, 1925
   Xenopera insolita Nicoll, 1915 (fig. 903)
Monorchidae Odhner, 1911
   Pseudoproctotrema parupenei Yamaguti, 1942 (fig. 904)
   Botulisaccus pisceus Caballero, Bravo, and Grocott, 1955 (fig. 905)
   Brahamputrotrema punctata Gupta, 1953 (fig. 906)
   Opisthomonorchis carangis Yamaguti, 1952 (fig. 907)
   Diplolasiotocus chaetodontis Yamaguti, 1952 (fig. 908)

PART XV

KEY TO THE GENERA OF THE FAMILY MASENIIDAE YAMAGUTI, 1953 (XV:60)

1 (2) Spines of oral sucker forming continuous crown; diverticulum in pars prostatica lacking.
          Masenia Chatterji, 1933 (fig. 585)

2 (1) Spines of oral sucker interrupted mediodorsally; special diverticulum present at base at pars prostatica.
          Eumasenia Srivastava, 1951 (fig. 586)

KEY TO THE SPECIES OF THE GENUS MASENIA CHATTERJI, 1953 modified from Gupta (1953) (XV:61)

K. I. Skrjabin

1 (2) Excretory bladder tubular; vitellaria originating at level of middle of ventral sucker, extending to middle of posterior testis.
          M. collata Chatterji, 1933 (fig. 585)

2 (1) Excretory bladder saccular.
3 (4) Vitellaria originating at level of middle of ventral sucker, extending to posterior edge of anterior testis; eggs with operculum.
                    M. dayali Gupta, 1953
4 (3) Vitellaria originating at level of anterior edge of ventral sucker, extending to middle of anterior testis; eggs not operculate.   M. fossilis Gupta, 1953

KEY TO THE FAMILIES OF THE SUPERFAMILY OPECOELOIDEA CABLE, 1956 (XV:77)

K. I. Skrjabin, A. M. Petrov and V. P. Koval

1 (2) Mature forms with pigmented spots concentrated near vitellaria; oral sucker with post-oral ring; intestinal ceca never forming anal pores or uroproct; ventral sucker in mid- or hind- third of body; flame cells usually complex with numerous cones of cilia. Parasites of marine fishes.
                    Opistholebetidae Fukui, 1929
2 (1) No pigmented spots or post-oral ring; intestinal ceca (in many genera) forming anal pores or uroproct; ventral sucker at considerable distance from posterior end of body; flame cells with single cone of cilia. Parasites of both fresh-water and marine fishes.   Opecoelidae Ozaki, 1925

KEY TO THE GENERA OF THE SUBFAMILY OPECOELINAE STUNKARD, 1931 from Harshey (1937) (XV:87)

1. Anal pore absent.
                    Coitocaecum Nicoll (fig. 587)
2. Anal pore present.   3
3. Genital sucker present.
                    Anisoporus Ozaki (fig. 588)
4. Genital sucker absent.   5
5. Body oval; vitellaria near intestinal bifurcation, or extending further anteriorly.
6. Body elongate; vitellaria entirely restricted posterior to ventral sucker.   7
7. Seminal receptacle present.
                    Opecoelina Manter (fig. 590)
8. Seminal receptacle absent.
                    Opecoelus Ozaki (fig. 591)

KEY TO THE SUBFAMILIES OF THE FAMILY OPECOELIDAE OZAKI, 1925 (XV:94)

K. I. Skrjabin and A. M. Petrov

1 (2) Intestinal ceca opening externally in one or two independent anuses or together with excretory pore to form uroproct.   Opecoelinae Stunkard, 1931
2 (1) Intestinal ceca ending blindly, not opening to exterior.
3 (4) Intestinal ceca uniting terminally to form arch.   Coitocaecinae Poche, 1925
4 (3) Intestinal ceca not uniting.
5 (6) Genital pore opening dorsally.
                    Notoporinae Srivastava, 1942

6 (5) Genital pore opening ventrally.
7 (8) Cirrus sac well-developed, large, containing all elements of male terminal genitalia; seminal receptacle present.   Plagioporinae Manter, 1947
8 (7) Cirrus sac lacking, or very rudimentary.
9 (10) Genital sucker and seminal receptacle lacking.   Horatrematinae Srivastava, 1942
10 (9) Genital sucker and seminal receptacle present. Genitocotylinae Skrjabin, Petrow and Koval, 1958

KEY TO THE GENERA OF THE SUBFAMILY OPECOELINAE STUNKARD, 1931 (XV:95)

K. I. Skrjabin and A. M. Petrov

1 (2) Two vitelline reservoirs present, lateral and anterior to ovary; seminal vesicle wholly enclosed within small cirrus sac; seminal receptacle present.
                    Dideutosaccus Acena, 1941 (fig. 592)
2 (1) Single vitelline reservoir present.
3 (6) Large oral sucker equipped with special, strong sphincter-like organ on anterior portion; cirrus sac absent.
4 (5) Intestinal ceca opening into uroproct; two testes present.
                    Sphincterostoma Yamaguti, 1937 (fig. 593)
5 (4) Intestinal ceca opening to exterior independently in two anuses; uroproct absent; eight testes present.   Megacreadium Nagaty, 1956 (fig. 594)
6 (3) Oral sucker of usual construction.
7 (16) Intestinal ceca joining with excretory bladder, forming uroproct.
8 (13) Ventral sucker sessile; cirrus sac well-developed, equipped with muscular cirrus; external seminal vesicle lacking.
9 (10) Esophagus short, bulbous; pars prostatica lacking; shell of eggs thick, with marginal ridges.
                    Lucknoides Gupta, 1953 (fig. 595)
10 (9) Esophagus short, of usual appearance; pars prostation present, eggs without marginal ridges.
11 (12) Seminal receptacle absent; cirrus sac long, extending far beyond posterior edge of ventral sucker; genital pore anterior to intestinal bifurcation, directly posterior to pharynx.
                    Pseudopecoelina Yamaguti, 1942 (fig. 596)
12 (11) Seminal receptacle present; cirrus sac weakly developed, not extending to anterior edge of ventral sucker; genital pore posterior to intestinal bifurcation.   Neopecoelina Gupta, 1953 (fig. 597)
13 (8) Ventral sucker pedunculate; cirrus sac absent or present; external seminal vesicle present.
14 (15) Ventral sucker without papillae; accessory sucker lacking.
                    Pseudopecoeloides Yamaguti, 1940 (fig. 598)
15 (14) Ventral sucker with papillae; accessory sucker present. Opecoeloides Odhner, 1928 (fig. 599)
16 (7) Intestinal ceca opening to exterior independently, without junction with excretory bladder, forming one or two anuses.
17 (26) Intestinal ceca uniting at posterior end, forming single medial anus.

18 (19) Accessory sucker present; ventral sucker pedunculate, with papillae; lateral sucker-like structure present.   Anisoporus Ozaki, 1928 (fig. 588)

19 (18) Accessory suckers lacking.

20 (23) Ventral sucker pedunculate.

21 (22) Ventral sucker with lateral digitiform papillae; cirrus sac present.
Opecoelus Ozaki, 1925 (fig. 591)

22 (21) Muscular collar of ventral sucker forming two appendages projecting out over surface of ventral sucker; cirrus sac lacking.
Anomalotrema Zhukov, 1953 (fig. 600)

23 (20) Ventral sucker sessile.

24 (25) Cirrus sac well-developed; seminal receptacle present; anus dorsal, posterior to excretory pore.   Opecoelina Manter, 1934 (fig. 590)

25 (24) Cirrus sac rudimentary; seminal receptacle lacking; anus ventral, anterior to excretory pore.
Opegaster Ozaki, 1928 (fig. 589)

26 (17) Intestinal ceca not uniting, two independent anuses present.

27 (28) Ventral sucker with papillae; accessory sucker present.   Fimbriatus Wicklen, 1946 (fig. 601)

28 (27) Ventral sucker without papillae; accessory sucker lacking.

29 (30) Cirrus sac and seminal receptacle absent.
Neopecoelus Manter, 1947 (fig. 602)

30 (29) Cirrus sac and seminal receptacle present.
Pellamyzon Montgomery, 1957 (fig. 603)

KEY TO THE SPECIES OF THE GENUS OPECOELUS OZAKI, 1925 (XV:97)

K. I. Skrjabin and A. M. Petrov

1 (12) Testes lobed.

2 (5) Vitellaria not extending anteriorly beyond ovary.

3 (4) Ventral sucker with twelve papillae; eight papillae in peripheral pairs; two medial pairs nearer to aperture of sucker, one pair posterior and other anterior to aperture.   O. adelongatus Nagaty, 1956

4 (3) Two medial pairs of papillae absent.
O. elongatus Ozaki, 1925

5 (2) Vitellaria extending anteriorly beyond ovary.

6 (11) Seminal vesicle extending posteriorly beyond ventral sucker.

7 (8) Ventral sucker with five pairs of papillae.
O. xenistii Manter, 1940

8 (7) Ventral sucker with three pairs of papilla.

9 (10) Vitellaria bordering on posterior edge of ventral sucker; gonads closely adjacent.
O. himezi Yamaguti, 1951

10 (9) Vitellaria falling slightly short of ventral sucker; gonads dispersed spatially.
O. lobatus Ozaki, 1925 and O. mutu Yamaguti, 1940

11 (6) Seminal vesicle not extending posterior to ventral sucker.   O. tasmanicus Crowcroft, 1947

12 (1) Testes entire.

13 (26) Ventral sucker with four to five pairs of papillae.

14 (21) Vitellaria not reaching ventral sucker.

15 (16) Testes adjacent; ovary bilobed.
O. gonistii Yamaguti, 1938

16 (15) Testes not adjacent; ovary not bilobed.

17 (18) Vitellaria originating at level of ovary, not extending anterior to ovary.
O. upenoides Nagaty, 1954

18 (17) Vitellaria originating anterior to ovary.

19 (20) Vitellaria lateral, in four groups: anterior to ovary, between ovary and anterior testis, between testes, and posterior to posterior testes.
O. thapari Nagaty, 1954

20 (19) Vitellaria not in separate groups, continuously filling space between gonads.
O. lotellae Manter, 1954

21 (14) Vitellaria reaching ventral sucker.

22 (23) Genital pore at level of prepharynx.
O. acutus (Manter, 1940)

23 (22) Genital pore posterior to prepharynx.

24 (25) Five pairs of papillae present on ventral sucker, with three pairs elongated.
O. mexicanus Manter, 1940

25 (24) All five pairs of papillae short.
O. pentedactylus (Manter, 1940)

26 (13) Three pairs of papillae present on ventral sucker, or papillae lacking.

27 (32) Ovary deeply lobed.

28 (29) Ovary separated into four lobes.
O. quadratus Ozaki, 1928

29 (28) Ovary distinctly tri-lobed.

30 (31) Testes adjacent; vitellaria interrupted at level of testes.   O. nipponicus Yamaguti, 1951

31 (30) Testes distinctly separated; vitellaria not interrupted at level of testes.
O. sphaericus Ozaki, 1925 (fig. 591)

32 (27) Ovary compact, entire.

33 (38) Gonads adjacent.

34 (35) Papillae on ventral sucker not evident.
O. ozakii (Layman, 1930)

35 (34) Three pairs of papillae present on ventral sucker.

36 (37) Vitellaria originating at level of anterior edge of ventral sucker; body pyriform.
O. pyriformis Yamaguti, 1952

37 (36) Vitellaria originating posterior to ventral sucker; body elongate.   O. inimici Yamaguti, 1934

38 (33) Gonads distinctly separated.

39 (40) Papillae on ventral sucker very long, pedunculate.   O. minor Yamaguti, 1934

40 (39) Papillae on ventral sucker short.
O. adsphaericus Manter and Van Cleave, 1951

KEY TO THE SPECIES OF THE GENUS NEOPECOELUS MANTER, 1947 (XV:175)

K. I. Skrjabin and A. M. Petrov

1 (2) Testes and ovary lobed; intestinal ceca broad.
N. holocentri Manter, 1947

2 (1) Testes and ovary entire; intestinal ceca narrow.   N. scorpaenae Manter, 1947 (fig. 602)

KEY TO THE SPECIES OF THE GENUS GENITOCOTYLE PARK, 1937 (XV:280)

K. I. Skrjabin and A. M. Petrov

1 (2) Vitellaria originating anterior to ventral sucker; ovary far posterior to ventral sucker; genital pore at level of posterior limit of pharynx, occasionally anterior to genital sucker.
G. atlantica Manter, 1947

2 (1) Vitellaria originating posterior to ventral sucker; genital pore posterior to pharynx, anterior to genital sucker.

3 (4) Ovary considerably posterior to ventral sucker; vitellaria originating anterior to ovary.
G. acirrus Park, 1937 (fig. 604)

4 (3) Ovary near posterior edge of ventral sucker; vitellaria originating at level of posterior testis, posterior to ovary.
G. heterostichi Montgomery, 1957

KEY TO THE GENERA OF THE SUBFAMILY HORATREMATINAE SRIVASTAVA, 1942 (XV:288)

K. I. Skrjabin and A. M. Petrov

1 (2) Cuticle with small spines; testes in posterior portion of body, nearly symmetrical.
Horatrema Srivastava, 1942 (fig. 605)

2 (1) Cuticle smooth; testes tandem.

3 (4) Ventral sucker with two large lobes, anterior and posterior; posterior end of body with papilla-like appendages. Parvacreadium Manter, 1940 (fig. 915)

4 (3) Ventral sucker of ordinary construction; posterior papilla-like structures lacking.
Pseudopecoelus Wicklen, 1946 (fig. 606)

KEY TO THE SPECIES OF THE GENUS HORATREMA SRIVASTAVA, 1942 (XV:289)

K. I. Skrjabin and A. M. Petrov

1 (2) Seminal vesicle not extending beyond level of middle of ventral sucker; esophagus short; testes displaced towards posterior end of body.
H. crassum Manter, 1947

2 (1) Seminal vesicle extending beyond level of middle of ventral sucker; esophagus long; testes slightly distant from posterior end of body.
H. pristopomatis Srivastava, 1942 (fig. 605)

KEY TO THE SPECIES OF THE GENUS PSEUDOPECOELUS WICKLEN, 1946 from Manter (1954) (XV:296)

1 (10) Ovary lobed.

2 (3) Papillae present on posterior lip of ventral sucker. P. hemilobatus Manter, 1954

3 (2) Papillae on ventral sucker lacking.

4 (7) Vitellaria extending anterior to ventral sucker.

5 (6) Genital pore at level of mid-pharynx; ovary dextral to anterior testis.
P. umbrinae Manter and Van Cleave, 1951

6 (5) Genital pore at level of mid-esophagus; ovary medial, anterior to anterior testis.
P. brevivesiculatus Hanson, 1955

7 (4) Vitellaria not extending anterior to ventral sucker.

8 (9) Ventral sucker two to three times larger than oral. P. vulgaris (Manter, 1934) (fig. 606)

9 (8) Ventral sucker slightly larger than oral.
P. japonicus (Yamaguti, 1938)

10 (1) Ovary entire.

11 (12) Vitellaria extending anterior to ventral sucker. P. gibbonsiae Manter and Van Cleave, 1951

12 (11) Vitellaria not extending anterior to ventral sucker.

13 (14) Vitellaria interrupted at level of gonads.
P. elongatus (Yamaguti, 1938)

14 (13) Vitellaria not interrupted at level of gonads.

15 (16) Ventral sucker with lateral pouch.
P. priacanthi (MacCallum, 1921)

16 (15) Ventral sucker without lateral pouch.

17 (18) Testes smooth, entire; eggs: 0.044-0.051 mm. long. P. barkeri Hanson, 1950

18 (17) Testes lobed, with uneven contours; eggs: 0.057-0.066 mm. long. P. tortugae Wicklen, 1946

KEY TO THE GENERA OF THE SUBFAMILY NOTOPORINAE SRIVASTAVA, 1942 (XV:319)

K. I. Skrjabin and A. M. Petrov

1 (2) Cirrus aac and prostatic bursa absent; prostatic cells surrounding seminal vesicle, extending along voluminous pars prostatica; pars prostatica opening with metraterm into genital atrium.
Notoporus Yamaguti, 1938 (fig. 14)

2 (1) Cirrus sac lacking; so-called prostatic bursa present, surrounding prostatic vesicle, pars prostatica and seminal vesicle.
Neonotoporus Srivastava, 1942 (fig. 607)

KEY TO THE SPECIES OF THE GENUS NEONOTOPORUS SRIVASTAVA, 1942 (XV:323)

K. I. Skrjabin and A. M. Petrov

1 (2) Genital pore at level of mid-ventral sucker; gonads not lobed; maximal width of body at level of ventral sucker.
N. trachuri (Yamaguti, 1938) (fig. 607)

2 (1) Genital pore anterior to anterior edge of ventral sucker; gonads lobed; maximal body width posterior to testes.

3 (4) Body less than 2 mm. long; ventral sucker equatorial; genital pore dorsal near left edge of body, at level of anterior edge of ventral sucker; prostatic bursa membranous, without muscular elements.
N. yamagutii, Manter, 1947

4 (3) Body exceeding 3 mm. in length; ventral

sucker in anterior third of body; genital pore dorsal, near left edge of body, anterior to ventral sucker; prostatic bursa composed of weak longitudinal and strong circular external muscles.

N. carangis (Yamaguti, 1951)

KEY TO THE GENERA OF THE SUBFAMILY COITOCAECINAE POCHE, 1925 (XV:332)

K. I. Skrjabin and V. P. Koval

1 (2) Ventral sucker with digitiform papillae; genital pore medial or sinistral.

Dactylostomum Woolcock, 1935 (fig. 608)

2 (1) Ventral sucker without papillae; genital pore lateral.

3 (4) Cirrus sac short, reduced, enclosing cirrus (if present), pars prostatica, ejaculatory canal, and internal seminal vesicle; external seminal vesicle present.   Coitocaecum Nicoll, 1915 (fig. 587)

4 (3) Cirrus sac long, enclosing cirrus, ejaculatory canal, pars prostatica and all of seminal vesicle.

Crowcrocaecum Skrjabin and Koval, 1956 (fig. 609)

KEY TO THE SPECIES OF THE GENUS COITOCAECUM NICOLL, 1915 (XV:333)

K. I. Skrjabin and V. P. Koval

1 (4) Vitellaria exclusively posterior to ventral sucker.

2 (3) Eggs: 0.081-0.084 x 0.042-0.043 mm.

C. gymnophallum Nicoll, 1915 (fig. 587)

3 (2) Eggs: 0.054-0.057 x 0.036 mm.

C. callyodontis Yamaguti, 1942

4 (1) Vitellaria posterior and anterior to ventral sucker.

5 (8) Vitellaria interrupted in area of ventral sucker.

6 (7) Ovary entire. C. glandulosum Yamaguti, 1934

7 (6) Ovary deeply lobed.

C. tylogonium Manter, 1954

8 (5) Vitellaria continuous in region of ventral sucker.

9 (10) Testes tandem, with weakly indented edges.

C. orthorchis Ozaki, 1926

10 (9) Testes entire.

11 (12) Body round.   C. latum Ozaki, 1929

12 (11) Body elongate, oval.

13 (14) Pharynx with constriction.

C. diplobulbosum Ozaki, 1929

14 (13) Pharynx without constriction.

15 (16) Ventral sucker equatorial.

C. plagiorchis Ozaki, 1926

16 (15) Ventral sucker at boundary of anterior and middle thirds of body.

17 (18) Testes oblique.

C. leptoscari Yamaguti, 1940

18 (17) Testes tandem.

19 (20) Eggs: 0.048-0.051 x 0.026-0.032 mm.

C. tropicum Manter, 1940

20 (19) Eggs larger.

21 (22) Ventral sucker with papilla-like appendages; posterior testis serrate.

C. xesuri Yamaguti, 1940

22 (21) Ventral sucker without appendages; posterior testis round.

23 (24) Cirrus present.

C. anaspidis Hickman, 1934

24 (23) Cirrus lacking.

C. unibulbosum Ozaki, 1929

Note: C. acanthogobium Park, 1939; C. koreanum Park, 1939; C. palaoensis Ogata, 1942; and C. parvum Crowcroft, 1944 omitted from key.

KEY TO THE SPECIES OF THE GENUS DACTYLOSTOMUM WOOLCOCK, 1935 (XV:420)

K. I. Skrjabin and V. P. Koval

1 (2) Eggs: 0.053-0.054 x 0.027-0.030 mm.

D. vitellosum Manter, 1940

2 (1) Eggs: 0.07-0.08 x 0.05-0.06 mm.

D. gracile Woolcock, 1935 (fig. 608)

KEY TO THE GENERA OF THE SUBFAMILY PLAGIOPORINAE MANTER, 1947 (XV:425)

K. I. Skrjabin and V. P. Koval

1 (4) Ventral sucker pedunculate.

2 (3) Excretory bladder very long, extending to level of ventral sucker; posterior testis not reaching end of body.

Podocotyloides Yamaguti, 1934 (fig. 610)

3 (2) Excretory bladder of medium size, at considerable distance from acetabular peduncle; posterior testis reaching posterior end of body.

Pedunculacetabulum Yamaguti, 1934 (fig. 611)

4 (1) Ventral sucker sessile.

5 (8) Many testes present.

6 (7) Eggs with filaments; genital pore posterior to intestinal bifurcation.

Helicometrina Linton, 1910 (fig. 612)

7 (6) Eggs without filaments; genital pore submedial, at level of pharynx.

Decemtestis Yamaguti, 1934 (fig. 613)

8 (5) Two testes present.

9 (12) Ovary between testes.

10 (11) Testes symmetrical, in posterior portion of body.   Hysterogonia Hanson, 1955 (fig. 614)

11 (10) Testes medial, not reaching posterior portion of body.

Pseudoplagioporus Yamaguti, 1938 (fig. 615)

12 (9) Ovary anterior to testes.

13 (16) Eggs with filaments.

14 (15) Genital pore medial, posterior to intestinal bifurcation.   Helicometra Odhner, 1902 (fig. 616)

15 (14) Genital pore medial or submedial, anterior to intestinal bifurcation.

Stenopera Manter, 1933 (fig. 617)

16 (13) Eggs without filaments.

17 (18) Muscular fold surrounding ventral sucker.
            Pachycreadium Manter, 1954 (fig. 618)
18 (17) Ventral sucker lacking muscular fold.
19 (20) Cuticle armed with spines.
Spinoplagioporus Skrjabin and Koval, 1958 (fig. 619)
20 (19) Cuticle smooth.
21 (22) Eggs with tapering terminal projection opposite operculum. Eucreadium Dayal, 1950 (fig. 620)
22 (21) Eggs without terminal projection.
23 (26) Vitellaria reaching posterior edge of ventral sucker.
24 (25) Loops of uterus extending to level of ovary.
            Podocotyle (Dujardin, 1845) (fig. 621)
25 (24) Loops of uterus extending to level of testes.
            Neopodocotyle Dayal, 1950 (fig. 622)
26 (23) Vitellaria reaching level of intestinal bifurcation and beyond.
            Hamacreadium Linton, 1910 (fig. 623) and
            Plagioporus Stafford, 1904 (fig. 624)

KEY TO THE SUBGENERA OF THE GENUS PLAGIOPORUS STAFFORD, 1904 (XV:431)

K. I. Skrjabin and V. P. Koval

1 (2) Excretory bladder short, not reaching level of ventral sucker. Plagioporus (Stafford, 1904)
2 (1) Excretory bladder long, extending anteriorly beyond ventral sucker.
            Paraplagioporus Yamaguti, 1939

KEY TO THE SPECIES OF THE SUBGENUS PLAGIOPORUS (Stafford, 1904) (XV:431)

K. I. Skrjabin and V. P. Koval

1 (56) Intestinal ceca posteriorly extending considerable distance beyond testes.
2 (5) Genital pore opposite oral sucker.
3 (4) Testes lobed. P. preporatus Manter, 1954
4 (3) Testes entire. P. dactylopagri Manter, 1954
5 (2) Genital pore posterior to oral sucker.
6 (15) Ovary lobed.
7 (10) Testes lobed.
8 (9) Sucker ratio, 1:1.8-2:3.6.
            P. lobatus (Yamaguti, 1934)
9 (8) Sucker ratio, 1:1.4-1.6.
            P. acanthogobii Yamaguti, 1951
10 (7) Testes entire.
11 (12) Eggs about 0.022 mm. long.
            P. choerodontis (Yamaguti, 1934)
12 (11) Eggs at least 0.054 mm. long, usually more than 0.07 mm. long.
13 (14) Genital pore posterior to pharynx; eggs: 0.098 mm.
            P. elongatus (Goto and Ozaki, 1930)
14 (13) Genital pore at level of pharynx; eggs: 0.075-0.082 mm. P. ira Yamaguti, 1940
15 (6) Ovary entire.
16 (21) Vitellaria interrupted at level of ventral sucker.

17 (20) Testes tandem; vitellaria extending to level of pharynx.
18 (19) Vitellaria interrupted at level of testes.
            P. interruptus Manter, 1954
19 (18) Vitellaria not interrupted at level of testes.
            P. issaitschikowi (Layman, 1930)
20 (17) Testes oblique; vitellaria not extending to pharynx. P. macassarensis Yamaguti, 1952
21 (16) Vitellaria continuous along ventral sucker.
22 (27) Genital pore at level of pharynx.
23 (24) Ventral sucker less than twice diameter of oral sucker. P. calotomi (Yamaguti, 1934)
24 (23) Ventral sucker at least twice diameter of oral.
25 (26) Ventral sucker equatorial; uterus reaching posterior testis. P. branchiostegi Yamaguti, 1937
26 (25) Ventral sucker pre-equatorial; uterus not reaching posterior testis.
            P. japonicus Yamaguti, 1938
27 (22) Genital pore posterior to pharynx.
28 (35) Vitellaria reaching base of oral sucker.
29 (3) Cirrus sac reaching posterior edge of ventral sucker or beyond.
            P. angusticolle (Hausmann, 1896)
30 (29) Cirrus sac not reaching posterior edge of ventral sucker.
31 (32) Eggs: 0.054-0.057 mm. long.
            P. apogonichthydis Yamaguti, 1938
32 (31) Eggs: 0.075 mm. long.
33 (34) Testes and ovary tandem; vitellaria longer on right side than on left. P. imanensis Belouss, 1954
34 (33) Testes oblique; ovary at same level as anterior testis; vitellaria of right and left sides of equal length. P. triangulogenitalis Belouss, 1954
35 (28) Vitellaria not reaching base of oral sucker.
36 (37) Uterus reaching posterior testis.
            P. macrouterinus Haderlie, 1953
37 (36) Uterus not reaching posterior testis.
38 (41) Vitellaria not extending anterior to ventral sucker.
39 (40) Excretory bladder reaching ovary.
            P. virens Sinitsin, 1931
40 (39) Excretory bladder short, extending only to posterior testis. P. lepomis Dobrovolny, 1939
41 (38) Vitellaria extending anterior to ventral sucker.
42 (47) Ovary medial directly anterior to testes.
43 (44) Vitellaria not extending anterior to intestinal bifurcation. P. siliculus Sinitsin, 1931
44 (43) Vitellaria extending anterior to intestinal bifurcation.
45 (46) Ventral sucker considerably larger than oral; uterus reaching anterior testis.
            P. pacificus Yamaguti, 1938
46 (45) Ventral sucker only slightly larger than oral; uterus wholly anterior to ovary.
            P. occidentalis Szidat, 1944
47 (42) Ovary slightly dextral.
48 (49) Genital pore posterior to intestinal bifurcation; vitellaria extending only to level of intestinal bifurcation. P. obductus (Nicoll, 1909)

49 (48) Genital pore anterior to intestinal bifurcation; vitellaria extending anterior to intestinal bifurcation.

50 (53) Testes tandem.

51 (52) Excretory bladder extending to posterior testis.   P. serotinus Stafford, 1940 (fig. 624)

52 (51) Excretory bladder reaching ovary.
          P. sillagonis Yamaguti, 1938

53 (50) Testes oblique.

54 (55) Vitellaria numerous in space posterior to testes, sparse or lacking in region of ventral sucker.
          P. varius (Nicoll, 1910)

55 (54) Vitellaria relatively sparse, absent posterior to testes, dispersed evenly through lateral fields.   P. alacris (Looss, 1901)

56 (1) Intestinal ceca not extending posterior to testes.

57 (62) Eggs small, about 0.027 mm. long.

58 (61) Genital pore at level of pharynx.

59 (60) Ovary tri-lobed.
          P. pachysomus Manter, 1954

60 (59) Ovary spherical, entire.
          P. thalasomatis Yamaguti, 1942

61 (58) Genital pore at level of intestinal bifurcation.   P. neopercis (Yamaguti, 1938)

62 (57) Eggs reaching at least 0.057 mm. in length.

63 (78) Vitellaria lateral, not merging posterior to testes.

64 (73) Vitellaria usually not extending posteriorly beyond posterior edge of posterior testis.

65 (66) Ovary separated from testes by several loops of uterus; vitellaria numerous, filling all space between ventral sucker and ovary.
          P. nicolli (Issaitschikoff, 1928)

66 (65) Loops of uterus not passing between ovary and testes; vitellaria in space between ventral sucker and ovary, restricted laterally.

67 (70) Eggs 0.07 mm. Parasitic in gall bladder of fishes.

68 (69) Cirrus not forming loops.
          P. sinitzini Mueller, 1934

69 (68) Cirrus forming complete loop.
          P. sinitizini huroni Dobrovolny, 1939

70 (67) Eggs 0.076-0.092 mm. Intestinal parasites of fishes.

71 (72) Ovary lobed. P. orientalis (Yamaguti, 1934)

72 (71) Ovary entire.   P. skrjabini Koval, 1951

73 (64) Vitellaria extending posteriorly beyond posterior edge of posterior testis for considerable distance.

74 (75) Body 0.85 mm. long; ovary entire; posterior end of cirrus sac in space between intestinal bifurcation and ventral sucker.   P. spari Yamaguti, 1951

75 (74) Body 1.27-2.10 mm. long; ovary tri-lobed; posterior end of cirrus sac extending beyond anterior edge of ventral sucker.

76 (77) Ventral sucker large, twice size of oral, equatorial; body fusiform.
          P. fusiformis Price, 1934

77 (76) Ventral sucker larger than oral by 1.2-1.5 times, at boundary of anterior and middle

thirds of body; body elongate, oval.
          P. azurionis Yamaguti, 1951

78 (63) Vitelline follicles merging medially posterior to testes.

79 (80) Ovary tri-lobed.
          P. zacconis (Yamaguti, 1934)

80 (79) Ovary entire.

81 (82) Vitellaria not extending anteriorly beyond level of ventral sucker.
          P. angulatus (Dujardin, 1845)

82 (81) Vitellaria extending anteriorly beyond level of ventral sucker, reaching pharynx.

83 (84) Esophagus present.
          P. synagris Yamaguti, 1952

84 (83) Esophagus absent.
          P. trachuri Pogorelzeva, 1954

KEY TO THE SPECIES OF THE SUBGENUS PARAPLAGIOPORUS YAMAGUTI, 1939 (XV:545)

1 (2) Excretory bladder reaching anterior edge of ventral sucker; ovary spherical.
          P. (P.) isagi Yamaguti, 1939

2 (1) Excretory bladder reaching intestinal bifurcation; ovary tri-lobed.
          P. (P.) longivesicula Yamaguti, 1952

KEY TO THE SPECIES OF THE GENUS DECEMTESTIS YAMAGUTI, 1934 from Manter (1954) (XV:551)

1 (4) Two concentric ventral suckers present.

2 (3) Vitellaria extending posterior to testes.
          D. biacetabulata Srivastava, 1936

3 (2) Vitellaria not extending posterior to testes.
          D. pseudolabri Manter, 1954

4 (1) Ventral sucker without double construction.

5 (8) Vitellaria interrupted in region of ventral sucker.

6 (7) Cirrus sac not extending posterior to ventral sucker.   D. kobayashii Park, 1939

7 (6) Cirrus sac extending posterior to ventral sucker.   D. callionymi Yamaguti, 1934

8 (5) Vitellaria continuous in region of ventral sucker.

9 (10) Cirrus sac not extending to ventral sucker.
          D. brevicirrus Srivastava, 1936

10 (9) Cirrus sac reaching ventral sucker, or extending more posteriorly.

11 (20) Ovary very weakly lobed.

12 (17) Testes in longitudinal, lateral rows.

13 (14) Ventral sucker nearly two times larger than oral.   D. megacotyle Yamaguti, 1958

14 (13) Ventral sucker only slightly larger than oral.

15 (16) Cirrus sac extending beyond posterior edge of ventral sucker.   D. gonistii Yamaguti, 1938

16 (15) Cirrus sac not extending beyond posterior edge of ventral sucker.   D. takanoha Yamaguti, 1951

17 (12) At least one testis displaced from longitudinal row.

18 (19) Eggs: 0.108-0.117 mm. long.
D. spari Yamaguti, 1938
19 (18) Eggs: 0.054-0.066 mm. long.
D. bera Yamaguti, 1938
20 (11) Ovary deeply lobed.
21 (22) Cirrus sac not extending posterior to ventral sucker.   D. mehrai Srivastava, 1936
22 (21) Cirrus sac extending posterior to ventral sucker.   D. ditrematis, Yamaguti, 1934
23 (24) Vitellaria not reaching genital pore.
D. sillagonis Yamaguti, 1934 (fig. 613)
24 (23) Vitellaria reaching genital pore.
25 (28) Muscular protuberance present in terminal portion of metraterm.
26 (27) Testes multi-lobed.
D. neopercis Yamaguti, 1938
27 (26) Testes entire.
D. pagrosomi Yamaguti, 1938
28 (25) Muscular protuberance not present in terminal portion of metraterm.
D. azumae (Layman, 1930)

KEY TO THE SPECIES OF THE GENUS HAMACREADIUM LINTON, 1910 (XV:581)

K. I. Skrjabin and V. P. Koval

1 (4) Testes lobed.
2 (3) Genital pore medial; cirrus sac straight, diagonal; excretory bladder reaching ovary.
H. lethrini Yamaguti, 1934
3 (2) Genital pore lateral; cirrus sac curved; excretory bladder reaching intestinal bifurcation.
H. mutabile Linton, 1910 (fig. 623)
4 (1) Testes entire.
5 (8) Genital pore lateral.
6 (7) Vitellaria reaching intestinal bifurcation; excretory bladder reaching intestinal bifurcation.
H. epinepheli Yamaguti, 1934
7 (6) Vitellaria reaching anterior edge of ventral sucker; excretory bladder reaching level of ovary.
H. oscitans Linton, 1910
8 (5) Genital pore medial.
9 (10) Excretory bladder reaching posterior edge of ventral sucker.   H. consuetum Linton, 1910
10 (9) Excretory bladder reaching level of ovary.
H. gulella Linton, 1910

KEY TO THE SPECIES OF THE GENUS HELICOMETRA ODHNER, 1902 (XV:606)

K. I. Skrjabin and V. P. Koval

1 (14) Vitellaria not extending anteriorly beyond anterior edge of ventral sucker.
2 (11) Ventral sucker larger or equal to oral.
3 (4) Ventral sucker equal in size to oral; oral sucker funnel-shaped, terminal.
H. insolita Poljansky, 1955
4 (3) Ventral sucker larger than oral; oral sucker round; sub-terminal.

5 (10) Ventral sucker at least two times larger than oral.
6 (7) Anterior border of vitellaria extending to posterior edge of ventral sucker.
H. bassensis Woolcock, 1935
7 (6) Anterior border of vitellaria not reaching posterior edge of ventral sucker.
8 (9) Anterior border of vitellaria midway between ovary and ventral sucker; eggs: 0.040-0.058 mm. long.   H. torta Linton, 1910
9 (8) Anterior border of vitellaria at level slightly posterior to ventral sucker; eggs: 0.065-0.078 mm. long.   H. pretiosa Bravo-Hollis and Manter, 1957
10 (5) Ventral sucker less than 1.5 times larger than oral; vitellaria extending anteriorly to center of ventral sucker.   H. plovmornini Issaitschikoff, 1928
11 (2) Ventral sucker smaller than oral.
12 (13) Vitellaria reaching anterior edge of ventral sucker.   H. grandora Manter, 1954
13 (12) Vitellaria not extending to anterior edge of ventral sucker.
H. neosebastodis Crowcroft, 1947 and H. tenuifolia Woolcock, 1935
14 (1) Vitellaria extending anteriorly beyond anterior edge of ventral sucker.
15 (16) Genital pore directly posterior to intestinal bifurcation; usually one testis present, or none.
H. execta Linton, 1910
16 (15) Genital pore at level of intestinal bifurcation or anterior; testes well developed.
17 (24) Genital pore at level of intestinal bifurcation or more anterior.
18 (21) Testes entire.
19 (20) Vitellaria continuous lateral to ventral sucker.   H. pulchella (Rudolphi, 1819) (fig. 616)
20 (19) Vitellaria interrupted at level of ventral sucker.   H. sinuata (Rudolphi, 1819)
21 (18) Testes lobed.
22 (23) Genital pore medial; ovary anterior to testes.   H. fasciata (Rudolphi, 1819)
23 (22) Genital pore slightly dextral; ovary wedged between testes. H. markewitschi Pogorelzeva, 1954
24 (17) Genital pore at level of pharynx, or at level of mid-esophagus.
25 (26) Vitelline follicles lateral, merging medially posterior to testes.   H. hypodytis Yamaguti, 1934
26 (25) Vitellaria lateral, not merging medially posterior to testes.   H. epinepheli Yamaguti, 1934
Note: H. gurnardus Thapar and Dayal, 1934 omitted from key.

KEY TO THE SPECIES OF THE GENUS PEDUNCULACETABULUM YAMAGUTI, 1934 (XV:687)

K. I. Skrjabin and V. P. Koval

1 (2) Cuticle armed with small spines; vitellaria occupying lateral fields anterior to testes.
P. pedicellata Srivastava, 1938
2 (1) Cuticle aspinose; vitellaria anterior to testes,

occupying all available space.

> P. opisthorchis Yamaguti, 1934 (fig. 611)

Note: P. manteri Nagaty, 1942 omitted from key.

KEY TO THE SPECIES OF THE GENUS PSEUDOPLAGIOPORUS YAMAGUTI, 1938 (XV:802)

K. I. Skrjabin and V. P. Koval

1 (2) Ovary smaller than testes.

> P. lethrini Yamaguti, 1938 (fig. 615)

2 (1) Ovary larger than testes.

> P. microrchis Yamaguti, 1942

LITERATURE ON THE TREMATODES OF THE FAMILY OPECOELIDAE OZAKI, 1925 (XV:812-813)

Bazikalova, A. Ya. 1932. Materials on the parasitology of fishes of Murmansk. Sbornik Nauchno-Promyslovykh Rabot na Murmane. pp. 136-153.

Belous, E. V. 1953. Parasitic worms of freshwater vertebrates of the Primorye region. Dissertatsiya.

Vlasenko, P. V. 1931. On the fauna of parasitic worms of fishes of the Black Sea. Trudy Karadagskoy Biologicheskoy Stantsii. No. 4:88-136.

Dogiel, V. A. and G. S. Markov. 1937. Variations in the parasite fauna with age of the char (Salvelinus alpineus) of Novaya Zemlya. Trudy Leningradskogo Obschestva Estestvoispytateley. 66(3):434-455.

Zhukov, E. V. 1953. Endoparasitic worms of fishes of the Sea of Japan and the Kurile shoal waters. Dissertatsiya.

Zernov, S. A. 1913. On the question of the study of life in the Black Sea. Zapiski Imperatorskoy Akad. Nauk. 32(1):

Zakhvatkin, V. A. 1951. Parasites of fishes of waters of the Transcarpathian district. Naukovi Zapiski Lvivskogo Naukovogo Prirodoznavchogo Muzeyu Akad. Nauk Ukr. RSR. 1:119-149. (In Ukrainian).

Zakhvatkin, V. A. and O. P. Kulakivskaya. 1951. Parasites of fishes of the upper Dniester. Naukovi Zapiski Lvivskogo Naukovogo Prirodoznavchogo Muzeyu Akad. Nauk Ukr. RSR. 1:150-155. (In Ukrainian).

Ivanitsky, S. V. 1928. On the trematode fauna of vertebrates of the Ukraine. Veterinarne Dilo. No. 2(51):30-48.

Isaychikov, I. M. 1928. On the knowledge of the parasitic worms of several groups of vertebrates of the Russian Arctic, A. Trematodes. Trudy Morskogo Nauchnogo Instituta. 3(2):5-79.

Isaychikov, I. M. 1933. On the parasitic worms of several groups of vertebrates of the Russian Arctic, II. Trudy Gosudarstvennogo Okeanograficheskogo Instituta. 3(1):3-44.

Koval, V. P. 1946. Variability of diagnostic characters in Coitocaecum skrjabini Iwa. (Trematoda: Digenea); Kievsky Derzhavni Universitet. Naukovi Zapiski. 5(2):237-243. (In Ukrainian).

Koval, V. P. 1949. The present status of the systematics of Coitocaecum skrjabini Iwan. Kievskogo Derzhavni Universitet. Biol. Zbirnik. No. 4:91-97. (In Ukrainian).

Koval, V. P. 1950. Digenetic trematodes of fishes of the lower Dnieper. Trudy Biologo-Gruntoznavchogo Fakultetu Kievskogo Derzhavnogo Universitetu. No. 5:187-207.

Koval, V. P. 1952. Digenetic trematodes of fishes of the Dnieper River. Dissertatsiya.

Koval, V. P. 1955. Critical survey of the species composition of the genus Plagioporus (Trematoda: Digenea). Naukovi Zapiski Kievskogo Derzhavnogo Universitetu Trudi Biologo-Gruntoznavchogo Fakultetu. No. 10:95-115. (In Ukrainian).

Koval, V. P. 1955a. Materials on the knowledge of the seasonal dynamics of the digenetic trematodes of fishes of the Dnieper River. Naukovi Zapiski Kievskogo Derzhavnogo Universitetu, 13(16). Trudi Biologo-Gruntoznavchogo Fakultetu. No. 10:87-94. (In Ukrainian).

Komarova, M. S. 1941. On the knowledge of the helminth fauna of percoid fishes of the Dnieper. Doklady Akad. Nauk Ukr. SSR. No. 1:29-34. (In Ukrainian).

Komarova, M. S. 1941. On the knowledge of the life cycle of Bunodera luciopercae Mull. (Trematoda: Digenea). Doklady Akad. Nauk SSSR. 31(2):184-185.

Komarova, M. S. 1951. On the life cycle of the trematode Coitocaecum skrjabini Ivanisky. Doklady Akad. Nauk SSSR. 77(6):1127-1128.

Kulakivskaya, O. P. 1949. Parasites of fishes of the upper Dniester. Naukovi Zapiski Lvivskogo Naukovogo Prirodoznavchogo Muzeyu Akad. Nauk Ukr. RSR. 1: (In Ukrainian).

Kulakivska, O. P. 1951. On the parasite fauna of trout and grayling of Transcarpathia. Naukovi Zapiski Lvivskogo Naukovogo Prirodoznavchogo Muzeyu Akad. Nauk URSS. 1:156-166. (In Ukrainian).

Kulakivskaya, O. P. 1955. Parasites of fishes of the Dniester. Dissertatsiya, Kiev. 280 pp. (In Ukrainian).

Layman, E. M. 1930. Parasitic worms of fishes of Peter the Great Bay. Izvestiya Tikhookeanskoy Nauchno-Promyslovoy Stantsii. 3(6):1-120.

Layman, E. M. and M. M. Borovkova. 1926. Parasitic worms of fishes of Murmansk, from materials of the 15th Union Helminthological Expedition in 1924. Raboty Parazitologicheskoy Laboratorii Moskovskogo I Gosudarstvennogo Universiteta. pp. 27-37.

Markevich, A. P. 1934. Parasitic diseases of fish and their control. KOIZ, Leningrad. 100 pp.

Markevich, A. P. 1951. The parasite fauna of fresh-water fishes of the Ukrainian S.S.R. Izdatelstvo Akad. Nauk Ukr. SSR, Kiev. 376 pp.

Osmanov, S. U. 1940. Materials on the parasite fauna of fishes of the Black Sea. Uchenye Zapiski Leningradskogo Pedagogicheskogo Instituta, Kafedra Zoologii i Darvinizma. 30:187-267.

Polyansky, Yu. I. 1952. Two new species of digenetic trematodes from fishes of the North Atlantic.

Parazitologichesky Sbornik Zoologicheskogo Instituta. Akad. Nauk SSSR. 14:266-280.

Polyansky, Yu. I. 1955. Materials on the parasite fauna of fishes of the northern seas of the U.S.S.R. Parasites of fishes of the Barents Sea. Trudy Zoologicheskogo Instituta Akad. Nauk SSSR. 19:1-170.

Pogoreltseva, T. P. 1952. The parasite fauna of fishes of the northeastern part of the Black Sea. Dissertatsiya.

Pogoreltseva, T. P. 1952. Materials on the parasite fauna of fishes of the northeastern part of the Black Sea. Trudy Zoologicheskogo Instituta Akad. Nauk SSSR. 8:100-120.

Pogoreltseva, T. P. 1952. New trematodes from fishes of the Black Sea. Trudy Karadagskoy Biologicheskoy Stantsii. No. 12:34-35.

Pogoreltseva, T. P. 1954. New species of digenetic trematodes from fishes of the Black Sea. Naukovi Zapiski Kievskogo Pedagog. Institutu, XV, biol. seriya. No. 2:133-137. (In Ukrainian).

Pigulevsky, S. V. 1931. Parasitic worms of fishes of the Dnieper basin. Ezhegodnik Zoologicheskogo Muzeya Akad. Nauk SSSR. 32(4):425-542.

Pigulevsky, S. V. 1931. A new species of trematode from fishes of the Dnieper basin. Zool. Anz., 96(1/2):9-18. (In German).

Petrushevsky, G. K. and I. E. Bykhovskaya (Pavlovskaya). 1935. Materials on the parasitology of fishes of Karelia, I. Parasites of fishes of lakes in the vicinity of Konchozero. Trudy Borodinskoy Biologicheskoy Stantsii. 8(1):15-77.

Reshetnikova, A. V. 1954. The parasite fauna of several commercial fishes of the Black Sea. Dissertatsiya.

Savina, N. V. 1927. On the knowledge of the parasitic worms of fishes of Murmansk. Sbornik Rabot po Gelmintologii, Posvyaschenny Prof. K. I. Skrjabinu. pp. 216-220.

Skrjabin, K. I. and V. P. Koval. 1956. Crowcrocaecum gen. nov., a new genus of the family Opecoelidae Ozaki, 1925. Naukovi Zapiski Kievskogo Derzhavnogo Universitetu, 15(12), Trudi Biol. Fakultetu. No. 13:93-94. (In Ukrainian).

Stsiborskaya, T. A. 1948. The parasite fauna of lump-sucker of the White Sea. Raboty Morskoy Biologicheskoy Stantsii, Karelo-Finskogo Universiteta. 1:145-151.

Strelkov, Yu. A. 1956. Endoparasitic worms of marine fishes of eastern Kamchatka. Avtoreferat dissertatsii.

Uspenskaya, A. V. 1950. On the question of the life cycle of Podocotyle atomon. Uchenye Zapiski Leningradskogo Gosudarstvennogo Universiteta, No. 133, seriya biologicheskaya. No. 23:129-134.

Shevchenko, N. N. 1956. Parasites of fishes of the mid-reaches of the North Donets River. Trudy Nauchno-Issledovatelskogo Instituta Biologii i Biologicheskogo Fakulteta Kharkovskogo Gosudarstvennogo Universiteta. 23:269-301.

Shulman-Albova, R. E. 1952. On the question of variability in the digentic trematode of fishes, Podocotyle atomon (Rud.) Odhner. Uchenye Zapiski Leningradskogo Gosudarstvennogo Universiteta, No. 141. No. 28:110-126.

Shulman, S. S. 1950. Parasites of fishes of bodies of water of the Latvian S. S. R. Trudy Gelmintologicheskoy Laboratorii Akad. Nauk SSSR. 7:278-281.

Shulman, R. E. 1948. The parasite fauna of commercial fishes of the White Sea. Avtoreferat dissertatsii.

Shulman, S. S. and R. E. Shulman-Albova. 1953. Parasites of fishes of the White Sea. Izdatelstvo Akad. Nauk SSSR, Moskva-Leningrad. 198 pp.

Shumilo, R. 1953. Parasites of fishes of the lower Dniester River. Dissertatsiya.

LIST OF SUPPLEMENTARY ILLUSTRATIONS

Thapariellidae Srivastava, 1953
  Thapariella anastomusa Srivastava, 1953 (fig. 909)
Trematobrienidae Dollfus, 1950
  Trematobrien hapiochromios Dollfus, 1950 (fig. 910)
Transversotrematidae Yamaguti, 1953
  Transversotrema haasi Witenberg, 1944 (fig. 911)
Deropristidae Skrjabin, 1958
  Deropristis inflata (Molin, 1899) (fig. 912)
  Pristicola sturionis (Little, 1930) (fig. 913)
Prosogonotrematidae Vigueras, 1940
  Prosogonotrema bilabiata Vigueras, 1940 (fig. 914)

PART XVI

LITERATURE ON THE TREMATODES OF THE ORDER FAUSTULIDA (POCHE, 1925) SKRJABIN AND SCHULZ, 1937 (XVI:12)

Skrjabin, K. I. and R. Ed. S. Schulz. 1937. Helminthiases of long-horned cattle and their young. Selkozgiz, Moskva. 723 pp.

KEY TO THE SUBFAMILIES OF THE FAMILY SCHISTORCHIDAE YAMAGUTI, 1942 (XVI:16)

K. I. Skrjabin

1 (2) Lymphatic system absent.
                    Schistorchinae Skrjabin, 1959

2 (1) Lymphatic system present.
                         Apocreadiinae Skrjabin, 1942

KEY TO THE SPECIES OF THE GENUS
SCHISTORCHIS LÜHE, 1906 (XVI:18)

K. I. Skrjabin

1 (6) Testes tandem, medial.
2 (3) Testes to left and right of medial line; uterus anterior to ovary.   S. haridis Nagaty, 1957
3 (2) Testes strictly medial, adjacent.
4 (5) Vitellaria originating posterior to ovary at level of anterior testis.   S. stenosoma Hanson, 1953
5 (4) Vitellaria originating anterior to ovary at level of posterior edge of ventral sucker.
                         S. zancli Hanson, 1953
6 (1) Testes partially or wholly in two longitudinal, medial or submedial rows.
7 (10) Testes in two sub-medial rows.
8 (9) Vitellaria originating posterior to ventral sucker; ventral sucker slightly posterior to intestinal bifurcation.   S. carneus Lühe, 1906 (fig. 625)
9 (8) Vitellaria originating at level of anterior edge of ventral sucker; ventral sucker directly adjacent to intestinal bifurcation.   S. oligorchis (Johnston, 1914)
10 (7) Part of testes medial, forming single row; second part in two rows in sub-medial fields.
11 (12) Ventral sucker adjacent to intestinal bifurcation; ovary equatorial.
                         S. callyodontis Yamaguti, 1942
12 (11) Ventral sucker at considerable distance from intestinal bifurcation; ovary in anterior half of body.   S. sigani Yamaguti, 1942

KEY TO THE SPECIES OF THE GENUS
APOCREADIUM MANTER, 1937 (XVI:35)

K. I. Skrjabin

1 (6) Vitellaria originating at considerable distance posterior to ventral sucker.
2 (3) Testes entire, elongate, oval, with equatorial swelling (so-called equatorial crest).
                         A. balistis Manter, 1947
3 (2) Testes irregularly lobed, without equatorial crest.
4 (5) Body length not exceeding 4.1 mm.; eggs: 0.061-0.067 x 0.031 x 0.034 mm.
                A. mexicanum Manter, 1937 (fig. 626)
5 (4) Body length reaching 6.57-9.65 mm.; eggs: 0.088-0.102 x 0.048-0.060.
                A. longisinosum Manter, 1937
6 (1) Vitellaria originating anterior to ventral sucker, or at same level.
7 (8) Testes entire, longitudinally oval; ovary adjacent to ventral sucker, at some distance from anterior testis.   A. synagris Yamaguti, 1953
8 (7) Testes deeply lobed, stellate, with rounded rays; ovary adjacent to anterior testis, considerably posterior to ventral sucker. A. caballeroi Bravo, 1953

KEY TO THE GENERA OF THE FAMILY
CALLODISTOMATIDAE POCHE, 1925 (XVI:56)

K. I. Skrjabin

1 (2) Cephalic end with muscular dorso-lateral ornamentations; intestinal parasites of turtles.
                Braunotrema Price, 1930 (fig. 627)
2 (1) Cephalic end lacking muscular ornamentation. Parasites in gall bladder of fishes.
3 (6) Loops of uterus inter- and extra-cecal.
4 (5) Testes extra-cecal; vitelline follicles lacking definite arrangement, surrounding intestinal ceca along both sides of ventral sucker.
                Callodistomum Odhner, 1902 (fig. 628)
5 (4) Testes inter-cecal and adjacent to intestinal ceca ventrally; vitellaria forming on each side of body one row of stellate follicles originating extra-cecally posterior to intestinal bifurcation and merging medially at level of Mehlis' gland.
                Prosthenhystera Travassos, 1930 (fig. 629)
6 (3) Loops of uterus strictly inter-cecal.
7 (8) Body attenuated, elongate; ovary and vitellaria in anterior half of body; intestinal ceca narrow, extending to posterior end of body.
                Cholepotes Odhner, 1911 (fig. 630)
8 (7) Body broad, oval; ovary and vitellaria in posterior part of body; intestinal ceca broad, not extending to posterior end of body.
Teratotrema Travassos, Artigas and Pereira, 1928
                         (fig. 631)

KEY TO THE SPECIES OF THE GENUS
OPISTHOLEBES NICOLL, 1915 from Cable
(1956) (XVI:90)

K. I. Skrjabin

1 (6) Ventral sucker surrounded by well-developed glandular disc.
2 (5) Posterior end of cirrus sac near level of ovary; vitelline follicles merging anterior to genital pore or adjacent to gonads posteriorly.
3 (4) Body 3.8 mm. long; ovary sub-medial; vitelline follicles merging anteriorly; ejaculatory duct nearly straight.   O. cotylophorus Ozaki, 1935
4 (3) Body 1.35 mm. long; ovary anterior to right testis; vitelline follicles merging anteriorly, adjacent to gonads posteriorly; ejaculatory duct sharply curved.   O. adcotylophorus Manter, 1947
5 (2) Cirrus sac noticeably distant from ovary; vitelline follicles not merging anteriorly, not adjacent to gonads posteriorly.
                         O. diodontis Cable, 1956
6 (1) Ventral sucker without glandular disc.
7 (8) Body oval; ovary anterior to right testis; cirrus sac reaching 0.45 mm. in length.
                O. amplicoelum Nicoll, 1915 (fig. 336)
8 (7) Body elongate; ovary sub-medial to right testis; cirrus sac reaching 0.67 mm. in length.
                         O. elongatus Ozaki, 1937

KEY TO THE SUBFAMILIES OF THE FAMILY ACCACOELIIDAE LOOSS, 1912 (XVI:109)

K. I. Skrjabin and L. Kh. Gushanskaya

1 (8) Hermaphroditic bursa absent.
2 (7) Pharynx of usual structure.
3 (4) Genital atrium with copulatory organ capable of eversion; vitellaria tubular or in separate groups of dendritically branched follicles.
                Accacoeliinae Odhner, 1911
4 (3) Genital atrium present; copulatory organ lacking.
5 (6) Vitellaria composed of pyriform follicles along dorsal and ventral sides of intestinal ceca in middle portion of body; oral sucker with special sphincter with two lips; esophagus short.
                Orophocotylinae Yamaguti, 1958
6 (5) Vitellaria tubular, equatorial; oral sucker of usual structure; esophagus long.
                Tetrochetinae Looss, 1912
7 (2) Pharynx of complex structure; muscular sphincter present anterior to pharynx, ventral wall of sphincter extending anteriorly to form proboscis-like structure; sometimes with only slender protuberance extending anteriorly from pharynx; muscular bulb present posterior to pharynx; vitellaria tubular.
                Rhynchopharynginae Yamaguti, 1958
8 (1) Hermaphroditic bursa present; pharynx weakly developed, of usual structure; vitellaria of two distinct parts: basal mass with branched character, grouped in cephalic portion of body, second rudimentary vitelline mass directly posterior to ovary, composed of single follicle with independent vitelline duct.   Guschanskianinae Skrjabin, 1959

KEY TO THE GENERA OF THE SUBFAMILY ACCACOELIINAE ODHNER, 1911 (XVI:110)

K. I. Skrjabin and L. Kh. Gushanskaya

1 (4) Cuticle anteriorly covered with papillae.
2 (3) Anterior and posterior extensions of intestinal ceca with diverticula; ventral sucker pedunculate; vitellaria tubular.
            Accacladocoelium Odhner, 1928 (fig. 632)
3 (2) Intestinal diverticula absent; ventral sucker sessile, slightly protuberant; vitellaria in separate groups of dendritically branched follicles.
            Accacoelium Monticelli, 1893 (fig. 633)
4 (1) Cuticle smooth; posterior extensions of intestinal ceca with diverticula; anterior extensions lacking diverticula; ventral sucker pedunculate; vitellaria tubular.   Accacladium Odhner, 1928 (fig. 634)

KEY TO THE SPECIES OF THE GENUS ACCACLADIUM ODHNER, 1928 (XVI:114)

K. I. Skrjabin and L. Kh. Gushanskaya

1 (2) Body 12-30 mm. long; ventral sucker 0.91-

1.25 x 0.7-0.8 mm.
                A. serpentulum Odhner, 1928 (fig. 634)
2 (1) Body 8.22-17.60 mm. long; ventral sucker 0.53-1.59 x 0.31-0.60 mm.; vas deferens functioning as seminal vesicle for most of its length.
            A. nematulum A. Noble and G. Noble, 1937

KEY TO THE GENERA OF THE SUBFAMILY RHYNCHOPHARYNGINAE YAMAGUTI, 1958 (XVI:139)

K. I. Skrjabin and L. Kh. Gushanskaya

1 (2) Genital atrium and genital papilla present; metraterm well-defferentiated; vitellaria composed of dendritically branched tubules, extending from ventral sucker to level of ovary, extra-cecal; pharynx globular; esophagus with muscular bulb at anterior end; cuticle covered with papillae anteriorly.
            Rhyncopharynx Odhner, 1928 (fig. 635)
2 (1) Genital atrium and papilla lacking; differentiated metraterm lacking; vitellaria tubular, originating posterior to anterior testis, terminating before reaching ventral sucker; pharynx elongate; muscular bulb of esophagus absent; cuticle smooth.
            Paratetrochetus Hanson, 1955 (fig. 636)

KEY TO THE GENERA OF THE SUBFAMILY TETROCHETINAE LOOSS, 1912 (XVI:148)

K. I. Skrjabin and L. Kh. Gushanskaya

1 (4) Anterior portion of body with sucker-like cervical crests on dorsal surface.
2 (3) Ventral sucker with large petal-shaped appendage in shape of cowl.
            Mneiodhneria Dollfus, 1935 (fig. 637)
3 (2) Ventral sucker pedunculate, without appendages.   Caballeriana Skrjabin and Guschanskaja, 1959
                                            (fig. 638)
4 (1) Anterior portion of body without sucker-like cervical crests; ventral sucker lacking appendages.
            Tetrochetus Looss, 1912 (fig. 639)

KEY TO THE SPECIES OF THE GENUS TETROCHETUS LOOSS, 1912 (XVI:149)

K. I. Skrjabin and L. Kh. Gushanskaya

1 (4) Ventral sucker larger than oral, pedunculate.
2 (3) Oral sucker 0.2 mm. long; ventral sucker 0.29 mm. long; body 3.37 mm. long.
                T. coryphaenae Yamaguti, 1934
3 (2) Oral sucker 0.187-0.277 mm. long; ventral sucker 0.277-0.472 mm. long; body 5.4 mm. long.
                T. proctocolus Manter, 1940
4 (1) Ventral sucker smaller than oral, slightly protuberant, not pedunculate; oral sucker 1.2-1.3 mm. long; ventral sucker 0.9-1.0 mm. long; body 10-12 mm. long.

                T. raynerius (Nardo, 1827) (fig. 639)

Note: T. hamadai Fukui and Ogata, 1935 omitted from key.

KEY TO THE SUBFAMILIES OF THE FAMILY LECITHOCHIRIIDAE SKRJABIN AND GUSCHANSKAJA, 1954 (XVI:189)

K. I. Skrjabin and L. Kh. Gushanskaya

1 (2) Anal appendage and hermaphroditic bursa lacking; metraterm uniting with ejaculatory duct, forming hermaphroditic duct.
　　　Myosacciinae Skrjabin and Guschanskaja, 1959
2 (1) Anal appendage present.
3 (4) Hermaphroditic bursa present.
　　　　　Lecithochiriinae Lühe, 1901
4 (3) Hermaphroditic bursa absent.
　　　Brachyphallinae Skrjabin and Guschanskaja, 1955

LITERATURE ON THE TREMATODES OF THE FAMILY ACCACOELIIDAE LOOSS, 1912 (XVI:182)

Markevich, A. P. 1951. The parasite fauna of fresh-water fishes of the Ukrainian S. S. R. Izdatelstvo Akad. Nauk Ukr. SSR, Kiev. 376 pp.

Skrjabin, K. I. and L. Kh. Gushanskaya. 1954. The suborder Hemiurata (Markevitsch, 1951) Skrjabin and Guschanskaja, 1954, Part I. In: Skrjabin, K. I., Trematodes of animals and man. Izdatelstvo Akad. Nauk SSSR. Moskva-Leningrad. 9:227-653.

Skrjabin, K. I. and L. Kh. Gushanskaya. 1956. Systematics of the trematodes of the suborder Hemiurata (Markevitsch, 1951) Skrjabin and Guschanskaja, 1954. Trudy Gelmintologicheskoy Laboratorii Akad. Nauk SSSR. 8:144-158.

Skrjabin, K. I. 1959. On the position of the trematode, Accacladocoelium alveolatum Robinson, 1934, in the systematics of the suborder Hemiurata. Trudy Gelmintologicheskoy Laboratorii Akad. Nauk SSSR. 9:26-27.

KEY TO THE SUBORDERS OF THE ORDER STRIGEIDIDA (LA RUE, 1926) (XVI:296)

V. E. Sudarikov

1 (2) Body divided morphologically and functionally into two segments; cirrus sac absent; ovary anterior to testes, or at level of anterior testis (exception: Mesoophorodiplostomum: ovary inter-cecal); single pair of lateral collecting vessels extending from excretory bladder in cercariae. Strigeata LaRue, 1926
2 (1) Body not divided into segments, small caudal appendage may be present; cirrus sac present; ovary never anterior to testes; two pairs of lateral collecting tubules extending from excretory bladder in cercariae. Cyathocotylata Sudarikov, 1959

KEY TO THE SUPERFAMILIES OF THE SUBORDER STRIGEATA LA RUE, 1926 (XVI:297)

V. E. Sudarikov

1 (2) Anterior segment cup-shaped; organ of Brandes composed of dorsal and ventral lobes rising from bottom of cavity (not lobed in Pseudapatemon; lobes reduced in Codonocephalus); proteolytic glands in cavity near inter-segmental boundary.
　　　　　Strigeoidea Railliet, 1919
2 (1) Anterior segment thickened, saucer-shaped, leaf-shaped or oval in outline; organ of Brandes round, divided by fissure into right and left portions or equipped with cavity.
3 (4) Paraprostatic gland with duct opening into genital atrium along with uterus and ejaculatory duct; testes entire, almost spherical. Sexually mature forms in reptiles.
　　　　Proterodiplostomatoidea Sudarikov, 1959
4 (3) Paraprostatic gland absent; testes multilobed, or irregular in outline; posterior testis or both testes horseshoe-shaped, protruding dorsally. Sexually mature forms found in birds and mammals.
　　　　　Diplostomatoidea Nicoll, 1937

KEY TO THE FAMILIES OF THE SUPERFAMILY STRIGEOIDEA RAILLIET, 1919 (XVI:298)

V. E. Sudarikov

1 (2) Anterior segment cup-shaped, globular, or funnel-shaped; vitelline follicles in both segments or only in posterior; paraprostatic gland lacking. Parasites of birds.　　　Strigeidae Railliet, 1919
2 (1) Anterior segment of body tubular; vitellaria in anterior segment; paraprostatic gland present. Parasites of mammals.
　　　　Duboisiellidae Sudarikov, 1959

KEY TO THE SUBFAMILIES OF THE FAMILY STRIGEIDAE RAILLIET, 1919 (XVI:298)

V. E. Sudarikov

1 (2) Vitelline follicles in both segments.
　　　　　Strigeinae Railliet, 1919
2 (1) Vitelline follicles concentrated in posterior segment with occasional follicles extending into basal portion of anterior segment.
3 (4) Organ of Brandes composed of dorsal and ventral lobes, separated by deep interlobular fissure.
　　　　Cotylurinae Sudarikov, 1959
4 (3) Organ of Brandes of different structure.
5 (6) Organ of Brandes without lobes; genital cone surrounded by high muscular fold in shape of cuff; ejaculatory bursa lacking.
　　　　Codonocephalinae Sudarikov, 1959
6 (5) Lobes of organ of Brandes merging into single structure, protruding from cavity of cephalic cup; genital cone with cuff lacking; ejaculatory bursa present.
　　　　Pseudapatemoninae Sudarikov, 1959

KEY TO THE GENERA OF THE SUBFAMILY STRIGEINAE RAILLIET, 1919 (XVI:299)

V. E. Sudarikov

1 (2) Pharynx lacking; oral and ventral suckers normally developed.
Apharyngostrigea Ciurea, 1927 (fig. 640)
2 (1) Pharynx present.
3 (4) Anterior body segment with two large lateral expansions; expansions apparently hypertrophic portions of base of dorsal lobe of organ of Brandes; basal mass of vitelline follicles concentrated in expansions; suckers weakly developed, usually within cephalic cup; aperture of cup usually constricted.
Parastrigea Szidat, 1928 (fig. 641)
4 (3) Anterior segment without lateral expansions enclosing vitelline follicles, relatively narrow.
5 (6) Vitelline follicles concentrated into two small symmetrical aggregates within lobes of organ of Brandes; genital cone lacking; opening of hermaphroditic duct at tip of broad papilla-like elevation found in base of genital atrium; posterior segment six to seventeen times longer than anterior.
Ophiosoma Szidat, 1928 (fig. 642)
6 (5) Vitelline follicles not forming paired symmetrical aggregates in anterior segment of body, dispersed unequally throughout walls of cephalic cup and in lobes of organ of Brandes; genital cone present.
7 (8) Lobes of organ of Brandes broad, not divided into right and left portions; seminal vesicle tubular, sinuous, posterior to testes.
Strigea Abildgaard, 1790 (fig. 643)
8 (7) Ventral lobe of organ of Brandes divided into two sub-lobes twisted into helix with common base; seminal vesicle tubular, slightly sinuous, with proximal portion lying at level between ovary and anterior testis. Chaubaustrigea Sudarikov, 1959 (fig. 644)

KEY TO THE GENERA OF THE SUBFAMILY COTYLURINAE SUDARIKOV, 1959 (XVI:468)

V. E. Sudarikov

1 (2) Muscular, eversible genital bulb present; hermaphroditic canal opening dorsal to bulb; genital pore subterminal, displaced dorsally.
Cotylurus Szidat, 1928 (fig. 645)
2 (1) Genital bulb absent; genital pore terminal.
3 (4) Two protruding, flexible lobes present posterior to pharynx, to right and left of medial line; anterior segment saccular, concave ventrally; lower boundary of concavity reaching level of one-fourth to one-half length of entire segment.
Swartzitrema Vigueras, 1941 (fig. 646)
4 (3) Lobes posterior to pharynx absent.
5 (6) Hermaphroditic duct opening at tip of genital papilla; genital papilla not clearly delimited from parenchyma by fibrilar wall.
Apatemon Szidat, 1928 (fig. 647)
6 (5) Hermaphroditic duct opening at tip of genital cone; genital cone distinctly delimited from parenchyma.
7 (10) Genital cone very large, not less than one-fifth length of posterior segment, greatly eversible through genital pore; hermaphroditic duct sinuous or folded in genital cone.
8 (9) Anterior segment relatively small, cardiform or pyriform, shorter than posterior segment by factor of 4.5-8.5; posterior segment with slender flexible neck piece; genital cone equal to or exceeding length of body segment containing testes; region of body containing genital atrium distinct from body proper; genital pore broad. Parasites of gulls and penguins. Cardiocephalus Szidat, 1928 (fig. 648)
9 (8) Anterior segment not more than four times smaller than posterior; posterior segment saccular, without flexible neck-piece, genital cone shorter than zone of testes; region of genital atrium not distinct from body; genital pore narrow. Parasites of swans (Australia).
Australapatemon Sudarikov, 1959 (fig. 649)
10 (7) Genital cone less than one-fifth length of posterior segment; hermaphroditic duct, simple, tubular.
11 (12) Body thick, both segments large; posterior segment without slender flexible neck-piece, not exceeding 3.5 times length of anterior segment.
Pseudostrigea Yamaguti, 1933 (fig. 650)
12 (11) Body slender, posterior segment with slender flexible neck-piece; length of posterior segment four or more times longer than anterior segment.
13 (14) Posterior segment 8.5-25 times longer than anterior segment; anterior segment in shape of shallow cup or funnel; tip of genital cone surrounded by muscular fold resembling cuff. Parasites of birds of the suborder Accipitres.
Nematostrigea Sandground, 1934 (fig. 651)
14 (13) Posterior segment four to five times longer than anterior; anterior segment cardiform or pyriform; fold surrounding genital cone lacking. Parasites of gulls.
Cardiocephaloides Sudarikov, 1959 (fig. 652)

KEY TO THE GENERA OF THE FAMILY MESOCOELIIDAE DOLLFUS, 1950 (XVI:636)

K. I. Skrjabin and F. N. Morozov

1 (2) Testes slightly oblique or parallel, lateral to medial line. Mesocoelium Odhner, 1910 (fig. 653)
2 (1) Testes tandem, medial.
Pintneria Poche, 1925 (fig. 654)

LITERATURE ON THE TREMATODES OF THE FAMILY MESOCOELIIDAE DOLLFUS, 1950 (XVI:703)

Skrjabin, K. I. 1916. Parasitic trematodes and nematodes collected by the expedition of Professors V. A. Dogiel and I. I. Sokolov in British East Africa

and Uganda. Nauchnye Rezultaty Zoologicheskoy Expeditsii Prof. V. A. Dogielya i I. I. Sokolova v Britanskuyu Vostochnuyu Afriku i Ugandu v 1914 g. 1(14):
1-157.

LIST OF SUPPLEMENTARY ILLUSTRATIONS

Faustulidae Poche, 1925
  Faustula keksooni (McCallum, 1918) (fig. 918)
Schistorchidae Yamaguti, 1942
  Choanodera caulolatili Manter, 1940 (fig. 919)
Accacoeliidae Looss, 1912

Guschanskiana alveolata (Robinson, 1934) (fig. 920)
  Orophocotyle planci (Stossich, 1899 (fig. 917)
Lecithochiriidae Skrjabin and Guschanskaja, 1954
  Myosaccium ecaude Montgomery, 1957 (fig. 901)
Strigeidae Railliet, 1919
  Codonocephalus urinigerus (Rudolphi, 1819) (fig. 879)
Duboisiellidae Sudarikov, 1959
  Duboisiella proloba Baer, 1938 (fig. 872)
Neostrigeidae Bisseru, 1956
  Neostrigea africana Bisseru, 1956 (fig. 832)

PART XVII

KEY TO THE GENERA OF THE SUBFAMILY ENCYCLOMETRINAE MEHRA, 1931 from Mehra (1937) (XVII:56)

1 (2) Cirrus sac transversely oriented anterior to
ventral sucker, sometimes partially superimposed on
anterior edge of sucker; eggs: 0.0748-0.095 x 0.03-
0.07 mm.
    Encyclometra Baylis and Cannon, 1924 (fig. 580)
2 (1) Cirrus sac sinistral, anterior to ventral
sucker; eggs: 0.0444-0.059 mm.
            Orthorchis Mödlinger, 1924

KEY TO THE SPECIES OF THE GENUS ENCYCLOMETRA BAYLIS AND CANNON, 1924 from Yeh (1958) (XVII:56)

1 (2) Intestinal ceca of equal size.
        E. colubrimurorum (Rudolphi, 1819) (fig. 580)
2 (1) Intestinal ceca of unequal length.
3 (4) Intestinal ceca sharply different in length.
                E. asymmetrica Wallace, 1936
4 (3) Intestinal ceca not excessively different in
length.   E. japonica Yoshida and Ozaki, 1929

KEY TO THE GENERA OF THE SUBFAMILY ENCYCLOMETRINAE MEHRA, 1931 (XVII:58)

K. I. Skrjabin and D. N. Antipin

1 (2) Cuticle without spines; cirrus sac transverse
to long body axis; seminal vesicle bulbous; uterus not
forming self-crossing loops, ascending and descending loops not inter-twined.
    Encyclometra Baylis and Cannon, 1924 (fig. 580)
2 (1) Cuticle with spines; cirrus sac oblique to long
body axis; seminal vesicle tubular, twisted into
spiral; ascending and descending limbs of uterus
inter-twined. Encyclobrephus Sinha, 1949 (fig. 655)

KEY TO THE GENERA OF THE SUBFAMILY

TRAVTREMATINAE GOODMAN, 1954 (XVII:110)

K. I. Skrjabin and D. N. Antipin

1 (2) Cuticle smooth, without spines; cirrus armed
with spines; metraterm exceptionally well-developed.
        Travtrema Pereira, 1929 (fig. 656)
2 (1) Cuticle armed with spines; cirrus unarmed;
metraterm relatively weakly developed.
        Paurophyllum Byrd, Parker and Reiber, 1940
                    (fig. 657)

KEY TO THE FAMILIES OF THE SUPERFAMILY DIPLOSTOMATOIDEA NICOLL, 1937 (XVII:158)

V. E. Sudarikov

1 (2) Parasites of mammals; vitelline follicles exclusively or predominantly in anterior segment of
body. Anurans: second intermediate host.
            Alariidae Tubangui, 1922
2 (1) Parasites of birds; vitelline follicles not in
anterior segment of body.
3 (4) Body spoon-shaped; anterior segment with
ventral cavity; organ of Brandes in shape of large
circular or oval sucker; vitelline follicles in both
segments or restricted to posterior.
            Diplostomatidae (Poirier, 1886)
4 (3) Body mushroom-shaped; anterior segment
modified into massive flattened proboscis capable of
penetrating deeply into mucus layers of intestine;
organ of Brandes of small lobes; vitelline follicles
concentrated in equatorial swelling at level of seg-
mental boundary.   Bolbocephalodidae Strand, 1935

KEY TO THE SUBFAMILIES OF THE FAMILY DIPLOSTOMATIDAE (POIRIER, 1886) (XVII:160)

V. E. Sudarikov

1 (2) Vitelline follicles in both segments; organ of

Brandes resembling sucker with well-developed cavity opening in medial fissure.
Diplostomatinae Monticelli, 1888
2 (1) Vitelline follicles restricted to posterior segment, sometimes extending into anterior region within limits of organ of Brandes.
Crassiphialinae Sudarikov, 1960

KEY TO THE GENERA OF THE SUBFAMILY DIPLOSTOMATINAE MONTICELLI, 1888 (XVII:161)

V. E. Sudarikov

1 (2) Ovary between testes. Parasites of gulls.
Mesoophorodiplostomum Dubois, 1936 (fig. 658)
2 (1) Ovary anterior to testes.
3 (20) Pseudo-suckers present (lateral suckers of homologs).
4 (5) Deep, tubular dorsal cavity present in posterior segment, at level of posterior testis; globular sphincter present in cavity; cavity not connected with genital ducts.
Sphincterodiplostomum Dubois, 1936 (fig. 659)
5 (4) Tubular cavity lacking in posterior segment.
6 (7) Body bent so that surfaces of segments parallel or touching. Harwardia Baer, 1932 (fig. 660)
7 (6) Body not bent, or else bent with dorsal surfaces forming obtuse or right angle, never parallel.
8 (9) Group of large single-celled glands present around ventral sucker; ducts of glands opening independently, along ventral surface of body.
Adenodiplostomum Dubois, 1937 (fig. 661)
9 (8) Glands around ventral sucker lacking.
10 (13) Segments of body separated by clearly visible constrictions; anterior segment leaf-shaped, lateral and posterior edges usually turned ventrally.
11 (12) Muscular genital bulb present, at bottom of genital atrium, dorsal to hermaphroditic duct.
Bolbophorus Dubois, 1935 (fig. 662)
12 (11) Genital bulb lacking.
Diplostomum Nordmann, 1832 (fig. 663)
13 (10) Body without external segmentation.
14 (15) Body cylindrical; diameters of anterior and posterior segments nearly equal; anterior segment short. Parasites of diurnal predators.
Glossodiplostomoides Bhalerao, 1942 (fig. 664)
15 (14) Body of different shape.
16 (17) Body fusiform; testes symmetrical; anterior testis wider than posterior. Parasites of wading birds and grebes, rarely of diurnal predators.
Tylodelphys Diesing, 1850 (fig. 665)
17 (16) Body pyriform or wedge-shaped, with broad anterior segment; testes asymmetrical. Parasites of Pelicaniformes.
18 (19) Ventral sucker distinct; vitelline follicles concentrated in organ of Brandes, descending upon posterior testis; uterus not reaching organ of Brandes. Hysteromorpha Lutz, 1931 (fig. 666)
19 (18) Ventral sucker rudimentary or lacking; vitelline follicles not entering organ of Brandes; posteriorly not extending beyond posterior testis; uterus extending to organ of Brandes.
Austrodiplostomum Szidat and Nani, 1951
20 (3) Pseudo-suckers or homologs lacking.
21 (22) Body elliptical, without external segmentation; ventral cavity deepening continuously to point about one-third of body length from posterior end, or to base of posterior segment; ovary lateral to anterior testis.
Ornithodiplostomum Dubois, 1936 (fig. 668)
22 (21) Body distinctly bi-segmented.
23 (24) Oral sucker elliptical, with conical base and ring-like thickening equatorially on posterior and lateral sides; ventral surface of sucker constricted.
Lophosicyadiplostomum Dubois, 1936 (fig. 669)
24 (23) Oral sucker without equatorial thickening.
25 (26) Large ejaculatory bursa present; genital atrium with papilla; hermaphroditic duct opening at tip of papilla. Prolobodiplostomum Baer, 1959
26 (25) Ejaculatory bursa absent.
27 (28) Genital atrium usually opening terminally, everting to free papilla with opening of hermaphroditic duct at tip; papilla often surrounded by preputial folds. Parasites of wading birds, rarely gulls.
Posthodiplostomum Dubois, 1936 (fig. 671)
28 (27) Genital atrium massive, opening subterminally, lacking papilla or papilla small, broad, without preputial folds, incapable of eversion. Parasites of predators, rarely of cuckoos, sparrows, woodpeckers and hoopoes.
Neodiplostomum Railliet, 1919 (fig. 672)

KEY TO THE GENERA OF THE SUBFAMILY CRASSIPHIALINAE SUDARIKOV, 1960 (XVII:477)

V. E. Sudarikov

1 (12) Vitelline follicles restricted in posterior segment. Parasites of sandpipers and kingfishers.
2 (5) Pseudo-suckers present.
3 (4) Genital atrium rudimentary; hermaphroditic duct opening subterminally on dorsal surface. Parasites of sandpipers.
Pulvinifer Yamaguti, 1933 (fig. 673)
4 (3) Genital atrium present, with genital papilla with ventral fold; fold lingulate in cross-section. Parasites of kingfishers.
Subuvulifer Dubois, 1952 (fig. 674)
5 (2) Pseudo-suckers absent.
6 (7) Organ of Brandes massive, bulbous, filling part of ventral cavity of segment, with anterior border nearly reaching pharynx; ventral sucker rudimentary or lacking; anterior segment saucer-shaped. Parasites of kingfishers.
Crassiphiala Haitsma, 1925 (fig. 675)
7 (6) Organ of Brandes small, with anterior border not extending beyond level of ventral sucker; anterior segment flattened or slightly curved, spoon-shaped.
8 (9) Relatively large atrial sucker present in cavity of genital atrium. Parasites of kingfishers.
Cercotyla Yamaguti, 1939 (fig. 676)
9 (8) Atrial sucker lacking.

10 (11) Muscular, genital bulb ventral to genital papilla present in genital atrium; ventral sucker smaller than oral or lacking; atrial pore usually opening terminally. Parasites of kingfishers.
Uvulifer Yamaguti, 1934 (fig. 677)

11 (10) Genital bulb lacking; ventral sucker larger than oral. Parasites of kingfishers.
Pseudodiplostomum Yamaguti, 1934 (fig. 678)

12 (1) Vitelline follicles descending into organ of Brandes. Parasites of sandpipers.

13 (14) Surface of organ of Brandes divided by fissures into three parts; vitelline follicles descending into posterior medial portion of organ.
Allodiplostomum Yamaguti, 1935 (fig. 679)

14 (13) Organ of Brandes mushroom-shaped, with groove along medial line; vitelline follicles filling entire expanded portion of organ.
Scolopacitrema Sudarikov and Rykovsky, 1958
(fig. 680)

LITERATURE ON THE ONTOGENY OF REPRESENTATIVES OF THE SUBORDER HEMIURATA (XVII:605)

Sinitsyn, D. F. 1905. Materials on the natural history of trematodes. Distomes of fishes and frogs in the vicinity of Warsaw. Varshava. 210 pp.

Sinitsyn, D. F. 1906. Distomes of fishes and frogs in the vicinity of Warsaw. On the intermediate hosts of distomes parasitizing frogs. Izvestiya Varshavskogo Universiteta. Nos. 1-2:140-144.

Sinitsyn, D. F. 1911. The parthenogenetic generation of trematodes and its offspring in molluscs of the Black Sea. Zapiski Imperatorskoy Akad. Nauk. 30(5); 127 pp.

Skrjabin, K. I. and L. Kh. Gushanskaya. 1956. Systematics of trematodes of the sub-order Hemiurata (Markevitsch, 1951) Skrjabin and Guschanskaja, 1954. Trudy Gelmintologicheskoy Laboratorii Akad. Nauk SSSR. 8:144-158.

Skrjabin, K. I. and L. Kh. Gushanskaya. 1959. Ontogeny and separate stages of development of representatives of the sub-order Hemiurata. Trudy Gelmintologicheskoy Laboratorii Akad. Nauk SSSR. 9:280-293.

Chubrik, G. K. 1952. Encysted cercariae from Nautica clausa Brod. and Sow. Doklady Akad. Nauk SSSR. 86(6):1233-1236.

KEY TO THE FAMILIES OF THE SUPERFAMILY HEMIUROIDEA FAUST, 1929 (XVII:618)

K. I. Skrjabin and L. Kh. Gushanskaya

1 (2) Intestinal cecum single, terminating blindly; hermaphroditic bursa absent; testis single; ovary anterior to testis; vitellaria single, compact, or composed of two groups of follicles.
Haplosplanchnidae Poche, 1925

2 (1) Two intestinal ceca present.

3 (4) Posterior region of body, including ovary, vitellaria, and terminal parts of intestinal ceca, separated from remainder of body by cuticular ridge. Parasites of swim-bladders of fishes.
Aerobiotrematidae Yamaguti, 1958

4 (3) Dividing cuticular ridge absent.

5 (10) Posterior ends of intestinal ceca uniting.

6 (7) Intestinal ceca uniting in posterior end of body, forming intestinal arch; uroproct lacking; hermaphroditic bursa usually lacking (except in subfamily Otiotrematinae); clustered ovary posterior to similarly-shaped testes; clustered vitellaria posterior to ovary.
Syncoeliidae Dollfus, 1923

7 (6) Posterior ends of intestinal ceca uniting with excretory bladder, forming uroproct.

8 (9) Intestinal ceca H-shaped; hermaphroditic bursa lacking (exception: Guschanskianinae); esophagus present; ovary posterior to testes; vitellaria tubular, dendritic, or follicular.
Accacoeliidae Looss, 1912

9 (8) Intestinal ceca lacking anterior extensions; hermaphroditic bursa lacking; esophagus lacking; ovary anterior to testes; vitellaria follicular.
Ptychogonimidae Dollfus, 1936

10 (5) Posterior ends of intestinal ceca not uniting, terminating blindly.

11 (12) Ovary in space between testes; hermaphroditic bursa lacking; vitellaria elongate, tubular, extending from level of anterior testis to posterior end of body. Gill parasites of fishes.
Bathycotylidae Dollfus, 1932

12 (11) Ovary posterior to posterior testis.

13 (16) Vitellaria single.

14 (15) Terminal component of genital apparatus composed of four parts: proximal hermaphroditic duct; thin-walled, hermaphroditic cirrus; hermaphroditic metraterm; and genital atrium; vitellaria of seven tubular lobes.
Elytrophallidae Skrjabin and Guschanskaja, 1954

15 (14) Terminal component of genital apparatus composed of ejaculatory duct and metraterm uniting to form hermaphroditic duct; hermaphroditic duct usually in hermaphroditic bursa (exception: subfamily Johniophyllinae); vitellaria stellate, single, composed of varying number of lobes.
Lecithasteridae Skrjabin and Guschanskaja, 1954

16 (13) Two vitellaria present (exception: Bunocotylinae, with single vitellaria).

17 (20) Vitellaria compact, entire.

18 (19) Hermaphroditic duct always enclosed within hermaphroditic bursa; ventral sucker in anterior part of body, near oral sucker. Hemiuridae Lühe, 1901

19 (18) Hermaphroditic duct present; hermaphroditic bursa usually lacking (exception: Derogenetinae); ventral sucker near middle of body or in posterior half of body. Halipegidae Poche, 1925

20 (17) Vitellaria differently constructed.

21 (22) Vitellaria lobed; prostatic vesicle present, enclosed within hermaphroditic bursa or free in parenchyma if bursa lacking; ventral sucker in anterior third of body-length.
Lecithochiriidae Skrjabin and Guschanskaja, 1954

22 (21) Vitellaria of thin, sinuous tubules or dentritically branched.

23 (24) Vitellaria dendritically branched, in posterior part of body, terminating near level of ends of intestinal ceca; ovary tubular, sinuous, posterior to testes in posterior half of body; testes symmetrical, directly posterior to ventral sucker; hermaphroditic bursa present; ejaculatory duct uniting with metraterm at base of bursa forming hermaphroditic duct. Parasites of swim-bladders of fishes.
Isoparorchidae Poche, 1925

24 (23) Vitellaria of slender, inter-winding tubules.

25 (26) Large specialized ejaculatory bursa containing long, muscular, twisting ejaculatory duct, with papilla protruding basally into hermaphroditic bursa; distal end of metraterm near base of hermaphroditic bursa; paired vitellaria narrow, tubular, lateral in posterior half of body.
Lampritrematidae Skrjabin and Guschanskaja, 1954

26 (25) Ejaculatory bursa lacking.

27 (28) Terminal component of genital apparatus composed of hermaphroditic bursa surrounding hermaphroditic duct; pars prostatica and metraterm leading from hermaphroditic duct; testes two; vitellaria paired, composed of long, slender, sinuous tubules, medial or lateral; excretory apparatus simple, Y-shaped, without lacunar system; body usually elongate with anal appendage (exception: Prosorchinae).
Dinuridae Skrjabin and Guschanskaja, 1954

28 (27) Terminal component of genital apparatus simple; hermaphroditic duct enclosed within hermaphroditic bursa or free in parenchyma when bursa lacking; vitellaria composed of elongate, densely inter-winding tubules, ventral, intercecal; excretory apparatus complex, with lacunar system; body elongate, oval; anal appendage absent.
Sclerodistomatidae Dollfus, 1932

LIST OF SUPPLEMENTARY ILLUSTRATIONS

Cortrematidae Yamaguti, 1958
 Cortrema corti Tang, 1951 (fig. 815)
Heronimidae Ward, 1917
 Heronimus chelydrae McCallum, 1902 (fig. 689)
Botulidae Guiart, 1938
 Botulus alepidosauri Guiart, 1938 (fig. 681)
Aphanhysteridae Yamaguti, 1958
 Aphanhystera monacensis Guiart, 1938 (fig. 670)

PART XVIII

KEY TO THE FAMILIES OF THE SUPERFAMILY LEPOCREADIOIDEA CABLE, 1956 (XVIII:16)

K. I. Skrjabin and V. P. Koval

1 (8) Loops of uterus between ovary or anterior testis and ventral sucker.

2 (7) Cirrus sac present (exception: several genera of Lepocreadiidae).

3 (4) Intestinal ceca opening externally through two anal pores.   Diploproctodaeidae Ozaki, 1928

4 (3) Intestinal ceca terminating blindly.

5 (6) Testes symmetrical; body round.
Dermadenidae Yamaguti, 1958

6 (5) Body elongate, oval; testes tandem or oblique.
Lepocreadiidae Nicoll, 1935

7 (2) Cirrus sac lacking.
Schistorchiidae Yamaguti, 1942

8 (1) Loops of uterus nearly reaching posterior end of body.

9 (10) Hermaphroditic duct present; anterior end of body covered with spines (exception: Skrjabinopsolus)
Deropristidae Skrjabin, 1958

10 (9) Hermaphroditic duct absent; anterior end of body without spines.
Orientocreadiidae Skrjabin and Koval, 1960

KEY TO THE SUBFAMILIES OF THE FAMILY LEPOCREADIIDAE NICOLL, 1935 (XVIII:19)

K. I. Skrjabin and V. P. Koval

1 (18) Genital pore anterior to ventral sucker.

2 (15) Cirrus sac present; internal seminal vesicle and cirrus enclosed within sac; external seminal vesicle present.

3 (12) Two testes present.

4 (11) Intestinal ceca terminating blindly; genital pore medial or sub-medial.

5 (10) External seminal vesicle without surrounding glandular cells and thin membrane.

6 (7) Ventral sucker with muscular lips.
Labriferinae Yamaguti, 1958

7 (6) Ventral sucker without muscular lips.

8 (9) Loops of uterus passing between ovary and ventral sucker.   Lepocreadiinae Odhner, 1905

9 (8) Loops of uterus passing between anterior testis and ventral sucker, mainly concentrated between anterior testis and ovary.
Aephnidiogenetinae Yamaguti, 1934

10 (5) External seminal vesicle surrounded by glandular mass of cells, usually enveloped by thin-walled membrane.   Lepidapedinae Yamaguti, 1958

11 (4) Intestinal ceca opening into excretory bladder forming uroproct; genital pore marginal.
Allolepidapedinae Skrjabin and Koval, 1960

12 (3) Testes single or many.

13 (14) Single testes present.
Spiritestinae Yamaguti, 1958

14 (13) Eleven or twelve testes present.
                    Folliorchinae Yamaguti, 1958
15 (2) Cirrus sac lacking or very rudimentary; only external seminal vesicle present.
16 (17) Prostatic cells free in parenchyma, especially well-developed, occupying entire inter-cecal space from center of ventral sucker and middle of seminal vesicle; seminal vesicle adjacent to intestinal ceca. Marsupioacetabulinae Skrjabin and Koval, 1960
17 (16) Prostatic cells weakly developed, of usual structure. Homalometrinae Cable and Hunninen, 1942
18 (1) Genital pore posterior to ventral sucker.
                    Postporinae Yamaguti, 1958

KEY TO THE GENERA OF THE SUBFAMILY LEPOCREADIINAE ÓDHNER, 1905 (XVIII:21)

K. I. Skrjabin and V. P. Koval

1 (2) Testes symmetrical.
                    Eocreadium Szidat, 1954
2 (1) Testes tandem or oblique.
3 (4) Genital pore marginal, near oral sucker.
                    Lepocreadioides Yamaguti, 1936 (fig. 682)
4 (3) Genital pore medial, submedial or sinistral, near ventral sucker.
5 (6) Intestinal ceca short, terminating at middle of ovary. Opechonoides Yamaguti, 1940 (fig. 683)
6 (5) Intestinal ceca long, reaching posterior end of body.
7 (8) Prepharynx long; body elongate; length six to seven times greater than width.
                    Opechona Looss, 1907 (fig. 684)
8 (7) Prepharynx short; body short, oval, length exceeding width by two to three times.
                    Lepocreadium Stossich, 1904 (fig. 685)

KEY TO THE SPECIES OF THE GENUS LEPOCREADIUM STOSSICH, 1904 (XVIII:22-27)

K. I. Skrjabin and V. P. Koval

1 (10) Ovary entire.
2 (3) Eggs in uterus few (one to two).
                    L. trullaforme Linton, 1940
3 (2) Many eggs in uterus.
4 (5) Vitellaria reaching level of pharynx.
                    L. ovalis Manter, 1931
5 (4) Vitellaria not reaching level of pharynx; cirrus sac not extending posterior to ventral sucker.
                    L. bimarinum Manter, 1940
6 (9) Oral and ventral suckers equal in size.
7 (8) Vitellaria not reaching level of intestinal bifurcation. L. album (Stossich, 1890) (fig. 685)
8 (7) Vitellaria reaching level of ventral sucker.
                    L. pyriforme (Linton, 1900)
9 (6) Oral sucker smaller than ventral.
                    L. retrusum Linton, 1940
10 (1) Ovary lobed.
11 (12) Testes entire. L. elongatum (Nagaty, 1942)
12 (11) Testes lobed.

13 (14) External seminal vesicle reaching level of posterior testis.   L. incisum Hanson, 1955
14 (13) External seminal vesicle not reaching level of posterior testis.
15 (16) Excretory bladder extending to intestinal bifurcation.
                    L. floridanum Sogandares-Bernal and Hutton, 1959
16 (15) Excretory bladder not extending to intestinal bifurcation.
17 (18) Excretory bladder reaching ventral sucker.
                    L. clavatum (Ozaki, 1932)
18 (17) Excretory bladder reaching level of anterior testis.   L. trulla (Linton, 1907)
Note: All known species of Lepocreadium not considered in key.

KEY TO THE SPECIES OF THE GENUS LEPOCREADIOIDES YAMAGUTI, 1936 (XVIII:57)

K. I. Skrjabin and V. P. Koval

1 (4) Excretory bladder reaching pharynx.
2 (3) Intestinal ceca not reaching posterior end of body; post-cecal distance exceeding diameter of testes.   L. branchiostegi Yamaguti, 1937
3 (2) Intestinal ceca reaching posterior end of body.
                    L. zebrini Yamaguti, 1936 (fig. 682)
4 (1) Excretory bladder extending to level of anterior edge of right testis. L. indicum Srivastava, 1941
Note: L. orientale Park, 1939 omitted from key.

KEY TO THE SPECIES OF THE GENUS OPECHONA LOOSS, 1907 (XVIII:66)

K. I. Skrjabin and V. P. Koval

1 (2) Four thin-walled, digitiform appendices, directed anteriorly, at anterior end of pharynx.
                    O. pharyngodactyla Manter, 1940
2 (1) Digitiform appendices on pharynx lacking.
3 (8) Excretory bladder extending anteriorly to oral sucker or pharynx.
4 (5) Vitellaria originating at level midway between intestinal bifurcation and ventral sucker.
                    O. xesuri Yamaguti, 1940
5 (4) Vitellaria extending anteriorly beyond anterior edge of ventral sucker.
6 (7) Excretory bladder anteriorly reaching middle of oral sucker; body oval; prepharynx short.
                    O. scombri Yamaguti, 1938
7 (6) Excretory bladder anteriorly reaching level of pharynx; body elongate; prepharynx long.
                    O. orientalis (Layman, 1930)
8 (3) Excretory bladder anteriorly not reaching oral sucker or pharynx.
9 (20) Oral sucker equal to or smaller than ventral.
10 (15) Vitellaria extending anteriorly beyond level of intestinal bifurcation.
11 (12) Testes lobed.   O. menidiae Manter, 1947
12 (11) Testes entire.
13 (14) Ovary trilobed; excretory bladder reaching

posterior edge of ventral sucker or slightly beyond; oral sucker smaller than ventral.

O. alaskensis Ward and Fillingham, 1934

14 (13) Ovary entire, or slightly lobed; excretory bladder extending slightly anterior to intestinal bifurcation; oral and ventral sucker almost equal in size.

O. hynnodi Yamaguti, 1938

15 (10) Vitellaria not reaching level of intestinal bifurcation anteriorly.

16 (17) Anterior border of vitellaria in posterior half of body, at level slightly anterior to ovary.

O. girellae Yamaguti, 1940

17 (16) Anterior border of vitellaria at boundary of anterior and middle thirds of body.

18 (19) Vitellaria originating near posterior edge of ventral sucker.   O. gracilis (Linton, 1910)

19 (18) Vitellaria originating at level of posterior limit of cirrus sac.   O. sebastodis (Yamaguti, 1934)

20 (9) Oral sucker larger than ventral.

21 (24) Vitellaria extending anteriorly to posterior limit of cirrus sac or to external seminal vesicle.

22 (23) Ovary tri-lobed; genital pore near anterior edge of ventral sucker.

O. bacillaris (Molin, 1859) (fig. 684)

23 (22) Ovary entire; genital pore at level of intestinal bifurcation.   O. olssoni (Yamaguti, 1934)

24 (21) Vitellaria anteriorly not reaching cirrus sac or external seminal vesicle; anterior border of vitellaria in posterior half of body.

O. occidentalis Montgomery, 1957

KEY TO THE GENERA OF THE SUBFAMILY AEPHNIDIOGENETINAE YAMAGUTI, 1934 (XVIII:108)

K. I. Skrjabin and V. P. Koval

1 (4) Ovary and testes entire; genital pore anterior to ventral sucker, near intestinal bifurcation.

2 (3) Testes separated by considerable distance.

Aephnidiogenes Nicoll, 1915 (fig. 686)

3 (2) Testes adjacent.

Holorchis Stossich, 1901 (fig. 687)

4 (1) Ovary and testes lobed; genital pore at level of pharynx.

Pseudoholorchis Yamaguti, 1958 (fig. 688)

KEY TO THE GENERA OF THE SUBFAMILY FOLLIORCHINAE YAMAGUTI, 1958 (XVIII:133)

K. I. Skrjabin and V. P. Koval

1 (2) Cuticle unarmed. Folliorchis Srivastava, 1948

2 (1) Cuticle armed anteriorly.

3 (4) Ventral sucker smaller than or approximately equal to oral; vitellaria originating at level of second third of body or anterior.

Multitestis Manter, 1931 (fig. 690)

4 (3) Ventral sucker larger than oral; vitellaria originating in posterior half of body.

Rhagorchis Manter, 1931 (fig. 691)

KEY TO THE SPECIES OF THE GENUS MULTITESTIS MANTER, 1931 (XVIII:134)

K. I. Skrjabin and V. P. Koval

1 (6) Oral and ventral sucker nearly equal in size.

2 (3) Testes in two lateral, rosette-shaped groups, in middle third of body; ovary posterior to testes.

M. nasusi Bravo-Hollis and Brenes, 1959

3 (2) Testes medial, intercecal, in posterior half of body; ovary anterior to testes or at level of anterior testes.

4 (3) Vitellaria extending from level slightly posterior to posterior edge of ventral sucker to posterior end of body.   M. chaetodoni Manter, 1947

5 (4) Vitellaria extending from level of intestinal bifurcation to posterior end of body.

M. inconstans (Linton, 1905) (fig. 690)

6 (1) Oral sucker larger than ventral; sucker ratio 3:2.   M. blennii Manter, 1931

Note: M. rotundus Sparks, 1954 omitted from key.

KEY TO THE GENERA OF THE SUBFAMILY HOMALOMETRINAE CABLE AND HUNNINEN, 1942 (XVIII:153)

K. I. Skrjabin and V. P. Koval

1 (8) Cuticle spinose.

2 (3) Paired, distinct outgrowths present around oral sucker.

Dactylotrema Bravo-Hollis and Manter, 1957 (fig. 692)

3 (2) Outgrowths around oral sucker lacking.

4 (7) Testes oblique or tandem.

5 (6) Testes tandem; ovary entire.

Homalometron Stafford, 1904 (fig. 693)

6 (5) Ovary lobed; testes oblique.

Pancreadium Manter, 1954 (fig. 694)

7 (4) Testes symmetrical.

Microcreadium Simer, 1929 (fig. 695)

8 (1) Spines on cuticle lacking or rudimentary.

9 (10) Cuticular bilobed valve present on each side of ventral sucker; esophagus lacking.

Myzotus Manter, 1940 (fig. 696)

10 (9) Cuticular valves absent, esophagus present.

Crassicutis Manter, 1936 (fig. 697)

KEY TO THE SPECIES OF THE GENUS HOMALOMETRON STAFFORD, 1904 (XVIII:154)

K. I. Skrjabin and V. P. Koval

1 (2) Oral and ventral sucker nearly equal in size.

H. pallidum Stafford, 1904 (fig. 693)

2 (1) Oral and ventral suckers differing considerably in size.

3 (4) Vitellaria not reaching level of ventral sucker, merging medially in space between anterior testis and ovary; oral sucker larger than ventral.

H. elongatum Manter, 1947

4 (3) Vitellaria reaching level of ventral sucker,

not merging medially between testis and ovary; oral
sucker smaller than ventral.
5 (6) Vitellaria reaching posterior edge of ventral
sucker.   H. pearsei (Hunter and Bangham, 1932)
6 (5) Vitellaria reaching middle of ventral sucker.
                    H. armatum (McCallum, 1895)

KEY TO THE SPECIES OF THE GENUS
CRASSICUTIS MANTER, 1936 (XVIII:169)

K. I. Skrjabin and V. P. Koval

1 (2) Vitellaria originating at level of intestinal bifurcation; testes slightly lobed; excretory pore dorsal, approximately at level of ends of intestinal ceca.
                C. cichlasomae Manter, 1936 (fig. 697)
2 (1) Vitellaria originating at level of posterior
half of oral sucker; testes entire; excretory pore
subterminal, at posterior end of body.
                    C. marina Manter, 1947

KEY TO THE GENERA OF THE SUBFAMILY
LABRIFERINAE YAMAGUTI, 1958 from Yamaguti
(1958) (XVIII:188)

1 (2) Ventral sucker with anterior and posterior
lips; prostatic cells present along both sides of external seminal vesicle, posterior and dorsal to ventral sucker.   Labrifer Yamaguti, 1936 (fig. 698)
2 (1) Ventral sucker with lateral lips; prostatic
cells situated external to cirrus sac.
                    Myzoxenus Manter, 1934 (fig. 699)

KEY TO THE SPECIES OF THE GENUS
LABRIFER YAMAGUTI, 1936 (XVIII:188)

K. I. Skrjabin and V. P. Koval

1 (2) Vitellaria originating posterior to level of
ventral sucker.
            L. semicossyphi Yamaguti, 1936 (fig. 698)
2 (1) Vitellaria originating at level of ventral
sucker or at level of intestinal bifurcation.
                    L. secundus Manter, 1940

KEY TO THE SPECIES OF THE GENUS
MYZOXENUS MANTER, 1934 (XVIII:195)

K. I. Skrjabin and V. P. Koval

1 (2) Vitellaria originating anterior to level of ventral sucker; testes slightly lobed.
                M. vitellosus Manter, 1934 (fig. 699)
2 (1) Vitellaria originating posterior to level of
ventral sucker; testes entire.
3 (4) External seminal vesicle tripartite; testes in
middle third of body; eggs: 0.057-0.074 x 0.028-0.042
mm.   M. crowcrofti Manter, 1954
4 (3) External seminal vesicle simple; testes in
posterior third of body; eggs: 0.049-0.055 x 0.025-
0.030 mm.   M. lachnolaimi Manter, 1947

Note: M. insolens (Crowcroft, 1945) omitted from
key.

KEY TO THE GENERA OF THE SUBFAMILY
LEPIDAPEDINAE YAMAGUTI, 1958 (XVIII:203)

K. I. Skrjabin and V. P. Koval

1 (2) Glandular cells surrounding external seminal
vesicle enveloped by common, thin membrane.
                Lepidapedon Stafford, 1904 (fig. 700)
2 (1) Glandular cells surrounding external seminal
vesicle lacking membrane.
                Neolepidapedon Manter, 1954 (fig. 701)

KEY TO THE SPECIES OF THE GENUS
LEPIDAPEDON STAFFORD, 1904 (XVIII:206)

K. I. Skrjabin and V. P. Koval

1 (20) Excretory bladder not reaching level of ventral sucker.
2 (11) Ventral sucker equal in size or slightly
smaller than oral.
3 (4) Genital pore dextral; part of uterus leading
from oviduct expanded.   L. calli Acena, 1947
4 (3) Genital pore sinistral; uterus not constructed
as above.
5 (6) Esophagus short.
                L. rachion (Cobbold, 1858) (fig. 700)
6 (5) Esophagus long.
7 (8) Vitellaria extending to level between ventral
sucker and ovary; prepharynx short.
                L. gymnocanthi (Issaitschikoff, 1928)
8 (7) Vitellaria extending to anterior edge of ventral sucker or to intestinal bifurcation; prepharynx
long.
9 (10) Vitellaria extending to anterior edge of ventral sucker.   L. lebouri Manter, 1934
10 (9) Vitellaria reaching intestinal bifurcation.
                    L. genge Yamaguti, 1938
11 (2) Ventral sucker larger than oral.
12 (13) Pre-oral lip present.
                    L. gadi (Yamaguti, 1934)
13 (12) Pre-oral lip absent.
14 (17) Excretory bladder extending to level of
posterior testis.
15 (16) Gonads located in middle third of body; vitellaria reaching level of ventral sucker.
                    L. luteum Yamaguti, 1938
16 (15) Gonads in posterior half of body; vitellaria
not reaching level of ventral sucker.
                    L. australis Manter, 1954
17 (14) Excretory bladder extending to level of anterior testis.
18 (19) Eggs: 0.09 x 0.045 mm.
                    L. pugetensis Acena, 1947
19 (18) Eggs: 0.06-0.065 x 0.030-0.036 mm.
                    L. elongatum (Lebour, 1908)
20 (1) Excretory bladder reaching ventral sucker
or intestinal bifurcation.

21 (26) Genital pore anterior to ventral sucker.
22 (23) Sucker-like lateral organ present.
L. trachynoti Hanson, 1950
23 (22) Sucker-like lateral organ absent.
24 (25) Ventral sucker larger than oral; genital pore nearly medial. L. congeri Manter, 1954
25 (24) Ventral sucker smaller than oral; genital pore sinistral. L. hancocki Manter, 1940
26 (21) Genital pore at level of anterior edge of ventral sucker, lateral.
27 (28) Vitellaria originating at level of anterior edge of external seminal vesicle.
L. epinepheli Bravo-Hollis and Manter, 1957
28 (27) Vitellaria originating at level of posterior edge of external seminal vesicle.
L. levenseni (Linton, 1907)

KEY TO THE SPECIES OF THE GENUS NEOLEPIDAPEDON MANTER, 1954 (XVIII:267)

K. I. Skrjabin and V. P. Koval

1 (8) Esophagus well-developed.
2 (5) Internal seminal vesicle surrounded by dense mass of circular muscle fibers.
3 (4) Excretory bladder reaching level of ovary.
N. polyprioni Manter, 1954 (fig. 701)
4 (3) Excretory bladder not reaching level of ovary, extending only to anterior testis.
N. sebastici (Yamaguti, 1938)
5 (2) Dense mass of circular muscle fibers surrounding internal seminal vesicle lacking.
6 (7) Ventral sucker pedunculate; length of body posterior to testes six to seven times greater than space between testes. N. cablei Manter, 1954
7 (6) Ventral sucker sessile; distance between testes equaling body posterior to testes.
N. medialunae Montgomery, 1957
8 (1) Esophagus absent.
N. haplognathi (Yamaguti, 1938)

KEY TO THE SPECIES OF THE GENUS POSTPORUS MANTER, 1949 (XVIII:285)

K. I. Skrjabin and V. P. Koval

1 (2) Excretory bladder reaching pharynx.
P. epinepheli (Manter, 1947) (fig. 702)
2 (1) Excretory bladder terminating directly posterior to intestinal bifurcation.
P. mycteropercae (Manter, 1947)

KEY TO THE GENERA OF THE SUBFAMILY SPIRITESTINAE YAMAGUTI, 1958 (XVIII:291)

K. I. Skrjabin and V. P. Koval

1 (2) Oral sucker with pre-oral lobes; intestinal ceca relatively short; vitellaria in posterior half of body. Spiritestis Nagaty, 1948 (fig. 703)
2 (1) Oral sucker without pre-oral lobes; intestinal ceca long, reaching posterior end of body; vitellaria extending to intestinal bifurcation.
Hairana Nagaty, 1948 (fig. 704)

LITERATURE ON THE TREMATODES OF THE FAMILY LEPOCREADIIDAE NICOLL, 1935 (XVIII:296-301)

Amosova, I. S. 1955. On the discovery of the metacercariae of digenetic trematodes in several polychaetes of the Barents Sea. Zoologichesky Zhurnal. 34:286-290.

Akhmerov, A. Kh. 1951. Some data on parasites of walleye pollack. Izvestiya Tikhookeanskogo Nauchno-Issledovatelskogo Instituta Rybnogo Khozyaystva i Okeanografii. 34:99-104.

Bazikalova, A. Ya. 1932. Materials on the parasitology of fishes of Murmansk. Sbornik Nauchno-Promyslovykh Rabot na Murmane. pp. 136-153.

Vlasenko, P. V. 1931. On the fauna of parasitic worms of fishes of the Black Sea. Trudy Karadagskoy Biologicheskoy Stantsii, Simferopol. No. 4:88-136.

Dogiel, V. A. 1936. Parasites of cod from Lake Mogilnoye. Uchenye Zapiski Leningradskogo Gosudarstvennogo Universiteta, No. 3, seriya biologicheskikh nauk. No. 7:125-133.

Dogiel, V. A. and A. Rozova. 1941. The parasite fauna of four-horned sculpin (Myoxocephalus Quadricornis) in different regions of its distribution. Uchenye Zapiski Leningradskogo Gosudarstvennogo Universiteta, No. 74, seriya biologicheskikh nauk. No. 18:4-19.

Zhukov, E. V. 1953. Endoparasitic worms of fishes of the Sea of Japan and the Kurile shoal-waters. Dissertatsiya.

Zhukov, E. V. 1956. New genera and species of digenetic trematodes of fishes of the Far East seas. Zoologichesky Zhurnal. 36(6):840-845.

Kurashvili, B. E. and N. A. Tabidze. 1947. Materials on the study of the helminth fauna of commercial fishes of the Black Sea. Soobscheniye Akad. Nauk Gruz. SSR. 8(1-2):

Isaychikov, I. M. 1928. On the knowledge of the parasitic worms of several groups of vertebrates of the Russian Arctic, A. Trematodes. Trudy Morskogo Nauchnogo Instituta. 3(2):5-79.

Layman, E. M. 1930. Parasitic worms of fishes of Peter the Great Bay. Izvestiya Tikhookeanskoy Nauchno-Promyslovoy Stantsii. 3(6):1-120.

Osmanov, S. U. 1940. Materials on the parasite fauna of fishes of the Black Sea. Uchenye Zapiski Leningradskogo Pedagogicheskogo Instituta, Kafedra Zoologii i Darvinizman. 30:187-267.

Pogoreltseva, T. P. 1952. New trematodes from fishes of the Black Sea. Trudy Karadagskoy Biologicheskoy Stantsii. No. 12:34-35.

Pogoreltseva, T. P. 1952. Materials on the parasite fauna of fishes of the north-eastern part of the Black Sea. Trudy Zoologicheskogo Instituta Akad. Nauk Ukr. SSR. 8:100-120.

Pogoreltseva, T. P. 1952. The parasite fauna of fishes of the north-eastern part of the Black Sea. Dissertatsiya.

Pogoreltseva, T. P. 1954. New species of digenetic trematodes from fishes of the Black Sea. Naukovi Zapiski Kievskogo Pedagog. Institutu, XV, biol. seriya. No. 2:133-137. (In Ukrainian).

Polyansky, Yu. I. 1955. Materials on the parasite fauna of fishes of the northern seas of the U. S. S. R. Parasites of fishes of the Barents Sea. Trudy Zoologicheskogo Instituta Akad. Nauk SSSR. 19:1-170.

Reshetnikova, A. V. 1954. The parasite fauna of several commercial fishes of the Black Sea. Avtoreferat dissertatsii.

Savina, N. V. 1927. On the knowledge of the parasitic worms of fishes of Murmansk. Sbornik Rabot po Gelmintologii, Posvyaschenny Prof. K. I. Skrjabinu. pp. 216-220.

Strelkov, Yu. A. 1956. Endoparasitic worms of marine fishes of eastern Kamchatka. Avtoreferat dissertatsii.

Strelkov, Yu. A. 1956. Endoparasitic worms of marine fishes of eastern Kamchatka. Dissertatsiya.

Shulman-Albova, R. E. 1952. The parasite fauna of fishes of the White Sea, in the vicinity of the village of Gridino, I. Monogenetic and digenetic trematodes. Uchenye Zapiski Karelo-Finskogo Gosudarstvennogo Universiteta. 4(2):78-97.

Shulman, S. S. and R. E. Shulman-Albova. 1953. Parasites of fishes of the White Sea. Izdatelstvo Akad. Nauk SSSR, Moskva-Leningrad. 198 pp.

Chernyshenko, A. S. 1955. Materials on the parasite fauna of fishes of the Gulf of Odessa. Trudy Odesskogo Universiteta, seriya biologicheskikh nauk. 145(7):211-222.

Chernyshenko, A. S. 1956. On the question of the parasite fauna of endemic, relict fishes. Zoologichesky Zhurnal. 35(8):1261.

Chulkova, V. N. 1939. The parasite fauna of fishes in the vicinity of the city of Batum. Uchenye Zapiski Leningradskogo Gosudarstvennogo Universiteta, No. 43, seriya biologicheskikh nauk. No. 11:21-32.

KEY TO THE GENERA OF THE FAMILY DERMADENIDAE YAMAGUTI, 1958 (XVIII:305)

K. I. Skrjabin and V. P. Koval

1 (2) Numerous cuticular glands present on ventral surface of body; pores located on special, more or less protruding papillae.
    Dermadena Manter, 1945 (fig. 705)
2 (1) Cuticular glands lacking ventrally.
    Pseudocreadium Layman, 1930 (fig. 706)

LITERATURE ON THE TREMATODES OF THE FAMILY DERMADENIDAE YAMAGUTI, 1958 (XVIII:346)

Layman, E. M. 1930. Parasitic worms of fishes of Peter the Great Bay. Izvestiya Tikhookeanskoy Nauchno-Promyslovoy Stantsii. 3(6):1-120.

KEY TO THE SPECIES OF THE GENUS BIVESICULA YAMAGUTI, 1934 (XVIII:382)

K. I. Skrjabin and A. A. Sobolev

1 (2) Vitellaria passing beyond level of posterior edge of testis; esophagus exceptionally long, seven times longer than oral sucker.
    B. tarponis Sogandares-Bernal and Hutton, 1959
2 (1) Vitellaria not passing beyond level of posterior edge of testis; esophagus of medium length.
3 (4) Intestinal ceca extending nearly to posterior end of body.   B. australis Crowcroft, 1947
4 (3) Intestinal ceca terminating at boundary of middle and posterior thirds of body.
5 (8) Testis medial or slightly submedial.
6 (7) Vitelline follicles lateral, merging along median line.   B. claviformis Yamaguti, 1938 (fig. 1)
7 (6) Vitelline follicles not merging medially.
            B. epinepheli Yamaguti, 1938
8 (5) Testis lateral, adjacent to medial line, or only slightly crossing.
9 (10) Vitellaria extending anteriorly to level of oral sucker; uterus extending posteriorly beyond testis.   B. synodi Yamaguti, 1938
10 (9) Vitellaria not extending anteriorly beyond level of intestinal bifurcation; uterus not extending posteriorly beyond testis. B. hepsetiae Manter, 1947

KEY TO THE SPECIES OF THE GENUS BIVESICULOIDES YAMAGUTI, 1938 (XVIII:406)

K. I. Skrjabin and A. A. Sobolev

1 (2) Average body length exceeding 3 mm.; external seminal vesicle lacking; vitelline follicles branched.   B. otagoensis Manter, 1954
2 (1) Body length less than 2 mm.; external seminal vesicle present; vitellaria composed of large spherical follicles.   B. atherinae Yamaguti, 1938 (fig. 2)

KEY TO THE SUBFAMILIES OF THE FAMILY DINURIDAE SKRJABIN AND GUSCHANSKAJA, 1954 (XVIII:419)

K. I. Skrjabin and L. Kh. Gushanskaya

1 (4) Anal appendage present; testes posterior to ventral sucker.
2 (3) Body elongate; vitellaria sinuous, tubular, medial (exception: Pseudostomachicola), posterior to ovary, not extending far posteriorly; pars prostatica compact.   Dinurinae Looss, 1907
3 (2) Trematodes with attenuated anterior portion, expanded posterior portion; vitellaria sinuous, tubular, lateral to intestinal ceca; pars prostatica composed of two distinct portions connected by long, narrow duct.
    Mecoderinae Skrjabin and Guschanskaja, 1954

4 (1) Anal appendage lacking.

5 (6) Testes posterior to ventral sucker; anterior expansions present in intestinal ceca; vitellaria slender, sinuous, tubular, occupying posterior half of body, medial, inter-cecal.

Profundiellinae A. Skrjabin, 1958

6 (5) Testes anterior to ventral sucker; intestinal ceca without expansions; vitellaria slender, sinuous, tubular, filling body posterior to ovary, partially extra-cecal. Prosorchinae Yamaguti, 1934

KEY TO THE SPECIES OF THE GENUS GRASSITREMA YEH, 1954 (XVIII:429)

K. I. Skrjabin and L. Kh. Gushanskaya

1 (2) Rudimentary hermaphroditic bursa present; esophagus absent; glandular expansions of intestinal ceca lacking. G. genypteri (Fife, 1954) (fig. 707)

2 (1) Hermaphroditic bursa absent; small esophagus present; small glandular expansions present at origin of each intestinal cecum.

G. prudhoei Yeh, 1954

KEY TO THE SUBFAMILIES OF THE FAMILY ALARIIDAE TUBANGUI, 1922 (XVIII:455)

V. E. Sudarikov

1 (2) Organ of Brandes of alariid type (exception: when of diplostomatid type, ventral cavity well-developed), lingulate, more rarely circular, usually covering ventral sucker; vitellaria in anterior segment (when isolated follicles descending into posterior segment, organ of Brandes always of alariid type). Alariinae Hall and Wigdor, 1918

2 (1) Organ of Brandes of diplostomatid type; vitellaria present in both segments.

Fibricolinae Sudarikov, 1960

LITERATURE ON THE TREMATODES OF THE SUBORDER HEMIURATA (MARKEVITSCH, 1951) SKRJABIN AND GUSCHANSKAJA, 1954 (XVIII:499)

Skrjabin, A. S. 1958. On the study of the helminth fauna of the deep-water marine fish, Alepisaurus aescularius. Raboty po Gelmintologii, Posvyaschenny 80-letiyu Akademika K. I. Skrjabina. pp. 340-344.

KEY TO THE GENERA OF THE SUBFAMILY ALARIINAE HALL AND WIGDOR, 1918 (XVIII:455)

V. E. Sudarkov

1 (4) Testes tandem.

2 (3) Aberrant forms; posterior segment subdivided into ventral and dorsal cone-shaped components, giving body foot-shaped appearance; pseudosuckers and homologs lacking. Parasites of marsupials.

Podospathalium Dubois, 1932 (fig. 708)

3 (2) Normally developed form; posterior segment

not subdivided; pseudosuckers or tab-like appendages present lateral to oral sucker. Parasites of predators. Alaria Shrank, 1788 (fig. 709)

4 (1) Testes symmetrical.

5 (6) Lateral suckers or homologs lacking; organ of Brandes cardiform. Parasites of dogs and cats.

Pharyngostomum Ciurea, 1922 (fig. 710)

6 (5) Lateral suckers present. Parasites of racoons.

7 (8) Body strongly elongate, nearly cylindrical, deep ventral cavity occupying about two-thirds length of anterior segment; organ of Brandes greatly attenuated, filling large part of ventral cavity; ejaculatory bursa lacking.

Procyotrema Harkema and Miller, 1959 (fig. 711)

8 (7) Body pyriform; ventral cavity of moderate depth; organ of Brandes round or elliptical; ejaculatory bursa present.

Pharyngostomoides Harkema, 1942 (fig. 712)

KEY TO THE GENERA OF THE SUBFAMILY FIBRICOLINAE SUDARIKOV, 1960 (XVIII:561)

V. E. Sudarikov

1 (2) Pseudosuckers lacking.

Fibricola Dubois, 1932 (fig. 713)

2 (1) Pseudosuckers present.

3 (4) Body distinctly divided into segments; anterior segment shorter than posterior; genital atrium with broad pore. Parasites of otters.

Enhydridiplostomum Dubois, 1944

4 (3) Body indistinctly divided into segments; anterior segment longer than posterior; genital atrium with small pore.

5 (6) Organ of Brandes large, broadly elliptical; border of vitellaria extending posteriorly beyond posterior testis. Parasites of marsupials.

Didelphodiplostomum Dubois, 1944 (fig. 714)

6 (5) Organ of Brandes round, relatively small; vitellaria terminating anterior to base of posterior segment. Parasites of predators (canids).

Cynodiplostomum Dubois, 1936 (fig. 715)

KEY TO THE FAMILIES OF THE SUPERFAMILY PROTERODIPLOSTOMATOIDEA SUDARIKOV, 1960 (XVIII:602)

V. E. Sudarikov

1 (2) Parasites of crocodiles and turtles; organ of Brandes small or of moderate size; digitiform papillae present on edges of organ (lacking in parasites of turtles).

Proterodiplostomatidae (Dubois, 1936)

2 (1) Parasites of snakes; organ of Brandes of moderate size or large; papillae lacking on edges of organ.

Ophiodiplostomatidae Sudarikov, 1960

KEY TO THE SUBFAMILIES OF THE FAMILY PROTERODIPLOSTOMATIDAE (DUBOIS, 1936) (XVIII:603)

V. E. Sudarikov

1 (2) Vitellaria present in both segments; posterior border of vitellaria posterior to level of posterior testis. Parasites of crocodiles.
          Proterodiplostomatinae Dubois, 1936
2 (1) Vitellaria in one segment only.
3 (4) Basal mass of vitellaria concentrated in anterior segment; posterior border of vitellaria not extending beyond posterior testis. Parasites of crocodiles and turtles.   Polycotylinae Monticelli, 1888
4 (3) Vitellaria restricted to posterior segment.
          Massoprostatinae Yamaguti, 1958

KEY TO THE GENERA OF THE SUBFAMILY PROTERODIPLOSTOMATINAE DUBOIS, 1936 (XVIII:603)

V. E. Sudarikov

1 (2) Paraprostate well-developed, with distinct walls, extending to level of seminal vesicle; duct of paraprostate opening with ejaculatory duct at tip of genital papilla; uterus opening independently; muscular sucker-like structure present in wall of genital atrium.   Proterodiplostomum Dubois, 1936 (fig. 716)
2 (1) Paraprostate small, sometimes poorly defined.
3 (4) Paraprostate club-shaped, with distinct walls; ejaculatory duct joining with duct of paraprostate and latter with uterus, forming single hermaphroditic duct.   Archaeodiplostomum Dubois, 1944 (fig. 717)
4 (3) Paraprostate indistinct; uterus and ejaculatory duct with common opening; region of genital atrium swollen; broad atrial pore with lobes; cavity of atrial diverticulum joined with cavity of atrium by narrow pore.
          Mesodiplostomum Dubois, 1936 (fig. 718)

KEY TO THE GENERA OF THE SUBFAMILY POLYCOTYLINAE MONTICELLI, 1888 (XVIII:622)

V. E. Sudarikov

1 (16) Papillae present on edges of organ of Brandes. Parasites of crocodiles.
2 (3) Fourteen or fifteen small suckers present medially on dorsal segment; Mehlis' gland and vitelline reservoir between ovary and anterior testis.
          Polycotyle Willemoes-Suhm, 1870 (fig. 719)
3 (2) Medial suckers absent; Mehlis' gland and vitelline reservoir between testes.
4 (5) Thick-walled, sucker-like capsule present on dorsal surface of posterior segment, opening medially in small pore.
          Cystodiplostomum Dubois, 1936 (fig. 720)
5 (4) Dorsal capsule lacking.

6 (7) Genital atrium very large, occupying expanded portion of posterior segment, filling area not less than one-third length of segment; testes oblique.
          Paradiplostomum La Rue, 1926 (fig. 721)
7 (6) Genital atrium of moderate size; testes tandem.
8 (9) Paraprostate long, tubular, with independent pore; uterus and ejaculatory duct with common hermaphroditic pore.
          Prolecithodiplostomum Dubois, 1936 (fig. 722)
9 (8) Paraprostate small, club-shaped, or oval.
10 (11) Paraprostate small, club-shaped, occupying axis of small genital papilla; duct of paraprostate opening independently through pore at tip of papilla; uterus and ejaculatory duct opening by means of hermaphroditic pore in ventral wall of papilla.
          Herpetodiplostomum Dubois, 1936 (fig. 723)
11 (10) Duct of paraprostate opening jointly with either uterus or ejaculatory duct; paraprostate very thick-walled.
12 (15) Vitellaria restricted to anterior segment.
13 (14) Ejaculatory duct joining paraprostate, paraprostate duct opening into uterus; small cavity formed at confluence, forming so-called secondary bursa with muscular walls; genital atrium reduced.
          Pseudocrocodilicola Byrd and Reiber, 1942 (fig. 724)
14 (13) Ejaculatory duct joining uterus; paraprostate duct joining uterus slightly posterior to confluence of uterus with ejaculatory duct; common hermaphroditic canal penetrating papilla, opening into genital atrium; secondary bursa lacking.
          Crocodilicola Poche, 1925 (fig. 725)
15 (12) Vitellaria entering posterior segment posteriorly, sometimes reaching level of anterior edge of posterior testis.
          Pseudoneodiplostomum Dubois, 1936 (fig. 726)
16 (1) Papillae lacking on edges of organ of Brandes. Parasites of turtles.
          Cheloniodiplostomum Sudarikov, 1960 (fig. 727)

KEY TO THE SUBFAMILIES OF THE FAMILY OPHIODIPLOSTOMATIDAE SUDARIKOV, 1960 (XVIII:677)

V. E. Sudarikov

1 (2) Pseudosuckers lacking on anterior portion of body; vitellaria present in both segments.
          Ophiodiplostomatinae Dubois, 1936
2 (1) Pseudosuckers present on anterior portion of body; vitellaria concentrated in anterior segment, with only solitary follicles passing into base of posterior segment.   Proalariodinae Sudarikov, 1960

KEY TO THE GENERA OF THE SUBFAMILY OPHIODIPLOSTOMATINAE DUBOIS, 1936 (XVIII:677)

V. E. Sudarikov

1 (2) Duct of paraprostate enclosed in muscular

bursa, capable of external eversion resembling cirrus; genital pore dorsal.

Heterodiplostomum Dubois, 1936

2 (1) Duct of paraprostate not in muscular bursa; genital pore subterminal.

3 (4) Basal mass of vitellaria concentrated in posterior segment, forming two parallel, elongate groups; paraprostate small.

Ophiodiplostomum Dubois, 1936 (fig. 729)

4 (3) Basal mass of vitellaria concentrated in organ of Brandes; paraprostate of medium size.

Petalodiplostomum Dubois, 1936 (fig. 730)

KEY TO THE GENERA OF THE SUBFAMILY OPISTHOGONIMINAE TRAVASSOS, 1928 (XVIII:699)

K. I. Skrjabin and D. N. Antipin

1 (2) Cirrus sac very elongate, sharply curved, reaching genital pore at level of testes.

Opisthogonimus Lühe, 1900 (fig. 731)

2 (1) Cirrus sac comparatively small, with curved distal end and genital pore reaching or falling short of level of ovary.

Westella Artigas, Ruiz and Leão, 1942 (fig. 732)

LITERATURE ON THE TREMATODES OF THE FAMILY OPISTHOGONIMIDAE FREITAS, 1956 (XVIII:732)

Skrjabin, K. I. 1920. Trematodes of snakes of Paraguay. Izvestiya Donskogo Veterinarnogo Instituta. 1(2):3-4.

LIST OF SUPPLEMENTARY ILLUSTRATIONS

Cylindrorchidae Poche, 1925
Cylindrorchis tenuicutis Southwell, 1913 (fig. 667)
Lepocreadiidae Nicoll, 1935
Allolepidapedon fistulariae Yamaguti, 1940 (fig. 546)
Marsupioacetabulum marinum Yamaguti, 1952 (fig. 540)
Diploproctodaeidae Ozaki, 1928
Diploproctodaeum haustrum (MacCallum, 1918) (fig. 444)
Dinuridae Skrjabin and Guschanskaja, 1954
Profundiella skrjabini A. Skrjabin, 1958 (fig. 432)
Aerobiotrematidae Yamaguti, 1958
Aerobiotrema muraenesocis Yamaguti, 1958 (fig. 408)
Alariidae Tubangui, 1922
Enhydridiplostomum fosteri (McIntosh, 1939) (fig. 289)
Bolbocephalodidae Strand, 1935
Bolbocephalodes intestiniforax (Dubois, 1934) (fig. 283)
Proterodiplostomatidae Dubois, 1936
Massoprostatum longum Caballero, 1947 (fig. 239)
Ophiodiplostomatidae Sudarikov, 1960
Proalarioides serpentis Yamaguti, 1933 (fig. 232)
Opisthogonimidae Freitas, 1956
Sticholecitha serpentis Prudhoe, 1949 (fig. 199)

PART XIX

KEY TO THE GENERA OF THE FAMILY PROSTHOGONIMIDAE NICOLL, 1924 (XIX:8)

K. I. Skrjabin

1 (6) Parasites of birds.
2 (5) Parasites of fabrician bursa and oviduct of birds.
3 (4) Pore of uterus opening closely adjacent to male genital pore, in anterior region of body, lateral to oral sucker. Prosthogonimus Lühe, 1899 (fig. 582)
4 (3) Male genital pore in anterior region of body, closely adjacent to oral sucker; pore of uterus not adjacent to male genital pore, but displaced for considerable distance, opening separately at anterolateral edge of body.

Schistogonimus Lühe, 1909 (fig. 584)

5 (2) Parasites of conjunctiva of birds; lateral edges of large ventral sucker crossing intestinal ceca on both sides; total length of greatly sinuous cirrus sac: nearly reaching half of body length, extending beyond anterior edge of ventral sucker; genital pores as in Prosthogonimus.

Ophthalmogonimus Oschmarin, 1961 (fig. 733)

6 (1) Parasites of mammals.
7 (8) Cirrus sac bent midway forming right angle; genital pores adjacent to left edge of oral sucker, at level of middle of sucker. Intestinal parasites.

Cephalotrema Baer, 1943 (fig. 734)

8 (7) Cirrus sac straight, medial; genital pore medial, posterior to oral sucker, at level of pharynx. Liver parasites.

Mediogonimus Woodhead and Malewitz, 1936 (fig. 735)

KEY TO THE SPECIES OF THE GENUS PROSTHOGONIMUS LÜHE, 1899 from Chauhan (1940) (XIX:11)

1 (8) Suckers nearly equal in size.
2 (5) Cirrus sac not extending posteriorly beyond level of intestinal bifurcation; vitellaria originating

posterior to level of intestinal bifurcation, at level of ventral sucker, or slightly posterior.

3 (4) Cirrus sac extremely sinuous; vitellaria originating at level of ovary, considerably posterior to posterior edge of ventral sucker.
P. japonicus Braun, 1901

4 (3) Cirrus sac not sinuous; vitellaria originating at level of ventral sucker.
P. pellucidus (Linstow, 1873)

5 (2) Cirrus sac extending beyond intestinal bifurcation, not reaching ventral sucker.

6 (7) Vitellaria originating at level of intestinal bifurcation.   P. folliculus Reid and Freeman, 1936

7 (6) Cirrus sac nearly reaching ventral sucker; vitellaria originating posterior to level of intestinal bifurcation at anterior edge of ventral sucker.
P. furcifer Railliet, 1925

8 (1) Ventral sucker not less than one and one-half times larger than oral.

9 (20) Ovary dorsal to, or considerably superimposed upon ventral sucker.

10 (13) Uterus forming massive loops anterior to ventral sucker.

11 (12) Vitellaria passing posteriorly far beyond posterior limit of testes.   P. dogieli Skrjabin, 1916

12 (11) Vitellaria not reaching posterior limit of testes.   P. ovatus (Rudolphi, 1803) (fig. 582)

13 (10) Uterus not forming massive loops anterior to ventral sucker.

14 (17) Cirrus sac reaching ventral sucker; esophagus exceptionally small.

15 (16) Vitellaria restricted to region posterior to ventral sucker.   P. leei Hsü, 1935

16 (15) Vitellaria not restricted posterior to ventral sucker.   P. macroacetabulus Chauhan, 1940

17 (14) Cirrus sac crossing intestinal bifurcation, not reaching ventral sucker.

18 (19) Testes and vitellaria restricted to anterior half of body.   P. vitellatus Nicoll, 1914

19 (18) Testes and vitellaria not restricted to anterior half of body.   P. indicus Srivastava, 1938

20 (9) Ovary wholly posterior to ventral sucker.

21 (26) Cirrus sac reaching ventral sucker.

22 (23) Ventral sucker directly posterior to intestinal bifurcation.   P. brauni Skrjabin, 1919

23 (22) Ventral sucker at some distance posterior to intestinal bifurcation.

24 (25) Sucker ratio about 1:1.5.
P. longusmorbificans Seifried, 1923

25 (24) Sucker ratio 1:1.23.
P. putschkowskii Skrjabin, 1911

26 (21) Cirrus sac not reaching ventral sucker.

27 (28) Anterior border of vitellaria posterior to ventral sucker; testes equatorial.
P. anatinus Markow, 1902

28 (27) Vitellaria originating at level of ventral sucker; testes posterior to ovary.

29 (30) Vitellaria terminating by posterior borders of testes, or anterior.   P. macrorchis Macy, 1934

30 (29) Vitellaria extending posteriorly considerably beyond testes.

31 (32) Loops of uterus entirely inter-cecal.
P. rudolphii Skrjabin, 1919

32 (31) Loops of uterus both inter-cecal and extra-cecal, filling greater part of posterior half of body.

33 (34) Cirrus sac reaching intestinal bifurcation, nearly straight; sucker ratio 1:2.
P. cuneatus (Rudolphi, 1809)

34 (33) Cirrus sac extending beyond boundary of intestinal bifurcation, very sinuous; sucker ratio 1:2.
P. fulleborni Skrjabin and Massino, 1925

KEY TO THE SPECIES OF THE GENUS PROSTHOGONIMUS LÜHE, 1899 modified from Jaiswal (1957) (XIX:12)

K. I. Skrjabin

1 (10) Suckers equal or nearly equal.

2 (5) Cirrus sac not extending beyond intestinal bifurcation; vitellaria originating far posterior to intestinal bifurcation, at level of ventral sucker or posterior to it.

3 (4) Cirrus sac sinuous; vitellaria originating near ovary, posterior to level of ventral sucker.
P. japonicus Braun, 1901

4 (3) Cirrus sac not sinuous; vitellaria originating at level of ventral sucker.
P. pellucidus (Linstow, 1873)

5 (2) Cirrus sac extending beyond intestinal bifurcation, sometimes reaching ventral sucker.

6 (7) Vitellaria originating anterior to level of ventral sucker, at level of intestinal bifurcation, terminating posteriorly at level of middle or posterior edges of testes.
P. pseudopellucidus Tubangui and Masilungan, 1941

7 (6) Vitellaria originating posterior to intestinal bifurcation.

8 (9) Vitellaria originating posterior to level of intestinal bifurcation, approximately at level of anterior edge of ventral sucker, terminating posteriorly slightly beyond testes.   P. furcifer Railliet, 1925

9 (8) Vitellaria originating far posterior to level of intestinal bifurcation, approximately at level of posterior edge of ventral sucker, terminating far posterior to testes.   P. sinensis Chang-Tung-Ku, 1941

10 (1) Suckers unequal; ventral sucker not less than one and one-half times larger than oral.

11 (32) Ovary predominantly or partially in zone of ventral sucker.

12 (15) Ovary not closely adjacent to ventral sucker.

13 (14) Ovary lateral to ventral sucker; vitellaria approximately at level of intestinal bifurcation; cirrus sac not reaching ventral sucker.
P. ketupi Jaiswal, 1957

14 (13) Ovary predominantly lateral to ventral sucker, not superimposed; vitellaria far posterior to intestinal bifurcation, approximately at level of ventral sucker; cirrus sac reaching ventral sucker.
P. penni Chang-Tung-Ku, 1951

15 (12) Ovary largely superimposed upon ventral sucker.

16 (19) Massive loops of uterus present anterior and posterior to ventral sucker.

17 (18) Vitellaria not extending to posterior borders of testes. **P. ovatus** (Rudolphi, 1803) (fig. 582)

18 (17) Vitellaria extending beyond posterior borders of testes. **P. dogieli** Skrjabin, 1916

19 (16) Massive loops of uterus absent anterior to ventral sucker.

20 (23) Cirrus sac reaching ventral sucker; esophagus small.

21 (22) Vitellaria restricted to zone posterior to ventral sucker. **P. leei** Hsü, 1935

22 (21) Vitellaria not restricted to zone posterior to ventral sucker. **P. macroacetabulus** Chauhan, 1940

23 (20) Cirrus sac not reaching ventral sucker.

24 (25) Gonads and vitellaria restricted to anterior half of body. **P. vitellatus** Nicoll, 1914

25 (24) Gonads in posterior or in middle part of body.

26 (27) Gonads limited to posterior half of body; vitellaria anteriorly extending to anterior edge of ventral sucker. **P. dollfusi** Jaiswal, 1957

27 (26) Gonads equatorial.

28 (29) Vitellaria anteriorly not reaching intestinal bifurcation, posteriorly terminating far posterior to testes; ventral sucker more than two times larger than oral. **P. indicus** Srivastava, 1938

29 (28) Vitellaria anteriorly extending to intestinal bifurcation.

30 (31) Vitellaria extending anteriorly to intestinal bifurcation, terminating slightly posterior to testes; ventral sucker two times larger than oral.
P. singhi Jaiswal, 1957

31 (30) Vitellaria extending anteriorly nearly to intestinal bifurcation, terminating approximately at level of posterior limit of testes; ventral sucker less than two times larger than oral.
P. folliculus Reid and Freeman, 1936

32 (11) Ovary always posterior to ventral sucker.

33 (40) Cirrus sac nearly reaching ventral sucker.

34 (37) Ventral sucker directly posterior to intestinal bifurcation.

35 (36) Vitellaria in groups, extending nearly to level of intestinal bifurcation.
P. brauni Skrjabin, 1919

36 (35) Vitellaria not in groups, extending only to level of ventral sucker.
P. mesolecithus Jaiswal, 1957

37 (34) Ventral sucker at some distance posterior to intestinal bifurcation.

38 (39) Sucker ratio 1:1.5.
P. longusmorbificans Seifried, 1923

39 (38) Sucker ratio 1:1.23.
P. putschkowskii Skrjabin, 1912

40 (33) Cirrus sac not reaching ventral sucker.

41 (46) Vitellaria originating posterior to ventral sucker.

42 (43) Testes post-equatorial vitellaria restricted to zone of testes. **P. anatinus** Markow, 1902

43 (42) Testes with different position.

44 (45) Testes nearly equatorial; vitellaria not restricted to zone of testes.
P. querquedulae Yamaguti, 1933

45 (44) Testes mostly pre-equatorial; vitelline follicles in definite groups anterior and posterior to testes. **P. horiuchii** Morishita and Tsuchimochi, 1925

46 (41) Vitellaria not originating posterior to ventral sucker.

47 (48) Vitellaria originating at considerable distance anterior to ventral sucker.
P. hyderabadensis Jaiswal, 1957

48 (47) Vitellaria originating in zone of ventral sucker.

49 (54) Vitellaria originating at level of middle of ventral sucker.

50 (51) Ovary directly anterior to zone of testes; testes equatorial; vitellaria evenly distributed.
P. orientalis Yamaguti, 1933

51 (50) Ovary differently placed.

52 (53) Ovary in zone of testes; testes very small, slightly post-equatorial; vitellaria in distinct groups.
P. skrjabini Zakharow, 1920

53 (52) Ovary wedged between testes; male genital organs in posterior spade-shaped part of body; vitellaria restricted, evenly dispersed.
P. karausiaki Layman, 1926

54 (49) Vitellaria originating at level of anterior edge of ventral sucker.

55 (56) Vitellaria terminating at level of posterior limit of testes, or slightly anterior.
P. macrorchis Macy, 1934

56 (55) Vitellaria extending considerably beyond testes.

57 (58) Loops of uterus wholly inter-cecal.
P. rudolphii Skrjabin, 1919

58 (57) Loops of uterus both inter-cecal and extra-cecal, filling entire posterior half of body.

59 (60) Cirrus sac sinuous, reaching intestinal bifurcation. **P. cuneatus** (Rudolphi, 1809)

60 (59) Cirrus sac not sinuous, extending slightly beyond intestinal bifurcation.
P. fulleborni Skrjabin and Massino, 1925

KEY TO THE SUBGENERA OF THE GENUS PROSTHOGONIMUS LÜHE, 1899 from Skrjabin (1961) (XIX:18)

1 (6) Gonads well-developed; vitelline follicles large.

2 (5) Uterus sinuous, passing anterior and posterior to ventral sucker.

3 (4) In posterior half of body uterus wholly inter-cecal. Prosthogenotrema Skrjabin and Gnedina, 1941 (typical species: **P. (P.) limani** Gnedina, 1941)

4 (3) Uterus inter-cecal and extra-cecal, filling entire posterior half of body.
Prosthogonimus (Lühe, 1899) Skrjabin and Baskakow, 1925
(typical species: **P. (P.) ovatus** (Rudolphi, 1803))

5 (2) Uterus broad, well-developed, posterior to ventral sucker, extra-cecal and inter-cecal, filling entire posterior half of body.

Macrogenotrema Skrjabin and Baskakow, 1925

(typical species: P. (M.) cuneatus (Rudolphi, 1803)

6 (1) Gonads weakly developed; vitelline follicles delicate, usually stellate.

7 (8) Uterus both inter-cecal and extra-cecal posteriorly.

    Politogenotrema Skrjabin and Baskakow, 1925
(typical species: P. (P.) gracilis Skrjabin and Baskakow, 1925)

8 (7) Uterus inter-cecal posteriorly.

    Primagenotrema Skrjabin and Baskakow, 1941
(typical species: P. (P.) skrjabini Zakharow, 1920)

KEY TO THE SPECIES OF THE SUBGENUS PROSTHOGONIMUS (LÜHE, 1899) SKRJABIN AND BASKAKOW, 1941 (XIX:27)

K. I. Skrjabin

1 (2) Vitellaria not extending beyond posterior limit of testes; loops of uterus inter-cecal and extra-cecal anterior to ventral sucker.

    P. (P.) ovatus (Rudolphi, 1803) (fig. 582)

2 (1) Posterior border of vitellaria considerably posterior to testes; loops of uterus inter-cecal anterior to ventral sucker. P. (P.) dogieli Skrjabin, 1916

LITERATURE ON THE TREMATODES OF THE FAMILY PROSTHOGONIMIDAE NICOLL, 1924 (XIX:183-185)

Ablasov, N. A. 1955. A new trematode from anatids. Trudy Instituta Zoologii i Parazitologii Akad. Nauk Kirgisk. SSR. No. 4:137-140.

Baskakov, V. P. 1927. On the analysis of individual variability of Prosthogonimus ovatus (Rud., 1803) Sbornik Rabot po Gelmintologii, Posvyachenny Akademiku K. I. Skrjabin. pp. 25-43.

Bykhovskaya-Pavlovskaya, I. E. 1955. Trematodes of birds of the fauna of the U. S. S. R. Avtoreferat dissertatsii, Leningrad.

Witenberg, G. G. and V. P. Podyapolskaya. 1926. The Eleventh Union Helminthological Expedition into the Zabaykalye region. Deyatelnost 28 Gelmintologicheskikh Expeditsii v SSSR (1919-1925). pp. 144-152.

Gvozdev, E. V. 1954. Prosthogonimiasis of hens and its control. Selskoye Skozyaystvo Kazakhstana. No. 11:41-43.

Gvozdev, E. V. 1954. Parasitic worms of gallinaceous birds of Kazakhstan. Izdatelstvo Akad. Nauk Kazakh. SSR, Alma-Ata.

Gorshkov, I. P. 1937. On the knowledge of the helminth fauna of domestic geese of the Omsk and Chelyabinsk districts. Sbornik Rabot po Gelmintologii, Posvyaschenny Akademiku K. I. Skrjabinu. pp. 191-202.

Dogiel, V. A. and Kh. Karolinskaya. 1936. The parasite fauna of swifts (Apus apus). Uchenye Zapiski Leningradskogo Gosudarstvennogo Universiteta, No. 7, seriya biologicheskaya. No. 3:43-79.

Zaskind, L. N. 1951. Helminthiases of geese and their agents. Dissertatsiya na Stepen Kandidata

Verterinarnykh Nauk Moskovskaya Veterinarnaya Akademiya.

Zakharov, N. P. 1920. Prosthogonimus skrjabini nov. sp. Materials on the knowledge of the helminth fauna of birds of Russia. Trudy Donskogo Veterinarnogo Instituta. 1(2):1-6.

Isaychikov, I. M. 1927. On the fauna of parasitic worms of domestic carnivores of the Crimea, II. Parasitic worms of cats. Trudy Sibirskogo Veterinarnogo Instituta. No. 9:132-170.

Isaychikov, I. M. 1931. Further consideration of prosthogonimiasis of poultry. Prakticheskaya Veterinariya. No. 12:381.

Kasimov, G. B. 1956. The helminth fauna of game birds of the order Galliformes. Izdatelstvo Akad. Nauk, Moskva. 554 pp.

Krasnolobova, T. A. 1935. On the development of the agent of oviduct disease in hens, Prosthogonimus cuneatus (Rudolphi, 1809). Vosmoye Soveschanie po Parazitologicheskim Problemam. Tezisy Dokladov. Izdatelstvo Akad. Nauk SSSR. pp. 80-81.

Krasnolobova, T. A. 1956. On the biology of development of the agent of oviduct disease in hens, Prosthogonimus cuneatus (Rudolphi, 1809) (Trematoda). Doklady Akad. Nauk SSSR. 106(1):165-168.

Krasnolobova, T. A. 1957. On the biology of Prosthogonimus pellucidus (Linst.) the agent of prosthogonimiasis in birds. Devyatoye Soveschanie po Parazitologicheskim Problemam. Tezisy Dokladov Zoologicheskogo Instituta Akad. Nauk SSSR. pp. 119-120.

Krasnolobova, T. A. 1959. On the biology of Prosthogonimus pellucidus (Lins., 1873), the agent of prosthogonimiasis in poultry. Raboty po Gelmintologii k 80-letiyu Akademika K. I. Skrjabina. pp. 172-175.

Krasnolobova, T. A. 1959. On the identity of Prosthogonimus pellucidus Linstow, 1873, and Prosthogonimus anatinus Markow, 1902. Mezhdunarodny Nauchny Zhurnal (Helmintologia). 1(1-4):113-119.

Krasnolobova, T. A. 1960. The biology of prosthogonimids, the agents of disease in poultry. Dissertatsiya, Moskva.

Kurashvili, B. E. 1957. Helminths of game birds of Georgia from the faunistic and ecological standpoints. Izdatelstvo Akad. Nauk SSSR. 434 pp.

Layman, E. M. 1926. On the fauna of parasitic worms of pheasants of Turkestan. Raboty Parazitologicheskoy Laboratorii I Moskovskogo Gosudarstvennogo Universiteta. pp. 50-58.

Markov, M. P. 1902. On a new representative of the genus Prosthogonimus, P. anatinus nov. sp. Trudy Ispytateley Prirody pri Kharkovskom Universitete. 38:287-298.

Machulsky, S. N., L. I. Etingov, and A. Ya. Gozha. 1950. Application of hexachlorethane in prosthogonimiasis of hens. Trudy Buryat-Mongoloskogo Zooveterinarnogo Instituta, Ulan-Ude. No. 6:

Mozgovoy, A. A. and Mishenina. 1959. Prosthogonimus macroskrjabini, a new species of trematode from hen in Yakutiya. Raboty po Gelmintologii k 80-letiyu Akademika K. I. Skrjabina. pp. 236-238.

Morozov, F. N. 1959. On the question of the presence of an anus in digenetic trematodes. Raboty po Gelmintologii k 80-letiyu Akademika K. I. Skrjabina. pp. 239-242.

Palimpsestov, M. A. 1937. On the characteristics of the helminth fauna of domestic animals in the Mordovian Autotomy, the Kuybyshev and Orenburg districts. Sbornik Rabot po Gelmintologii, Posvyaschenny Akademika K. I. Skrjabina. pp. 454-458.

Panin, V. Ya. 1957a. Variability in morphological traits and its significance in the systematics of the genus Prosthogonimus Lühe, 1909. Trudy Instituta Zoologii Akad. Nauk Kazakh. SSR. 7:170-215.

Panin, V. Ya. 1957b. On the natural focus of prosthogonimiasis of domestic hens. Tezisy Dokladov Zool. Institut. Akad. Nauk SSSR. p. 195.

Panin, V. Ya. 1957c. Biology of the trematodes, Prosthogomimus ovatus (Rudolphi, 1803) and P. cuneatus (Rudolphi, 1809), parasites of fabrician bursae and oviducts of wild and domestic birds. Izvestiya Akad. Nauk Kazakhsk. SSR, seriya biologicheskaya, 14. No. 2:53-65.

Panova, L. G. 1927. Helminthology in Kazakhstan. Sbornik Rabot po Gelmintologii, Posvyaschenny K. I. Skrjabinu. pp. 121-137.

Petrov, A. M. 1926. On the fauna of parasitic worms of domestic and wild geese of the Don district. Trudy Gosudarstvennogo Instituta Experimentalnoy Veterinarii. 3(1):99-113.

Potemkina, V. A. 1941. On the diagnosis and treatment of prosthogonimiasis in hens. Veterinariya. 18(4):20-21.

Potemkina, V. A. 1953. Helminthiases of poultry. Selkhozgiz, Moskva. 168 pp.

Semenov, V. D. 1927. Preliminary results of research on a helminth infestation in birds of the Zapadny Kray. Trudy Smolenskogo Obschestva Estestvoispytateley i Vrachey. 2:137-156.

Sizov, P. V. 1926. An epizootic of helminthic inflammation of the oviduct in hens. Trudy Gosudarstvennogo Instituta Experimentalnoy Veterinarii. 4(1):40-55.

Skrjabin, K. I. 1911. Helminthiasis of the hen egg. Vestnik Obschestvennoy Veterinarii. 23(5):304.

Skrjabin, K. I. 1912. Parasitic worms of Turkestan, A. Trematodes. I. Subfamily Prosthogoniminae Lühe. Arkhiv Veterinarnykh Nauk. 42(12):1270-1287.

Skrjabin, K. I. 1916a. On the knowledge of the helminth fauna of domestic animals of Turkestan. Dissertatsiya, Yuriev.

Skrjabin, K. I. 1916b. Parasitic trematodes and nematodes collected by the expedition of Professors V. A. Dogiel and I. I. Sokolov in British East Africa and Uganda. Nauchnye Rezultaty Zoologicheskoy Expeditsii Prof. V. A. Dogielya i I. I. Sokolova v Britanskuyu Vostochnuyu Afriku i Ugandu v 1914 g. 1(14):1-157.

Skrjabin, K. I. 1919. The first Don-Azov Helminthological Expedition. Izvestiya Donskogo Veterinarnogo Instituta. 1(1):1-10.

Skrjabin, K. I. 1920. Nematodes of poultry. Attempts in monographic elaboration. I. Roundworms of hens, turkeys, guinea fowl, peafowl, and pigeons. Izvestiya Donskogo Veterinarnogo Instituta. 1(2):1-32.

Skrjabin, K. I. 1923. Trematodes of poultry. Trudy Gosudarstvennogo Instituta Experimentalnoy Veterinarii. 1(2):193-256.

Skrjabin, K. I. 1941. Analysis of the phylogenetic evolution of trematodes of the genus Prosthogonimus Lühe. Doklady Akad. Nauk SSSR. 33(7-8):466-470.

Skrjabin, K. I. and N. P. Popov. 1924. Brief summary of the activities of the Helminthological Expedition in Armenia in 1923. Russky Zhurnal Tropicheskoy Meditsiny. No. 2:58-63.

Skrjabin, K. I. and R. Ed. S. Schulz. 1935. Control of helminthiases of birds. Trudy Moskovskogo Zooveterinarnogo Instituta. 1:3-23.

Strelkov, S. T. 1949. Prosthogonimiasis of turkeys. Veterinariya. No. 12:28-29.

Khuan, Shen-i. 1961. The helminth fauna of domestic and game birds of the lower Amur. Dissertatsiya na Stepen Kandidata Biologicheskikh Nauk. Gelmintologicheskaya Laboratoriya Akad. Nauk SSSR.

Chertkova, A. N. 1952. Helminth fauna of domestic gallinaceous birds. Dissertatsiya na Stepen Kandidata Biologicheskikh Nauk VIGIS, Moskva.

Chertkova, A. N. and A. M. Petrov. 1959. Helminths of domestic gallinaceous birds and diseases caused by them. Moskva. 1:103-132 and 318-324.

Shevtsov, A. A. 1952. Helminthiases of domestic ducks and their agents. Dissertatsiya, Moskva.

Shevtsov, A. A. and L. N. Zaskind. 1960. Helminths and helminthiases of domestic water-fowl. Izdatelstvo Kharkovskogo Gosudarstvennogo Universiteta. pp. 70-89.

KEY TO THE GENERA OF THE SUBFAMILY STYPHLODORINAE DOLLFUS, 1937 (XIX:206)

K. I. Skrjabin and D. N. Antipin

1 (8) Cirrus sac reaching level of posterior edge of ventral sucker or only slightly beyond.

2 (3) Genital pore medial, directly anterior to ventral sucker.   Styphlodora Looss, 1899 (fig. 575)

3 (2) Genital pore submedial.

4 (5) Ovary considerably posterior to ventral sucker. Parasites of bile ducts.
Allopharynx (Strom, 1928) (fig. 736)

5 (4) Ovary closely adjacent to posterior edge of ventral sucker.

6 (7) Uterus inter-cecal, reaching posterior end of body. Intestinal parasites of fishes.
Glossidium Looss, 1899 (fig. 737)

7 (6) Uterus extra-cecal and inter-cecal, not reaching posterior end of body. Lung parasites of snakes.

Glossidioides Yamaguti, 1958 (fig. 738)

8 (1) Cirrus sac extending considerably posterior to posterior edge of ventral sucker.

9 (10) Seminal receptacle lacking. Intestinal parasites of turtles.　Glossimetra Mehra, 1937 (fig. 576)

10 (9) Seminal receptacle present.

11 (12) Cirrus armed. Intestinal parasites of reptiles.　Spinometra Mehra, 1931 (fig. 577)

12 (11) Cirrus unarmed. Lung parasites of snakes.　Glossidiella Travassos, 1927 (fig. 578)

KEY TO THE SPECIES OF THE GENUS STYPHLODORA LOOSS, 1899 modified from Byrd, Parker, and Reiber (1940) (XIX:207)

K. I. Skrjabin and D. N. Antipin

1 (8) Vitellaria terminating anterior to testes.

2 (5) Testes lobed.

3 (4) Ovary round; ventral sucker near intestinal bifurcation.　S. similis Sonsino, 1890

4 (3) Ovary lobed; ventral sucker directly posterior to intestinal bifurcation.　S. persimilis Nicoll, 1914

5 (2) Testes usually entire or slightly lobed.

6 (7) Testes medial; ventral sucker far from intestinal bifurcation; prepharynx present; pharynx round.　S. najae Nicoll, 1912

7 (6) Testes widely separated; ventral sucker directly posterior to intestinal bifurcation; prepharynx lacking; pharynx elongate.　S. aspina Byrd, Parker, and Reiber, 1940

8 (1) Vitellaria extending to level of testes or beyond.

9 (22) Vitellaria terminating at level of testes.

10 (11) Vitellaria terminating in zone of posterior testis.　S. baskaniensis Goldberger, 1911

11 (10) Vitellaria terminating in zone of anterior testis.

12 (13) Testes and ovary nearly equal in size; body long and slender.　S. horridum Leidy, 1850

13 (12) Testes clearly larger than ovary.

14 (17) Genital pore directly posterior to intestinal bifurcation.

15 (16) Pharynx elongate; ventral sucker directly posterior to genital pore; testes large, round.　S. nicolli Bhalerao, 1936

16 (15) Pharynx round; ventral sucker posterior to genital pore; anterior testis transversely elongate; posterior with shape of elongate oval.　S. condita De Faria, 1911

17 (14) Genital pore posterior to intestinal bifurcation.

18 (19) Testes oblique, with transverse zones overlapping; genital pores dextral.　S. lachesidis MacCallum, 1921

19 (18) Testes oblique, with transverse zones separated; body spade-shaped; genital pores medial.

20 (21) Testes elongate, with irregular contours; genital pore midway between ventral sucker and intestinal bifurcation.　S. serrata Looss, 1899 (fig. 575)

21 (20) Testes round with regular or nearly regular contours; genital pore directly anterior to ventral sucker.　S. renalis Tubangui, 1933

22 (9) Vitellaria terminating posterior to level of testes.

23 (24) Vitellaria reaching ends of intestinal ceca.　S. floridanis Byrd, Parker, and Reiber, 1940

24 (23) Vitellaria not reaching ends of intestinal ceca.

25 (26) Ovary at considerable distance from ventral sucker; loops of uterus concentrated between ovary and ventral sucker; genital pore midway between ventral sucker and intestinal bifurcation.　S. natricis Byrd and Denton, 1938

26 (25) Ovary near posterior edge of ventral sucker.

27 (28) Testes close together, on medial line; vitelline follicles large, compact; uterus forming short, spiral loops anterior to testes; esophagus short or absent.　S. compactum Byrd, Parker, and Reiber, 1940

28 (27) Testes separated by loops of uterus, at considerable distance from each other; esophagus present.

29 (30) Body length exceeding 6.0 mm.; vitellaria in distinct groups.　S. magna Byrd and Denton, 1938

30 (29) Body length less than 6.0 mm.; vitellaria branched.　S. agkistrodontis Byrd, Parker, and Reiber, 1940

Note: S. elegans, Dawes, 1941; S. compressiae Dawes, 1942; and S. dentipharyngeata Chatterji, 1940 omitted from key.

KEY TO THE SPECIES OF THE GENUS ALLOPHARYNX (STROM, 1928) PRICE, 1938 from Price (1938) (XIX:237)

1. Cirrus sac extending posteriorly beyond ventral sucker.　2

Cirrus sac not extending posteriorly beyond ventral sucker.　3

2. Cirrus sac and metraterm separated by ventral sucker; uterus with four loops anterior to ovary.　A. tropidonoti (MacCallum, 1918)

Cirrus sac and metraterm not separated by ventral sucker; uterus with numerous loops anterior to ovary.　A. multispinosus (Bennet, 1935)

3. Genital pores at level of intestinal bifurcation; testes larger than ovary.　A. mehrai (Gogate, 1935)

Genital pores midway between intestinal bifurcation and ventral sucker; testes and ovary nearly equal in size.　A. amudariensis (Strom, 1928) (fig. 736)

Note: Soviet authors relate only two species to the above genus, namely A. amudariensis and A. tropidonoti.

KEY TO THE FAMILIES OF THE SUPERFAMILY CYATHOCOTYLOIDEA (DUBOIS, 1936) NICOLL, 1937 (XIX:283)

V. E. Sudarikov

1 (2) Body swollen, with deep, saccular cavity, cavity wall covering entire ventral side of body and organ of Brandes, opening externally through relatively narrow terminal pore; large cardiform organ of Brandes containing gonads, loops of uterus, and intestinal ceca; ovary dorsal to testes. Parasites of marine mammals.   Brauninidae Bosma, 1931

2 (1) Boundaries of ventral cavity (when present) never covering entire ventral surface of body; pore of ventral cavity wide; testes and intestine dorsal to organ of Brandes; ovary ventral to testes. Parasites of birds, reptiles, and terrestrial mammals.

3 (4) Vitelline follicles in anterior and posterior halves of body, anterior boundary reaching level of intestinal bifurcation or beyond; testes symmetrical or oblique; position of ovary variable; ventral sucker near intestinal bifurcation.
        Cyathocotylidae Poche, 1925

4 (3) Vitelline follicles surrounding gonads in posterior half of body, anterior boundary at level of ventral sucker; ventral sucker displaced toward middle of body; testes tandem, medial; ovary submedial, between anterior and posterior limits of testes.
        Prohemistomatidae Sudarikov, 1961

KEY TO THE SUBFAMILIES OF THE FAMILY CYATHOCOTYLIDAE POCHE, 1925 (XIX:285)

V. E. Sudarikov

1 (2) Body round, oval, or pyriform; vitelline follicles in periphery of body, surrounding gonads. Parasites of birds (rarely of reptiles and mammals).
        Cyathocotylinae Mühling, 1898

2 (1) Body bottle-shaped; vitelline follicles in two semi-elliptical aggregations, posterior to organ of Brandes. Parasites of mammals.
        Muhlingininae Mehra, 1950

KEY TO THE GENERA OF THE SUBFAMILY CYATHOCOTYLINAE MÜHLING, 1898 (XIX:285)

V. E. Sudarikov

1 (2) Body massive, without ventral cavity; large, sucker-like organ of Brandes present, with crater-like central concavity, organ protruding beyond ventral surface of body. Parasites of birds, more rarely, of reptiles.   Cyathocotyle Mühling, 1896 (fig. 739)

2 (1) Ventral cavity with basal, slightly protruding organ of Brandes. Parasites of birds, more rarely of mammals.

3 (6) Vitelline follicles peripheral, surrounding organ of Brandes; organ of Brandes round, with central concavity.

4 (5) Body subdivided with expanded anterior part, and tapering caudal part; testes symmetrical; organ of Brandes relatively small; vitelline follicles small, peripheral, in both portions of body.
        Pseudhemistomum Szidat, 1936 (fig. 740)

5 (4) Body simple, without subdivision; testes usually oblique, very rarely symmetrical; organ of Brandes relatively large, filling greater part of ventral cavity.   Holostephanus Szidat, 1936 (fig. 741)

6 (3) Vitelline follicles in two lateral groups, dorsal to organ of Brandes, or passing into it; organ of Brandes oval, without central concavity.
        Duboisia Szidat, 1936 (fig. 742)

KEY TO THE SUBFAMILIES OF THE FAMILY PROHEMISTOMATIDAE SUDARIKOV, 1961 (XIX:342)

V. E. Sudarikov

1 (2) Organ of Brandes relatively large, without medial fissure, plug-shaped, covering ventral cavity, protruding far beyond edges of cavity, covering gonads, with anterior edge reaching intestinal bifurcation or ventral sucker. Parasites of mammals, birds, and reptiles.   Prosostephaninae Szidat, 1936

2 (1) Organ of Brandes with medial fissure or with central concavity, anterior edge considerably distant from intestinal bifurcation. Parasites of birds and reptiles, rarely of mammals.

3 (4) Parasites of birds, rarely of mammals; vitelline follicles surrounding organ of Brandes, nearly forming complete ring, or concentrated within organ; large pharynx present when vitellaria in organ of Brandes, pharynx exceeding oral sucker in size.
        Prohemistomatinae Lutz, 1935

4 (3) Parasites of reptiles; vitelline follicles in two parallel bands, lateral to organ of Brandes, or concentrated within organ in horseshoe-shaped configuration surrounding anterior testis; pharynx smaller than oral sucker.   Szidatinae Dubois, 1938

KEY TO THE GENERA OF THE SUBFAMILY PROHEMISTOMATINAE LUTZ, 1935 (XIX:343)

V. E. Sudarikov

1 (6) Organ of Brandes covering only small portion of gonads, or not at all.

2 (5) Vaginal sphincter lacking.

3 (4) Ventral cavity a shallow chamber, with edges partially or wholly covering relatively small organ of Brandes; ventral sucker nearly equal in size to oral; vitellaria in two aggregations, lateral to organ of Brandes, united by narrow bridge at level of ventral sucker or anterior edge of organ; cercariae with ventral sucker and with lateral membranes on forked tail.   Prohemistomum Odhner, 1913 (fig. 743)

4 (3) Ventral cavity indistinct; organ of Brandes never covered by edges of ventral cavity; ventral sucker weakly developed or lacking; vitelline follicles in ring surrounding organ of Brandes; cercaria lacking ventral sucker and lateral membranes on tail.
        Paracoenogonimus Katsurada, 1914 (fig. 744)

5 (2) Vaginal sphincter present.
        Mesostephanus Lutz, 1935 (fig. 745)

6 (1) Organ of Brandes wholly or nearly wholly

covering testes and ovary; large portion of vitelline follicles concentrated within organ of Brandes.

Gelanocotyle Sudarikov, 1961 (fig. 746)

KEY TO THE GENERA OF THE SUBFAMILY PROSOSTEPHANINAE SZIDAT, 1936 (XIX:390)

V. E. Sudarikov

1 (4) Parasites of mammals.
2 (3) Organ of Brandes very large, filling ventral cavity and protruding beyond edges of cavity, with anterior edge at level of intestinal bifurcation, or anterior; ventral sucker lacking; testes in anterior and posterior halves of body.

Prosostephanus Lutz, 1935 (fig. 747)

3 (2) Organ of Brandes concealed within pouch-like ventral cavity, anterior edge at level of distinctly visible ventral sucker; testes occupying posterior half of body.   Tangiella Sudarikov, 1961 (fig. 748)

4 (1) Parasites of birds and reptiles.
5 (6) Parasites of snakes; organ of Brandes large, protruding far beyond edges of weakly developed ventral cavity; oral sucker larger than pharynx or equal to it; ventral sucker clearly distinguishable.

Serpentostephanus Sudarikov, 1961 (fig. 749)

6 (5) Parasites of birds; ventral cavity concealing organ of Brandes, supplemented by well-developed lateral and posterior edges of body; pharynx larger than oral sucker; ventral sucker lacking.

Neogogatea Chandler and Rausch, 1947 (fig. 750)

KEY TO THE GENERA OF THE SUBFAMILY SZIDATINAE DUBOIS, 1938 (XIX:401)

V. E. Sudarikov

1 (2) Vitelline follicles in two parallel bands, lateral to organ of Brandes. Parasites of African sna snakes.   Szidatia Dubois, 1938 (fig. 751)

2 (1) Vitelline follicles within organ of Brandes, in horseshoe configuration around anterior testis. Parasites of Asiatic snakes.

3 (4) Cirrus sac very large; cirrus reaching more than one-third body length, armed with spines; vitelline follicles only partially extending into relatively small organ of Brandes.

Mesostephanoides Dubois, 1951 (fig. 752)

4 (3) Cirrus and cirrus sac of moderate size; vitelline follicles nearly wholly within relatively large organ of Brandes.   Gogatea Lutz, 1935 (fig. 753)

LITERATURE ON THE TREMATODES OF THE ORDER STRIGEIDIDA (LA RUE, 1926) SUDARIKOV, 1959 (XIX:413-433)

Ablasov, N. A. 1953a. The helminth fauna of domestic and wild water-fowl of Kirgizia. Dissertatsiya, Moskva.

Ablasov, N. A. 1953b. The helminth fauna of domestic and wild water-fowl of Kirgizia. Avtoreferat dissertatsii, Moskva.

Agapova, A. I. 1945. The parasite fauna of Squalalburnus taeniatus, a Central Asian endemic. Izvestiya Akad. Nauk Kazakhsk. SSR, seriya zoologicheskaya. No. 4:20-26.

Agapova, A. I. 1956a. Parasites of fishes of bodies of water in western Kazakhstan. Trudy Instituta Zoologii Akad. Nauk Kazakhsk. SSR. 5:5-60.

Agapova, A. I. 1956b. Parasites of fishes of bodies of water in western Kazakhstan. Trudy Instituta Zoologii Akad. Nauk Kazakhsk. SSR. 5:5-60.

Agapova, A. I. 1956c. Parasites of wild carp of Lake Bymo-Kul. Sbornik Rabot po Ikhtiologii i Gidrobiologii Akad. Nauk Kazakhsk. SSR. 1:269-277.

Agapova, A. I. 1957. Results of the study of parasites of fishes in bodies of water of Kazakhstan. Trudy Instituta Zoologii Akad. Nauk Kazakhsk. SSR. 7:121-130.

Annenkova-Khlopina, N. P. 1918. A disease in the fingerlings of kutum caused by the parasite, Diplostomum cuticola (v. Nordm.). Izvestiya Prikladnoy Ikhtiologii. 1(1):1-7.

Astakhova, T. V. 1953. Influence of rearing conditions on the parasite fauna of wild carp. Doklady Akad. Nauk SSSR. 93(3):577-579.

Akhmerov, A. Kh. 1941. On the study of the parasite fauna of fishes of Lake Balkash. Uchenye Zapiski Leningradskogo Gosudarstvennogo Universiteta, 74, seriya biologicheskikh nauk. No. 18:37-51.

Akhmerov, A. Kh. 1954. On the parasite fauna of fishes of the Kamchatka River. Trudy Problemnogo i Tematicheskogo Soveschaniya Zoologicheskogo Instituta Akad. Nauk SSSR. No. 4:89-98.

Akhmerov, A. Kh. 1955. The parasite fauna of fishes of the Kamchatka River. Izvestiya Tikookeanskogo Nauchno-Issledovatelskogo Instituta Rybnogo Khozyaystva i Okeanografii. 93:99-136.

Akhmerov, A. Kh. 1956a. The parasite fauna of wild carp from the Amur River and its epizootical significance. Trudy Vsesoyuznogo Nauchno-Issledovatelskogo Instituta Prudovogo Rybnogo Khozyaystva. 8:206-218.

Akhmerov, A. Kh. 1956b. Parasites encountered in fish and in fish production. Pischepromizdat, Moskva.

Akhmerov, A. Kh. and E. A. Bogdanova. 1957. Materials on the parasite fauna of fishes. Izvestiya Vsesoyuznogo Instituta Nauchno-Issledovatelskogo Ozernogo i Rechnogo Rybnogo Khozyaystva. 92:146-158.

Akhmerov, A. Kh. and L. K. Grapmane. 1954. The parasite fauna of cyprinid fishes in pond cultures of the Latvian S. S. R. Questions of animal culture and veterinary medicine. Trudy Latvyskoy Selskokhozyaystvennoy Akademii, Riga. 3:271-281.

Badanin, N. V. and M. V. Nazarov. 1936. On the question of helminth infestations in Nyctereutes procyonoides Gray. Trudy Kazakhskogo Krayesvogo Nauchno-Issledovatelskogo Veterinarnogo Instituta. 1:299-300.

Barysheva, A. F. 1949. The parasite fauna of fishes of Lake Ladoga. Uchenye Zapiski Leningradskogo Gosudarstvennogo Universiteta, No. 101, seriya biologicheskikh nauk. No. 19:5-11.

Barysheva, A. F. and O. N. Bauer. 1957. Parasites of fishes of Lake Ladoga. Izvestiya Vsesoyuznogo Nauchno-Issledovatelskogo Instituta Ozernogo i Rechnogo Rybnogo Khozyaystva. 92:175-224.

Bauer, O. N. 1941. The parasite fauna of birds of the mountainous area of the Borzhomsky region. Uchenye Zapiski Leningradskogo Gosudarstvennogo Universiteta, No. 74. seriya biologicheskikh nauk. No. 18:63-92.

Bauer, O. N. 1946. The parasite fauna of cisco from various bodies of water of the U. S. S. R. Trudy Leningradskogo Obschestva Estestviospytateley. 19(4):7-21.

Bauer, O. N. 1948a. Parasites of fishes of the Yenisei River. Izvestiya Vsesoyuznogo Nauchno-Issledovatelskogo Instituta Ozernogo i Rechnogo Rybnogo Khozyaystva. 27:97-157.

Bauer, O. N. 1948b. Parasites of fishes of the Lena River. Izvestiya Vsesoyuznogo Nauchno-Issledovatelskogo Instituta Ozernogo i Rechnogo Rybnogo Khozyaystva. 27:157-174.

Bauer, O. N. 1950. The parasite fauna of whitefish of the U. S. S. R., its zoogeography and commercial fisheries significance. Trudy Barabinskogo Otdeleniya Vsesoyuznogo Nauchno-Issledovatelskogo Institut Ozernogo i Rechnogo Rybnogo Khozyaystva. 4:59-76.

Bauer, O. N. 1953. Prophylactic measures in pond cultures against parasitic diseases of fishes. Gizlegpischepromizdat. pp. 1-34.

Bauer, O. N. 1954. The formation of the parasite fauna of fishes in new reservoirs. Trudy Problemnogo i Tematicheskogo Soveschaniya Zoologicheskogo Instituta. No. 4:47-53.

Bauer, O. N. 1957a. Diseases of pond carp in fish-culture ponds of the Leningrad and Novgorod districts. Izvestiya Vsesoyuznogo Nauchno-Issledovatelskogo Ozernogo i Rechnogo Rybnogo Khozyaystva. 92:67-88.

Bauer, O. N. 1957b. The parasite fauna of salmon fingerlings (Salmo salar) in early stages of their development. Trudy Leningradskogo Obschestva Estestvoispytateley. 23(4):159-163.

Bauer, O. N. 1958a. Interrelationship between parasites and hosts (fishes). In: Basic problems of fish parasitology. Izdatelstvo Leningradskogo Gosudarstvennogo Universiteta. pp. 90-108.

Bauer, O. N. 1958b. Parasitic diseases of fishes in fish-culture ponds and hatcheries, and methods of control. In: Basic problems of fish parasitology. Izdatelstvo Leningradskogo Gosudarstvennogo Universiteta. pp. 267-300.

Bauer, O. N. 1959. The influence of environmental factors on reproduction of parasites of fishes. Voprosy Ekologii. Kievsky Universitet. 3:132-141.

Bauer, O. N. 1960. Ecology of parasites of freshwater fishes. (Interrelationships between parasite and environment). Izvestiya Vsesoyuznogo Nauchno-Issledovatelskogo Instituta Ozernogo i Rechnogo Rybnogo Khozyaystva. 99:186-194.

Bauer, O. N. and V. N. Greze. 1948. Parasites of fishes of Lake Taymyr. Izvestiya Vsesoyuznogo Nauchno-Issledovatelskogo Instituta Ozernogo i Rechnogo Rybnogo Khozyaystva. 27:186-194.

Bauer, O. N. and N. P. Nikolskaya. 1958. The dynamics of the parasite fauna of Lake Ladoga whitefish and its epizootical significance. Izvestiya Vsesoyuznogo Nauchno-Issledovatelskogo Ozernogo i Rechnogo Rybnogo Khozyaystva. 92:227-242.

Bauer, O. N. and V. P. Stolyarov. 1928. Formation of the parasite fauna and parasitic diseases of fishes in reservoirs. In: Basic problems of fish parasitology. Izdatelstvo Leningradskogo Gosudarstvennogo Universiteta. pp. 247-255.

Bauer, O. N. and S. S. Shulman. 1948. On the question of ecological classification of fish parasites. Izvestiya Vsesoyuznogo Nauchno-Issledovatelskogo Ozernogo i Rechnogo Rybnogo Khozyaystva. 27:239-243.

Belopolskaya, M. M. 1952. The parasite fauna of marine water-fowl. Uchenye Zapiski Leningradskogo Gosudarstvennogo Universiteta, 141, seriya biologicheskikh nauk. No. 28:127-180.

Belopolskaya, M. M. 1953. On the helminth fauna of sand-papers of the U. S. S. R. Raboty po Gelmintologii k 75-letiyu Akademika K. I. Skrjabina. pp. 47-65.

Belopolskaya, M. M. 1954. The parasite fauna of birds of the Sudzukhinsky Preserve (Primorye). Uchenye Zapiski Leningradskogo Gosudarstvennogo Universiteta, (172), seriya biologicheskikh nauk. No. 35:3-34.

Belopolskaya, M. M. 1957. The larval trematode fauna of amphipods (Gammarus locusta L.) from the Baltic Sea. Trudy Leningradskogo Obschestva Estestvoispytateley. 23(4):164-169.

Bidulina, M. I. 1955. The larval trematode fauna of molluscs of the Dnieper River. Avtoreferat kandidata dissertatsii, Kiev.

Bidulina, M. I. 1956. Larval trematodes of molluscs of the Dnieper River and peculiarities of their habitat. Trudy 2 Nauchnoy Konferentsii Parazitologov Ukr. SSR. pp. 24-26.

Bogatova, Z. K. 1936. The parasite fauna of native fish and of acclimztized whitefish of Lake Turgoyak. Uchenye Zapiski Leningradskogo Gosudarstvennogo Universiteta, 7, seriya biologicheskikh nauk. No. 3:144-155.

Bogdanova, E. A. 1957a. Parasites of whitefish and cisco of Lake Baykal. Izvestiya Vsesoyuznogo Nauchno-Issledovatelskogo Ozernogo i Rechnogo Rybnogo Khozyaystva. 92:315-322.

Bogdanova, E. A. 1958b. Materials on the parasite fauna of roach fingerlings from a series of Volga rearing ponds. Izvestiya Vsesoyuznogo Nauchno-Issledovatelskogo Ozernogo i Rechnogo Rybnogo Khozyaystva. 92:323-325.

Bogdanova, E. A. 1957c. The parasite fauna of

bream and carp fingerlings of rearing ponds of the Volga delta, and their epizootical condition. Izvestiya Vsesoyuznogo Nauchno-Issledovatelskogo Ozernogo i Rechnogo Rybnogo Khozyaystva. 93(2):1-70.

Bogdanova, E. A. 1959. Seasonal variation in the parasite fauna of pike and bream of the Volga River. Raboty po Gelmintologii k 80-letiyu Akademika K. I. Skrjabina. pp. 72-78.

Bozhkov, D. K. 1957. The helminth fauna of Rana ridibunda from the vicinity of Sofia. Izvestiya Zoologicheskogo Instituta Bolgarskoy Akad. Nauk. 6:491-518.

Borovitskaya, M. P. 1952. Comparison of the parasite fauna of commercial fishes of the Danube estuaries and the Danube River. Trudy Leningradskogo Obschestva Estestvoispytateley. 21(4):10-25.

Burzhanadze, P. L. 1939. The main helminthiases of farm animals of the Georgian S. S. R. Rukopis dissertatsii, Moskva.

Butskaya, N. A. 1952. The parasite fauna of commercial fishes of the Black Sea near the mouth of the Danube. Trudy Leningradskogo Obschestva Estestvoispytateley. 71(4):30-52.

Bykova, E. V. 1939. On the knowledge of the parasite fauna of commercial fishes of Lake Charkhal. Uchenye Zapiski Leningradskogo Gosudarstvennogo Universiteta, 43, seriya biologicheskikh nauk. No. 11:33-43.

Bykhovskaya-Pavlovskaya, I. E. 1935. Materials on the endoparasite fauna of fishes of Lake Issyk-Kul. Trudy Kirgizskoy Komplexnoy Expeditsii v 1932-1933 gg. 3(2):65-71.

Bykhovskaya, I. E. 1936a. On the influence of the size of the habitat on the parasite fauna of fishes. Uchenye Zapiski, No. 3, seriya biologicheskaja. Problemy Ekologicheskoy Parazitologii. No. 3:163-166.

Bykhovskaya, I. E. 1936b. Materials on the parasitology of fishes of Karelia, II. The parasite fauna of fishes of small bodies of water. Trudy Borodinskoy Biologicheskoy Stantsii. 8(2):123-138.

Bykhovskaya-Pavlovskaya, I. E. 1936c. The fauna of endoparasites of fishes of the River Chu. Trudy Kirgizskoy Komplexnoy Expeditsii. 3(1):277-294.

Bykhovskaya, I. E. 1940. On the influence of age on the variability of the parasite fauna of perch. Parazitologichesky Sbornik Zoologicheskogo Instituta Akad. Nauk SSSR. 8:99-130.

Bykhovskaya-Pavlovskaya, I. E. 1949. The parasite fauna of perch and its variation under the influence of several ecological factors. Izvestiya Akad. Nauk SSSR, seriya biologicheskaya. No. 3:316-339.

Bykhovskaya-Pavlovskaya, I. E. 1953a. The trematode fauna of birds of western Siberia, and its dynamics. Parazitologichesky Sbornik Zoologicheskogo Instituta Akad. Nauk SSSR. 15:5-116.

Bykhovskaya-Pavlovskaya, I. E. 1953b. On the trematode fauna of birds of the Leningrad district. Raboty po Gelmintologii k 75-letiyu Akademika K. I. Skrjabina. pp. 85-92.

Bykhovskaya-Pavlovskaya, I. E. 1955a. Trema-

todes of birds of Tadzhikistan. Trudy Zoologicheskogo Instituta Akad. Nauk SSSR. 21:125-151.

Bykhovskaya-Pavlovskaya, I. E. 1955b. Trematodes of birds of the fauna of the U. S. S. R. Avtoreferat dissertatsii, Leningrad.

Bykhovskaya-Pavlovskaya, I. E. 1957. On the question of specificity of trematodes. Trudy Leningradskogo Obschestva Estestvoispytateley. 73(4): 171-177.

Bykhovskaya (Pavlovskaya), I. E. and B. E. Bykhovsky. 1940. The parasite fauna of fishes of the Akhtarinskie estuaries (Sea of Azov, delta of the River Kuban). Parazitologichesky Sbornik Zoologicheskogo Instituta Akad. Nauk SSR. 8:131-161.

Bykhovskaya-Pavlovskaya, I. E. and E. V. Zhukov. 1953. On the systematics of the genera Apharnygostrigea Ciurea, 1927 and Parastrigea Szidat, 1928 (Trematoda:Strigeidae). Trudy Zoologicheskogo Instituta Akad. Nauk SSSR. 13:163-170.

Bykhovsky, B. E. 1933. The trematode fauna of amphibians in the vicinity of Kiev. Zool. Anz. 102: 44-58. (In German).

Bykhovsky, B. E. 1936. Parasitological research on the Barabinskiye lakes, I. The parasite fauna of fishes. Parazitologichesky Sbornik Zoologicheskogo Instituta Akad. Nauk SSSR. 6:437-482.

Bykhovsky, B. E. 1949. The parasitic worms. In: Fresh-water life of the U. S. S. R. Pod Redaktsii Prof. Zhadina Zoologichesky Institut Akad. Nauk SSSR. 2:69-110.

Bykhovsky, B. E. and G. K. Petrushevsky. 1958. The work of member-correspondent of the Academy of Sciences of the U. S. S. R., Valentin Alexandrovich Dogiel, on the parasitology of fishes. Izvestiya Vsesoyuznogo Nauchno-Issledovatelskogo Ozernogo i Rechnogo Rybnogo Khozyaystva. 12:7-13.

Vergun, G. I. 1956. On the larval trematode fauna of several molluscs in the vicinity of the mid-reaches of the North Donets River. Trudy 2 Nauchnoy Konferentsii Parazitologov Ukr. SSR. pp. 30-32.

Vergun, G. I. 1957. On the larval trematode fauna of molluscs of the North Donets River and flood plains in the vicinity of its mid-reaches. Trudy Nauchno-Issledovatelskogo Instituta Biologii Biologicheskogo Fakulteta Kharkovskogo Gosudarstvennogo Universiteta. 30:147-166.

Vildanov, M. G. 1938. The helminth fauna of poultry of the Bashkir A. S. S. R. Trudy Bashkirskoy Gelmintologicheskoy Expeditsii. pp. 360-371.

Vildemann, L. 1957. Kodupartidel esinevad parasitaarsed helmindis Eesti NSV-s Eesti Põllum. Akadem. teaduslike tööde Koduwik 3, pp. 278-282. (In Estonian).

Vinogradova, V. 1957. Peculiarities in development and migrations of alariids in the terminal host. Sbornik Studencheskikh Rabot Vologodskogo Gosudarstvennogo Pedagogicheskogo Instituta. No. 3:89-92.

Witenberg, G. G. and V. P. Podyapolskaya. 1927. The Eleventh Union Helminthological Expedition into the Zabaykalye region. Deyatelnost 28-y

Gelmintologicheskoy Expeditsii v SSSR (1919-1925). pp. 144-152.

Volgar-Pastukhova, L. G. 1959. The parasite fauna of tail-less amphibians of the Danube delta. Ekologichesky Parazitologichesky Sbornik Statey. Izdatelstvo Leningradskogo Gosudarstvennogo Universiteta. pp. 58-95.

Volkova, M. M. 1941. The parasite fauna of fishes of the Ob River basin. Uchenye Zapiski Leningradskogo Gosudarstvennogo Universiteta, (74), seriya biologicheskikh nauk. No. 18:20-36.

Gagarin, V. G., N. A. Ablasov, and N. T. Chibichenko. 1957. The helminth fauna of wild birds of southern Kirgizia. Trudy Instituta Zoologii i Parazitologii Akad. Nauk Kirgizsk. SSR. No. 6:105-120.

Gagarin, V. G. and K. I. Iksanov. 1954. Materials on the helminth fauna of carnivores and their veterinary-sanitary significance in conditions of the Kirgiz S. S. R. Trudy Instituta Zoologii i Parazitologii Akad. Nauk Kirgizsk. SSR. No. 2:113-117.

Gvozdev, E. V. 1945. The parasite fauna of fishes of the Nagorno-Aziatskaya (Asian Uplands) subdistrict. Izvestiya Akad. Nauk Kazakhsk. SSR, seriya zoologicheskya. No. 4:38-44.

Gvozdev, E. V. 1950. Materials on the parasite of fishes of Lake Marka-Kul. Izvestiya Akad. Nauk Kazakhsk. SSR, 75, seriya parazitologicheskaya. No. 8:167-225.

Gvozdev, E. V. 1953. On the study of the parasite fauna of the spiny sturgeon, Acipenser nudiventris Lov., of the Il River. Trudy Instituta Zoologii Akad. Nauk Kazakhsk. SSR. 1:167-169.

Gvozdev, E. V., A. I. Agapova, and P. F. Martekhov. 1953. Parasites of fishes of the Il River basin. Izvestiya Akad. Nauk Kazakhsk. SSR, 125, seriya biologicheskaya. No. 8:92-114.

Getsevichute, S. I. 1954. The parasite fauna of fishes of Kurshyu Mares Zaliv. Avtoreferat dissertatsii, Vilnyus.

Ginetsinskaya, T. A. 1949a. The parasite fauna of anatids of the Volga delta. Uchenye Zapiski Leningradskogo Gosudarstvennogo Universiteta, No. 101, seriya biologicheskikh nauk. No. 19:81-109.

Ginetsinskaya, T. A. 1949b. New data on life cycles of several trematodes of birds. Doklady Akad. Nauk SSSR. 66(5):1017-1020.

Ginetsinskaya, T. A. 1952a. Parasites of rails and grebes of the Astrakhan Preserve. Trudy Leningradskogo Obschestva Estestvoispytateley. 71(4):53-72.

Ginetsinskaya, T. A. 1952 b. Interchange of parasitic worms in birds of the Volga delta. Uchenye Zapiski Leningradskogo Gosudarstvennogo Universiteta, No. 141, seriya biologicheskikh nauk. No. 28: 181-187.

Ginetsinskaya, T. A. 1953. The helminth fauna of migratory sand-pipers of the Volga delta. Raboty po Gelmintologii k 75-letiyu Akademika K. I. Skrjabina. pp. 147-156.

Ginetsinskaya, T. A. 1956. Biological adaptations of the larval stages and parthenitae of trematodes in searching for and infecting animal hosts. Vestnik Leningradskogo Universiteta. 11(3):71-84.

Ginetsinskaya, T. A. 1958. The life cycles and biology of larval stages of parasitic worms of fishes. In: Basic problems of fish parasitology. Izdatelstvo Leningradskogo Gosudarstvennogo Universiteta. pp. 144-183.

Ginetsinskaya, T. A. and A. F. Kosheva. 1959. On the question of the life cycle and systematic position of Paracoenogonimus ovatus Katsurada (Trematoda) and on the identity of the metracercaria of this species with Neodiplostomum hughesi Markewitsch. Vestnik Leningradskogo Universiteta, 14(9), seriya biologicheskaya. No. 2:68-75.

Glukhova, V. M. 1956. The parasite fauna of flatfishes of the White Sea. Trudy Karelo-Finskogo Filiala Akad. Nauk SSSR. 4:27-49.

Gnedina, M. P. 1938. On the study of the helminth fauna of fishes of the Bashkir A. S. S. R. Trudy Bashkirskoy Gelmintologicheskoy Expeditsii, Ufa. pp. 395-396.

Gnedina, M. P. and L. F. Potekhina. 1950. On the trematode fauna of birds of the Kirgiz S. S. R. Trudy Gelmintologicheskoy Laboratorii. 4:75-83.

Gnedina, M. P. and N. V. Savina. 1930. On the fauna of parasitic worms of fishes of the North Dvina basin. Rabota 32-y i 38-y Soyuznykh Gelmintologicheskikh Expeditsy. pp. 87-106.

Golovin, O. V. 1958. On the helminth fauna of the white-tailed eagle in the Kalinin district. Byulleten Moskovskogo Obschestva Ispytateley Prirody, Kalininskoye Otdeleniye. 1:93-96.

Golovin, O. V. and V. A. Savinov. 1957. On the question of specificity in the trematode Strigea strigis. Tezisy Dokladov Nauchnoy Konferentsii Vsesoyuznogo Obschestva Gelmintologov. pp. 88-89.

Golovin, O. V. and V. A. Savinov. 1958a. New hosts of the agent of alariasis in animals. Byulleten Moskovskogo Obschestva Ispytateley Priorody, Kalininskoye Otdeleniye. 1:6-66.

Golovin, O. V. and V. A. Savinov. 1958b. On the specificity of helminths and the formation of hosts of parasites. Byulleten Obschestva Ispytateley Priorody, Kalininskoye Otdeleniye. 1:85-92.

Gorbunova, M. 1936. Variation in the parasitic fauna with age of pike and roach. Uchenye Zapiski Leningradskogo Gosudarstvennogo Universiteta, No. 7, seriya biologicheskaya. No. 3:5-30.

Gorshunov, E. I. 1937. On the helminth fauna of dogs of the Gorky district. Trudy Gorkovskogo Pedagogicheskogo Instituta. 1:141-143.

Gubanov, N. M. and K. M. Ryzhikov. 1958. On the trematode fauna of geese of Verkhoyanye. Nauchnye Soobscheniya Yakutskogo Filiala Akad. Nauk SSSR. No. 1:109-114.

Gubsky, V. O. 1957. Wild birds as distributors of helminths. Nauchny Ezhegodnik Odesskogo Gosudarstvennogo Universiteta. pp. 249-250.

Gusev, A. V. 1951. On the parasite fauna of the Ussurysky racoon (Nyctereutes procyonoides Gray, 1834). Parazitologichesky Sbornik

Zoologicheskogo Instituta Akad. Nauk SSSR. 13:96-104.

Delyamure, S. L. 1953a. Morphological-systematic review of the helminth fauna of marine mammals (Pinnipedia, Cetacea), in light of their ecology and phylogeny. Rukopis dissertatsii, Moskva.

Delyamure, S. L. 1953b. Morphological-systematic review of the helminth fauna of marine mammals (Pinnipedia, Cetacea), in light of their ecology and phylogeny. Avtoreferat dissertatsii, Moskva.

Delyamure, S. L. 1956. Helminth fauna of marine mammals, in light of their ecology and phylogeny. Izdatelstvo Akad. Nauk SSSR. 517 pp.

Delyanova, R. Sh. 1957. The distribution of helminths of dogs throughout various geographical zones of the U. S. S. R. Doklady Akad. Nauk Uzbek. SSR. No. 10:65-71.

Delyanova, R. Sh. 1958. The helminth fauna of dogs in the territory of Uzbekistan. Uzbeksky Biologichesky Zhurnal. No. 5:47-57.

Delyanova, R. Sh. 1959. The distribution of helminths of dogs throughout various geographical zones of the U. S. S. R. Trudy Vsesoyuznogo Instituta Gelmintologii im. Akademika K. I. Skrjabina. 6:115-120.

Dobrokhotova, O. V. 1953a. The parasite fauna of fishes of Lake Zaysan, with reference to the reconstruction of its ichthyofauna. Avtoreferat dissertatsii, Alma-Ata.

Dobrokhotova, O. V. 1953b. The parasite fauna of wild carp of Lake Zaysan-Nor. Trudy Instituta Zoologii Akad. Nauk Kazakhsk. SSR. 1:170-174.

Dogiel, V. A. 1932. Parasitic diseases of fishes. Selkhozgiz, Moskva-Leningrad. 151 pp.

Dogiel, V. A. 1936. Changes in the parasite fauna with age of eel, in connection with its migrations. Uchenye Zapiski Leningradskogo Universiteta, No. 7, seriya biologicheskaya. No. 3:114-122.

Dogiel, V. A. 1941. Course in general parasitology. Leningrad. 287 pp.

Dogiel, V. A. 1945a. The influence of discontinuous distribution of a host on its parasite fauna. Izvestiya Akad. Nauk Kazakhsk. SSR, seriya zoologicheskaya. No. 4:5-8.

Dogiel, V. A. 1945b. Analysis of the parasite fauna of acipenserids, and an evaluation of its pathogenic significance. Izvestiya Akad. Nauk Kazakhsk. SSR, seriya zoologicheskaya. No. 4:9-19.

Dogiel, V. A. 1947. Course in general parasitology. Second Ed. Uchpedgiz, Leningrad. 371 pp.

Dogiel, V. A. 1950. Diseases of fishes of the northwest U. S. S. R.: means of controlling these diseases in fish-culturing ponds and in cases involving the introduction of acclimatization measures. Vestnik Leningradskogo Gosudarstvennogo Universiteta. 8:201-208.

Dogiel, V. A. 1954. Problems and perspectives of parasitological research of fishes in the southern rivers, with reference to the reconstruction of the fish industry. Trudy Problemnogo i Tematicheskogo Soveschaniya Zoologicheskogo Instituta Akad. Nauk SSSR. No. 4:43-46.

Dogiel, V. A. 1958. The parasite fauna and the environment. Some questions of the ecology of parasites of fresh-water fishes. In: Basic problems of fish parasitology. Izdatelstvo Leningradskogo Gosudarstvennogo Instituta. pp. 9-54.

Dogiel, V. A. and A. Kh. Akhmerov. 1946. The parasite fauna of fishes of the Amur and its zoogeographical significance. Trudy Yubileynoy Nauchnoy Sessii Leningradskogo Gosudarstvennogo Universiteta 1814-1944, sektsia biologicheskikh nauk. pp. 171-173.

Dogiel, V. A. and O. N. Bauer. 1955. Control of parasitic diseases of fishes in fish-culture ponds. Moskva-Leningrad. 87 pp.

Dogiel, V. A. and O. N. Bauer. 1955. Control of parasitic diseases of fishes in fish-culture ponds. Akad. Nauk SSSR Nauchno-Populyarnaya Seriya.

Dogiel, V. A. and I. I. Bogolepova. 1957. The parasite fauna of fishes of Lake Baykal. Trudy Baykalskoy Limnologicheskoy Stantsii. 15:427-464.

Dogiel, V. A., I. I. Bogolepova, and K. V. Smirnova. 1949. The parasite fauna of fishes of Lake Baykal and its zoogeographical significance. Vestnik Leningradskogo Gosudarstvennogo Universiteta. No. 7:13-34.

Dogiel, V. A. and B. E. Bykhovsky. 1934. Parasite fauna of fishes of the Aral Sea. Parazitologichesky Sbornik Zoologicheskogo Instituta. 4:241-344.

Dogiel, V. A. and B. E. Bykhovsky. 1939. Parasites of fishes of the Caspian Sea. Trudy Komissii Kompleksnomu Izucheniya Kospyskogo Morya. No. 7:1-149.

Dogiel, V. A. and E. V. Gvozdev. 1945. On the desirability of rejecting the Nagorno-aziatskaya (Asian Uplands) sub-district as an independent unit in the zoogeography of fishes. Izvestiya Akad. Nauk Kazakhsk. SSR, seriya zoologicheskaya. 4:49-52.

Dogiel, V. A. and G. K. Petrushevsky. 1933. The parasite fauna of fishes of the Neva Gulf. Trudy Leningradskogo Obschestva Estestvoispytateley. 62(3):366-434.

Dogiel, V. A. and G. K. Petrushevsky. 1935. Experiment in ecological research on the parasite fauna of the White Sea salmon. In: Voprosy Ekologii i Biotsenologii. Sbornik Statey. Biomedgiz, Leningrad. pp. 137-169.

Dogiel, V. A., K. V. Smirnova, and L. K. Roznachenko. 1945. Parasites of commerical fishes of Lake Zaysan. Izvestiya Akad. Nauk Kazakhsk. SSR, seriya zoologicheskaya. No. 4:31-37.

Dubinin, V. B. 1936. Research on the parasite fauna of grayling in different periods of its life. Uchenye Zapiski Leningradskogo Gosudarstvennogo Universiteta, 7, seriya biologicheskaya. No. 3:31-48.

Dubinin, V. B. 1938. Changes in the parasite fauna of the glossy ibis (Plegadis falcinellus) brought about with age and migration of the host. Trudy Astrankhanskogo Gosudarstvennogo Zapovednika. 2:108-212.

Dubinin, V. B. 1939. The life cycle of ecto- and endo-parasites of colonial birds of the Astrakhan

Preserve. Dissertatsiya, Leningradskogo Gosudarstvennogo Universitet.

Dubinin, V. B. 1941. New data on age localization of parasitic worms in the intestine of birds. Doklady Akad. Nauk SSSR. 30(4):377-380.

Dubinin, V. B. 1948a. The significance of animal migrations in the distribution of diseases. Izvestiya Akad. Nauk Kazakhsk. SSR, 43, seriya parazitologicheskaya. No. 5:13-22.

Dubinin, V. B. 1948b. The effect of increased salinity of the Maly Uzen River on the parasite fauna of the fishes. Zoologichesky Zhurnal. 27(4):335-341.

Dubinin, V. B. 1949a. The dependence of the distribution of larval parasitic worms of fishes of the Volga delta, on the variability in the places of concentrations of birds. Zoologichesky Zhurnal. 28(2):131-136.

Dubinin, V. B. 1949b. Experimental research on the life cycles of several parasitic worms of animals of the Volga River delta. Parazitologichesky Sbornik Zoologicheskogo Instituta Akad. Nauk SSSR. 11:126-160.

Dubinin, V. B. 1952. The fauna of larval parasitic worms of vertebrate animals of the Volga River delta. Parazitologichesky Sbornik Zoologicheskogo Instituta Akad. Nauk SSSR. 14:203-265.

Dubinin, V. B. 1953. The parasite fauna of murine rodents and its variability in the Volga River delta. Parazitologichesky Sbornik Zoologicheskogo Instituta Akad. Nauk SSSR. 15:252-301.

Dubinin, V. B. 1954. Dynamics of the parasite fauna of pelicans of the Volga River delta. Uchenye Zapiski Leningradskogo Gosudarstvennogo Universiteta, 172, seriya biologicheskikh nauk. No. 35:203-243.

Dubinin, V. B. and M. N. Dubinina. 1940. The parasite fauna of colonial birds of the Astrakhan Preserve. Trudy Astrakhanskogo Gosudarstvennogo Zapovednika. 3:190-298.

Dubinin, V. B. and M. N. Dubinina. 1951. The parasite fauna of mammals of the Daurskaya Steppe. In: Materials on the knowledge of the fauna and flora of the U. S. S. R. Izdatelstvo Moskovskogo Obschestva Ispytateley Prirody. Material po Gryzunam. 4:98-156.

Dubinina (Gorbunova), M. N. 1937. The parasite fauna of the black-crowned night heron (Nycticorax nycticorax L.) and its variability in connection with migration of the host. Zoologichesky Zhurnal. 16(3):547-573.

Dubinina, M. N. 1947. The parasitic worms of mammals of the Daurskaya Steppe. Referaty Nauchno-Issledovatelskikh Rabot za 1945 g. Otdel Biologicheskikh Nauk Akad. Nauk SSSR. pp. 178-179.

Dubinina, M. N. 1948. The parasite fauna of the wild gray-lay goose. Parazitologichesky Sbornik Zoologicheskogo Instituta Akad. Nauk SSSR. 10:165-188.

Dubinina, M. N. 1949. The influence on the parasite fauna of fishes of their wintering in pools of the Volga River delta. Parazitologichesky Sbornik Zoologicheskogo Instituta Akad. Nauk SSSR. 11:104-125.

Dubinina, M. N. 1950. Ecological research on the parasite fauna of the lake frog (Rana ridibunda Pall.) of the Volga River delta. Parazitologichesky Sbornik Zoologicheskogo Instituta Akad. Nauk SSSR. 12:300-350.

Dubinina, M. N. 1953. Dynamics of the parasite fauna of water snakes of the coastal region of the Volga River delta. Trudy Zoologicheskogo Instituta Akad. Nauk SSSR. 13:171-187.

Dubinina, M. N. 1955. Parasitological research on birds. Izdatelstvo Akad. Nauk SSSR, Moskva-Leningrad. 133 pp.

Dubinina, M. N. 1956. Hyper-parasitism of the metacercaria of Tetracotyle variegata (Creplin) on cestodes. Zoologichesky Zhurnal. 35(8):1139-1145.

Dubnitsky, A. A. 1953. A new helminth disease of the Ussurysky raccoon, a metaceracrial alariasis. Karakulevodstvo i Zverovodstvo. 6(6):57.

Dubnitsky, A. A. 1956. The fate of imaginal forms of gastrointestinal heminths in cannibalism of carnivorous animals. Zoologichesky Zhurnal. 35(11):1626-1628.

Evdokimova, L. I. 1954. Materials on the helminth fauna of fur-bearing animals of the Tatar A. S. S. R. Trudy Kazanskogo Filiala Akad. Nauk SSSR, seriya biologicheskaya. No. 3:227-230.

Efimov, A. V. 1936. On the question of the distribution of parasitic worms of terrestrial and aquatic birds of the Tatar Republic. Trudy Kazanskogo Nauchno-Issledovatelskogo Veterinarnogo Instituta. 2:162-177.

Zhadnov, A. P. and G. M. Gayfutdinova. 1954. Metacercarial alariasis of badgers in the Bashkir A. S. S. R. Veterinariya. 31(4):25.

Zhukov, E. V. 1956. Materials on the parasite fauna of predatory birds. Parazitologichesky Sbornik Zoologicheskogo Instituta Akad. Nauk SSSR. 16:264-279.

Zaskind, L. N. 1951. Helminthiases of geese and their agents. Rukopis dissertatsii, Moskva.

Zaskind, L. N. 1952. Helminthiases of geese and their agents. Tezisy dissertatsii. Trudy Gelmintologicheskoy Laboratorii Akad. Nauk SSSR. 6:407-409.

Zaskind, L. N. 1958. On the question of the study of the helminth fauna of domestic geese. Trudy Moskovskoy Veterinarnoy Akademii. 27:132-138.

Zakhvatkin, V. A. 1936. The parasite fauna of fishes of the Kama River, I. Uchenye Zapiski Permskogo Gosudarstvennogo Universiteta. 2(3):175-199.

Zakhvatkin, V. A. 1938. The parasite fauna of fishes of Lake Zaysan and of the Black Irtysh River. Uchenye Zapiski Permskogo Gosudarstvennogo Universiteta. 3(2):193-249.

Zakhvatkin, V. A. 1951. Parasites of fishes of waters of the Transcarpathian district. Naukovi Zapiski Lvivskogo Naukovogo Prirodoznavchogo Muzeyu Akad. Nauk Ukr. RSR. 1:119-155. (In Ukrainian).

Zakhvatkin, V. A. and N. S. Azheganova. 1940.
Parasites of fishes of the lakes of the Ilmensky Preserve in the Urals. Uchenye Zapiski Permskogo Gosudarstvennogo Universiteta. 4(1):3-31.

Zakhvatkin, V. A. and O. P. Kulakivska. 1951.
Parasites of fishes of the upper Dniester. Naukovi
Zapiski Lvivskogo Naukovogo Prirodoznavchogo Muzeyu Akad. Nauk Ukr. RSR. 1:150-155. (In Ukrainian).

Zakhvatkin, V. A. and G. K. Petrushevsky. 1952.
On the parasite fauna of several endemic fishes of
the Danube basin and the Black Sea. Trudy Leningradskogo Obschestva Estestvoispytateley. 71(4):82-
85.

Zdun, V. I. 1951a. The larvae of trematodes in
molluscs of the family Melanidae of the lower Dniester. Naukovi Zapiski Prirodoznavchogo Muzeyu
Akad. Nauk Ukr. SSR. 2:93-113. (In Ukrainian).

Zdun, V. I. 1951b. The larval trematode fauna of
molluscs of Transcarpathia. Naukovi Zapiski Lvivskogo Prirodoznavchogo Muzeyu Akad. Nauk Ukr. RSR.
1:167-189.

Zdun, V. I. 1952. The larval trematode fauna of
molluscs in bodies of water of the western districts
of the Ukrainian S. S. R. Kandidat dissertatsii, Lvov.

Zdun, V. I. 1956a. On the infestation of molluscs
of Transcarpathia with larval forms of the agents of
fascioliasis, dictylocauliasis, and paramphistomiasis.
Nauchnye Zapiski Uzhgorodskogo Gosudarstvennogo
Universiteta. 21:123-133.

Zdun, V. I. 1956b. Cercaria of the lower Danube
basin. Trudy 2 Nauchnoy Konferentsii Parazitologov
Ukr. SSR. pp. 59-60.

Zdun, V. I. 1957a. On parasitism by larval trematodes of fresh-water molluscs. Devyatoye Soveschanie po Parazitologicheskim Problemam Zoologicheskogo Instituta Akad. Nauk SSSR. pp. 98-99.

Zdun, V. I. 1957b. Trematode cercaria of fishes
of the western districts of the Ukrainian S. S. R.
Tezisy Dokladov Soveschaniya po Boleznyam Ryb,
Leningrad. pp. 34-34.

Zdun, V. I. 1959. Cercaria from Coretus corneus
(L.) in the environs of Warsaw. Acta Parasitologica
Polonica. 7(2):95-114. (In English).

Zekhnov, M. I. 1953. Variations in the helminth
fauna with age of the gray crow (Corvus cornix L.).
Zoologichesky Zhurnal. 32(1):53-59.

Zekhnov, M. I. 1955. Seasonal variations in the
helminth fauna of the gray crow (Corvus cornix L.).
Uchenye Zapiski Vologodskog Pedagogicheskogo Instituta. 15:353-374.

Zekhnov, M. I. 1958. The parasite fauna of the
lamprey. Uchenye Zapiski Vitebskogo Veterinarnogo
Instituta. 16(1):137-141.

Ivanitsky, S. V. 1927. On the trematode fauna of
vertebrates of the Ukraine. Veterinarne Dilo. 5(42):
36-42.

Ivanitsky, S. V. 1928. On the trematode fauna of
vertebrates of the Ukraine. Veterinarne Dilo. No.
2(51):30-48.

Ivanov, A. S. 1946. On the helminth fauna of

cyprinid fishes of the Volga delta. Sbornik Rabot po
Gelmintologii, Posvyaschenny Akademiku K. I. Skrjabinu. pp. 121-125.

Ivasik, V. M. 1953. Parasites of pond carp in
fish-cultures of the western districts of the Ukraine
and diseases caused by them. Trudy Vsesoyuznogo
Nauchno-Issledovatelskogo Instituta Prudovogo i
Ozernogo Rybnogo Khozyaystva Ukr. SSR. 8:

Ivasik, V. M. 1954. Parasites and parasitic diseases of pond carp under pond culture in the western
districts of the U. R. S. R. Pratsi Institutu Agrobiologii Akad. Nauk URSR. 5:57-68. (In Ukrainian).

Ivasik, V. M. 1955. Diseases and parasites of
fishes and measures of controlling them in fish-
culture ponds of the western districts of the Ukrainian S. S. R. Avtoreferat dissertatsii, Leningrad.

Ivasik, V. M. and A. P. Kholod. 1957. Experiment
in sanitation of ponds in the Ukrainian woodlands
(Polesie). Izvestiya Vsesoyuznogo Nauchno-
Issledovatelskogo Instituta Ozernogo i Rechnogo
Rybnogo Khozyaystva. 12:89-98.

Izyumova, N. A. 1959. On the question of the dynamics of the parasite fauna of fishes of the Rybinskoye reservoir. Trudy Instituta Biologii Vodokhra-
nilisch Akad. Nauk SSSR. No. 2:174-190.

Isaychikov, I. M. 1922. On the knowledge of the
helminth fauna of amphibians of Russia. Centralb. f.
Bakt. Parasitenk. Abt. 2, 57:272-274. (In German).

Isaychikov, I. M. 1923. On the knowledge of the
helminth fauna of amphibians of Russia. Centralb.
Bakt. Abt. 2, 59:19-26. (In German).

Isaychikov, I. M. 1924. On the fauna of parasitic
worms of domestic carnivores of the Crimea, I.
Parasitic worms of dogs. Uchenye Zapiski Sibirskogo Veterinarnogo Instituta. No. 6:47-105.

Isaychikov, I. M. 1927. On the fauna of parasitic
worms of domestic carnivores of the Crimea, II.
Parasitic worms of cats. Trudy Sibirskogo Veterinarnogo Instituta. No. 9:132-170.

Isaychikov, I. M. and N. P. Zakharov. 1929. On
the fauna of parasitic worms of Rana esculenta of the
Don district. Russky Gidrobiologichesky Zhurnal.
8(1-3):49-54.

Kadenatsii, A. N. 1957. The helminth fauna of
mammals of the Crimea. Omsk. 124 pp.

Kadenatsii, A. N. 1958a. The helminth fauna of
mammals of the Crimea and an experiment in ridding
domestic animals of the basic helminthiases. Rukopis
dissertatsii, Moskva.

Kadenatsii, A. N. 1958b. The helminth fauna of
the Crimea and an experiment in ridding domestic
animals of the basic helminthiases. Avtoreferat dissertatsii, Moskva.

Kazadeyev, V. I. 1954. Infestations of tench and
their influence on the organism. Avtoreferat dissertatsii, Moskva.

Kalantaryan, E. V. 1924. On the knowledge of the
trematodes of birds in the vicinity of the city of Erevan. Trudy Tropicheskogo Instituta Armenii. 1:74-
75.

Kaletskaya, S. L. 1958. Parasites of fishes of

Lake Bolshoy Ivan. Uchenye Zapiski Vitebskogo Veterinarnogo Instituta. 16(1):142-159.

Kamenev, V. P. and Z. M. Sakhnina. 1953. The parasite fauna of the vimba, Vimba vimba carinata and the shemaia, Chalcalburnus chalcoides schischkovi Drensky in connection with their migrations. Uchenye Zapiski Krasnodarskogo Pedagogicheskogo Instituta. No. 11:

Kamenev, V. P. and Z. M. Sakhnina. 1956. The parasite fauna of the acipenserid fishes, the stellate sturgeon Acipenser stellatus Pall. and A. guldenstadti Br., and its variation in connection with migrations. Uchenye Zapiski Krasnodarskogo Pedagogicheskogo Instituta. No. 17:97-103.

Karokhin, V. I. 1933. On the fauna of platyhelminths of fishes of the central Povolzhie district. Uchenye Zapiski Kazanskogo Veterinarnogo Instituta. 12:191-194.

Karpovich, V. N. 1953. On the helminth fauna of the desman (Desmana moschata L.). Raboty po Gelmintologii k 75-letiyu Akademika K. I. Skrjabina. pp. 293-300.

Kasimov, G. B. 1956. The helminth fauna of game birds of the order Galliformes. Izdatelstvo Akad. Nauk SSSR, Moskva. 554 pp.

Kaschenko, N. F. 1892. Account of the research on a helminth epizootic of fishes in the Barabinskiye lakes. Izvestiya Imperatorskogo Tomskogo Universiteta. 4:184-213.

Koval, V. P. 1950. Digenetic trematodes of fishes of the lower Dnieper. Trudy Biologo-Gruntoznavchogo Fakultetu Kievskogo Derzhavnogo Universitetu. 5:187-207.

Koval, V. P. 1952. Digenetic trematodes of fishes of the Dnieper River. Avtoreferat dissertatsii, Kiev.

Koval, V. P. 1955a. Materials on the knowledge of the seasonal dynamics of digenetic trematodes of fishes of the Dnieper River. Trudy Biologo-Gruntoznavchogo Fakultetu. Naukovi Zapiski Kievskogo Derzhavnogo Universitetu. 10:87-94. (In Ukrainian).

Koval, V. P. 1955b. Seasonal dynamics of digenetic trematodes of fishes of the Dnieper River. Naukovi Zapiski Kievskogo Universitetu. 12(16): 95-114. (In Ukrainian).

Koval, V. P. 1959. Digenetic trematodes of fishes of the Dnieper River. Voprosy Ekologii Kievsky Universitet. 3:167-216.

Kogteva, E. P. 1957. Parasites of fishes of the Pskovsk-Chudsky reservoir. Izvestiya Vsesoyuznogo Nauchno-Issledovatelskogo Instituta Ozernogo i Rechnogo Rybnogo Khozyaystva. 12:243-269.

Korneev, A. P. 1954. Nyctereutes procyonoides Gray in the Ukraine. (Results of works on acclimatization). Trudy Zoologicheskogo Muzeya Kievskogo Gosudarstvennogo Universiteta. No. 4:

Korneev, A. P. and V. P. Koval. 1959. On the study of the helminth fauna of fur-bearing animals of the Ukrainian S. S. R. Raboty po Gelmintologii k 80-letiyu Akademika K. I. Skrjabina. pp. 161-166.

Kotova, E. I. 1936. Parasitic worms of fishes and amphibians of the Klyazma River in the vicinity of the Bolshevskaya Biological Station. Zapiski Bolshevskoy Biologicheskoy Stantsii. No. 9:125-140.

Kotova, E. I. 1939. The larval trematode fauna of the Klyazma River. Zapiski Bolshevskoy Biologicheskoy Stantsii. No. 11:75-106.

Kosheva, A. F. 1951. The role of feeding and of the mode of life in the formation of the parasite fauna of cyprinid fishes. Trudy Tatarskogo Vsesoyuznogo Nauchno-Issledovatelskogo Ozernogo i Rechnogo Rybnogo Khozyaystva. No. 4:196-216.

Kosheva, A. F. 1955. Parasites of fishes of the central Volga and their epidemiological and epizootical significance. Avtoreferat dissertatsii, Leningrad.

Kosheva, A. F. 1957. The formation of the parasite fauna of fishes in the Kutuluzhskoye reservoir. Izvestiya Vsesoyuznogo Nauchno-Issledovatelskogo Instituta Ozernogo i Rechnogo Rybnogo Khozyaystva. 12:124-131.

Krotov, A. I. and S. L. Delyamure. 1952. On the fauna of parasitic worms of mammals and birds of the U. S. S. R. Trudy Gelmintologicheskoy Laboratorii Akad. Nauk SSSR. 6:278-292.

Kudryavtseva, E. S. 1954. The parasite fauna of the inconnu, Stenodus leucichtys nelma, and of the whitefish, Coregonus lavaretus nelmuscha, of Kubenskoye Lake. Uchenye Zapiski Vologodskogo Pedagogicheskogo Instituta. No. 15:307-319.

Kudryavtseva, E. S. 1955. The parasite fauna of fishes of the Sukhona River and of Kubenskoye Lake. Avtoreferat dissertatsii, Leningrad.

Kudryavtseva, E. S. 1957a. The dependence of the parasite fauna of fishes of the Sukhona River upon changes in hydrological and geomorphological conditions. Trudy Leningradskogo Obschestva Estestvoispytateley. 73(4):193-197.

Kudryavtseva, E. S. 1957b. The parasite fauna of fishes of the Sukhona River and Kubenskoye Lake. Zoologichesky Zhurnal. 36(9):1292-1303.

Kudryavtseva, E. S. 1959. Faunal survey of the parasites of fishes of the Sukhona River and Kubenskoye Lake. Uchenye Zapiski Vologodskogo Pedagogicheskogo Instituta. 24:175-185.

Kuzmenko, M. L. 1945. The parasite fauna of the ostroluchka, Capoetobrama cuschakewichi, a Central Asian endemic. Izvestiya Akad. Nauk Kazakhsk. SSR, seriya zoologicheskaya. No. 4:27-30.

Kulakivaka, O. P. 1951. Parasite fauna of trout and grayling of several rivers of Transcarpathia. Naukovi Zapiski Lvivskogo Naukovogo Prirodoznavchogo Muzeyu. Akad. Nauk URSR. 1:156-166. (In Ukrainian).

Kulakivskaya, O. P. 1955. Parasites of fishes of the basin of the upper Dniester. Avtoreferat dissertatsii, Kiev.

Kulachkova, V. G. 1950. The parasite fauna of gulls and terns of the Danube delta. Uchenye Zapiski Leningradskogo Gosudarstvennogo Universiteta, 133, seriya biologicheskaya. No. 23:123-128.

Kupriyanova, R. A. 1957. The trematode larvae of fresh-water molluscs of several regions of the central Povolzhie district. Devyatoye Soveschanie po Parazitologicheskim Problemam Zoologicheskogo Instituta Akad. Nauk SSSR. pp. 127-128.

Kurashvili, B. E. 1941. On the study of the helminth fauna of birds of Georgia. Trudy Zoologicheskogo Instituta Akad. Nauk Gruz. SSR. 4:53-100.

Kurashvili, B. E. 1953. The helminth fauna of game birds of Georgia. Raboty po Gelmintologii k 75-letiyu Akademika K. I. Skrjabina. pp. 340-346.

Kurashvili, B. E. 1956. Zoogeography of the helminth fauna of game birds of Georgia. Soobschenie Akad. Nauk Gruz. SSR. 17(10):935-940.

Kurashvili, B. E. 1957. Helminths of game birds of Georgia, with reference to the fauna and ecology. Izdatelstvo Akad. Nauk SSSR, Moskva. 434 pp.

Kurashvili, B. E., T. E. Rodanaya, and L. I. Konava. 1951. On the study of the helminth fauna of fishes of several bodies of water in the interior of Georgia. Trudy Zoologicheskogo Instituta Akad. Nauk Gruz. SSR. 10:

Lavrov, G. D. 1949. Parasitic infestation in the European pike-perch from the Volga River in the Saratov district. Uchenye Zapiski Saratovskogo Gosudarstvennogo Pedagogicheskogo Instituta. No. 13: 129-140.

Lavrov, G. D. 1955a. Seasonal and age variability in the parasite fauna of the European pike-perch. Uchenye Zapiski Saratovskogo Gosudarstvennogo Pedagogicheskogo Instituta. No. 19:98-158.

Lavrov, G. D. 1955b. Parasitic infestation of perch from the Volga River in the Saratov district. Uchenye Zapiski Saratovskogo Gosudarstvennogo Pedagogicheskogo Instituta. No. 19:159-173.

Lavrov, S. D. 1909. Results of the research on the fauna of worms of the Volga River and of flood plains near Saratov. (Trematodes, cestodes, nemathelminthes, and Oligochaeta). Raboty Volzhskoy Biologicheskoy Stantsii. 3(3):1-86.

Latysheva, N. V. 1939. The parasite fauna of several invertebrates of the Sea of Azov, with reference to the question of their transplantation into the Caspian. Uchenye Zapiski Leningradskogo Gosudarstvennogo Universiteta, 43, seriya biologicheskikh nauk. No. 11:213-232.

Levashov, M. M. 1950a. The status of the helminth fauna of the U. S. S. R. and an attempt in characterizing the helminths by ecological-geographical zones. Rukopis dissertatsii, Moskva.

Levashov, M. M. 1950b. The status of the helminth fauna of the U. S. S. R. and an attempt to characterize the helminths by ecological-geographical zones. Avtoreferat dissertatsii, Moskva.

Levashov, M. M. 1952. The status of the helminth fauna of the U. S. S. R. and an attempt to characterize the helminths by ecological-geographical zones. Tezisy dissertatsii. Trudy Gelmintologicheskoy Laboratorii Akad. Nauk SSSR. 6:329-396.

Leonov, V. A. 1958. The helminth fauna of larid birds of the Black Sea Preserve, and of the neighboring territory of the Khersonskaya district. Uchenye Zapiski Gorkovskogo Gosudarstvennogo Pedagogicheskogo Instituta. 20:266-296.

Linstov, O. 1886. Roundworms, trematodes and acanthocephalans from materials collected on the travels of A. P. Fedchenko in Turkestan. Izvestiya Obschestva Lyubiteley Estestvoznaniya Antropologii i Etnografii. 34(3); 40 pp.

Lutta, A. S. 1934. The fauna of parthenogenetic generations of trematodes in fresh-water molluscs of Petergofsk. Trudy Leningradskogo Obschestva Estestvoispytateley. 63(3):261-310.

Layman, E. M. 1933. Parasitic worms of fishes of Lake Baykal. Trudy Baykalskoy Limnologicheskoy Stantsii. 4:5-98.

Layman, E. M. 1934. Diseases of fishes caused by parasitic worms. (Helminthiases of fishes). Snabtekhizdat, Moskva-Leningrad. 135 pp.

Layman, E. M. 1938. Some new data on the development of Neodiplostomum cuticola in fishes and the inter-relationship between parasite and host. Trudy Mosrybvtuza. No. 1:

Layman, E. M. 1939. Disease of fishes (A course of lectures on fish disease). Pischepromizdat, Moskva.

Layman, E. M. 1946. The influence of age of carp on its infestation with parasites. Sbornik Rabot po Gelmintologii, Posvyaschenny Akademiku K. I. Skrjabiniu. pp. 171-177.

Layman, E. M. 1951. A practical guide to the disease of fishes. Pischepromizdat, Moskva. 150 pp.

Layman, E. M. 1955. The dynamics of parasite infestation of fishes in relation to age (on the question of preventing epizootics). Trudy Mosrybvtuza. No. 7:162-165.

Layman, E. M. and O. D. Sadkovskaya. 1952. Black-spot disease of carp and means of controlling it. Trudy Nauchno-Issledovatelskogo Instituta Prudovogo i Ozernogo Rechnogo Rybnogo Khozyaystva. 8:108-116.

Mazurmovich, B. N. 1951. Parasitic worms of amphibians and their inter-relationships with the host and with the external environment. Izdatelstvo Kievskogo Gosudarstvennogo Universiteta, Kiev. 99 pp.

Mailyan, R. A. 1956. The parasite fauna of whitefish of Lake Sevan. Doklady Akad. Nauk Armyansk. SSR. 23(1):45-48.

Maximova, A. P. 1957. The parasite fauna of ide from bodies of water in central Kazakhstan. Trudy Instituta Zoologii Akad. Nauk Kazakhsk. SSR. 7:141-150.

Maximova, E. A. 1955. Parasites of perch and their influence on the fish. Avtoreferat dissertatsii, Moskva.

Maximova, E. A. 1957. New data on the dynamics of infestation of perch with eye parasites of the class of Trematoda and their effect on the fish. Uchenye Zapiski Chelyabinskogo Gosudarstvennogo Pedagogicheskogo Instituta. 3(1):167-172.

Maximova, E. A. 1959. Age dynamics of an infestation in perch with the metacercaria of Tylodelphys clavata. Raboty po Gelmintologii k 80-letiyu Akademika K. I. Skrjabina. pp. 216-218.

Malevitskaya, M. A. 1952. Parasitic diseases of pond carp fingerlings in fish farms of the eastern districts of the Ukrainian S. S. R. Trudy Nauchno-Issledovatelskogo Instituta Prudovogo i Ozerno-Rechnogo Rybnogo Khozyaystva. 8:117-126.

Malevitskaya, M. A. and A. M. Lopukhina. 1955. Materials on the study of the parasites of fishes of the lower Dnieper. Trudy Nauchno-Issledovatelskogo Instituta Prudovogo i Ozerno-Rechnogo Rybnogo Khozyaystva. No. 10:40-49.

Malevitska, M. O. 1938. On the presence of Prohemistomum appendiculatum Ciurea, 1916 (Trematoda) in the territory of the U. R. S. R. Zbirnik Prats Zoologichnogo Muzeyu Akad. Nauk Ukr. SSR (21-22). Trudi Institutu Zoologii ta Biologii. 19:193-195. (In Ukrainian).

Mamayev, Yu. L. 1960a. The helminth fauna of hogs and swamp game of eastern Siberia. Rukopis dissertatsii, Moskva.

Mamayev, Yu. L. 1960b. The helminth fauna of hogs and swamp game of eastern Siberia. Avtoreferat dissertatsii, Moskva.

Marits, N. M. 1958. The parasite fauna of fishes of the Prut River. Uchenye Zapiski Tiraspolskogo Pedagogicheskogo Instituta. No. 5:209-224.

Markevich, A. P. 1934. Parasitic diseases of fishes and their control. KOIZ, Leningrad. 100 pp.

Markevich, A. P. 1947. The parasite fauna of fishes of the Dnieper River and of flood plains in the vicinity of Kanev. Zbirnik Prats Kanivsk. Biogeogr. Zapov. 2(1):21-23. (In Ukrainian).

Markevich, A. P. 1949b. The helminth fauna of fishes of the Dnieper River in the vicinity of Kanev. Naukovi Zapiski Kievskogo Derzhavnogo Universitetu. 8(6):1-12. (In Ukrainian).

Markevich, A. P. 1951. The parasite fauna of fresh-water fishes of the Ukrainian S. S. R. Izdatelstvo Akad. Nauk Ukr. SSR, Kiev. 376 pp.

Markov, G. S. 1937. Variations in the parasite fauna with age of the guillemot (Urialomvia lomvia lomvia) of Novaya Zemlya. Trudy Leningradskogo Obschestva Estestvoispytateley. 64:456-465.

Markov, G. S. 1939. The dynamics of the parasite fauna of the starling. Uchenye Zapiski Leningradskogo Gosudarstvennogo Universiteta, (43), seriya biologicheskikh nauk. No. 11:172-212.

Markov, G. S. 1941. Parasitic worms of birds of a nameless bay of Novaya Zemlya. Doklady Akad. Nauk SSSR, novaya seriya. 30(6):573-576.

Markov, G. S. 1950. The parasite fauna of reptiles of the Leningrad district. Doklady Akad. Nauk SSSR. 70(3):541-543.

Markov, G. S. 1952. The parasite fauna of reptiles of the Leningrad district. Uchenye Zapiski Leningradskogo Gosudarstvennogo Universiteta, (141), seriya biologicheskikh nauk. No. 28:217-229.

Markov, G. S. 1958. Physiology of parasites of fishes. In: Basic problems of fish parasitology.

Izdatelstvo Leningradskogo Gosudarstvennogo Universiteta. pp. 122-143.

Markov, G. S. and M. L. Rogoza. 1955. Annual variations in the parasite fauna of the grass frog, Rana temporaria L. Zoologichesky Zhurnal. 34(6):1203-1209.

Massino, B. G. 1927a. The Seventh Russian Helminthological Expedition into the Moscow Province. Deyatelnosti 28-y Gelmintologicheskoy Expeditsii v SSSR. pp. 103-110.

Massino, B. G. 1927b. The Ninth Union Helminthological Expedition into Old Bukhara. Deyatelnosti 28-y Gelmintologicheskay Expeditsii v SSSR. pp. 126-133.

Matevosyan, E. M. 1938. The helminth fauna of wild birds of Bashkiria. Trudy Bashkirskoy Gelmintologicheskoy Expeditsii. pp. 372-391.

Machulsky, S. N. 1959. The helminth fauna of rodents of the Buryat A. S. S. R. Raboty po Gelmintologii k 80-letiyu Akademika K. I. Skrjabina. pp. 219-224.

Mashkov, V. V. 1947. On the helminth fauna of birds of the Gorky district. Trudy Gorkovskogo Gosudarstvennogo Pedagogicheskogo Instituta. 12:59-63.

Merkusheva, I. V. 1959. On the trematode fauna of rodents and insectivores in the White Russian S. S. R. Raboty po Gelmintologii k 80-letiyu Akademika K. I. Skrjabina. pp. 225-227.

Mironchenko, O. A. 1938. The parasite fauna of the goldfish (Carassius carassius L.) and the silver goldfish (Carassius auratus gibelio Bloch) of Lake Zaysan and the Black Irtysh River. Uchenye Zapiski Permskogo Gosudarstvennogo Universiteta. 3(2):277-283.

Morozov, F. N. 1937. On a case of discovering encysted trematodes in the internal organs of skunks. Trudy Gorkovskogo Gosudarstvennogo Pedagogicheskogo Instituta. 1:115-120.

Morozov, F. N. 1939. Parasitic worms of fur-bearing animals of the family Mustelidae of the Gorky district. Trudy Gorkovskogo Gosudarstvennogo Pedagogicheskogo Instituta. 4:3-44.

Mosevich, M. V. 1948. On the parasite fauna of fishes of lakes of the Ob-Irtysh basin. Izvestiya Vsesoyuznogo Nauchno-Issledovatelskogo Instituta Ozernogo i Rechnogo Rybnogo Khozyaystva. 27:177-185.

Musselius, V. A. 1957a. Variations in helminth infestations with age of bream in reservoirs of the Moscow district, and the in vivo diagnosis of eye diseases of fishes. Tezisy Dokladov Nauchnoy Konferentsii Vsesoyuznogo Obschestva Gelmintologii. pp. 213-214.

Musselius, V. A. 1957b. Eye diseases of bream in reservoirs of the Moscow district. Rybnoye Khozyaystvo. No. 9:

Musselius-Bogoyavlenskaya, V. A. 1957c. Infestations of bream and their effect on the fish. Avtoreferat dissertatsii, Moskva.

Nagibina, L. F. 1957. The parasite fauna of fishes of Novoye Vygozero. Izvestiya Vsesoyuznogo

Nauchno-Issledovatelskogo Instituta Ozernogo i Rechnogo Rybnogo Khozyaystva. 13:132-145.

Nikolskaya, N. P. 1939. The parasite fauna of the cormorant (Phalacrocorax carbo) of the Astrakhan Preserve. Uchenye Zapiski Leningraskogo Gosudarstvennogo Universiteta, (43), seriya biologicheskikh nauk. No. 11:58-66.

Novikova, K. M. 1936. The parasite fauna of stint and smelt under natural and artificial conditions. Uchenye Zapiski Leningradskogo Gosudarstvennogo Universiteta, (7), seriya biologicheskikh nauk. No. 3:156-162.

Osmanov, S. O. 1954. On the helminth fauna of fishes of the Amu-Darya delta (the helminth fauna of fishes of Lake Mochankul and other lakes in the Kungradsky region of the Kara Kalpak. A. S. S. R.). Trudy Instituta Zoologii i Parazitologii Akad. Nauk Uzbek. SSR, Tashkent. 3:99-115.

Osmanov, S. O. 1958. The parasite fauna and parasitic diseases of fishes of the Aral Sea. Uzbeksky Biologichesky Zhurnal. 2:71-78.

Oshmarin, P. G. 1957. On the helmintho-geography of the Primorye region. Uchenye Zapiski Dalnevostochnogo Gosudarstvennogo Universiteta. No. 1:179-189.

Oshmarin, P. G. 1958. On the differ (sic) of the body of trematoda into motor and genital parts and on the phylogenetical age of this property. Acta Veterin. Acad. Scien. Hung. 8(3):257-263. (In English).

Pavlov, N. N. 1932. On the question of the parasitology of fishes. Trudy Dalnevostochnogo Pedagogicheskogo Instituta. 5(2):1-25.

Pavlov, Yu. S. 1956. On the helminth fauna of wolves of the Saratov district. Sbornik Nauchnykh Studencheskikh Rabot Saratovskogo Zooteknicho-Veterinarnogo Instituta. No. 1:52-53.

Pavlova, I. A. 1958. Parasites of whitefish acclimatized in Lake Sevan. Izvestiya Vsesoyuznogo Nauchno-Issledovateslskogo Instituta Ozernogo i Rechnogo Rybnogo Khozyaystva. 12:160-165.

Pavlovsky, E. N. and N. N. Anichkov. 1922. Tetracotyle sogdiana a new trematode parasite of the fish, Schizothorax intermedius, with a description of adhesive peritonitis produced by the parasite in its host. Parasitology, Cambridge. 14:309-314. (In English).

Pavlovsky, E. N. and N. N. Anichikov. 1923. Tetracotyle sogdiana, a new parasite of the marinka (Schizothorax intermedius) and a case of adhesive peritonitis produced by the parasite in its host. Russky Gidrobiologichesky Zhurnal. 2(11-12):219-228.

Paly, M. A. 1949. The parasites of fishes of the Ivano-Frankivsky culture pond. Naukovi Zapiski Lvovsk. Vsk. Derzhavnogo Universitetu. 16(5):179-191. (In Ukrainian).

Paly, M. A. 1952. The parasite fauna of pond fishes of the western districts of the Ukrainian S.S.R. Avtoreferat dissertatsii, Odessa.

Paly, M. A. 1959. Seasonal dynamics in the parasite fauna of the brook trout (Salmo trutta m. fario

L.) of the upper Seret River. Nauchnye Zapiski Uzhgorodskogo Universiteta. 4:301-308.

Palimpsestov, M. A. 1929. A new species of trematode, Plagiorchis popovi n. sp. from the intestine of a dog. Rabota 74-y Soyuznoy Gelmintologicheskoy Expeditsii v Astrakhanskom Okruge Nizhne-Volzhskogo Kraya. pp. 48-52.

Palimpsestov, M. A. 1937. On the characteristics of the helminth fauna of domestic animals in the Mordovian Autotomy, the Kuybyshev and Orenburg districts. Sbornik Rabot po Gelmintologii, Posvyaschenny Akademiku K. I. Skrjabinu. pp. 454-458.

Panova, L. G. 1927a. On the trematode fauna of gulls of the Don district. Trudy Leningradskogo Gosudarstvennogo Veterinarnogo Instituta. 1(1):52-61.

Panova, L. G. 1927b. Helminthology in Kazakhstan. Sbornik Rabot po Gelmintologii, Posvyaschenny Prof. K. I. Skrjabinu. pp. 121-137.

Pastukhova, L. P. 1950. Ecological analysis of the parasite fauna of amphibians of the Danube delta. Avtoreferat kandidata dissertatsii, Leningrad.

Paschenko, L. F. 1952a. The helminth fauna of poultry of the Kiev district. Tezisy dissertatsii, Kiev.

Paschenko, L. F. 1952b. On the helminth fauna of farm birds of the Kiev district. Trudi Institutu Zoologii. Sviyskikh Promislovikh Tvarin. Vidovaniya Akad. Nauk Ukr. SSR. 8:43-53. (In Ukrainian).

Perevezyantseva, Yu. N. 1945. Parasitic diseases of fingerlings of several fishes of the Syr-Darya River. Izvestiya Akad. Nauk Kazakhsk. SSR, seriya zoologicheskaya. No. 4:53-55.

Petrov, A. M. 1926. On the fauna of parasitic worms of domestic carnivores of Turkestan. Trudy Gosudarstvennogo Instituta Experimentalnoy Veterinarii. 2(2):88-101.

Petrov, A. M. 1930. On the fauna of parasitic worms of domestic carnivores of the North Dvina province. Rabota 32-y i 38-y Soyuznykh Gelmintologicheskikh Expeditsy g. Vyatka. pp. 56-67.

Petrov, A. M. 1940. Parasitic worms of mustelids of the Moscow Zoological Park. Trudy Moskovskogo Zooparka. 1:202-231.

Petrov, A. M. 1941. Helminth diseases of fur-bearing animals. Mezhdunarodnaya Kniga, Moskva. 228 pp.

Petrov, A. M. 1950. A new trematode, Mesostephanus skworzowi nov. sp. (Strigeata), from the intestine of a cat. Trudy Vsesoyuznogo Instituta Gelmintologii im. Akademika K. I. Skrjabina. 4:81-82.

Petrov, A. M. 1956. Helminthiases. Infectious and invasive diseases of dogs. Selkhozgiz, Moskva. 243 pp.

Petrov, A. M. and A. A. Dubnitsky. 1950a. A helminth disease of sables, metacercarial alariasis. Karakulevodstvo i Zverovodstvo. No. 4:70-71.

Petrov, A. M. and A. A. Dubnitsky. 1950b. The diagnosis, epizootology and therapy of alariasis of foxes. Trudy Tsentralnoy Nauchno-Issledovatelskoy Laboratorii Pushnogo Zverovodstva. No. 6:300-317.

Petrov, A. M. and A. A. Dubnitsky. 1950c.

Metacercarial alariasis of sables. Trudy Vsesoyuznogo Instituta Gelmintologii im. Akademika K. I. Skrjabina. 4:20-21.

Petrushevsky, G. K. 1940. Materials on the parasitology of fishes of Karelia, II. Parasites of fishes of Lake Onega. Uchenye Zapiski Leningradskogo Gosudarstvennogo Pedagogicheskogo Instituta, Kafedra Zoologii i Darvinizma. 30:133-186.

Petrushevsky, G. K. 1954. Studies on the parasite fauna of fishes, with reference to their acclimatization. Trudy Problemnogo i Tematicheskogo Soveschaniya. No. 4:29-38.

Petrushevsky, G. K. 1957a. The parasite fauna of clupeid fishes of the Black Sea. Izvestiya Vsesoyuznogo Nauchno-Issledovatelskogo Instituta Ozernogo i Rechnogo Rybnogo Khozyaystva. 42:304-313.

Petrushevsky, G. K. 1957b. On the parasite fauna of the Baltic Sea herring. Izvestiya Vsesoyuznogo Nauchno-Issledovatelskogo Instituta Ozernogo i Rechnogo Rybnogo Khozyaystva. 42:332.

Petrushevsky, G. K. 1958. Variation in the parasite fauna of fishes with their acclimatization. In: Basic problems of fish parasitology. Izdatelstvo Leningradskogo Gosudarstvennogo Universiteta. pp. 256-266.

Petrushevsky, G. K. and O. N. Bauer. 1948a. Parasitic diseases of fishes of Siberia, and their commercial and medical significance. Izvestiya Vsesoyuznogo Nauchno-Issledovatelskogo Instituta Ozernogo i Rechnogo Rybnogo Khozyaystva. 27:195-216.

Petrushevsky, G. K. and O. N. Bauer. 1948b. Zoogeography of parasites of fishes of Siberia. Izvestiya Vsesoyuznogo Nauchno-Issledovatelskogo Instituta Ozernogo i Rechnogo Rybnogo Khozyaystva. 27:217-231.

Petrushevsky, G. K. and O. N. Bauer. 1953. The effect of acclimatization of fishes on their parasite fauna. Izvestiya Vsesoyuznogo Nauchno-Issledovatelskogo Instituta Ozernogo i Rechnogo Rybnogo Khozyaystva. 32:259-273.

Petrushevsky, G. K. and I. E. Bykhovskaya-Pavlovskaya. 1935. Materials on the parasitology of fishes of Karelia, I. Parasites of fishes of the lakes of the Konchozero region. Trudy Borodinskoy Biologicheskoy Stantsii. 8(1):15-77.

Petrushevsky, G. K. and E. L. Kogteva. 1954. The effect of parasitic diseases on the condition of fishes. Zoologichesky Zhurnal. 33(2):395-405.

Petrushevsky, G. K., M. V. Mosevich, and I. G. Schupakov. 1948. The parasite fauna of fishes of the Ob and Irtysh Rivers. Izvestiya Vsesoyuznogo Nauchno-Issledovatelskogo Instituta Ozernogo i Rechnogo Rybnogo Khozyaystva. 27:67-96.

Petrushevsky, G. K., M. N. Pozdnyakova (Vikhrova), and S. S. Shulman. 1957. Parasites of fishes of the Braslavskie lakes of White Russia. Izvestiya Vsesoyuznogo Nauchno-Issledovatelskogo Instituta Ozernogo i Rechnogo Rybnogo Khozyaystva. 42:337-338.

Petrushevsky, G. K. and S. S. Shulman. 1958.

Parasitic diseases of fishes in natural bodies of water of the U. S. S. R. In: Basic problems of fish parasitology. Izdatelstvo Leningradskogo Gosudarstvennogo Universiteta. pp. 301-338.

Petryaev, P. A. and I. D. Starkov. 1934. Disease and parasites of fur-bearing animals. Vneshtorgizdat, Moskva-Leningrad.

Petukhova, L. G. 1950. Ecological analysis of the parasite fauna of amphibians of the Danube delta. Avtoreferat dissertatsii, Moskva.

Pozdnyakova (Vikhrova), M. M. 1957. Parasites of fishes of Lakes Pastovo and Velie (Novgorad district). Izvestiya Vsesoyuznogo Nauchno-Issledovatelskogo Instituta Ozernogo i Rechnogo Rybnogo Khozyaystva. 12:335-336.

Polyansky, Yu. I. 1955. Materials on the parasite fauna of fishes of the northern seas of the U. S. S. R. Parasites of fishes of the Barents Sea. Trudy Zoologicheskogo Instituta Akad. Nauk SSSR. 19:1-170.

Polyansky, Yu. I. 1958a. The parasite fauna and the surrounding environment. Some questions of the ecology of parasites of marine fishes. In: Basic problems of fish parasitology. Izdatelstvo Leningradskogo Gosudarstvennogo Universiteta. pp. 55-89.

Polyansky, Yu. I. 1958b. Zoogeography of the parasite fauna of marine fishes of the U. S. S. R. In: Basic problems of fish parasitology. Izdatelstvo Leningradskogo Gosudarstvennogo Universiteta. pp. 231-246.

Pomryaskinskaya, N. A. 1959. Helminths of fishes of the central Volga. Uchenye Zapiski Maryskogo Pedagogicheskogo Instituta. 25:38-39.

Popov, K. K. 1957. On the question of the distribution of trematodes of amphibians of the eastern and central Caucasus. Devyatoye Soveschanie po Parazitologicheskim Problemam. Tezisy Dokladov. pp. 203-204.

Pospelova-Strom, M. V. and N. K. Strom. 1940. The parasite fauna of animals, predominantly of native and migratory birds of Talysh (Trans-Caucasus.) Parazitologichesky Sbornik Zoologicheskogo Instituta Akad. Nauk SSSR. 8:7-24.

Potekhina, L. F. 1949. Paths of infection in foxes with alariasis. Karakulevodstvo i Zverovdstvo.

Potekhina, L. F. 1950a. The life cycle of the agent of alariiasis of fur-bearing animals. Avtoreferat dissertatsii, Moskva.

Potekhina, L. F. 1950b. Life cycle of the agent of alariiasis of foxes and dogs. Trudy Vsesoyuznogo Instituta Gelmintologii im. Akademika K. I. Skrjabina. 4:7-17.

Potekhina, L. F. 1951. The life cycle of Alaria alata, and alariiasis of foxes and dogs. Doklady Akad. Nauk SSSR. 76(2):325-327.

Potekhina, L. F. 1953. The paths of infection in fur-bearing animals with alariiasis. Karakulevodstvo i Zverovodstvo. 6(3):75-76.

Prendel, A. R. 1930. Contribution to the study of the helminth fauna of dogs of the Ukrainian S. S. R. (southern Ukraine). Zool. Anz., Leipzig. 89:323-326. (In German).

Prendel, A. R. 1927. Summary of the helminth fauna of cats of Odessa. Sbornik Rabot po Gelmintologii, Posvyaschenny Akademiku K. I. Skrjabinu. pp. 542-546.

Rakova, V. M. 1954. Age dynamics of an infestation of ide. Raboty po Gelmintologii k 75-letiyu Akademika K. I. Skrjabina. pp. 575-581.

Rakova, V. M. 1954. Infestations of ide (orfe), and their effects on the fish. Avtoreferat dissertatsii, Moskva.

Reshetnikova, A. V. 1955. On the knowledge of the parasite fauna of the bonito (Sarda sarda Bloch) of the Black Sea. Trudy Karadagskoy Biologicheskoy Stantsii. No. 13:97-104.

Roberman, S. L. 1939. Materials on the helminth fauna of dogs. Trudy Kirgizskogo Selskokhozyaystvennogo Instituta. No. 1:153-156.

Roman, E. 1953. On the question of the parasite fauna of the sunfish, Lepomis gibbosus (L.) acclimatized in the Danube. Doklady Akad. Nauk. SSSR. 89(4):765-768.

Romanov, I. V. 1957. On the helminth fauna of wild and domestic carnivorous mammals cf the Gorky district. Tezisy Dokladov Nauchnoy Konferentsii Vsesoyuznogo Obschestva Gelmintologii, Posvyaschenny 40-letiyu Velikoy Oktyabrskoy Sotsialisticheskoy Revolutsii. Art. 2; pp. 36-37.

Romanov, I. V. 1958. The helminth fauna of Vulpes vulpes of the Krasnoyarsk region. Raboty po Gelmintologii k 80-letiyu Akademika K. I. Skrjabina. pp. 297-301.

Romanova, G. P. 1957. Intestinal parasites of fingerlings of the European pike-perch of the Rybinskoye reservoir. Doklady Akad. Nauk SSSR. 117(1):157-160.

Roslyakov, V. 1954. The establishment of a new reservoir host in the life cycle of the agent of animal alariiasis. Sbornik Studencheskikh Rabot Vologodskogo Gosudarstvennogo Pedagogicheskogo Instituta. No. 2:99-103.

Ruzsky, M. D. 1934. Helminthiases in fishes and piscivorous birds of the Karachinskie lakes. Trudy Tomskogo Gosudarstvennogo Instituta. 86:143-147.

Rukhlyadev, D. P. 1956. On the helminth fauna of foxes of the Voronezh district. Trudy Khoperskogo Zapovednika. No. 2:169-172.

Ruchieva, G. I. 1938. The parasite fauna of the Siberian roach, Rutilus rutilus lacustris of Lake Zaysan and the Black Irtysh River. Uchenye Zapiski Permskogo Gosudarstvennogo Universiteta. 3(2):267-276.

Ryzhova, A. A. 1945a. Parasitic worms of poultry of the Gorky district. Dissertatsiya, Moskva.

Ryzhova, A. A. 1945b. Parasitic worms of poultry of the Gorky district. Avtoreferat dissertatsii.

Ryzhova, A. A. 1948. Parasitic worms of poultry of the Gorky district. Trudy Gelmintologicheskoy Laboratorii Akad. Nauk SSSR. 1:195-197.

Saakova, E. O. 1952. The fauna of parasitic worms of birds of the Danube delta. Avtoreferat dissertatsii, Leningrad.

Savinov, V. A. 1952. Development of Alaria alata (Goeze, 1782) in the definitive host. Avtoreferat dissertatsii, Moskva.

Savinov, V. A. 1953a. Development of Alaria alata (Goeze, 1782) in dogs. Trudy Vsesoyuznogo Instituta Gelmintologii im. Akademika K. I. Skrjabina. 5:63-64.

Savinov, V. A. 1953b. Variation in the helminth fauna of the raccoon dog as a result of its acclimatization in the Kalinin district. Trudy Vsesoyuznogo Instituta Gelmintologii im. Akademika K. I. Skrjabina. 5:99-102.

Savinov, V. A. 1954. Peculiarities of development of Alaria alata (Goeze, 1782) in the definitive and reservoir hosts. Raboty po Gelmintologii k 75-letiyu K. I. Skrjabina. pp. 611-616.

Savinov, V. A. 1954. On the question of some peculiarities of the life cycle of strigeids and of the role of different hosts in development. Uchenye Zapiski Vologodskogo Pedagogicheskogo Instituta. 15:245-306.

Savinov, V. A. 1958a. On the question of development of helminths in reservoir hosts. Raboty po Gelmintologii k 80-letiyu Akademika K. I. Skrjabina. pp. 315-319.

Savinov, V. A. 1958b. On the possibility of repeated migration and accelerated development of the agent of alariiasis in the definitive host. (The biology of the trematode Alaria alata (Goeze, 1782)). Byulleten Moskovskogo Obschestva Ispytateley Prirody, Kalininskoye Otdelenie. 1:59-64.

Savinov, V. A. 1958c. Partial substitution of hosts of helminths. Byulleten Moskovskogo Obschestva Ispytateley Prirody, Kaliniskoye Otdelenie. 1:67-72.

Savinov, V. A. 1958d. On the biological essence and origin of reservoir parasitism in helminths. Byulleten Moskovskogo Obschestva Ispytateley Priorody, Kalininskoye Otdelenie. 1:73-83.

Savinov, V. A. 1960. Experimental study of the possibility of infecting mammals with the cercaria of Alaria alata. Nauchnye Trudy Kalininskogo Otdeleniya Ispytateley Prirody. No. 2:82-88.

Sadovskaya, N. P. 1952. Parasitic worms of rodents and insectivores of the Primorye region. Avtoreferat dissertatsii. Trudy Gelmintologicheskoy Laboratorii Akad. Nauk SSSR. 7:388-390.

Sadovskaya, N. P. 1956. On the helminth fauna of murine rodents of the Primorye region. Trudy Dalnevostochnogo Filiala Akad. Nauk SSSR. 3(6):269-279.

Sadykov, I. E. 1958. The role of fur-bearing animals of Azerbaydzhan in the distribution of several helminths among domestic animals and man. Izvestiya Akad. Nauk Azerbay. SSR, seriya biologicheskikh nauk i selskokhozyaystvennykh. No. 5:49-54. (In Azerbaydzhanian, Russian resume).

Saidov, Yu. S. 1953a. The helminth fauna of fishes and piscivorous birds of Dagestan. Dissertatsiya, Moskva.

Saidov, Yu. S. 1953b. The helminth fauna of fishes and piscivorous birds of Dagestan. Avtoreferat dissertatsii, Moskva.

Semenov, V. D. 1927. Trematodes of birds of the western U. S. S. R. Sbornik Rabot po Gelmintologii, Posvyaschenny Prof. K. I. Skrjabinu. pp. 221-271.

Sidorov, E. G. 1956. Parasites of fishes of bodies of water of the Irgiz-Turgay basin. Sbornik Rabot po Ikhtiologii i Gidrobiologii Akad. Nauk Kazakhsk. SSR. 1:232-251.

Sidorov, E. G. 1957. The parasite fauna of fishes of Lake Kurgaldzhin. Trudy Instituta Zoologii Akad. Nauk Kazakhsk. SSR. 7:131-140.

Sinitsyn, D. F. 1896. Worm endoparasites of birds in the vicinity of Warsaw. Izvestiya Varshavskogo Universiteta. No. 7:1-32.

Sinitsyn, D. F. 1910. Studies concerning the phylogeny of trematodes. Cercaria plicata mihi and Tetracotyle brandes as dimorphic larvae of distomes, furthering a hypothesis concerning the origin of host alternation in the trematodes. Biologichesky Zhurnal. 1:106-144; 169-190 (191-193). (In German).

Skarbilovich, T. S. 1950. On the knowledge of the helminth fauna of amphibians and reptiles of southern Kirgizia. Trudy Gelmintologicheskoy Laboratorii Akad. Nauk SSSR. 4:108-132.

Skvortsov, A. A. 1924. Materials on the larval trematode fauna of molluscs of the Volga and Vetluga Rivers. Raboty Volzhskoy Biologicheskoy Stantsii. 7(4-5):201-211.

Skirta, O. M. 1955. On the morphology of alariasis of the lungs of Nyctereutes procyonoides Gray. Trudy Kievskogo Veterinarnogo Instituta. 12:264-268.

Skrjabin, K. I. 1913. Bird trematodes of Turkestan. Zool. Jahrb., Atb. Syst. 35:351-388. (In German).

Skrjabin, K. I. 1915. Trematodes of birds of the Urals. Ezhegodnik Zoologicheskogo Muzeya Akad. Nauk. SSSR. 20(3):395-417.

Skrjabin, K. I. 1916a. On the knowledge of the helminth fauna of domestic animals of Turkestan. Dissertatsiya, Yuriev.

Skrjabin, K. I. 1916b. Parasitic trematodes and nematodes collected by the expedition of Prof. V. A. Dogiel and I. I. Sokolov in British East Africa and Uganda. Nauchnye Rezultaty Zoologicheskoy Expeditsii Prof. V. A. Dogielya i I. I. Sokolova v Britanskuyu Vostochnuyu Afriku i Ugandu v 1914 g. 1(14): 1-157.

Skrjabin, K. I. 1917a. On the knowledge of helminth diseases of several fishes of Russia. Arkhiv Veterinarnykh Nauk. pp. 522-542.

Skrjabin, K. I. 1917b. On the knowledge of the helminth fauna of domestic animals of Turkestan. Zhurnal Nauchnoy i Prakticheskoy Veterinarnoy Meditsiny, Yuriev. pp. 151-241.

Skrjabin, K. I. 1923a. The Fifth Russian Helminthological Expedition into the Turkestan region in 1921. Trudy Gosudarstvennogo Instituta Experimentalnoy Veterinarii. 1(1):12-47.

Skrjabin, K. I. 1923b. Works on the study of parasitic worms of carnivores, II. Hemistomum azoviensis n. sp. Trudy Gosudarstvennogo Instituta Experimentalnoy Veterinarii. 1(1):67-71.

Skrjabin, K. I. 1923c. Trematodes of poultry. Trudy Gosudarstvennogo Instituta Experimentalnoy Veterinarii. 1(2):193-256.

Skrjabin, K. I. 1923d. Successes of experimental helminthology. Uspekhi Experimentalnoy Biologii. 1(3-4):1-15.

Skrjabin, K. I. 1923e. Parasitic worms of dogs of the Don district. Nauchnye Izvestiya Smolenskogo Gosudarstvennogo Universiteta. 1:56-59.

Skrjabin, K. I. 1924. Works on the study of parasitic worms of birds of Russia, I. Parasitic worms of Pelecanus onocrotalus. Trudy Gosudarstvennogo Instituta Experimentalnoy Veterinarii. 2(1):149-157.

Skrjabin, K. I. 1927a. The Fourth Russian Helminthological Expedition into the Don district (Novocherkassk). Deyatelnosti 28-y Gelmintologicheskoy Expeditsii v SSSR. pp. 32-40.

Skrjabin, K. I. 1927b. The Nineteenth Union Helminthological Expedition on the study of the helminth fauna of Armenia in 1924 conducted by Dr. E. V. Kalantaryan. Deyatelnosti 28-y Gelmintologicheskoy Expeditsii v SSSR. pp. 184-191.

Skrjabin, K. I. 1928. On the trematode fauna of birds of Transbaikalia. Ann. Parasitol. 6(1):80-87. (In French).

Skrjabin, K. I. 1932. Helminth infestations of pigeons. Selkhozgiz, Moskva-Leningrad. 124 pp.

Skrjabin, K. I. and B. G. Massino. 1925. Trematodes of birds of the Moscow district. Centralbl. Bakt. Abt. 2. 64(5):453-462. (In German).

Skrjabin, K. I. and N. P. Popov. 1927. The Tenth Union Helminthological Expedition into Armenia in 1923. Deyatelnosti 28-y Gelmintologicheskoy Expeditsii v SSSR. pp. 133-143.

Skrjabin, K. I. and N. P. Popov. 1930. Pharyngostomum fausti n. sp., a new trematode from the intestine of domestic cat. Tierärztl. Rundschau Jahrg. 36(42):709-710. (In German).

Smirnova, K. V. 1944. The parasite fauna of fishes of the Ala-Kulskie lakes. Izvestiya Kazakhskogo Filiala Akad. Nauk SSSR, seriya biologicheskaya. No. 3:49-80.

Smirnova, K. V. 1954. Parasitic diseases of fishes of the Don River in the vicinity of the Tsimlyansk reservoir (prior to its formation). Trudy Problemnogo i Tematicheskogo Soveschaniya Zoologicheskogo Instituta Akad. Nauk SSSR. No. 4:61-65.

Smirnova, K. V. 1957. On the parasite fauna of the Charkhal herring, Clupeonella delicatula tscharchalensis and several other fishes of Lake Charkhal. Izvestiya Vsesoyuznogo Nauchno-Issledovatelskogo Instituta Ozernogo i Rechnogo Rybnogo Khozyaystva. 12:332-333.

Smogorzhevskaya, L. A. 1953a. Materials on the trematode fauna of piscivorous birds of the central Dnieper valley. Nauchnye Zapiski Kievskogo Universiteta, Trudy Biol. Pochv, Fakulteta, No. 9. 12(7): 173-177.

Smogorzhevskaya, L. A. 1953b. Digenetic trematodes of piscivorous birds of the central Dnieper valley. Desyataya Nauchnaya Sessiya Kievskogo

Gosudarstvennogo Universiteta, sektsiya biologicheskaya. pp. 54-55.

Smogorzhevskaya, L. A. 1954. The helminth fauna of piscivorous birds of the Dnieper valley. Avtoreferat dissertatsii, Kiev.

Smogorzhevskaya, L. A. 1955. The helminth fauna of piscivorous birds of the Dnieper valley. Tezisy Dokladov. Vosmoye Soveschanie po Parazitologicheskim Problemam. pp. 140-144.

Smogorzhevskaya, L. A. 1956. Trematodes of piscivorous birds of the Dnieper valley. Parazitologichesky Sbornik Zoologicheskogo Instituta Akad. Nauk SSSR. No. 16:244-263.

Smogorzhevskaya, L. A. 1959. Ecological characteristics of helminths of piscivorous birds of the Dnieper valley. Voprosy Ekologii. Kievsky Universitet. 3:222-231.

Sobolev, A. A. 1940. Parasitic worms of marsh fowl of the order Chadradriformes. Dissertatsiya, Gorky.

Sobolev, A. A., V. V. Mashkov, and N. V. Mashkov. 1940. A new species of trematode from desman. Trudy Gorkovskogo Gosudarstvennogo Pedagogicheskogo Instituta. 5:57-60.

Soloviev, P. F. 1912. Parasitic worms of Turkestan. Ezhegodnik Zoologicheskogo Muzeya Imperatorskoy Akad. Nauk. 17(2):86-115.

Solonitsyn, I. A. 1928a. On the knowledge of the helminth fauna of birds of the Volzhsko-Kamsky region (nematodes and trematodes). Trudy 3 Vserossyskogo Sezda Zoologov, Anatomov, i Gistologov v Leningrade. pp. 155-156.

Solonitsyn, I. A. 1928b. On the knowledge of the helminth fauna of birds of the Volzhsko-Kamsky region (Nematodes and trematodes of birds of the Chuvashskaya and Tatar Republics.). Uchenye Zapiski Kazanskogo Gosudarstvennogo Veterinarnogo Instituta. 38(1):75-99.

Sosnina, E. F. 1952. On the fauna of parasitic worms of amphibians of Tadzhikistan. Trudy Akad. Nauk Tadzhiksk. SSR. 5:109-117.

Spasskaya, L. P. 1952. The helminth fauna of birds of the Barabinskaya Steppe. Avtoreferat dissertatsii.

Spassky, A. A. and P. G. Oshmarin, 1939. The parasitic worms of corvid birds. (On the helminth fauna of birds of the Gorky district.) Trudy Gorkovskogo Gosudarstvennogo Pedagogicheskogo Instituta. 4:45-70.

Spassky, A. A., K. M. Ryzhikov, and V. E. Sudarikov. 1952. The helminth fauna of wild mammals in the vicinity of Lake Baykal. Trudy Gelmintologicheskoy Laboratorii Akad. Nauk SSSR. 6:85-113.

Stolyarov, V. P. 1952. On the parasite fauna of fishes of the Rybinskoye reservoir. Trudy Leningradskogo Obschestva Estestvoispytateley. 71(4): 261-285.

Stolyarov, V. P. 1954. Dynamics of the parasite fauna of commercial fishes of the Rybinskoye reservoir. Trudy Leningradskogo Obschestva Estestvoispytateley. 72(4):160-189.

Stolyarov, V. P. 1955. Parasitic diseases of fishes of the upper Volga in the Yaroslav and Kalinin districts. Zapiski Leningradskogo Selskokhozyaystvennogo Instituta. No. 9:180-201.

Storozheva, A. M. 1958. The helminth fauna of domestic water-fowl of the Grodnenskaya district, woodland region (Polesie) of the White Russian S. S. R., and its seasonal dynamics. Avtoreferat dissertatsii, Moskva.

Storozheva, A. M. 1959. The helminth fauna of domestic water-fowl of the Grodnenskaya district, wood-land region (Polesie) of the White Russian S. S. R., and its seasonal dynamics. Trudy Vsesoyuznogo Instituta Gelmintologii im. Akademika K. I. Skrjabina. 6:177-182.

Sudarikov, V. E. 1950a. The helminth fauna of vertebrates of the central Povolzhie district. Dissertatsiya, Moskva.

Sudarikov, V. E. 1950b. The helminth fauna of vertebrates of the central Povolzhie district. Avtoreferat dissertatsii, Moskva.

Sudarikov, V. E. 1954. Biological peculiarities of trematodes of the order Strigeata. Trudy Problemnogo i Tematicheskogo Soveschaniya Zoologicheskogo Instituta Akad. Nauk SSSR. No. 4:110-113.

Sudarikov, V. E. 1956. On the identity of the genera Linstowiella and Paracoenogonimus (Trematoda: Cyathocotylidae). Trudy Gelmintologicheskoy Laboratorii Akad. Nauk SSSR. 8:240-247.

Sudarikov, V. E. 1959a. Biological peculiarities of the trematodes of the genus Alaria. Trudy Gelmintologicheskoy Laboratorii Akad. Nauk SSSR. 9: 326-332.

Sudarikov, V. E. 1959b. The order Strigeidida (La Rue, 1926) Sudarikov, 1959. In: Skrjabin, K. I., Trematodes of animals and man. Izdatelstvo Akad. Nauk SSSR, Moskva-Leningrad. 16:219-631.

Sudarikov, V. E. 1960a. On the biology of the trematodes, Strigea strigis (Shrank, 1788) and S. sphaerula (Rud., 1803). Trudy Gelmintologicheskoy Laboratorii Akad. Nauk SSSR. 10:217-226.

Sudarikov, V. E. 1960b. Experimentally obtaining sexually mature forms of the metacercaria of Tetracotyle ardae (Trematoda:Strigeidae). Trudy Gelmintologicheskoy Laboratorii Akad. Nauk SSSR. 10:227-230.

Sudarikov, V. E. and E. M. Karmanova. 1960. The oligochaete, Criodrilus lacuum Hoffmeister, 1845 as a supplementary host of trematodes of the families Echinostomatidae and Strigeidae. Trudy Gelmintologicheskoy Laboratorii Akad. Nauk SSSR. 10:231-234.

Sudarikov, V. E. and P. G. Oshmarin. 1954. A new trematode from birds, Duboisia skrjabini n. sp. Trudy Gelmintologicheskoy Laboratorii Akad. Nauk SSSR. 7:217-219.

Sudarikov, V. E. and A. S. Rykovsky. 1958. Scolopacitrema cubrensis nov. gen., nov. sp., a new trematode of the family Diplostomatidae Poirier, 1866. Raboty po Gelmintologii k 80-letiyu Akademika K. I. Skrjabina. pp. 360-363.

Sultanov, M. A. 1958. Trematodes of domestic and

wild birds of Uzbekistan. Raboty po Gelmintologii k 80-letiyu Akademika K. I. Skrjabina. pp. 363-369.

Sukhanova, K. M. 1958. Materials on the larval and parthenital fauna of digenetic trematodes of the Odredzha River (Varlitskoye reservoir). Uchenye Zapiski Leningradskogo Gosudarstvennogo Pedagogicheskogo Instituta. pp. 143 and 167-215.

Tell, Kh. I. 1955. The parasite fauna of fishes of Lake Vyrtsyarv. Avtoreferat dissertatsii, Moskva.

Timofeev, V. E. 1900. Trematodes of amphibians and reptiles in the vicinity of Kharkov. Trudy Obschestva Ispytateley Prirody pri Kharkovskom Universitete. 34:137-166.

Titova, S. D. 1946. Parasites of fishes of the Tom River basin. Trudy Tomskogo Gosudarstvennogo Universiteta. 97:137-150.

Titova, S. D. 1947. The parasite fauna of salmonid fishes of the Ob River basin. Uchenye Zapiski Tomskogo Gosudarstvennogo Universiteta. No. 6:76-83.

Titova, S. D. 1954. Parasites of fishes of Teletskoye Lake. Trudy Problemnogo i Tematicheskogo Soveschaniya Zoologicheskogo Instituta Akad. Nauk SSSR. No. 4:79-84.

Titova, S. D. 1955. The parasite fauna of cyprinid fishes acclimatized in western Siberia. Tezisy Dokladov 8-go Soveschaniya po Parazitologicheskim Problemam.

Titova, S. D. 1957. The parasite fauna of bream of Ubinskoye Lake. Izvestiya Vsesoyuznogo Nauchno-Issledovatelskogo Instituta Ozernogo i Rechnogo Rybnogo Khozyaystva. 42:166-173.

Uspenskaya, A. V. 1957. Some data on the effect of helminthic cataracts of the eyes on the condition of rainbow trout. Izvestiya Vsesoyuznogo Nauchno-Issledovatelskogo Instituta Ozernogo i Rechnogo Rybnogo Khozyaustva. 42:330-331.

Fedyushin, A. V. 1937. The helminth fauna of geese and ducks of western Siberia with reference to problems of utilizing natural bodies of water for purposes of poultry production. Sbornik Rabot po Gelmintologii, Posvyaschenny 30-letnikh Deyatelnost Akademika K. I. Skrjabina. pp. 167-177.

Kholodkovsky, N. A. 1921. Parasitic worms of the Petrograd province. Fauna Petrogradskoy Gubernii. 2(8):3-6.

Chernogorenko-Bidulina, M. 1958a. The larval trematode fauna of molluscs of the Dnieper River. Izdatelstvo Akad. Nauk Ukr. SSR. 106 pp.

Chernogorenko-Bidulina, M. 1958b. On the distribution of digenetic trematode larvae in molluscs of the Dnieper River. Trudy Instituta Gidrobiologii Akad. Nauk Ukr. SSR. 34:215-223.

Chernyshenko, A. S. 1956a. Materials on the parasite fauna of fishes of the Dniester estuary. Trudy 2 Parazitologicheskoy Konferentsii Ukr. SSR. pp. 288-289.

Chernyshenko, A. S. 1956b. On the question of the parasite fauna of endemic, relict fishes. Zoologichesky Zhurnal. 35(8):1261.

Chernyshenko, A. S. 1957. Trematodes of fishes of the Dniester estuary. Trudy Odesskogo Universiteta, seriya biologicheskikh nauk. 147:195-200.

Chertkova, A. N. 1959. Trematodes: In: Chertkova, A. N. and A. M. Petrov, Helminths of domestic gallinaceous birds and diseases caused by them. Moskva. 363 pp.

Chechina, A. S. 1954. Fish diseases in the White Russian S. S. R. in the post-war years. Trudy Problemnogo i Tematicheskogo Soveschaniya Zoologicheskogo Instituta Akad. Nauk SSSR. No. 4:39-42.

Chechina, A. S., M. A. Malevitskaya, and N. E. Kononeva. 1953. The effect of acclimatization of the brown bullhead on its parasite fauna. Doklady Akad. Nauk SSSR. 88(1):173-175.

Shaldybin, L. S. 1957. Parasitic worms of wolves of the Mordova A. S. S. R. Uchenye Zapiski Gorkovskogo Gosudarstvennogo Pedagogicheskogo Instituta. 19:65-70.

Sharpilo, V. P. 1959a. On the knowledge of the helminth fauna of snakes in the territory of the Ukrainian R. S. R. Pratsi Instituta Zoologii Akad. Nauk Ukr. SSR. 15:59-63. (In Ukrainian).

Sharpilo, V. P. 1959b. On the knowledge of the helminth fauna of water snakes of the Ukrainian S. S. R. Voprosy Ekologii Kievsky Universitet. 3:232-239.

Shakhtakhtinskaya, Z. M. 1953. The helminth fauna of domestic and game water-fowl of the Azerbaydzhanian S. S. R. Avtoreferat dissertatsii, Baku.

Shats, M. F. 1947. Parasitic diseases of geese in the Soletsky region of the Leningrad district. Trudy Leningradskogo Obschestva Estestvoispytateley. 69(4):202-222.

Shevtsov, A. A. 1952a. Helminthiases of domestic ducks and their agents. Rukopis dissertatsii, Moskva.

Shevtsov, A. A. 1952a. Helminthiases of domestic ducks and their agents. Avtoreferat dissertatsii, Moskva.

Shevtsov, A. A. 1955. On the question of the study of the helminth fauna of domestic ducks in the territory of the U. S. S. R. Trudy Kievskogo Veterinarnogo Instituta. 12:157-204.

Shevtsov, A. A. 1958a. The helminth fauna of domestic ducks of the Moscow district. Trudy Moskovskoy Veterinarnoy Akademii. 27:246-252.

Shevtsov, A. A. 1958b. On the disease of domestic ducks, cyathocotylosis. Veterinariya. 35(5):82.

Shevtsov, A. A. and L. N. Zaskind. 1960. Helminths and helminthiases of domestic water-fowl. Izdatelstvo Kharkovskogo Universiteta.

Shevchenko, N. N. 1954. On the parasites of fishes of the North Donets River. Soobschenie 1 Trudy Nauchno-Issledovatelskogo Instituta Biologii Kharkovskogo Gosudarstvennogo Universiteta. 19:73-86.

Shevchenko, N. N. 1956a. Parasites of fishes of the mid-reaches of the North Donets River. Trudy Nauchno-Issledovatelskogo Instituta Biologii i Biologicheskogo Fakulteta Kharkovskogo Gosudarstvennogo Universitet. 23:269-301.

Shevchenko, N. N. 1956b. The parasite fauna of several species of amphibians and aquatic reptiles in the vicinity of the mid-reaches of the North Donets River. Trudy 2 Parazitologicheskoy Konferentsii Ukr. SSR. pp. 117-118.

Shevchenko, N. N. 1957a. On the spring parasite fauna of several species of fishes of the lower reaches of the North Donets River. Trudy Instituta Biologii Kharkovskogo Gosudarstvennogo Universiteta. 26:5-12.

Shevchenko, N. N. 1957b. On some geographical peculiarities of the parasite fauna of aquatic reptiles in the vicinity of the mid-reaches of the Donets (Kharkov district). Trudy Instituta Biologii Kharkovskogo Gosudarstvennogo Universiteta. 30:129-145.

Shevchenko, N. N. and V. N. Barabasheva. 1958. On the helminth fauna of the hooded lizard, Lacerta agilis L. and the common adder (Vipera berus L.) of the Kharkov district. Raboty po Gelmintologii k 80-letiyu Akademiku K. I. Skrjabina. pp. 389-394.

Sivickis, P. 1954. Moliuskai-trematodu, platintojai. Gyvulininkystes ir veterinarijos instituto Darbai. 1:15.

Šivickis, P. 1959. Lietuvos Zasiniu pabksciur parazitiniia Kirminai. Acta parasitologica Lithnanica. 2:25-38.

Shigin, A. A. 1954a. The helminth fauna of piscivorous birds of the Rybinskoye reservoir. Avtoreferat dissertatsii, Moskva.

Shigin, A. A. 1954b. Results of helminthological researches on piscivorous birds of the Rybinskoye reservoir for three years (1949-1951). Trudy Problemnogo i Tematicheskogo Soveschaniya Zoologicheskogo Instituta Akad. Nauk SSSR. 4:57-60.

Shigin, A. A. 1957. Parasitic worms of herons and grebes of the Rybinskoye reservoir. Trudy Darvinskogo Gosudarstvennogo Zapovednika. No. 4:245-289.

Shigin, A. A. 1959. On the helminth fauna of piscivorous birds of the orders Anseriformes and Accipitriformes of the Rybinskoye reservoir. Trudy Darvinskogo Gosudarstvennogo Zapovednika. No. 5:315-331.

Shlyapnikova, R. L. 1957. Materials on the parasite fauna of fishes of Lake Vyrtsyarv. Izvestiya Vsesoyuznogo Nauchno-Issledovatelskogo Instituta Ozernogo i Rechnogo Rybnogo Khozyaystva. 42:270-277.

Shmidt, G. A. 1923. On the study of the trematode fauna of the Volga River delta. Russky Gidrobiologichesky Zhurnal. 2(1):30-31.

Shulman, S. S. 1949. Parasites of fishes of bodies of water of the Latvian S. S. R. Avtoreferat dissertatsii, Moskva.

Shulman, S. S. 1950. Parasites of fishes of bodies of water of the Latvian S. S. R. Trudy Gelmintologicheskoy Laboratorii Akad. Nauk SSSR. 4:278-281.

Shulman, S. S. 1954. The significance of data on parasites of fishes for related disciplines. Trudy Problemnogo i Tematicheskogo Soveschaniya Zoologicheskogo Instituta Akad. Nauk SSSR. 4:153-162.

Shulman, S. S. 1957a. Materials on the parasite fauna of lampreys of the basins of the Baltic and White Seas. Izvestiya Vsesoyuznogo Nauchno-Issledovatelskogo Instituta Ozernogo i Rechnogo Rybnogo Khozyaystva. 10(2):287-302.

Shulman, S. S. 1957b. Parasites of fishes of lakes of the Velikolutskaya district. Izvestiya Vsesoyuznogo Nauchno-Issledovatelskogo Instituta Ozernogo i Rechnogo Rybnogo Khozyaystva. 42:336-337.

Shulman, S. S. 1958a. Specificity of the parasites of fishes. In: Basic problems of fish parasitology. Izdatelstvo Leningradskogo Gosudarstvennogo Universiteta. pp. 109-121.

Shulman, S. S. 1958b. Zoogeographical analysis of the parasites of fresh-water fishes of the Soviet Union. In: Basic problems of fish parasitology. Izdatelstvo Leningradskogo Gosudarstvennogo Universiteta. pp. 184-230.

Shulman, S. S. and R. E. Shulman-Albova. 1953. Parasites of fishes of the White Sea. Izdatelstvo Akad. Nauk SSSR, Moskva-Leningrad. 198 pp.

Shulman-Albova, R. E. 1954. The parasite fauna of the pheasant (Phasianus colchicus L.) Uchenye Zapiski Leningradskogo Gosudarstvennogo Universiteta, 172, seriya biologicheskikh nauk. No. 35:185-202.

Schulz, R. Ed. S., M. P. Gnedina, and A. N. Kadenatsii. 1938. Materials on the study of the helminth fauna of animals of Bashkiria. Trudy Bashkirskoy Gelmintologicheskoy Expeditsii, Ufa. pp. 18-37.

Scherbina, A. K. 1952. Diseases of pond fishes. Selkhozgiz, Moskva.

Scherbovich, I. A. 1946. Trematodes of birds of the Far East. Sbornik Rabot po Gelmintologii, Posvyaschenny Akademiku K. I. Skrjabinu. pp. 296-300.

Schupakov, I. G. 1953. The parasite fauna of native and acclimatized fishes of Lake Zauralye, its dependence upon the action of the external environment, and its commercial and epidemiological significance. Avtoreferat dissertatsii, Leningrad.

Schupakov, I. G. 1954. New data on the parasite fauna of coregonid fishes acclimatized in the Urals. Trudy Problemnogo i Tematicheskogo Soveschaniya Zoologicheskogo Instituta Akad. Nauk SSSR. 4:24-28.

Yanchev, Ya. 1958.

LIST OF SUPPLEMENTARY ILLUSTRATIONS

PART XX

KEY TO THE SUBFAMILIES OF THE FAMILY
LIOLOPIDAE DOLLFUS, 1934 from Yamaguti,
1958 (XX:8)

1 (2) External seminal vesicle present; vitellaria
well-developed.   Liolopinae Odhner, 1912
2 (1) External seminal vesicle lacking; vitellaria
more weakly developed.
                    Harmotrematinae Yamaguti, 1933

KEY TO THE SPECIES OF THE GENUS
LIOLOPE COHN, 1902 (XX:10)

K. I. Skrjabin

1 (2) Testes and ovary entire; intestinal ceca
broad. Parasites of amphibians.
            L. copulans Cohn, 1902 (fig. 754)
2 (1) Testes and ovary sharply lobed; intestinal
ceca narrow. Parasites of turtles.
                    L. dollfusi Skrjabin, 1962

KEY TO THE GENERA OF THE SUBFAMILY
HARMOTREMATINAE YAMAGUTI, 1933 from
Yamaguti, 1958 (XX:14)

1 (2) Body constricted; ovary and testes equatorial
or pre-equatorial, ventral sucker displaced towards
anterior end of body.
            Helicotrema Odhner, 1912 (fig. 755)
2 (1) Body not constricted, lingulate; ovary and
testes equatorial or post-equatorial; ventral sucker
not anteriorly displaced.
            Harmotrema Nicoll, 1914 (fig. 8)

KEY TO THE GENERA OF THE FAMILY
AURIDISTOMATIDAE STUNKARD, 1924 modified
from Yamaguti, 1958 (XX:30)

K. I. Skrjabin

1 (2) Anterior end with tab-like appendages present
on dorsal and ventral sides; esophagus with paired
lateral diverticula; bifurcation of excretory bladder
posterior to testis. Calycodes Looss, 1901 (fig. 756)
2 (1) Anterior end differently constructed; lateral
diverticula of esophagus lacking.
3 (4) Anterior end with lateral tab-like appendages; bifurcation of excretory bladder posterior to
ovary.   Auridistomum Stafford, 1905 (fig. 757)
4 (3) Anterior end with one dorsal and two ventral
appendages; bifurcation of excretory bladder in inter-
testicular space.
            Petagium Heymann, 1905 (fig. 758)

KEY TO THE SPECIES OF THE GENUS
AURIDISTOMUM STAFFORD, 1905 (XX:31)

K. I. Skrjabin

1 (2) Testes oblique; genital pore directly posterior
to intestinal bifurcation.
            A. chelydrae (Stafford, 1900) (fig. 757)
2 (1) Testes tandem; genital pore far from intestinal bifurcation.   A. thomasi Dollfus, 1950

KEY TO THE SUBGENERA OF THE GENUS
HAEMATOLOECHUS LOOSS, 1899 from Odening,
1958 (XX:53)

1 (6) Loops of uterus present anterior to and external to intestinal ceca along both sides of body
(rarely, only on one side).
2 (5) Vitelline follicles extending into posterior
part of body, posterior to testes and to posterior
limits of extracecal loops of uterus.
3 (4) Vitelline follicles grouped in rosette-like
configurations, or in regular clusters.
                    Haematoloechus (Looss, 1899)
4 (3) Vitelline follicles in irregularly dispersed
clusters, or in isolated aggregations.
                    Anomolecithus Odening, 1958
5 (2) Vitelline follicles exclusively in anterior half
of body, not extending beyond level of limits of extra-
cecal loops of uterus, usually reaching mid-level of
posterior testis.   Skrjabinoeces (Sudarikov, 1950)
6 (1) Extracecal loops of uterus lacking on both
sides of body.   Ostiolum (Pratt, 1903)

KEY TO THE GENERA OF THE SUBFAMILY
PNEUMONOECINAE MEHRA, 1937 (XX:56)

K. I. Skrjabin and D. N. Antipin

1 (6) Lateral, anteriorly directed extracecal loops
of uterus present, usually on both sides of posterior
part of body, more rarely only on one side.
2 (3) Ventral sucker lacking in adults.
            Neohaematoloechus Odening, 1960 (fig. 759)
3 (2) Ventral sucker present.
4 (5) Vitellaria present in anterior half of body
only, not descending posteriorly beyond level of anterior limit of extracecal loops of uterus.
            Skrjabinoeces Sudarikov, 1950 (fig. 760)
5 (4) Vitellaria extending into posterior part of
body, posterior to testes and to anterior limit of
extracecal loops of uterus.
            Pneumonoeces Looss, 1902 (fig. 761)
6 (1) Lateral, anteriorly directed extracecal loops
of uterus lacking.   Ostiolum Pratt, 1902 (fig. 762)

KEY TO THE SUBSPECIES OF THE SPECIES
PNEUMONOECES VARIEGATUS
(RUDOLPHI, 1819) (XX:60)

K. I. Skrjabin and D. N. Antipin

1 (4) Cuticle smooth, aspinose.
2 (3) Anterior testis oval, entire, transversely oriented; posterior testis with three large sinistral, lateral protuberances longitudinally oriented, adjacent to intestinal cecum.
P. variegatus abbreviatus Bychowsky, 1932
3 (2) Both testes elongate-oval, oblique.
P. variegatus variegatus (Rudolphi, 1819) (fig. 761)
4 (1) Cuticle armed with delicate, weakly distinguishable spines.
P. variegatus dubininae Odening, 1958

KEY TO THE SPECIES OF THE GENUS SKRJABINOECES SUDARIKOV, 1950 (XX:153)

K. I. Skrjabin and D. N. Antipin

1 (4) Body seven to ten mm. long; testes nearly symmetrical.
2 (3) Ovary anterior to limits of extracecal loops of uterus.   S. similis (Looss, 1899) (fig. 760)
3 (2) Ovary posterior to limits of extracecal loops of uterus.   S. ellipticus (Eckstein, 1922)
4 (1) Length of body not more than five mm.; testes oblique, predominantly in posterior third of body.
5 (6) Cuticle smooth; oral sucker not less than one and one-half times larger than ventral; extracecal loops of uterus short, not extending beyond level of posterior edge of anterior testis, without transverse folds; cirrus sac not reaching level of ventral sucker.
S. breviansa Sudarikov, 1950
6 (5) Cuticle with spines to posterior end of body; oral sucker only slightly larger than ventral; extracecal loops of uterus forming transverse folds, reaching middle or anterior edge of anterior testis; cirrus sac reaching level of ventral sucker.
S. volgensis Sudarikov, 1950

LITERATURE ON THE TREMATODES OF THE SUBFAMILY PNEUMONOECINAE MEHRA, 1937 (XX:161)

Sinitsyn, D. F. 1905. Materials on the natural history of trematodes. Distomes of fishes and frogs in the vicinity of Warsaw. Izvestiya Varshavskogo Universiteta, Varshava. 210 pp.

KEY TO THE SUBFAMILIES OF THE FAMILY BUCEPHALIDAE POCHE, 1907 (XX:184)

K. I. Skrjabin and L. Kh. Gushanskaya

1 (10) Testes and ovary oval, entire. Esophageal parasites of fishes (exceptionally of amphibians).
2 (5) Ovary anterior to testes.
3 (4) Anterior fixatory organ a muscular sucker, with or without tentacles; intestine saccular, anteriorly or posteriorly directed.   Bucephalinae Nicoll, 1914
4 (3) Anterior fixatory organ a special proboscis, with or without tentacles, or with crown of spines; organ sometimes a funnel-shaped sucker, with cowl;

intestine saccular, usually posteriorly directed, more rarely anteriorly directed.
Prosorhynchinae Nicoll, 1914
5 (2) Ovary with other position.
6 (9) Ovary between testes.
7 (8) Anterior fixatory organ a funnel-shaped sucker, with semi-circle of several cornate protuberances; protuberances antero-dorsally situated; intestine a long canal, terminating blindly near posterior end of body.   Dolichoenterinae Yamaguti, 1958
8 (7) Anterior fixatory organ a disc-shaped or conical proboscis; intestine saccular, anteriorly directed.   Neidhartiinae Yamaguti, 1958
9 (6) Ovary posterior to testes; anterior fixatory organ an inverted conical proboscis; intestine saccular, anteriorly directed.
Neoprosorhynchinae Yamaguti, 1958
10 (1) Testes and ovary lobed; ovary dextral, at level of anterior testis; anterior fixatory organ a small weakly distinguishable proboscis; intestine saccular, elongate, bent. Parasites of body cavities of fishes.   Paurorhynchinae Dickerman, 1954

KEY TO THE GENERA OF THE SUBFAMILY BUCEPHALINAE NICOLL, 1914 (XX:184-185)

K. I. Skrjabin and L. Kh. Gushanskaya

1 (2) Seminal receptacle present; anterior fixatory organ a muscular sucker, without tentacles.
Neobucephalopsis Dayal, 1948 (fig. 763)
2 (1) Seminal receptacle lacking.
3 (4) Anterior fixatory organ a muscular sucker with tentacles.   Bucephalus Baer, 1827 (fig. 764)
4 (3) Anterior fixatory organ a muscular sucker without tentacles.
Bucephalopsis (Diesing, 1855) (fig. 765)

KEY TO THE GENERA OF THE SUBFAMILY DOLICHOENTERINAE YAMAGUTI, 1958 from Yamaguti, 1958 (XX:362)

1 (2) Proboscis funnel-shaped, with cornate protuberances; testes entire; ovary between testes.
Dolichoenterum Ozaki, 1924 (fig. 766)
2 (1) Proboscis weakly developed; testes extensively lobed; ovary opposite anterior testis.
Paurorhynchus (Yamaguti, 1958) (fig. 767)

KEY TO THE GENERA OF THE SUBFAMILY NEIDHARTIINAE YAMAGUTI, 1958 from Yamaguti, 1958 (XX:370)

1 (2) Proboscis discoid; ovary between testes.
Pseudoprosorhynchus Yamaguti, 1938 (fig. 768)
2 (1) Proboscis unusually large, conical; ovary opposite testes.   Neidhartia Nagaty, 1937 (fig. 769)

KEY TO THE GENERA OF THE SUBFAMILY PROSORHYNCHINAE NICOLL, 1914 (XX:390)

K. I. Skrjabin and L. Kh. Gushanskaya

1 (8) Anterior fixatory organ a proboscis.
2 (5) Crown of spines on proboscis lacking.
3 (4) Proboscis without tentacles; vitellaria follicular, in two groups, lateral.
Prosorhynchus Odhner, 1905 (fig. 770)
4 (3) Proboscis with tentacles; vitellaria follicular,
forming two lateral groups.
Alcicornis MacCallum, 1917 (fig. 771)
5 (2) Proboscis with a crown of spines.
6 (7) Proboscis thickened, resembling sucker, with
crown of three rows of small spines; vitellaria lateral. Dollfustrema Eckmann, 1934 (fig. 772)
7 (6) Proboscis an elongate, internally tapering
cone; spines present on proboscis, large, in crown of
single medio-ventrally interrupted row; vitellaria
forming arch in anterior half of body, follicular.
Telorhynchus Crowcroft, 1947 (fig. 773)
8 (1) Anterior fixatory organ a funnel-shaped
sucker with cowl; appendages on sucker present or
absent; vitellaria follicular, forming two lateral
groups.   Rhipidocotyle Diesing, 1858 (fig. 774)

LITERATURE ON THE TREMATODES OF THE ORDER BUCEPHALIDA (ODENING, 1960) SKRJABIN AND GUSCHANSKAJA, 1962 (XX:553)

Bauer, O. N. 1948. Parasites of fishes of the Yenesei River. Izvestiya Vsesoyuznogo Nauchno-Issledovatelskogo Instituta Ozernogo i Rechnogo Rybnogo Khozyaystva. 27:97-156.

Bidulina, M. I. 1955. The larval trematode fauna in molluscs of the Dnieper River. Dissertatsiya.

Vergun, G. I. 1957. On the larval trematode fauna in molluscs of the North Donets River and of its flood-plains in the vicinity of its mid-reaches. Trudy Nauchno-Issledovatelskogo Instituta Biologii i Biofaka Kharkovskogo Universiteta. 30:147-166.

Vlasenko, P. V. 1931. On the fauna of parasitic worms of fishes of the Black Sea. Trudy Karadagskoy Biologicheskoy Stantsii, Simferopol. 4:88-134.

Ginetsinskaya, T. A. 1958. The life cycles and biology of the larval stages of parasitic worms of fishes. In: Basic problems of the parasitology of fishes. pp. 144-183.

Dogiel, V. A. and B. Bykhovsky. 1934. The parasite fauna of fishes of the Aral Sea. Parazitologichesky Sbornik Zoologicheskogo Instituta Akademiya Nauk SSSR. 4:241-346.

Dubinin, V. B. 1952. The fauna of larval parasitic worms of vertebrates of the Volga River Delta. Parazitologichesky Sbornik Zoologicheskogo Instituta Akad. Nauk SSSR. 14:218.

Zhukov, E. V. 1960. Endoparasitic worms of the Sea of Japan and the south Kurile shoal-waters. Materials on the parasitology of the far-eastern seas. Trudy Zoologicheskogo Instituta Akad. Nauk SSSR. 28:3-146.

Zdun, V. I. 1952. The larval trematode fauna in molluscs of water-bodies of the western districts of the Ukrainian S. S. R. Dissertatsiya.

Zdun, V. I. 1956. Cercariae of the basin of the lower Danube. Problems of parasitology. Trudy Vtoroy Nauchnoy Konferentsii Parasitologov Ukr. SSR. Akad. Nauk Ukr. SSR., Institut Zoologii, pp. 59-60.

Isaychikov, I. M. 1928. On the knowledge of the parasitic worms of several groups of vertebrates of the Russian Arctic. A. Trematodes. Trudy Morskogo Nauchnogo Instituta. 3(2):5-79.

Koval, V. P. 1949. A new species of Bucephalus in fishes of the Dnieper. Doklady Akad. Nauk SSSR. 18(1):205-208.

Koval, V. P. 1955. Materials on the knowledge of the seasonal dynamics of digenetic trematodes of the Dnieper River. Zapiski Kievskogo Universiteta. 13(16):87-94. (In Ukrainian).

Koval, V. P. 1959. Digenetic trematodes of fishes of the Dnieper River. Voprosy Ekologii po Materialam Tretyei Ekologicheskoy Konferentsii. 3:165-217.

Koval, V. P. 1960. The parasite fauna of fishes of the Kakhovskoye Reservoir (in the vicinity of its lower reaches) during the first five years of its existence. Problems of parasitology. Trudy Tretyei Konferentsii Parazitologov Ukr. SSR., Kiev. pp. 393-396.

Kotova, E. I. 1939. The larval trematode fauna of the Klyazma River. Zapiski Bolsheskoy Biologicheskoy Stantsii. 2(2):

Lutta, A. S. 1934. The fauna of the parthenogenetic generations of trematodes in molluscs of Petergofsk. Trudy Leningradskogo Obschestva Estestvoispytateley. 13(3):

Layman, E. M. 1930. Parasitic worms of fishes of Peter the Great Bay. Izvestiya Tikhookeanskoy Nauchno-Issledovatelskoy Stantsii. 3(6):1-120.

Markevich, A. P. The parasite fauna of fresh-water fishes of the Ukrainian S. S. R. Izdatelstvo Akad. Nauk Ukr. SSR. 375 pp.

Pigulevsky, S. V. 1931. Parasitic worms of fishes of the Dnieper Basin. Ezhegodnik Zoologicheskogo Muzeya Akad. Nauk SSSR. 32:425-452.

Petrushevsky, G. K., M. V. Mosevich and I. G. Schupakov. 1948. The parasite fauna of fishes of the Ob and Irtysh Rivers. Izvestiya Vsesoyuznogo Nauchno-Issledovatelskogo Instituta Ozernogo i Rechnogo Rybnogo Khozyaystva. 27:67-96.

Polyansky, Yu. I. 1955. Materials on the parasite fauna of fishes of the northern seas of the U. S. S. R. Parasites of fishes of the Barents Sea. Trudy Zoologicheskogo Instituta Akad. Nauk SSSR. 19:5-170.

Roytman, V. A. 1960. Preliminary results of the ichthyological research in the basin of the Zeya River. Problems of parasitology. Trudy Tretey Nauchnoy Konferentsii Parazitologov Ukr. SSR, Kiev. pp. 407-408.

Sidorov, E. G. 1957. The parasite fauna of fishes of Lake Kurgaldzha. Trudy Instituta Zoologii Akad. Nauk Kazakhskoy SSR. Parazitologiya. 3:

Skrjabin, K. I. and R. Ed. S. Schulz. 1937. Helminthiases of cattle and their young. Selkhozgiz. 714 pp.

Skrjabin, K. I. and R. Ed. S. Schulz. 1940. Fundamentals of general helminthology. Selkhozgiz. 465 pp.

Shakhmatova, R. A. 1962. Larval trematodes of fresh-water molluscs of the central Povolzhie district and the experimental study of their biology. Dissertatsiya.

Shulman-Albova, R. E. 1952. Parasites of fishes of the White Sea in the vicinity of the village of Gridino. Ucheniye Zapiski Karelo-Finskogo Universiteta. 4(3):78-97.

Schulman, S. S. and R. E. Schulman-Albova. 1953. Parasites of fishes of the White Sea. Izdatelstvo Akad. Nauk SSSR.

Chubrik, G. K. 1952. On the life cycle of the fish trematode, Prosorhynchus squamatus Odhner, 1905. Doklady Akad. Nauk SSSR. 83(2):327-329. (In Ukrainian).

LIST OF SUPPLEMENTARY ILLUSTRATIONS

Bucephalidae Poche, 1907
Neoprosorhynchus purius Dayal, 1948 (fig. 46)

LITERATURE CITED

Baer, J. G. 1933. Note sur un noveau trematode *Clinostomum lophophallum* sp. nov. avec quelques considerations sur la famille des Clinostomidae. Revue Suisse Zool. 40(23):317-343. (In French).

Bashkirova, E. Ya. 1941. Echinostomatids of birds of the U.S.S.R., and a review of their life cycles. Trudy Bashkirskoy Nauchno-Issledovatelskoy Stantsii. 3:243-300. (In Russian).

Bhalerao, G. D. 1936. Studies on the helminths of India. Trematoda I. Journ. Helminthol. 14:163-180.

Bhalerao, G. D. 1937. Studies on the helminths of India. Trematoda IV. Journ. Helminthol. 15(2):97-124.

Byrd, E. E. and J. F. Denton. 1938. New trematodes of the subfamily Reniferinae with a discussion of the genera and the species assigned to the subfamily group. Journ. Parasitol. 24:379-401.

Caballero, E. 1952. Revision de generos y especies que integran la familia Acanthocolpidae Lühe, 1909 (Trematoda:Digenea). Nota Previa. Publ. Lab. Helminthol. Inst. Biol. Mexico. pp. 1-14. (In Spanish).

Cable, R. M. 1956. *Opistholebes diodontis* n. sp., its development in the final host, the affinities of some amphistomatous trematodes from marine fishes and the allocreadioid problem. Parasitol. 46(1-2):1-13.

Chauhan, B. S. 1940. Two new species of avian trematodes. Proc. Indian Acad. Sci. 12(3) sect. B:75-83.

Fischthal, J. H. 1942. *Triganodistomum hypentelii* n. sp. (Trematoda:Lissorchidae) from the hog sucker, *Hypentelium nigricans* (Le Seur). Journ. Parasitol. 28(5):389-393.

Fukui, T. 1929. Studies on Japanese amphistomatous parasites, with revision of the group. Jap. Journ. Zool. 2(3):219.

Harshey, K. R. 1937. On two new trematodes of the genus *Opegaster* Ozaki, with a systematic discussion on the families Opecoelidae Ozaki, 1925 and Coitocaecidae Ozaki, 1928. Proc. Indian Acad. Sci. 18:64-75.

Ishii, N. 1935. Studies on the family Didymozooidae (Monticelli, 1888). Jap. Journ. Zool. 6:278-335.

Kurashvili, B. E. 1941. On the study of the helminth fauna of birds of Georgia. Trudy Zoologicheskogo Instituta Akad. Nauk. 4:53-100. (In Russian).

Lewis, F. J. 1935. The trematode genus *Phyllodistomum* Braun. Trans. Amer. Micr. Soc. 54(2):103-117.

Manter, H. W. 1954. Some digenetic trematodes from fishes of New Zealand. Trans. Roy. Soc. New Zealand. 82(2):475-568.

Maplestone, P. A. 1923. A revision of the Amphistomata of mammals. Ann. Trop. Med. Parasitol. 17:113-166.

Mehra, H. R. 1937. Certain new and already known distomes of the family Lepodermatidae Odhner (Trematoda) with a discussion on the classification of the family. Zeitschr. f. Parasitenk. 9:429-469.

Mendheim, H. 1943. Beiträge zur Systematik und Biologie der Familie Echinostomatidae. Arch. f. Naturgesch. 12(2):175-302. (In German).

Nǎsmark, K. E. 1937. A revision of the trematode family Paramphistomidae. Inaug. Diss., Uppsala.

Odening, K. 1958. Zur Systematik von *Haematoloechus* (Trematoda:Plagiorchiidae). Mitteilungen Zool. Mus., Berlin. 34(1):63-108. (In German).

Olsen, O. W. 1937a. A systematic study of the trematode subfamily Plagiorchiinae Pratt, 1902. Trans. Amer. Micr. Soc. 56(3):311-339.

Olsen, O. W. 1937b. Description and life history of the trematode *Haplometrana utahensis* sp. nov. (Plagiorchiidae) from *Rana pretiosa*. Journ. Parasitol. 23:13-28.

Osmanov, S. U. 1940. Materials on the parasite fauna of fishes of the Black Sea. Uchenye Zapiski Leningradskogo Pedagogicheskogo Instituta, Kafedra Zoologii i Darvinizma. 30:187-267. (In Russian).

Popova, K. A. 1937. *Paramphistomum (Cautiorchis) skrjabini* n. sp. from the rumen of cattle. In: Skrjabin, K. I. and R. Ed. S. Schulz. Helminthiases of cattle and their young. Selkhozgiz, Moskva. 723 pp. (In Russian).

Price, E. W. 1929. Synopsis of the trematode family Schistosomatidae with a description of new genera and species. Proc. U. S. Nat. Mus. 75(art. 18):1-39.

Price, E. W. 1936. Two new trematodes from African reptiles. Proc. Helminthol. Soc. Wash. 3(2):76-78.

Price, E. W. 1939. A new genus and two new species of digenetic trematodes from a marine turtle. Proc. Helminthol. Soc. Wash. 6(1):24-25.

Ruiz, J. M. 1943. *Catadiscus freitaslenti* sp. n. (Trematoda:Paramphistomoidea) parasito de ofidio neotropico; observacao sobre a presenca de dois canais deferentes no genero *Catadiscus* Cohn, 1904. Mem. Inst. Butantan, S. Paulo. 17:29-34. (In Portugese).

Skrjabin, K. I. 1949. Trematodes of animals and man. Izdatelstvo Akad. Nauk SSSR, Moskva-Leningrad. vol. 3, 623 pp. (In Russian).

Skrjabin, K. I. 1951. Trematodes of animals and man. Izdatelstvo Akad. Nauk SSSR, Moskva-Leningrad. vol. 5, 624 pp. (In Russian).

Skrjabin, K. I., et al. 1947. Trematodes of animals and man. Izdatelstvo Akad. Nauk SSSR, Moskva-Leningrad. vol. 1, 515 pp. (In Russian).

Skrjabin, K. I., et al. 1948. Trematodes of animals and man. Izdatelstvo Akad. Nauk SSSR, Moskva-Leningrad. vol. 2, 600 pp. (In Russian).

Skrjabin, K. I., et al, 1950. Trematodes of

animals and man. Izdatelstvo Akad. Nauk SSSR, Moskva-Leningrad. vol. 4, 475 pp. (In Russian).

Skrjabin, K. I., et al. 1952. Trematodes of animals and man. Izdatelstvo Akad. Nauk SSSR, Moskva-Leningrad. vol. 6, 759 pp. (In Russian).

Skrjabin, K. I., et al. 1952. Trematodes of animals and man. Izdatelstvo Akad. Nauk SSSR, Moskva-Leningrad. vol. 7, 762 pp. (In Russian).

Skrjabin, K. I., et al. 1953. Trematodes of animals and man. Izdatelstvo Akad. Nauk SSSR, Moskva-Leningrad. vol. 8, 618 pp. (In Russian).

Skrjabin, K. I., et al. 1954. Trematodes of animals and man. Izdatelstvo Akad. Nauk SSSR, Moskva-Leningrad. vol. 9, 656 pp. (In Russian).

Skrjabin, K. I., et al. 1955. Trematodes of animals and man. Izdatelstvo Akad. Nauk SSSR, Moskva. vol. 10, 653 pp. (In Russian).

Skrjabin, K. I., et al. 1955. Trematodes of animals and man. Izdatelstvo Akad. Nauk SSSR, Moskva. vol. 11, 751 pp. (In Russian).

Skrjabin, K. I., et al. 1956. Trematodes of animals and man. Izdatelstvo Akad. Nauk SSSR, Moskva. vol. 12, 932 pp. (In Russian).

Skrjabin, K. I., et al. 1957. Trematodes of animals and man. Izdatelstvo Akad. Nauk SSSR, Moskva. vol. 13, 783 pp.

Skrjabin, K. I., et al. 1958. Trematodes of animals and man. Izdatelstvo Akad. Nauk SSSR, Moskva. vol. 14, 934 pp. (In Russian).

Skrjabin, K. I., et al. 1958. Trematodes of animals and man. Izdatelstvo Akad. Nauk SSSR, Moskva. vol. 15, 812 pp. (In Russian).

Skrjabin, K. I., et al. 1959. Trematodes of animals and man. Izdatelstvo Akad. Nauk SSSR, Moskva. vol. 16, 706 pp. (In Russian).

Skrjabin, K. I., et al. 1960. Trematodes of animals and man. Izdatelstvo Akad. Nauk SSSR, Moskva. vol. 17, 643 pp. (In Russian).

Skrjabin, K. I., et al. 1960. Trematodes of animals and man. Izdatelstvo Akad. Nauk SSSR, Moskva. vol. 18, 746 pp. (In Russian).

Skrjabin, K. I., et al. 1961. Trematodes of animals and man. Izdatelstvo Akad. Nauk SSSR, Moskva. vol. 19, 471 pp. (In Russian).

Skrjabin, K. I., et al. 1962. Trematodes of animals and man. Izdatelstvo Akad. Nauk SSSR, Moskva. vol. 20, 563 pp. (In Russian).

Sudarikov, V. E. and K. M. Ryzhikov. 1951. On the helminth fauna of ungulates of Pribaykalye (the Baikal region). Trudy Gelmintologicheskoy Laboratorii Akad. Nauk SSSR. 5:53-58. (In Russian).

Van Cleave, H. J. and J. F. Mueller. 1934. Parasites of Oneida Lake fishes. Part III. A biological and ecological survey of the worm parasites. Roosevelt Wildlife Ann. 3:161-334.

Wallace, F. C. 1935. A morphological and biological study of the trematode, Sellacotyle mustelae n. g., n. sp. Journ. Parasitol. 21(3):143-164.

Whitfield, F. J. 1958. A history of Russian literature (edited from D. S. Mirsky). A. A. Knopf, Inc., New York. 383 pp.

Witenberg, G. G. 1925. Versuch einer Monographie der Trematodenunterfamilie Harmostominae Braun. Zool. Jahrb. Abt. Syst., Jena. 51(2-3):167-254. (In German).

Yamaguti, S. 1958. Systema helminthum. The digenetic trematodes of vertebrates. Interscience Publishers, New York-London. Vol. 1, pts. 1 and 2, 1575 pp.

Yeh, L. S. 1954. On a new trematode Allechinostomum renale sp. n. (Trematoda:Echinostomidae) from Pelcanus erythrorhynchos. Journ. Helminthol. 28:159-164.

Yeh, L. S. 1958. A review of the trematode genus Encyclometra Baylis and Cannon, 1924. Journ. Helminthol. 32(1-2):99-114.

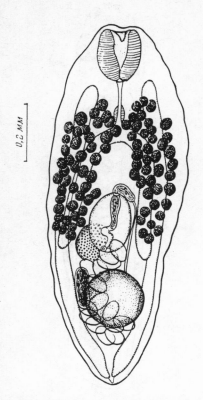

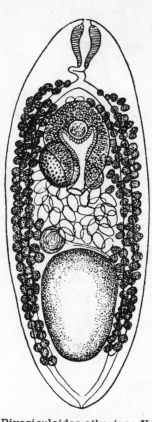

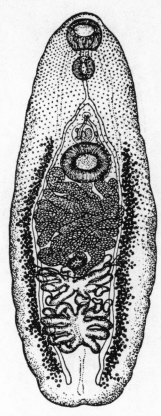

1. Bivesicula claviformis Yamaguti, 1934 (from Skrjabin and Sobolev, 1960, after Nagaty, 1948)

2. Bivesiculoides atherinae Yamaguti, 1938 (from Skrjabin, 1947, after Yamaguti, 1938)

3. Cathaemasia hians (Rudolphi, 1819) (from Skrjabin, 1947)

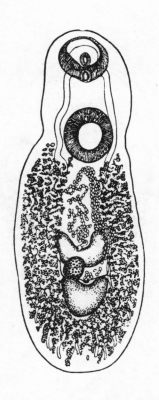

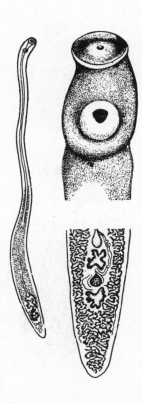

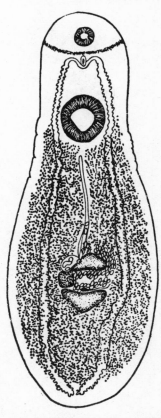

4. Euclinostomum heterostomum (Rudolphi, 1809) (from Skrjabin, 1947, after Braun, 1901)

5. Ithyoclinostomum dimorphum (Diesing, 1850) (from Skrjabin, 1947, after Braun, 1901)

6. Clinostomum complanatum (Rudolphi, 1819) (from Skrjabin, 1947, after Braun, 1901)

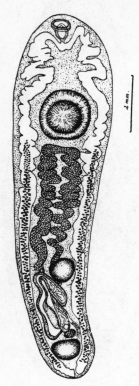

7. **Odhneriotrema microcephala** (Travassos, 1922) (from Skrjabin, 1947, after Travassos, 1922)

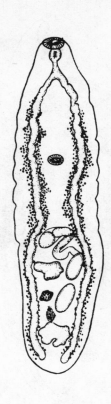

8. **Harmotrema infecundum** Nicoll, 1914 (from Skrjabin, 1947, after Nicoll, 1914)

9. **Eucotyle nephritica** (Creplin, 1846) (from Skrjabin, 1947, after Cohn, 1904)

10. **Tanaisia fedtschenkoi** Skrjabin, 1924 (from Skrjabin, 1947, after Skrjabin, 1924)

11. **Tamerlania zarudnyi** Skrjabin, 1924 (from Skrjabin, 1947, after Kalantaryan, 1927)

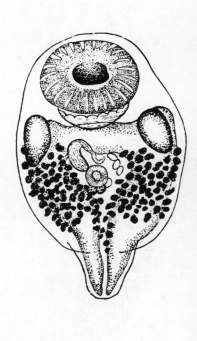

12. **Megapera pseudura** (Manter, 1933) (from Skrjabin, 1947, after Manter, 1933)

184

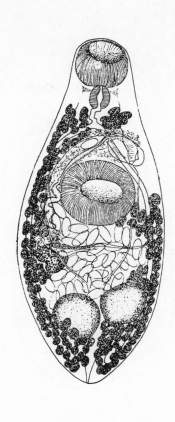

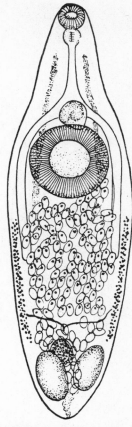

13. Thysanopharynx elongatus
Manter, 1933 (from Skrjabin, 1947,
after Manter, 1933)

14. Notoporus leiognathi Yamaguti,
1938 (from Skrjabin, 1947, after
Yamaguti, 1938)

15. Ommatobrephus singularis
Nicoll, 1914 (from Skrjabin, 1947,
after Nicoll, 1914)

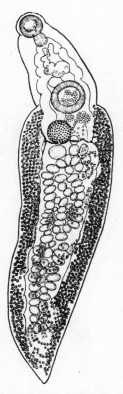

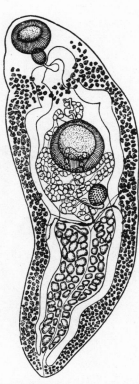

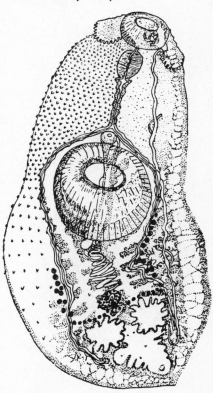

16. Orchipedum tracheicola Braun,
1901 (from Skrjabin, 1947, after
Braun, 1902)

17. Mammorchipedum isostomum
(Rudolphi, 1819) (from Skrjabin, 1947,
after Dollfus, Callot and Desportes,
1935)

18. Parorchis avitus Linton, 1914
(from Skrjabin, 1947, after Stunkard
and Cable, 1932)

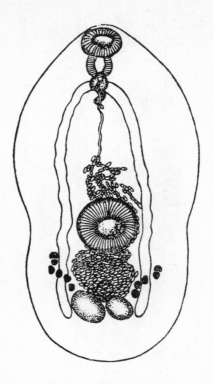

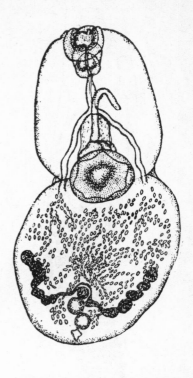

19. **Philophthalmus lucipetus** (Rudolphi, 1819) (from Skrjabin, 1947, after Braun, 1902)

20. **Cloacitrema ovatum** Yamaguti, 1938 (from Skrjabin, 1947, after Yamaguti, 1935)

21. **Ophthalmotrema numenii** Sobolev, 1943 (from Skrjabin, 1947, after Sobolev, 1943)

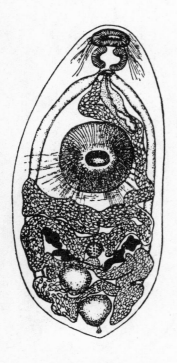

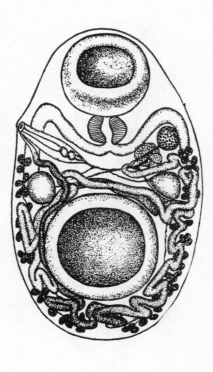

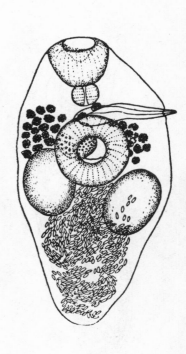

22. **Pygorchis affixus** Looss, 1899 (from Skrjabin, 1947, after Looss, 1899)

23. **Stomylotrema perpastum** Braun, 1902 (from Skrjabin, 1947, after Looss, 1899)

24. **Laterotrema vexans** (Braun, 1901) (from Skrjabin, 1947, after Semenov, 1928)

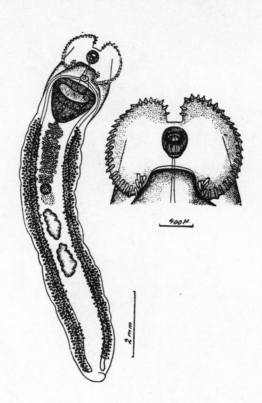

25. Nephrostomum ramosum (Son-sino, 1895) (from Bashkirova, 1947, after Odhner, 1911)

26. Patagifer bilobus (Rudolphi, 1819) (from Bashkirova, 1947, after Bash-kirova, 1941)

27. Prionosoma serratum (Diesing, 1850) (from Bashkirova, 1947, after Dietz, 1910)

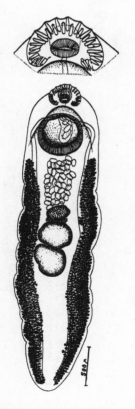

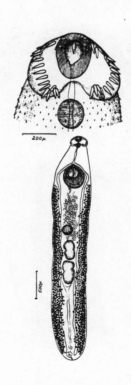

28. Skrjabinophora eroliae Bash-kirova, 1941 (from Bashkirova, 1947, after Bashkirova, 1941)

29. Echinostoma revolutum Frŏelich, 1802) (from Bashkirova, 1947, after Bashkirova, 1941)

30. Petasiger exaeretus Dietz, 1909 (from Bashkirova, 1947, after Bash-kirova, 1941)

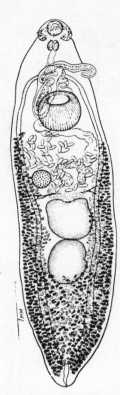

31. Paryphostomum radiatum (Dujardin, 1845) (from Bashkirova, 1947,
after Bashkirova, 1941)

32. Euparyphium melis (Goeze, 1782)
(from Skrjabin and Bashkirova, 1956,
after Skrjabin and Petrov)

33. Echinoparyphium elegans (Looss,
1899) (from Skrjabin and Bashkirova,
1956, after Looss, 1899)

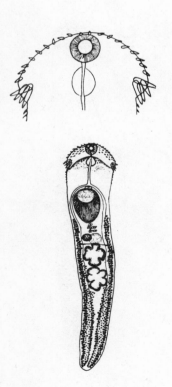

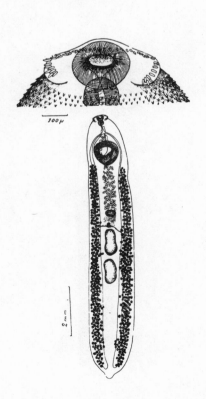

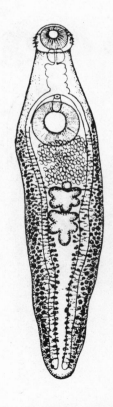

34. Drepanocephalus spathans Dietz,
1909 (from Bashkirova, 1947, after
Dietz, 1910)

35. Hypoderaeum conoideum (Bloch,
1782) (from Bashkirova, 1947, after
Bashkirova, 1941)

36. Microparyphium facetum Dietz,
1909 (from Skrjabin and Bashkirova,
1956, after Dietz, 1910)

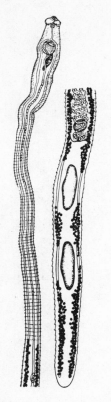

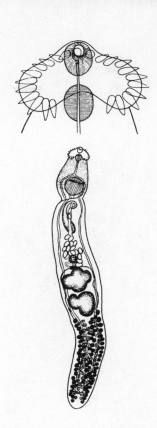

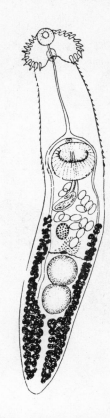

37. Himasthla rhigedana Dietz, 1909
(from Skrjabin and Bashkirova, 1956,
after Dietz, 1910)

38. Cleophora micata Dietz, 1909
(from Skrjabin and Bashkirova, 1956,
after Dietz, 1910)

39. Acanthoparyphium phoenicopteri
(Lühe, 1898) (from Skrjabin and Bashkirova, 1956, after Dietz, 1910)

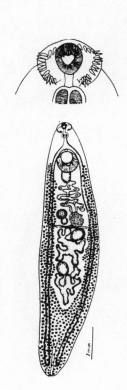

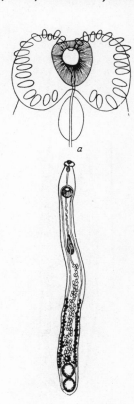

40. Artyfechinostomum sufrartyfex
Lane, 1915 (from Skrjabin and Bashkirova, 1956, after Faust, 1929)

41. Reptiliotrema indicum (Bhalerao,
1931) (from Bashkirova, 1947, after
Bhalerao, 1931)

42. Pelmatostomum episemum Dietz,
1909 (from Skrjabin and Bashkirova,
1947, after Dietz, 1910)

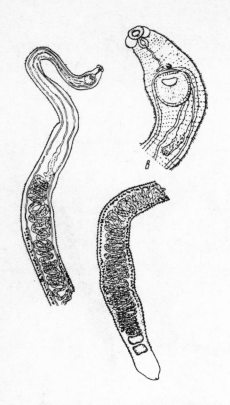

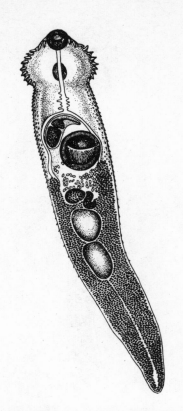

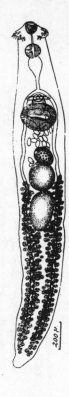

43. **Aporchis rugosus** Linton, 1928
(from Skrjabin and Bashkirova, 1947,
after Linton, 1928)

44. **Allechinostomum crocodili**
(Poirier, 1886) (from Bashkirova,
1947, after Odhner, 1911)

45. **Mesorchis pseudoechinatus**
(Olsson, 1876) (from Bashkirova,
1947, after Bashkirova, 1941)

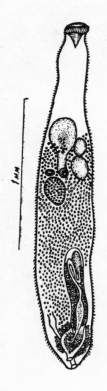

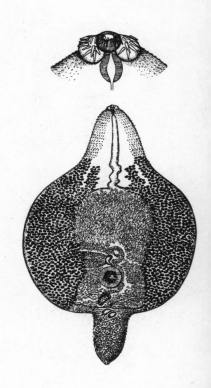

46. **Neoprosorhynchus purius** Dayal,
1948 (from Skrjabin and Gushanskaya,
1962, after Dayal, 1948)

47. **Echinochasmus coaxatus** Dietz,
1909 (from Bashkirova, 1947, after
Dietz, 1910)

48. **Balfouria monogama** Leiper,
1908 (from Bashkirova, 1947, after
Odhner, 1911)

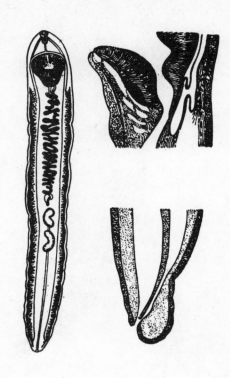

49. Chaunocephalus ferox (Rudolphi, 1795) (from Bashkirova, 1947, after Dietz, 1910)

50. Cotylotretus grandis (Rudolphi, 1819) (from Bashkirova, 1947, after M. Braun, 1902)

51. Pseudoechinostomum incoronatum (Odhner, 1911) (from Bashkirova, 1947, after Odhner, 1911)

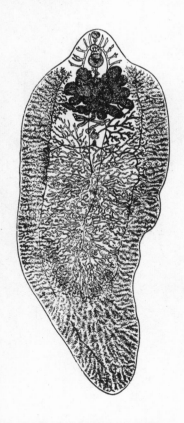

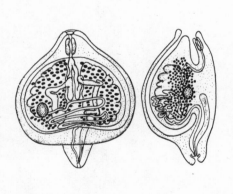

54. Fasciolopsis buski (Lankaster, 1857) (from Skrjabin, 1948, after Skrjabin, Podyapolskaya and Statirova, 1929)

52. Fasciola hepatica Linnaeus, 1758 (from Skrjabin, 1948, after Skrjabin and Schulz, 1926)

53. Braunina cardiformis Wolf, 1903 (from Sudarikov, 1961, Szidat, 1936)

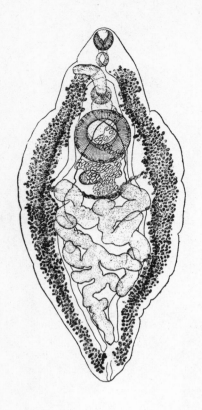

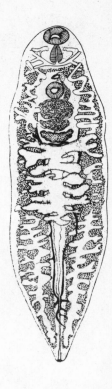

55. Parafasciolopsis fasciolaemorpha Ejsmont, 1932 (from Skrjabin, 1948)

56. Lecithodesmus goliath (Beneden, 1858) (from Skrjabin, 1948, after Odhner, 1905)

57. Zalophotrema hepaticum Stunkard and Alvey, 1929 (from Skrjabin, 1948, after Stunkard and Alvey, 1929)

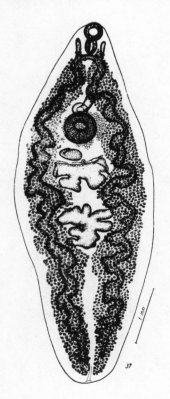

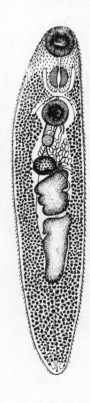

58. Campula oblonga Cobbold, 1858 (from Skrjabin, 1948, after Skrjabin and Schulz, 1935)

59. Synthesium tursionis (Marchi, 1872) (from Skrjabin, 1948, after Poirier, 1886)

60. Orthosplanchnus arcticus Odhner, 1905 (from Skrjabin, 1948, after Odhner, 1905)

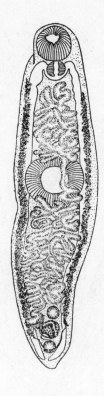

61. Oschmarinella sobolevi Skrjabin, 1947 (from Skrjabin, 1948, after Skrjabin, 1947)

62. Odhneriella rossica Skrjabin, 1915 (from Skrjabin, 1948, after Skrjabin, 1935)

63. Glaphyrostomum adhaerens Braun, 1901 (from Skrjabin, 1948, after Braun, 1902)

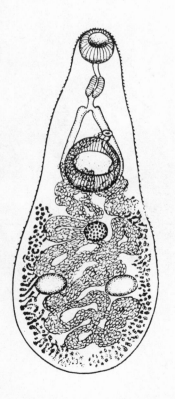

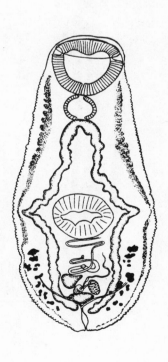

64. Aptorchis aequalis Nicoll, 1914 (from Skrjabin and Antipin, 1961, after Nicoll, 1914)

65. Ectosiphonus rhomboideus Sinitsin, 1931 (from Skrjabin, 1948, after Sinitsin, 1931)

66. Entosiphonus thompsoni Sinitsin, 1931 (from Skrjabin, 1948, after Sinitsin, 1931)

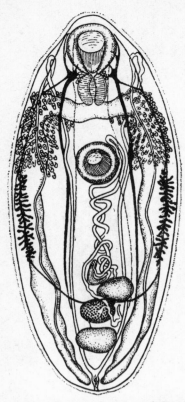

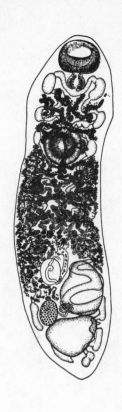

67. Brachylaemus helicis (Meckel, 1846) (from Skrjabin, 1948, after Hoffmann, 1899)

68. Postharmostomum gallinum Witenberg, 1923 (from Skrjabin, 1948, after Witenberg, 1923)

69. Ithyogonimus lorum (Dujardin, 1845) (from Skrjabin, 1948, after Looss, 1907)

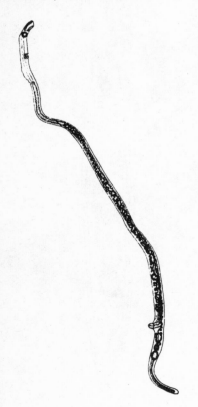

70. Scaphiostomum illatabile Braun, 1901 (from Skrjabin, 1948, after Braun, 1902)

71. Urotocus rossitensis (Mühling, 1898) (from Skrjabin, 1948, after Mühling, 1898)

72. Hasstilesia tricolor (Stiles and Hassall, 1894) (from Skrjabin, 1948, after Stiles and Hassall, 1894)

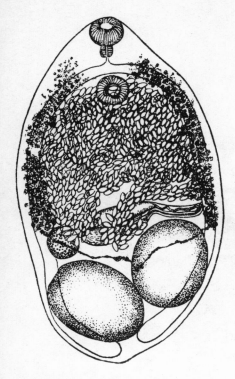

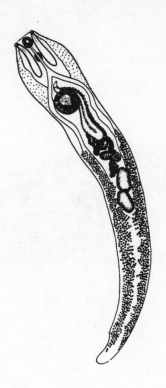

73. Skrjabinotrema ovis Orloff,
Erschoff and Badanin, 1934 (from
Skrjabin, 1948, after Orlov, Ershov
and Badanin, 1934)

74. Rhopalias coronatus (Rudolphi,
1819) (from Skrjabin, 1948, after
Braun, 1901)

75. Rhytidodes gelatinosus (Rudolphi,
1819) (from Skrjabin, 1948, after
Braun, 1901)

76. Rhytidodoides intestinalis Price,
1939 (from Skrjabin, 1948, after
Price, 1939)

77. Sphaerostomum bramae (Müller,
1776) (from Skrjabin, 1948, after
Looss, 1894)

78. Cotylogonoporum orfeum Thapar
and Dayal, 1934 (from Skrjabin, 1948,
after Thapar and Dayal, 1934)

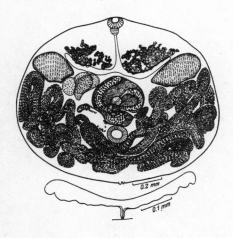

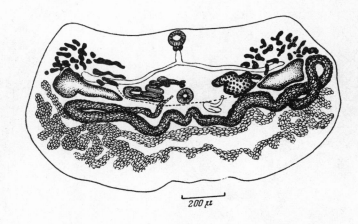

79. **Paralecithodendrium aranhai**
Lent, Teixeira and Proenca, 1945
(from Skarbilovich, 1948, after Lent,
Teixeira and Proenca, 1945)

80. **Castroia silvae** Travassos, 1928
(from Skarbilovich, 1948, after Travassos, 1928)

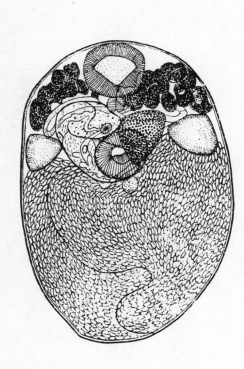

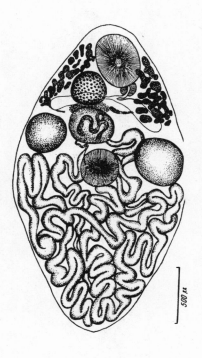

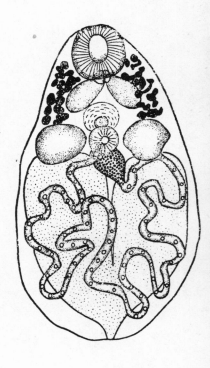

81. **Glyptoporus noctophilus** Macy,
1936 (from Skarbilovich, 1948, after
Macy, 1936)

82. **Travassodendrium bhaleraoi**
(Pande, 1935) (from Skarbilovich,
1948, after Pande, 1935)

83. **Prosthodendrium dinanatum**
(Bhalerao, 1926) (from Skarbilovich,
1948, after Bhalerao, 1926)

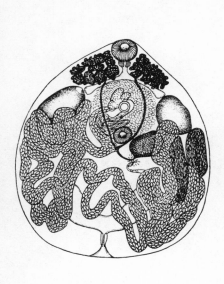

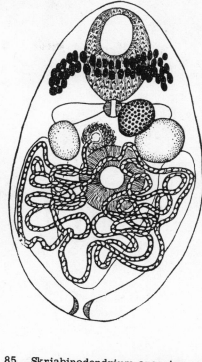

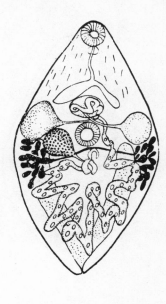

84. Acanthatrium nycteridis Faust, 1919 (from Skarbilovich, 1958, after Faust, 1919)

85. Skrjabinodendrium orospinosa (Bhalerao, 1926) (from Skarbilovich 1948, after Bhalerao, 1926)

86. Lecithodendrium linstowi Dollfus, 1931 (from Skarbilovich, 1948, after Linstow, 1894)

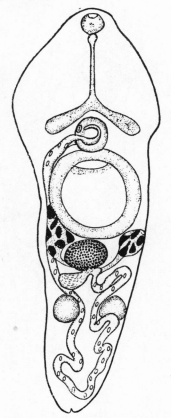

87. Pycnoporus heteroporus (Dujardin, 1845) (from Skarbilovich, 1948, after Looss, 1899)

88. Lecithoporus inversus (Looss, 1907) (from Skarbilovich, 1948, after Looss, 1907)

89. Anchitrema sanguineum (Sonsino, 1894) (from Skarbilovich, 1948, after Pande, 1935)

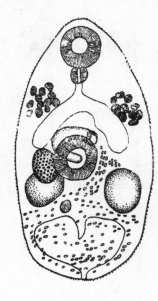

90. <u>Phaneropsolus sigmoideus</u>
Looss, 1899 (from Skarbilovich,
1948, after Looss, 1899)

91. **Pleuropsolus insolens** (Bhalerao,
1926) (from Skarbilovich, 1948, after
Bhalerao, 1926)

92. **Loxogenes arcanum** (Nickerson,
1900) (from Skarbilovich, 1948, after
Nickerson, 1900)

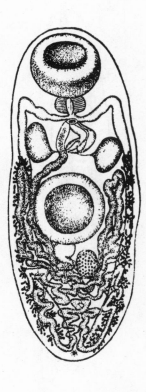

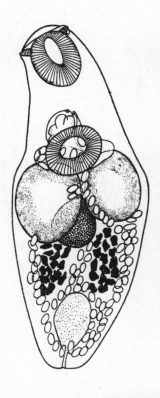

93. **Chiroptodendrium luzonicum**
(Tubangui, 1928) (from Skarbilovich,
1948, after Tubangui, 1928)

94. **Eumegacetes emendatus** Braun,
1901 (from Skarbilovich, 1948, after
Braun, 1901)

95. **Anenterotrema auritus** Stunkard,
1938 (from Skarbilovich, 1948, after
Stunkard, 1938)

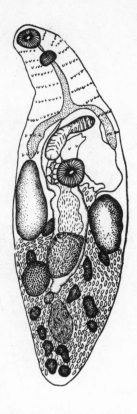

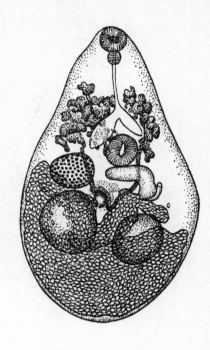

96. Exotidendrium gharialii Mehra, 1935 (from Skarbilovich, 1948, after Mehra, 1935)

97. Mosesia mosesi (Travassos, 1921) (from Skarbilovich, 1948, after Travassos, 1921)

98. Gyrabascus brevigastrus Macy, 1935 (from Skarbilovich, 1948, after Macy, 1935)

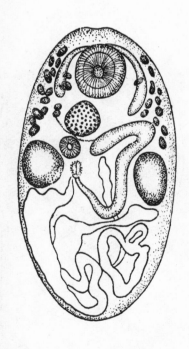

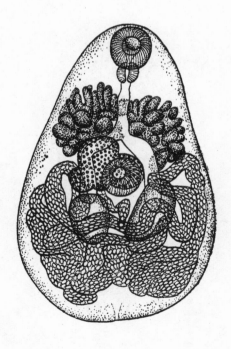

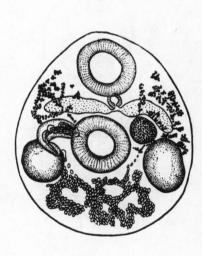

99. Ophiosacculus mehelyi (Mödlinger, 1930) (from Skarbilovich, 1948, after Mödlinger, 1930)

100. Echinuscodendrium echinus (McIntosh, 1936) (from Skarbilovich, 1948, after McIntosh, 1936)

101. Limatulum limatulum (Braun, 1900) (from Skarbilovich, 1948, after Travassos, 1921)

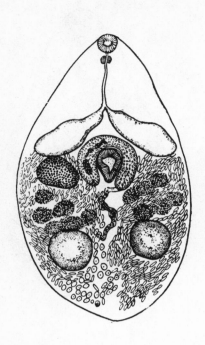

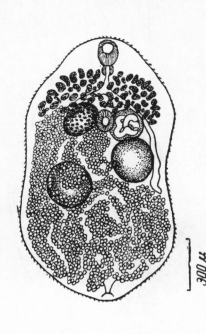

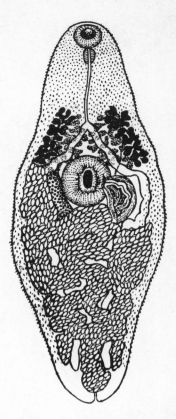

102. Basantisia ramai Pande, 1938 (from Skarbilovich, 1948, after Pande, 1938)

103. Postorchigenes ovatus Tubangui, 1928 (from Skarbilovich, 1948, after Tubangui, 1928)

104. Parabascus lepidotus Looss, 1907 (from Skarbilovich, 1948, after Looss, 1907)

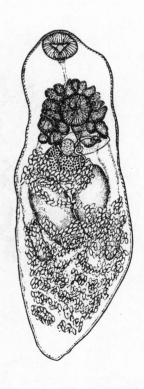

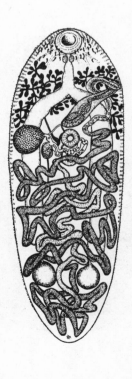

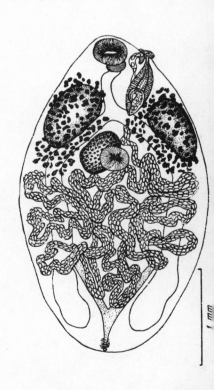

105. Parabascoides yucatanensis Stunkard, 1938 (from Skarbilovich, 1948, after Stunkard, 1938)

106. Pleurogenes claviger (Rudolphi, 1819) (from Skarbilovich, 1948, after Lühe, 1909)

107. Mehraorchis ranarum Srivastava, 1934 (from Skarbilovich, 1948, after Srivastava, 1934)

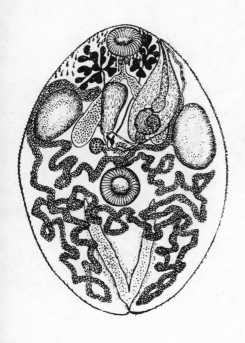

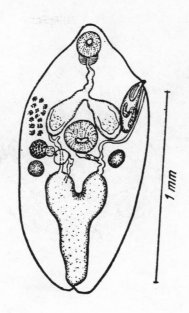

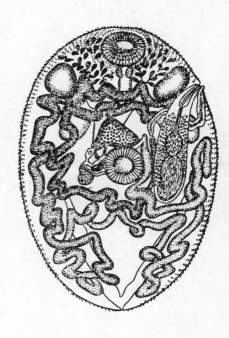

108. Pleurogenoides tener (Looss, 1898) (from Skarbilovich, 1948, after Travassos, 1930)

109. Sonsinotrema tacapense (Sonsino, 1894) (from Skarbilovich, 1948, after Balozet and Callot, 1938)

110. Prosotocus confusus (Looss, 1894) (from Skarbilovich, 1948, after Travassos, 1930)

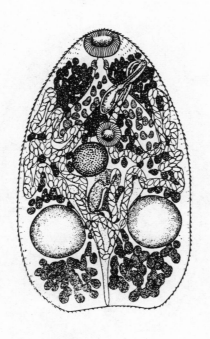

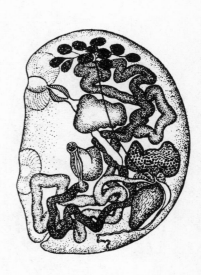

111. Ganeo glottoides Klein, 1905 (from Skarbilovich, 1948, after Klein, 1905)

112. Cryptotropa kuretanii (Ozaki, 1926) (from Skarbilovich, 1948, after Ozaki, 1926)

113. Brandesia turgida (Brandes, 1888) (from Skarbilovich, 1948, after Looss, 1899)

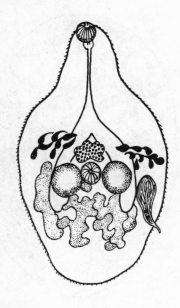

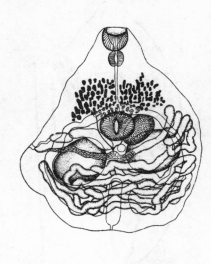

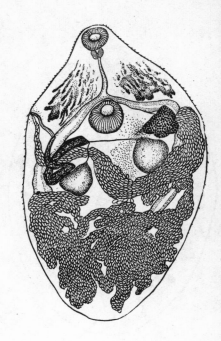

114. Leyogonimus polyoon (Braun, 1902) (from Skarbilovich, 1948, after Ginetsinskaya, 1947)

115. Allassogonoporus marginalis Olivier, 1938 (from Skarbilovich, 1948, after Olivier, 1938)

116. Myotitrema asymmetrica Macy, 1940 (from Skarbilovich, 1948, after Macy, 1940)

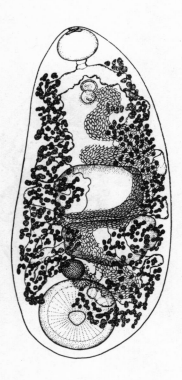

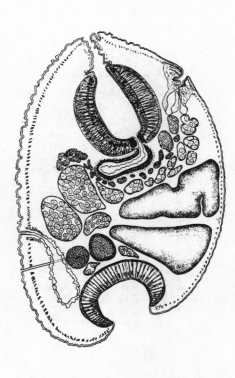

117. Paramphistomum cervi (Schrank, 1790) (from Skrjabin, 1949, after Stunkard, 1929)

118. Ugandocotyle pisom (Leiper, 1910) (from Skrjabin, 1949, after Näsmark, 1937)

119. Calicophoron calicophorum (Fischoeder, 1901) (from Skrjabin, 1949, after Fischoeder, 1903)

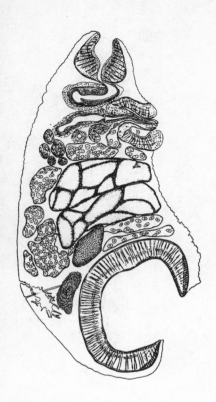

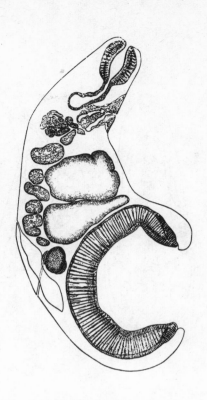

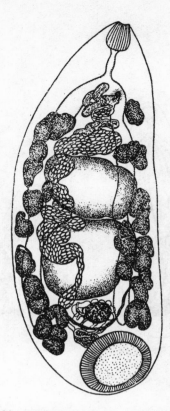

120. Cotylophoron cotylophorum (Fischoeder, 1901) (from Skrjabin, 1949, after Näsmark, 1937)

121. Gigantocotyle explanatum (Creplin, 1847) (from Skrjabin, 1949, after Näsmark, 1937)

122. Ceylonocotyle scoliocoelium (Fischoeder, 1901) (from Skrjabin, 1949, after Yamaguti, 1939)

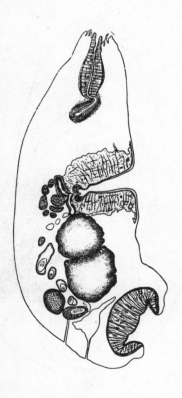

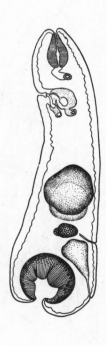

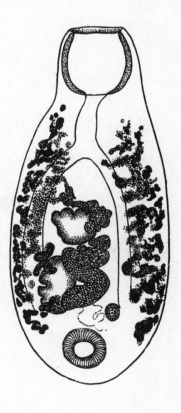

123. Nilocotyle gigantoatrium Näsmark, 1937 (from Skrjabin, 1949, after Näsmark, 1937)

124. Buxifrons buxifrons (Leiper, 1910) (from Skrjabin, 1949, after Leiper, 1910)

125. Macropharynx sudanensis Näsmark, 1937 (from Skrjabin, 1949, after Näsmark, 1937)

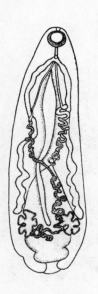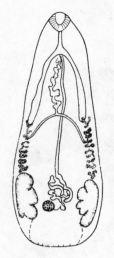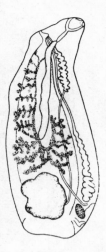

126. **Gastrothylax crumenifer** (Creplin, 1847) (from Skrjabin, 1949, after Fischoeder, 1901)

127. **Carmyerius gregarius** (Looss, 1896) (from Skrjabin, 1949, after Looss, 1896)

128. **Fischoederius elongatus** (Poirier, 1883) (from Skrjabin, 1949, after Yamaguti, 1939)

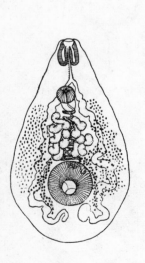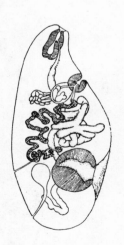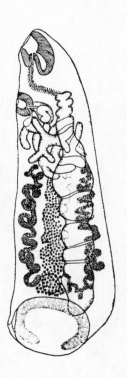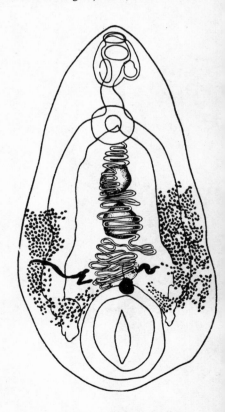

129. **Cladorchis pyriformis** (Diesing, 1838) (from Skrjabin, 1949, after Fischoeder, 1901)

130. **Taxorchis schistocotyle** (Fischoeder, 1901) (from Skrjabin, 1949, after Fischoeder, 1901)

131. **Chiostichorchis myopotami** (Artigas and Pacheco, 1932) (from Skrjabin, 1949, after Artigas and Pacheco, 1932)

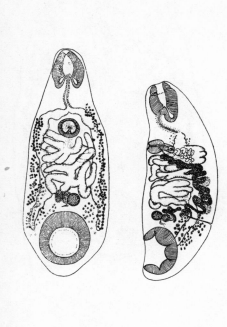

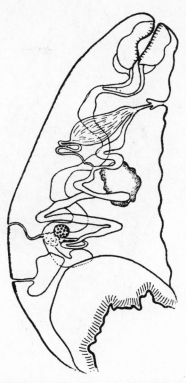

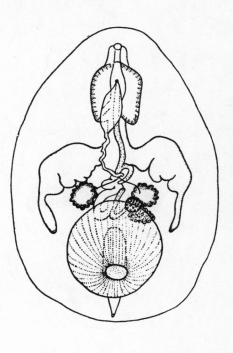

132. **Stichorchis giganteus** (Diesing, 1835) (from Skrjabin, 1949, after Fischoeder, 1901)

133. **Pfenderius papillatus** (Cobbold, 1882) (from Skrjabin, 1949, after Stiles and Goldberger, 1910)

134. **Tugumea heteroceca** Fukui, 1926 (from Skrjabin, 1949, after Fukui, 1929)

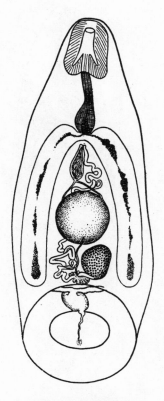

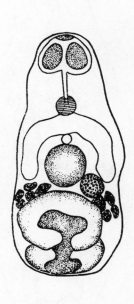

135. **Megalodiscus americanus** Chandler, 1923 (from Skrjabin, 1949, after Chandler, 1923)

136. **Diplodiscus subclavatus** (Goeze, 1782) (from Skrjabin, 1949, after Looss, 1892)

137. **Catadiscus dolichocotyle** (Cohn, 1903) (from Skrjabin, 1949, after Cohn, 1903)

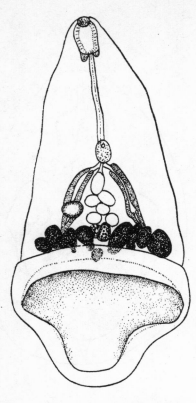

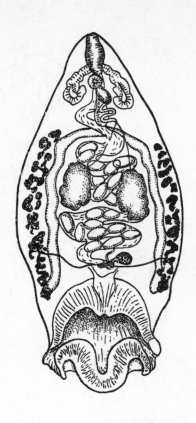

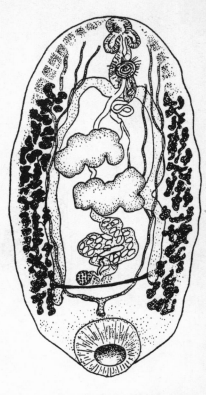

138. **Dermatemytrema trifoliata** Price, 1937 (from Skrjabin, 1949, after Price, 1937)

139. **Helostomatis helostomatis** (MacCallum, 1905) (from Skrjabin, 1949, after MacCallum, 1905)

140. **Protocladorchis pangasii** (MacCallum, 1905) (from Skrjabin, 1949, after MacCallum, 1905)

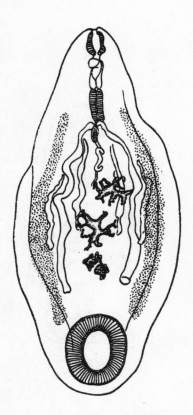

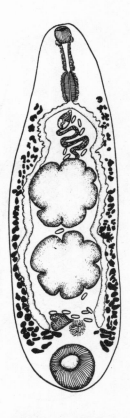

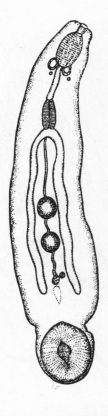

141. **Nematophila grande** (Diesing, 1839) (from Skrjabin, 1949, after Travassos, 1934)

142. **Orientodiscus lobatum** Srivastava, 1938 (from Skrjabin, 1949, after Srivastava, 1938)

143. **Schizamphistomoides constrictus** Price, 1936 (from Skrjabin, 1949, after Price, 1936)

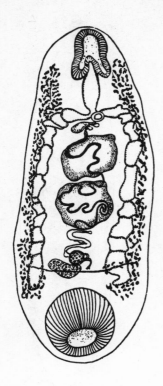

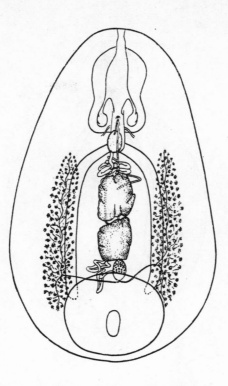

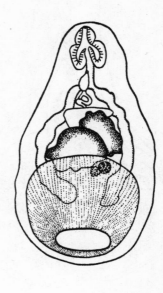

144. Wardius zibethicus Barker and East, 1915 (from Skrjabin, 1949, after Barker and East, 1915)

145. Watsonius watsoni (Cunningham, 1904) (from Skrjabin, 1949, after Stiles and Goldberger, 1910)

146. Hawkesius hawkesii (Cobbold, 1875) (from Skrjabin, 1949, after Stiles and Goldberger, 1910)

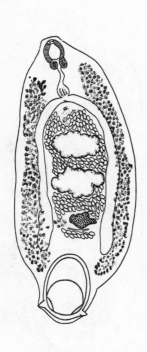

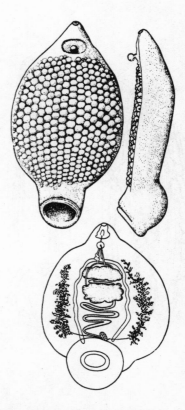

147. Zygocotyle lunatum (Diesing, 1835) (from Skrjabin, 1949, after Travassos, 1934)

148. Stunkardia dilymphosa Bhalerao, 1931 (from Skrjabin, 1949, after Bhalerao, 1931)

149. Homalogaster paloniae Poirier, 1883 (from Skrjabin, 1949, after Travassos, 1934)

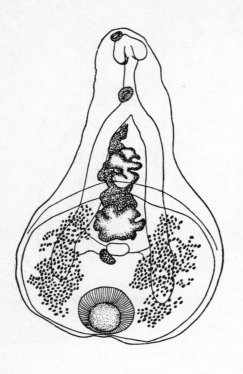

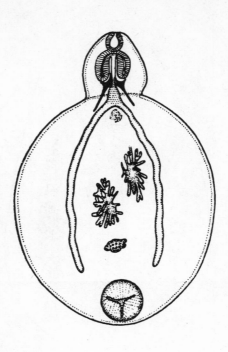

150. Gastrodiscoides hominis (Lewis and McConnal, 1876) (from Skrjabin, 1949, after Badanin, 1929)

151. Gastrodiscus aegyptiacus (Cobbold, 1876) (from Skrjabin, 1949, after Stunkard, 1929)

152. Neoctangium travassosi Ruiz, 1943 (from Skrjabin, 1949, after Ruiz, 1943)

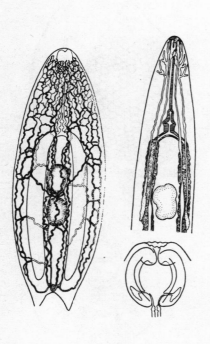

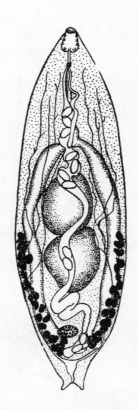

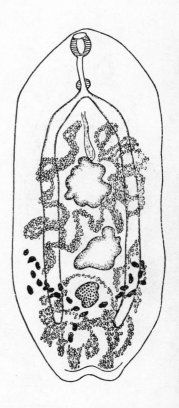

153. Octangium sagitta (Looss, 1899) (from Skrjabin, 1949, after Looss, 1902)

154. Hexangitrema pomacanthi Price, 1937 (from Skrjabin, 1949, after Price, 1937)

155. Parabaris parabaris Travassos, 1922 (from Skrjabin, 1949, after Travassos, Artigas and Pereora, 1928)

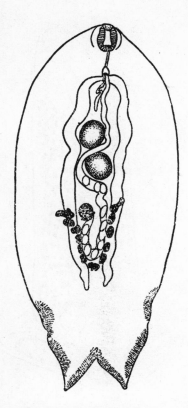

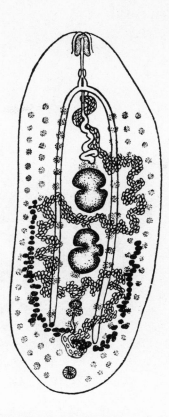

156. Octangioides skrjabini Price, 1937 (from Skrjabin, 1949, after Price, 1937)

157. Deuterobaris proteus (Brandes, 1891) (from Skrjabin, 1949, after Looss, 1899)

158. Hexangium sigani Goto and Ozaki, 1929 (from Skrjabin, 1949, after Goto and Ozaki, 1929)

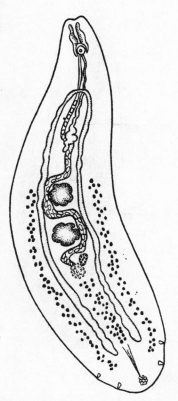

159. Microscaphidium reticulare (Beneden, 1859) (from Skrjabin, 1949, after Looss, 1899)

160. Angiodictyum parallelum (Looss, 1901) (from Skrjabin, 1949, after Looss, 1902)

161. Polyangium linguatula (Looss, 1899) (from Skrjabin, 1949, after Looss, 1902)

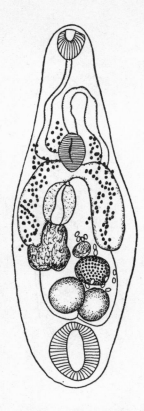

162. **Gyliauchen tarachodes** Nicoll, 1915 (from Skrjabin, 1949, after Nicoll, 1915)

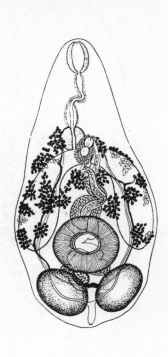

163. **Paragyliauchen chaetodontis** Yamaguti, 1934 (from Skrjabin, 1949, after Yamaguti, 1934)

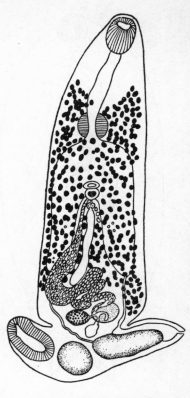

164. **Telotrema caudatum** Ozaki, 1933 (from Skrjabin, 1949, after Ozaki, 1933)

165. **Cephalogonimus amphiumae** Chandler, 1923 (from Skrjabin, 1950, after Chandler, 1923)

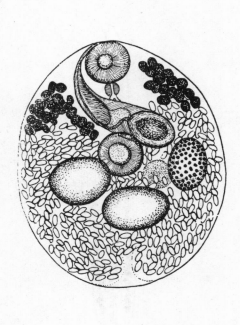

166. **Paracephalogonimus minutum** (Mehra, 1937) (from Skrjabin, 1950, after Mehra, 1937)

167. **Emoleptalea exilis** (Looss, 1899) (from Skrjabin, 1950, after Looss, 1899)

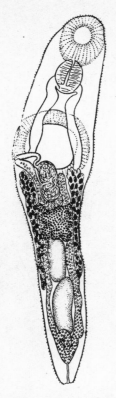

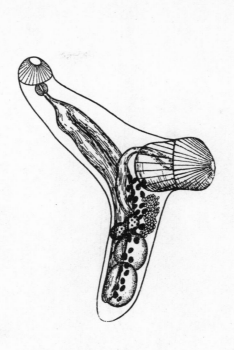

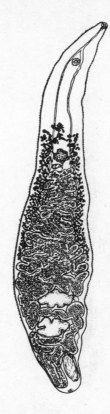

168. Lissorchis fairporti Magath, 1917 (from Skrjabin, 1950, after Magath, 1917)

169. Triganodistomum translucens Simer, 1929 (from Skrjabin, 1950, after Simer, 1929)

170. Urotrematulum attenuatum Macy, 1933 (from Skrjabin, 1950, after Macy, 1933)

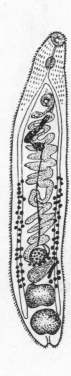

171. Urotrema scabridum Braun, 1900 (from Skrjabin, 1950, after M. Braun, 1900)

172. Evranorchis ophidiarum (Tubangui and Masilungan, 1935) (from Skrjabin and Petrov, 1950, after Tubangui and Masilungan, 1935)

173. Gomtia pisicola Thapar, 1930 (from Skrjabin and Petrov, 1950, after Thapar, 1930)

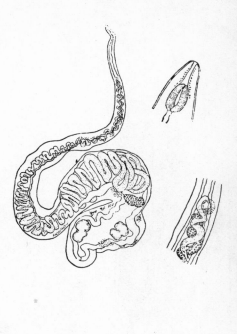

174. Euamphimerus nipponicus Yamaguti, 1941 (from Skrjabin and Petrov, 1950, after Yamaguti, 1941)

175. Amphimerus ovalis Barker, 1911 (from Skrjabin and Petrov, 1950, after Barker, 1911)

176. Erschoviorchis lintoni Skrjabin, 1945 (from Skrjabin and Petrov, 1950, after Linton, 1928)

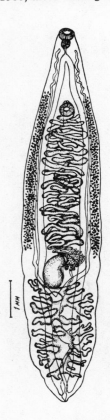

177. Clonorchis sinensis (Cobbold, 1875) (from Skrjabin and Petrov, 1950, after Skrjabin and Schulz, 1926)

178. Notaulus asiaticus Skrjabin, 1913 (from Skrjabin and Petrov, 1950, after Skrjabin, 1913)

179. Opisthorchis felineus (Rivolta, 1884) (from Skrjabin and Petrov, 1950, after Skrjabin and Schulz, 1926)

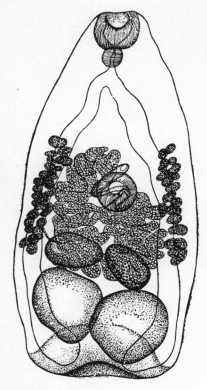

180. *Pseudamphistomum truncatum*
(Rudolphi, 1819) (from Skrjabin and
Petrov, 1950, after Skrjabin and
Schulz, 1929)

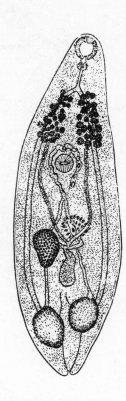

181. *Holometra exigua* (Mühling,
1898) (from Skrjabin and Petrov, 1950,
after Mühling, 1898)

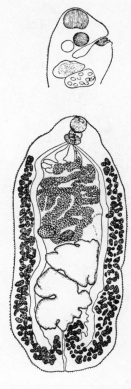

182. *Tubangorchis caintaensis*
(Tubangui, 1928) (from Skrjabin and
Petrov, 1950, after Tubangui, 1928)

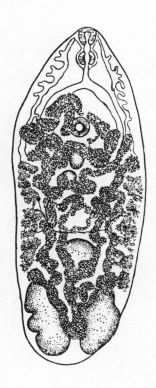

183. *Cladocystis trifolium* (Braun,
1901) (from Skrjabin and Petrov, 1950,
after M. Braun, 1902)

184. *Parametorchis complexus*
(Stiles and Hassall, 1894) (from
Skrjabin and Petrov, 1950, after
Stiles and Hassall, 1894)

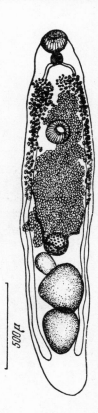

185. *Metametorchis skrjabini*
(Morosov, 1939) (from Skrjabin and
Petrov, 1950, after Morosov, 1939)

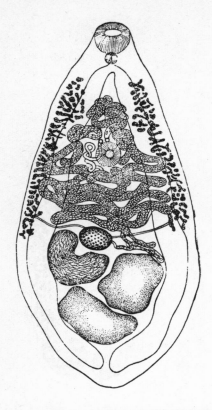

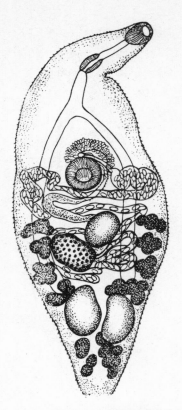

186. **Metorchis albidus** (Braun, 1893) (from Skrjabin and Petrov, 1950, after Skrjabin and Schulz, 1937)

187. **Phocitrema fusiforme** Goto and Ozaki, 1930 (from Skrjabin and Petrov, 1950, after Goto and Ozaki, 1930)

188. **Witenbergia witenbergi** Vaz, 1932 (from Skrjabin and Petrov, 1950, after Vaz, 1932)

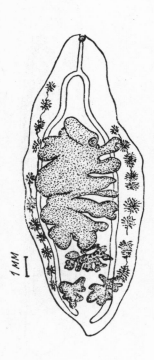

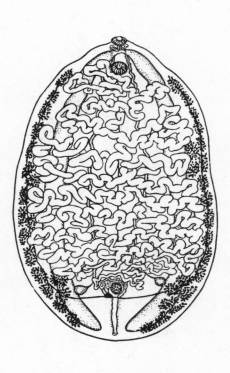

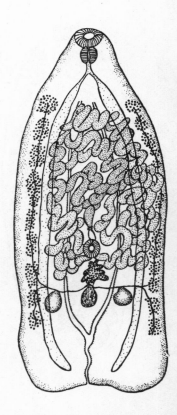

189. **Diasia diasi** Travassos, 1922 (from Skrjabin and Petrov, 1950, after Travassos, 1922)

190. **Pachytrema calculus** Looss, 1907 (from Skrjabin and Petrov, 1950, after Looss, 1907)

191. **Microtrema truncatum** Kobayashi, 1920 (from Skrjabin and Petrov, 1950, after Kobayashi, 1920)

192. Ratzia parva (Stossich, 1904) (from Skrjabin and Petrov, 1950, after Dollfus, 1929)

193. Cyclorchis campula (Cobbold, 1876) (from Skrjabin and Petrov, 1950, after Cobbold, 1876)

194. Cyclocoelum mutabile (Zeder, 1800) (from Bashkirova, 1950, after Harrah, 1922)

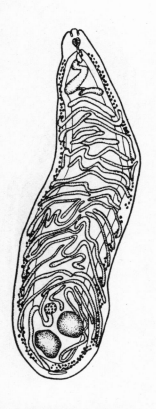

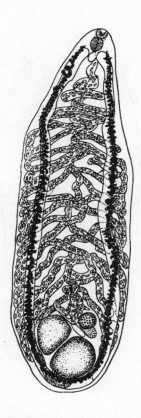

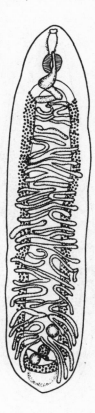

195. Haematotrephus similis Stossich, 1902 (from Bashkirova, 1950, after Kossack, 1911)

196. Uvitellina pseudocotylea Witenberg, 1923 (from Bashkirova, 1950, after Witenberg, 1923)

197. Hyptiasmus arcuatus (Stossich, 1902) (from Bashkirova, 1950, after Kossack, 1911)

215

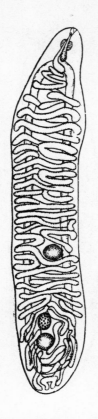

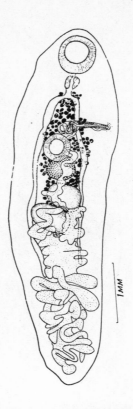

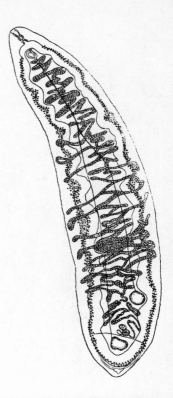

198.   Transcoelum oculeus (Kossack, 1911) (from Bashkirova, 1950, after Kossack, 1911)

199.   Sticholecitha serpentis Prudhoe, 1949 (from Skrjabin and Antipin, 1960, after Prudhoe, 1949)

200.   Allopyge antigones Johnston, 1913 (from Bashkirova, 1950, after Johnston, 1913)

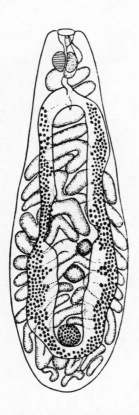

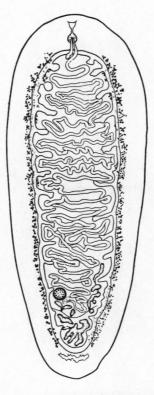

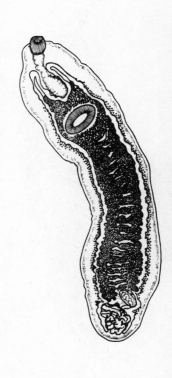

201.   Ophthalmophagus singularis Stossich, 1902 (from Bashkirova, 1950, after Kossack, 1911)

202.   Typhylocoelum cucumerinum (Rudolphi, 1809) (from Bashkirova, 1950, after Kossack, 1911)

203.   Hemiorchis hardelli (Mehra, 1934) (from Skrjabin, 1951, after Mehra, 1940)

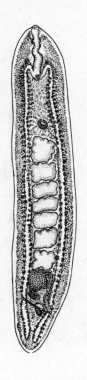

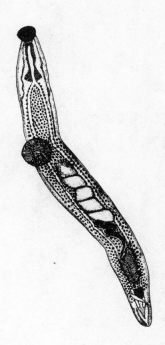

204.   Plasmiorchis orientalis Mehra, 1934 (from Skrjabin, 1951, after Mehra, 1934)

205.   Spirorchis innominata Ward, 1921 (from Skrjabin, 1951, after MacCallum, 1918)

206.   Monticellius indicum Mehra, 1939 (from Skrjabin, 1951, after Mehra, 1939)

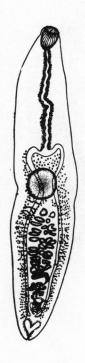

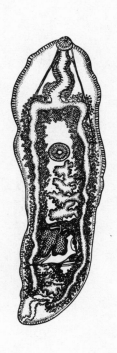

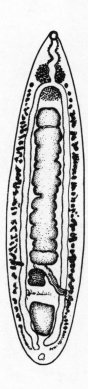

207.   Learedius learedi Price, 1934 (from Skrjabin, 1951, after Price, 1934)

208.   Spirhapalum polesianum Ejsmont, 1927 (from Skrjabin, 1951, after Ejsmont, 1927)

209.   Diarmostorchis blandingi (MacCallum, 1926) (from Skrjabin, 1951, after MacCallum, 1926)

210. Vasotrema amydae Stunkard, 1926 (from Skrjabin, 1951, after Stunkard, 1928)

211. Hapalotrema loossi Price, 1934 (from Skrjabin, 1951, after Looss, 1899)

212. Hapalorhynchus gracilis Stunkard, 1922 (from Skrjabin, 1951, after Stunkard, 1923)

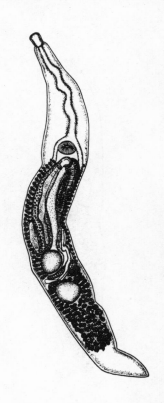

213. Coeuritrema lyssimus Mehra, 1933 (from Skrjabin, 1951, after Mehra, 1933)

214. Amphiorchis amphiorchis Price, 1934 (from Skrjabin, 1951, after Price, 1934)

215. Enterohaematotrema palaeorticum Mehra, 1940 (from Skrjabin, 1951, after Mehra, 1940)

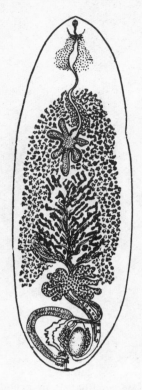

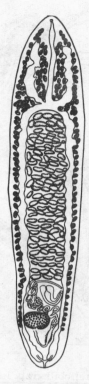

216. Plehniella coelomicola
Szidat, 1951 (from Skrjabin, 1951)

217. Sanguinicola inermis Plehn,
1905 (from Skrjabin, 1951, after
Scheuring, 1922)

218. Aporocotyle simplex Odhner,
1900 (from Skrjabin, 1951, after
Odhner, 1911)

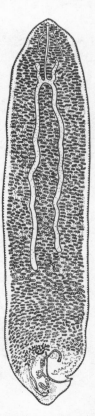

219. Paradeontacylix
sanguinicoloides McIntosh, 1934
(from Skrjabin, 1951, after Mcintosh,
1934)

220. Deontacylix ovalis Linton,
1910 (from Skrjabin, 1951, after
Linton, 1910)

221. Psettarium japonicum (Goto
and Ozaki, 1929) (from Skrjabin, 1951,
after Goto and Ozaki, 1929)

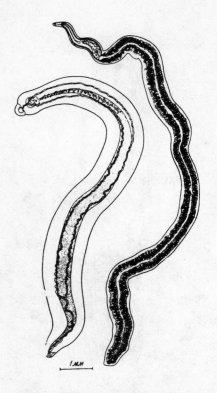

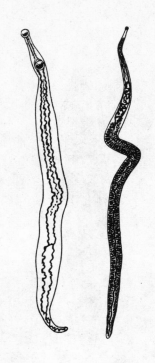

222. Bivitellobilharzia loxodontae
Vogel and Minning, 1940 (from
Skrjabin, 1951, after Vogel and
Minning, 1940)

223. Ornithobilharzia intermedia
Odhner, 1912 (from Skrjabin, 1951,
after Odhner, 1929)

224. Macrobilharzia macrobilharzia
Travassos, 1923 (from Skrjabin, 1951,
after Price, 1929)

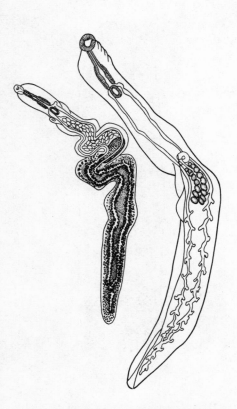

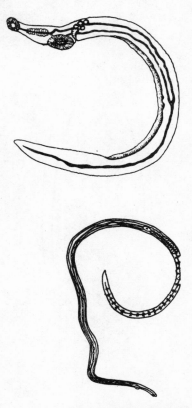

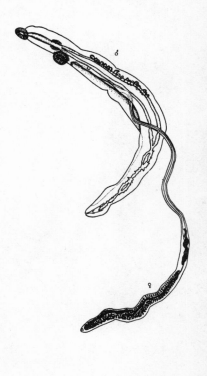

225. Schistosomatium pathlocopticum
Tanabe, 1923 (from Skrjabin, 1951,
after Tanabe, 1923)

226. Schistosoma haematobium
(Bilharz, 1852) (from Skrjabin,
1951, after Manson-Bahr and
Fairley, 1920)

227. Austrobilharzia terrigalensis
Johnston, 1917 (from Skrjabin, 1951,
after Johnston, 1917)

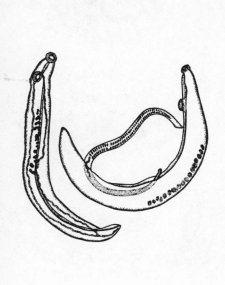

228. Microbilharzia chapini Price, 1929 (from Skrjabin, 1951, after Price, 1929)

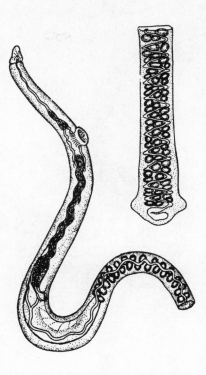

229. Trichobilharzia physellae (Talbot, 1936) (from Skrjabin, 1951)

230. Pseudobilharziella kowalewskii Ejsmont, 1929 (from Skrjabin, 1951, after Ejsmont, 1929)

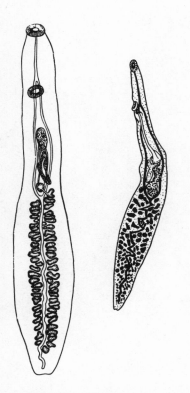

231. Bilharziella polonica (Kowalewsky, 1895) (from Skrjabin, 1951, after Zakharov, 1920 and Kowalewsky, 1895)

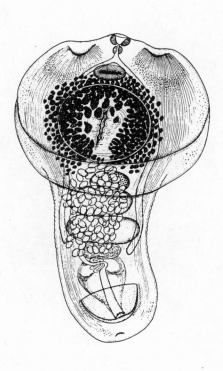

232. Proalarioides serpentis Yamaguti, 1933 (from Sudarikov, 1960. after Yamaguti, 1933)

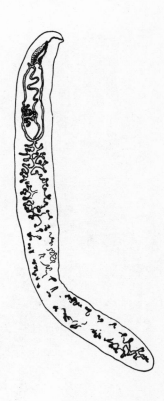

233. Dendritobilharzia pulverulenta (Braun, 1901) (from Skrjabin, 1951, after Braun, 1902)

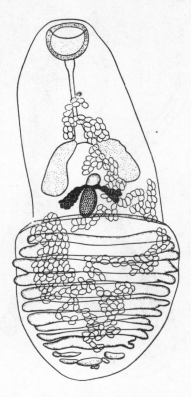

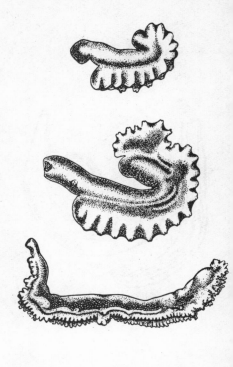

234. Gigantobilharzia gyrauli
(Brackett, 1940) (from Skrjabin,
1951, after Brackett, 1942)

235. Zonocotyle bicaecata
Travassos, 1947 (from Skrjabin,
1952, after Travassos, 1947)

236. Macraspis elegans Olsson,
1868 (from Skrjabin, 1952, after
Jägerskiöld, 1899)

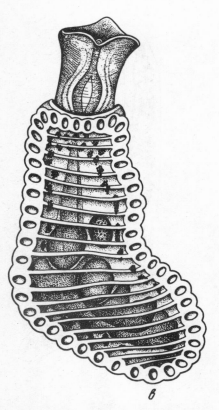

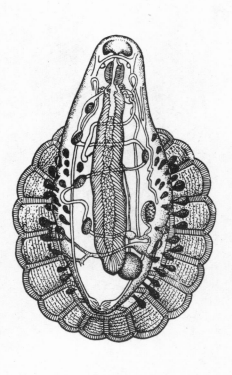

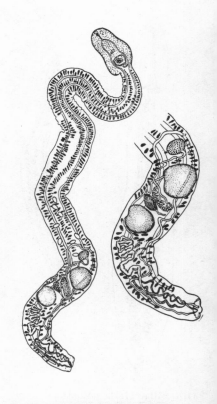

237. Cotylogaster michaelis
Monticelli, 1892 (from Skrjabin,
1952, after Monticelli, 1892)

238. Cotylaspis insignis Leidy,
1857 (from Skrjabin, 1952, after
Osborn, 1904)

239. Massoprostatum longum
Caballero, 1947 (from Sudarikov,
1960, after Caballero, 1947)

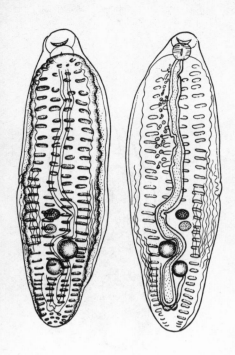

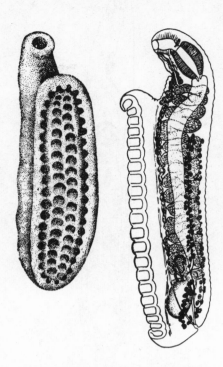

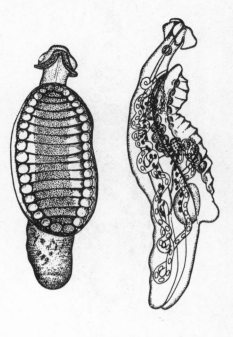

240. Multicotyle purvisi Dawes, 1941 (from Skrjabin, 1952, after Dawes, 1941)

241. Lophotaspis vallei (Stossich, 1899) (from Skrjabin, 1952, after Looss, 1902)

242. Lobatostoma ringens (Linton, 1907) (from Skrjabin, 1952, after MacCallum, 1913)

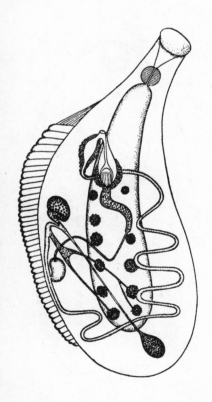

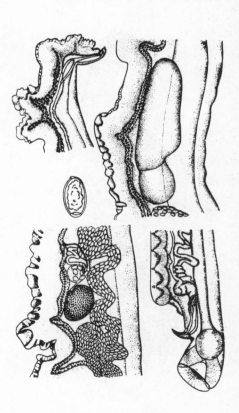

243. Aspidogaster conchicola K. Baer, 1927 (from Skrjabin, 1952, after Voeltzkov, 1888)

244. Stichocotyle nephropis Cunningham, 1884 (from Skrjabin, 1952, after Odhner, 1909)

245. Multicalyx cristatus (Faust and Tang, 1936) (from Skrjabin, 1952, after Faust and Tang, 1936)

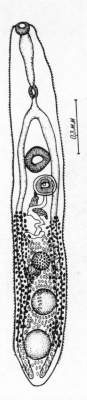

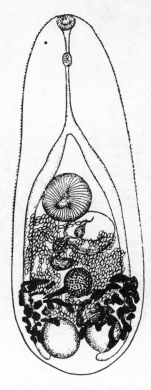

246. **Heterophyopsis expectans**
(Africa and Garcia, 1935) (from
Morozov, 1952, after Tubangui and
Africa, 1938)

247. **Pseudoheterophyes continua**
(Onji and Nishio, 1924) (from
Morozov, 1952, after Yamaguti, 1939)

248. **Heterophyes heterophyes**
(Siebold, 1852) (from Morozov, 1952,
after Witenberg, 1929)

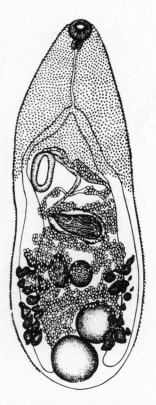

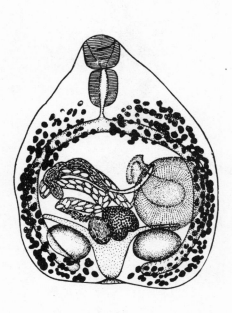

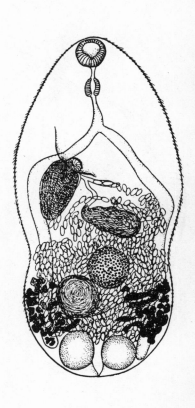

249. **Metagonimus yokogawai**
(Katsurada, 1912) (from Morozov,
1952, after Skrjabin, Podyapolskaya
and Schulz, 1930)

250. **Metagonimoides oregonensis**
Price, 1931 (from Morozov, 1952,
after Price, 1931)

251. **Dexiogonimus ciureanus**
Witenberg, 1929 (from Morozov,
1952, after Witenberg, 1929)

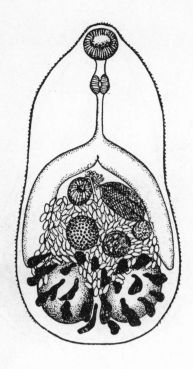

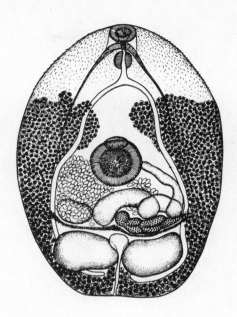

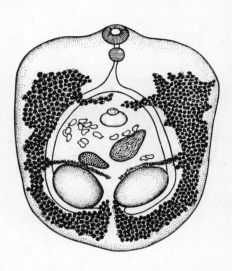

252. Diorchitrema pseudocirrata
Witenberg, 1929 (from Morozov,
1952, after Witenberg, 1929)

253. Cryptocotyle cancavum
(Creplin, 1825) (from Morozov,
1952, after Isaychikov, 1925)

254. Ciureana quinqueangularis
Skrjabin, 1923 (from Morozov,
1952, after Skrjabin, 1923)

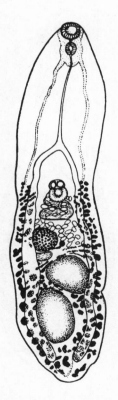

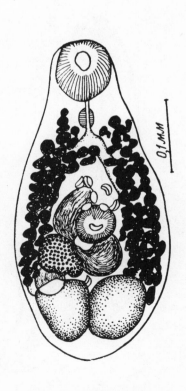

255. Rossicotrema donicum
Skrjabin and Lindtrop, 1919 (from
Morozov, 1952, after Ciurea, 1934)

256. Pricetrema zalophi (Price,
1932) (from Morozov, 1952, after
Price, 1932)

257. Apophallus muhlingi
(Jägerskiöld, 1899) (from Morozov,
1952, after Mühling, 1898)

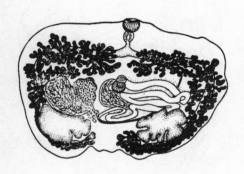

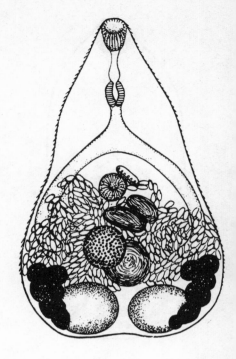

258. Euryhelmis squamula
(Rudolphi, 1819) (from Morozov, 1952, after Baer, 1931)

259. Parascocotyle minuta (Looss, 1899) (from Morozov, 1952, after Neveu-Lemarie, 1936)

260. Pygidiopsis genata Looss, 1907 (from Morozov, 1952, after Witenberg, 1929)

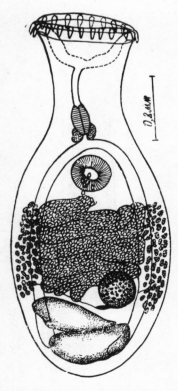

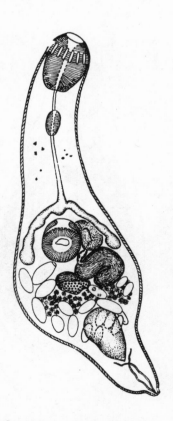

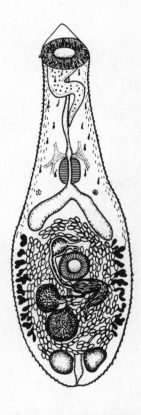

261. Caimanicola majoroara Freitas and Lent, 1938 (from Morozov, 1952, after Freitas and Lent, 1938)

262. Pygidiopsoides spindalis Martin, 1951 (from Morozov, 1952)

263. Ascotyle coleostoma (Looss, 1896) (from Morozov, 1952, after Ransom, 1920)

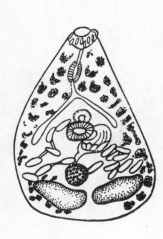

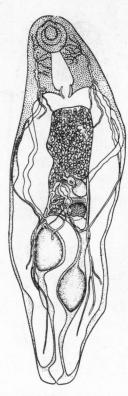

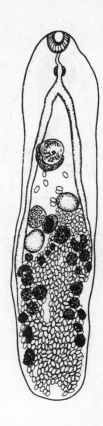

264.   Centrocestus cuspidatus
(Looss, 1896) (from Morozov, 1952,
after Balozet and Callot, 1939)

265.   Galactostomum lacteum
(Jägerskiöld, 1896) (from Morozov,
1952, after Jägerskiöld, 1896)

266.   Sobolephya oschmarini
Morosov, 1952 (from Morosov, 1952)

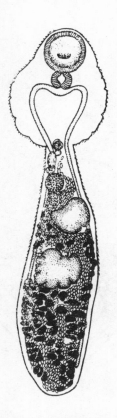

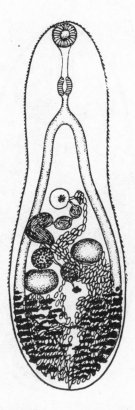

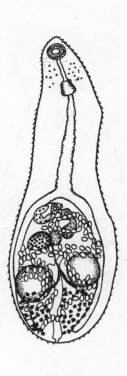

267.   Cercarioides aharoni
Witenberg, 1929 (from Morozov,
1952, after Witenberg, 1929)

268.   Stictodora sawakinensis
Looss, 1899 (from Morozov, 1952,
after Witenberg, 1929)

269.   Parastictodora hancocki
Martin, 1950 (from Morozov, 1952,
after Martin, 1950)

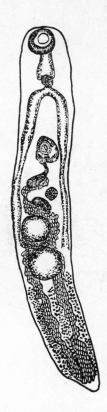

270. Ponticotrema euxini
Issaitschikoff, 1927 (from Morozov,
1952, after Isaychikov, 1927)

271. Tauridiana pontica
Issaitschikoff, 1925 (from Morozov,
1952, after Isaychikov, 1925)

272. Knipowitschetrema nicolai
Issaitschikoff, 1927 (from Morozov,
1952, after Isaychikov, 1927)

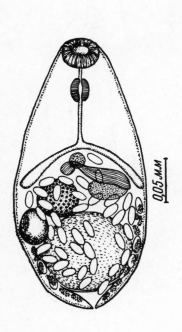

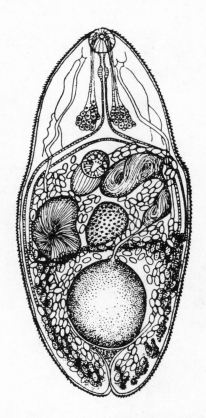

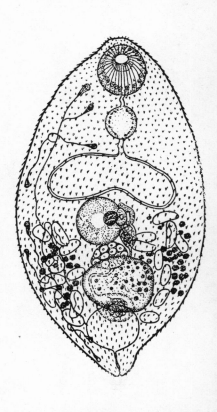

273. Procerovum sisoni (Africa and
Garcia, 1935) (from Morozov, 1952,
after Chen, 1949)

274. Haplorchis pumilo (Looss, 1896)
(from Morozov, 1952, after Faust and
Nishigori, 1926)

275. Euhaplorchis californiensis
Martin, 1950 (from Morozov, 1952,
after Martin, 1950)

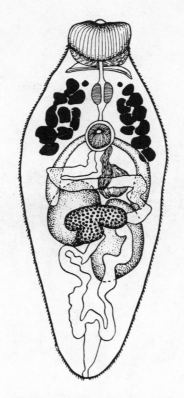

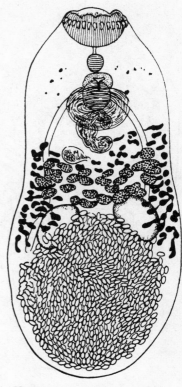

276. Cryptogonimus chili Osborn, 1903 (from Morozov, 1952, after Van Cleave and Mueller, 1934)

277. Caecincola parvulus Marshal and Gilbert, 1905 (from Morozov, 1952, after Marshal and Gilbert, 1905)

278. Neochasmus umbellus Van Cleave and Mueller, 1932 (from Morozov, 1952, after Van Cleave and Mueller, 1932)

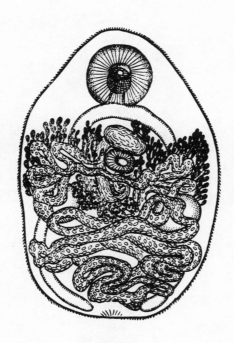

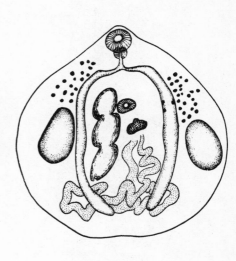

279. Allocanthochasmus artus Mueller and Van Cleave, 1932 (from Morozov, 1952, after Mueller and Van Cleave, 1932)

280. Metadena crassulata Linton, 1910 (from Morozov, 1952, after Linton, 1910)

281. Exorchis oviformis Kobayashi, 1918 (from Morozov, 1952, after Kobayashi, 1921)

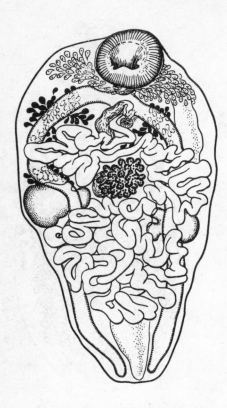

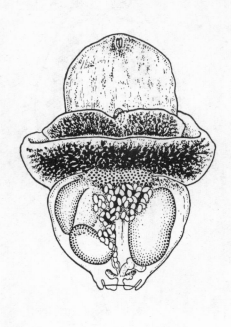

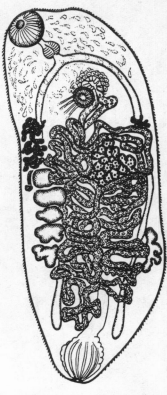

282. Siphoderina brotulae Manter,
1934 (from Morozov, 1952, after
Manter, 1934)

283. Bolbocephalodes intestiniforax
(Dubois, 1934) (from Sudarikov, 1960,
after Dubois, 1938)

284. Siphodera vinaledwardsi
(Linton, 1901) (from Morozov,
1952, after Linton, 1910)

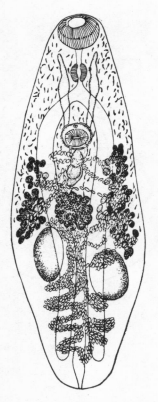

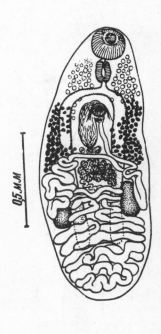

285. Paracryptogonimus
acanthostomus Yamaguti, 1934 (from
Morozov, 1952, after Yamaguti, 1934)

286. Biovarium cryptocotyle
Yamaguti, 1934 (from Morozov, 1952,
after Yamaguti, 1934)

287. Siphoderoides vancleavei
Manter, 1940 (from Morozov, 1952,
after Manter, 1940)

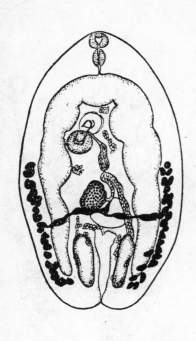

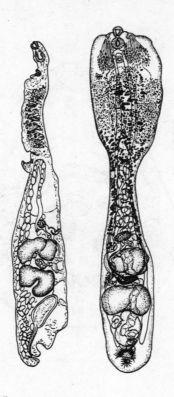

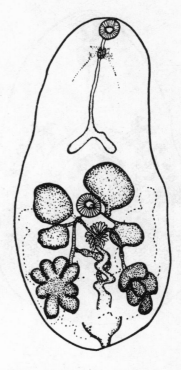

288. Acetodextra amiuri (Stafford, 1900) (from Morozov, 1952, after Van Cleave and Mueller, 1932)

289. Enhydridiplostomum fosteri (McIntosh, 1939) (from Sudarikov, 1960, after McIntosh, 1940)

290. Microphallus opacus (Ward, 1894) (from Belopolskaya, 1952, after Ward, 1901)

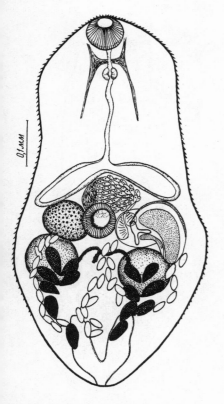

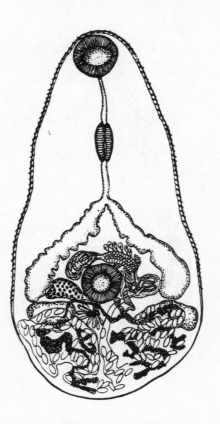

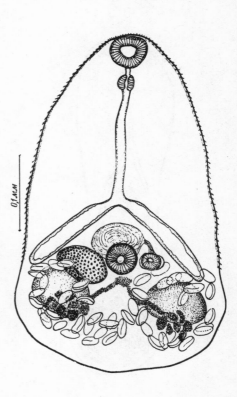

291. Spiculotrema litoralis Belopolskaia, 1949 (from Belopolskaya, 1952, after Belopolskaya, 1949)

292. Levinseniella brachysoma (Creplin, 1837) (from Belopolskaya, 1952, after Jägerskiöld, 1907)

293. Spelotrema pygmaeum (Levinsen, 1881) (from Belopolskaya, 1952)

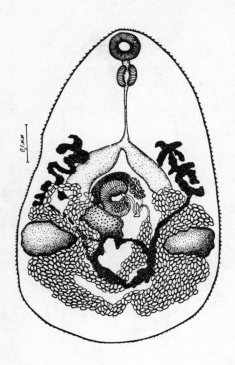

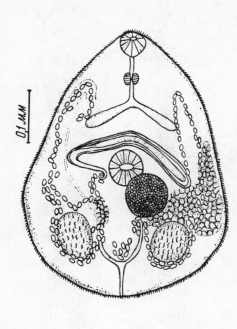

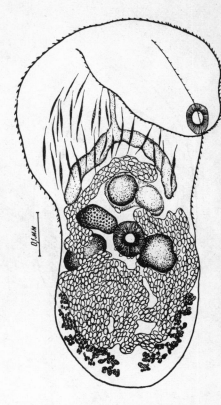

294. Endocotyle incana Belopolskaia, 1952 (from Belopolskaya, 1952)

295. Maritreminoides medium (Van Cleave and Mueller, 1932) (from Belopolskaya, 1952, after Sheldon, 1938)

296. Numeniotrema musculosa Belopolskaia, 1952 (from Belopolskaya, 1952)

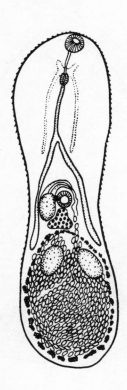

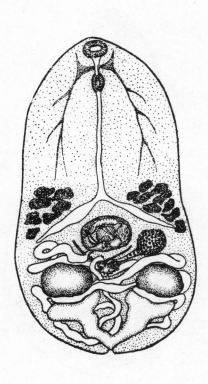

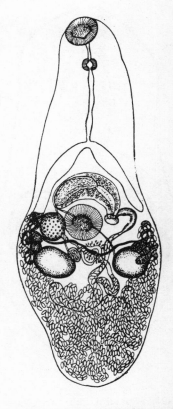

297. Maritrema gratiosum Nicoll, 1907 (from Belopolskaya, 1952, after Nicoll, 1909)

298. Microphalloides japonicus (Osborn, 1919) (from Belopolskaya, 1952, after Yoshida, 1938)

299. Pseudospelotrema japonicum Yamaguti, 1939 (from Belopolskaya 1952, after Yamaguti, 1939)

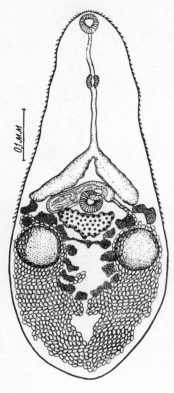

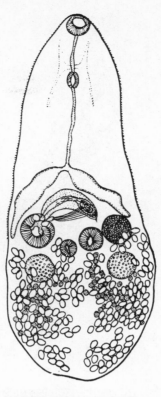

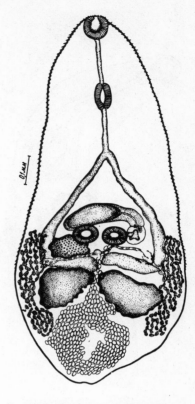

300. **Pseudomaritrema posterolecithale** Belopolskaia, 1952 (from Belopolskaya, 1952)

301. **Gynaecotyla squatorale** (Yamaguti, 1934) (from Belopolskaya, 1952, after Yamaguti, 1934)

302. **Diacetabulum curvicolon** Belopolskaia, 1952 (from Belopolskaya, 1952)

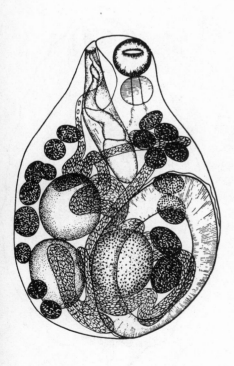

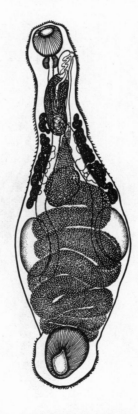

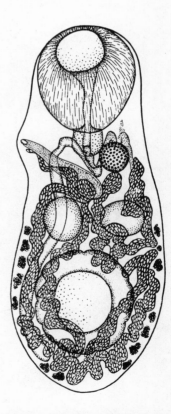

303. **Plectognathotrema cephalopora** Layman, 1930 (from Skrjabin, 1952, after Layman, 1930)

304. **Cephaloporus monacanthi** Yamaguti, 1934 (from Skrjabin, 1952, after Yamaguti, 1934)

305. **Khalilloossia aliibrahimi** Hilmy, 1948 (from Skrjabin, 1952, after Hilmy, 1948)

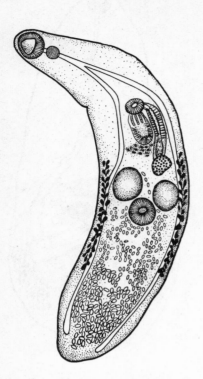

306. **Mehratrema dollfusi**
Srivastava, 1939 (from Skrjabin, 1952,
after Srivastava, 1939)

307. **Dicrocoelium lanceatum** Stiles
and Hassall, 1896 (from Skrjabin and
Evranova, 1952, after Skrjabin and
Schulz, 1928)

308. **Athesmia heterolecithodes**
(Braun, 1899) (from Skrjabin and
Evranova, 1952, after Braun, 1902)

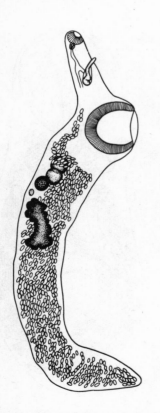

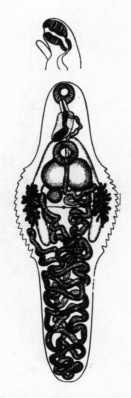

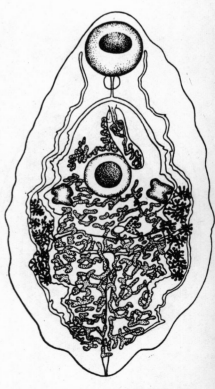

309. **Brachydistomum microscelis**
(Yamaguti, 1933) (from Skrjabin and
Evranova, 1952, after Yamaguti, 1933)

310. **Brodenia serrata** Gedoelst, 1913
(from Skrjabin and Evranova, 1952,
after Gedoelst, 1913)

311. **Eurytrema pancreaticum**
(Janson, 1889) (from Skrjabin and
Evranova, 1952, after Travassos,
1944)

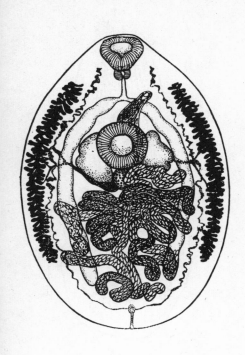

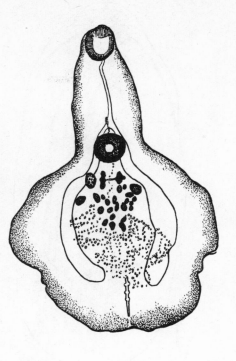

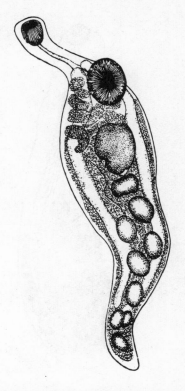

312. **Infidum infidum** (Faria, 1910)
(from Skrjabin and Evranova, 1952,
after Faria, 1910)

313. **Gorgotrema barbius** Dayal, 1938
(from Pigulevsky, 1952, after Dayal,
1938)

314. **Gorgodera cygnoides** (Zeder,
1800) (from Pigulevsky, 1952, after
Pigulevsky, 1945)

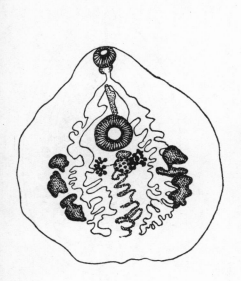

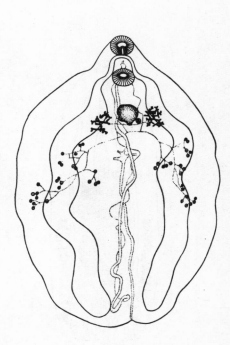

315. **Petalodistomum polycladum**
Johnston, 1913 (from Pigulevsky,
1952, after Johnston, 1913)

316. **Probolitrema richardii**
(Lopez, 1888) (from Pigulevsky,
1952, after Monticelli, 1893)

317. **Anaporrhutum albidum**
Ofenheim, 1900 (Pigulevsky, 1952,
after Ofenheim, 1900)

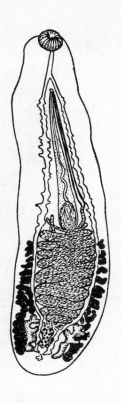

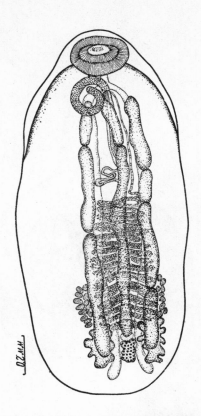

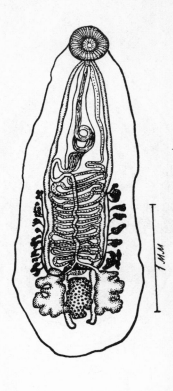

318.   Hofmonostomum himantopodis Harwood, 1939 (from Skrjabin, 1953, after Harwood, 1939)

319.   Tristriata anatis Belopolskaia, 1953 (from Skrjabin, 1953, after Belopolskaya, 1953)

320.   Quinqueserialis quinqueserialis (Barker and Laughlin, 1911) (from Skrjabin, 1953, after Barker, 1915)

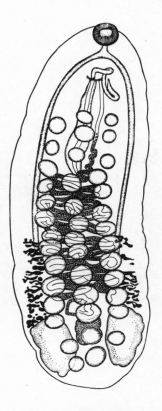

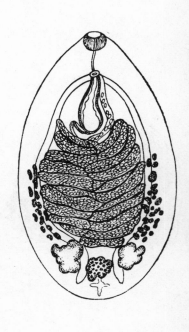

321.   Catatropis verrucosa (Frölich, 1789) (from Skrjabin, 1953, after Odhner, 1905)

322.   Notocotylus attenuatus (Rudolphi, 1809) (from Skrjabin, 1953, after Gorshkov, 1937)

323.   Paramonostomum alveatum (Mehlis, 1846) (from Skrjabin, 1953, after Mühling, 1898)

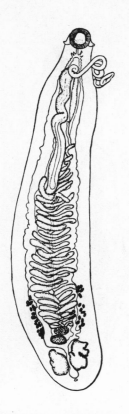

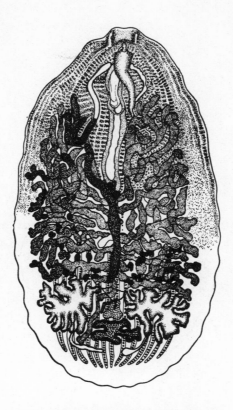

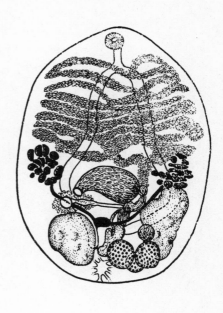

324. **Hippocrepis hippocrepis** (Diesing, 1850) (from Skrjabin, 1953, after Braun, 1901)

325. **Ogmogaster plicatus** (Creplin, 1829) (from Skrjabin, 1953 after Jägerskiöld, 1891)

326. **Nudacotyle novicia** Barker, 1916 (from Skrjabin, 1953, after Barker, 1916)

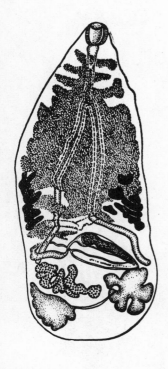

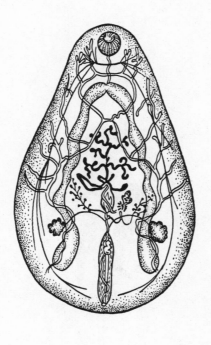

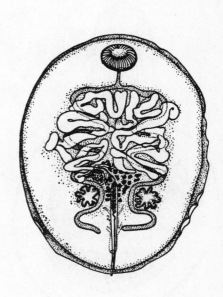

327. **Neocotyle neocotyle** Travassos, 1922 (from Skrjabin, 1953, after Travassos, 1939)

328. **Opisthotrema dujonis** (Leuckart, 1874) (from Skrjabin, 1953, after Fischer, 1883)

329. **Cochleotrema cochleotrema** Travassos and Vogelsang, 1931 (from Skrjabin, 1953, after Price, 1932)

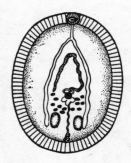

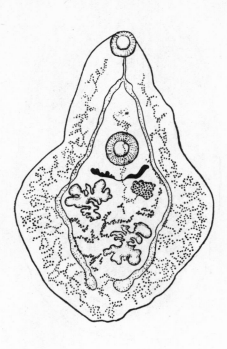

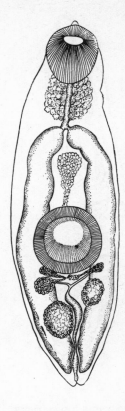

330. Pulmonicola pulmonalis
(Linstow, 1904) (from Skrjabin, 1953,
after Linstow, 1904)

331. Dendorchis neivai Travassos,
1926 (from Pigulevsky, 1953, after
Travassos, 1928)

332. Phyllodistomum folium
(Olfers, 1816) (from Pigulevsky, 1953)

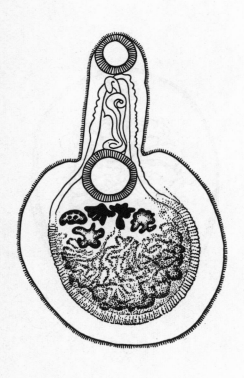

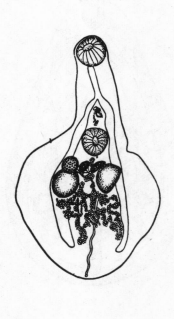

333. Xystretum solidum Linton, 1910
(from Pigulevsky, 1953, after Linton,
1910)

334. Phyllochorus macronius Dayal,
1938 (from Pigulevsky, 1953, after
Dayal, 1938)

335. Gorgoderina simplex (Looss,
1899) (from Pigulevsky, 1953, after
Stafford, 1903)

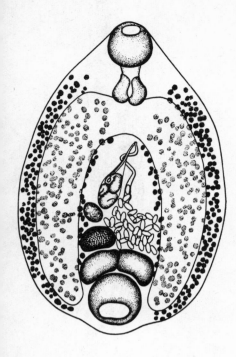

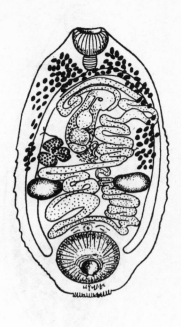

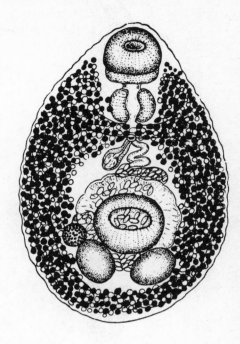

336. Opistholebes amplicoelum
Nicoll, 1915 (from Skrjabin, 1954,
after Nicoll, 1915)

337. Choanomyzus tasmaniae
Manter and Crowcroft, 1950 (from
Skrjabin, 1954, after Manter and
Crowcroft, 1950)

338. Heterolebes maculosus Ozaki,
1935 (from Skrjabin, 1954, after
Ozaki, 1935)

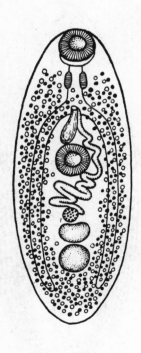

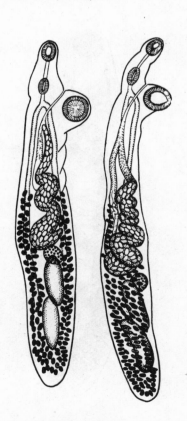

339. Maculifer subaequiporus
Nicoll, 1915 (from Skrjabin, 1954,
after Nicoll, 1915)

340. Acanthocolpus liodorus Lühe,
1906 (from Skrjabin, 1954, after
Lühe, 1906)

341. Paratormopsolus siluri
Dubinina and Bychovsky, 1954
(from Skrjabin, 1954, after Dubinina
and Bykhovsky, 1954)

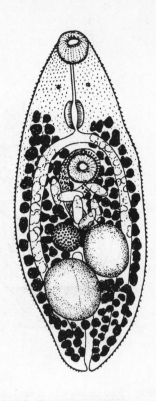

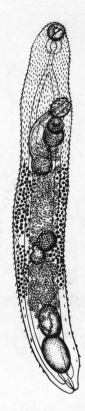

342. **Tormopsolus osculatus** (Looss, 1901) (from Skrjabin, 1954, after Looss, 1901)

343. **Acanthopsolus oculatus** (Levinsen, 1881) (from Skrjabin, 1954, after Odhner, 1905)

344. **Skrjabinopsolus acipenseris** Ivanov, 1935 (from Skrjabin, 1954, after Ivanov and Murygin, 1937)

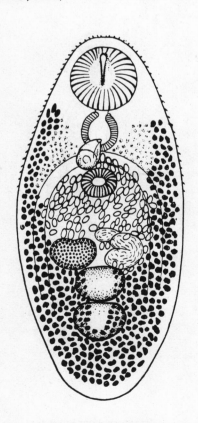

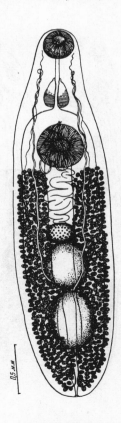

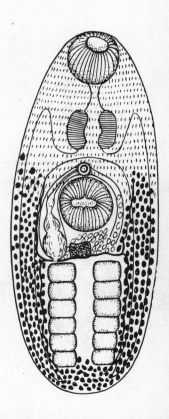

345. **Lepidauchen stenostoma** Nicoll, 1913 (from Skrjabin, 1954, after Nicoll, 1913)

346. **Pseudolepidapedon paralichthydis** Yamaguti, 1938 (from Skrjabin, 1954, after Yamaguti, 1938)

347. **Pleorchis polyorchis** (Stossich, 1888) (from Skrjabin, 1954, after Stossich, 1888)

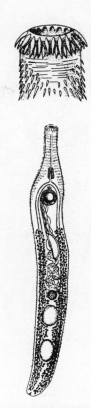

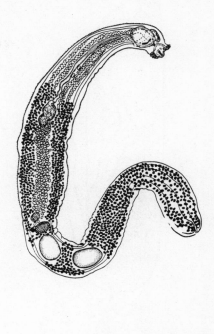

348. <u>Monorchistephanostomum gracile</u> Vigueras, 1942 (from Skrjabin, 1954, after Vigueras, 1942)

349. <u>Stephanostomum cesticillum</u> (Molin, 1858) (from Skrjabin, 1954, after Looss, 1899)

350. Manteria brachydera (Manter, 1940) (from Skrjabin, 1954, after Manter, 1940)

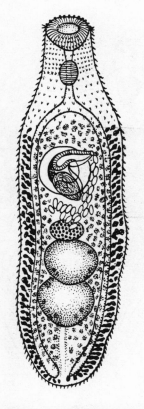

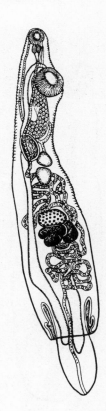

351. Dihemistephanus lydiae (Stossich, 1896) (from Skrjabin, 1954, after Nicoll, 1909)

352. Hemiuris appendiculatus (Rudolphi, 1802) (from Skrjabin and Gushanskaya, 1954, after Looss, 1908)

353. Parahemiuris merus (Linton, 1910) (from Skrjabin and Gushanskaya, 1954, after Linton, 1910)

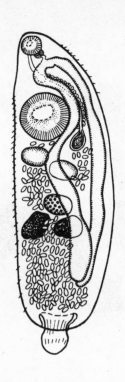

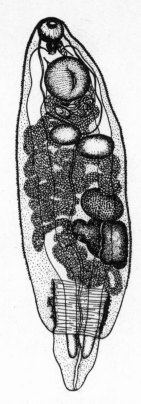

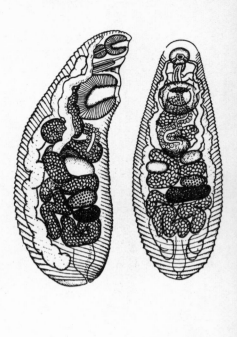

354. Anahemiuris microcercus
Manter, 1947 (from Skrjabin and
Gushanskaya, 1954, after Manter,
1947)

355. Glomericirrus amadai
Yamaguti, 1937 (from Skrjabin and
Gushanskaya, 1954, after Yamaguti,
1937)

356. Aphanurus stossichi (Monticelli,
1891) (from Skrjabin and Gushanskaya,
1954, after Looss, 1908)

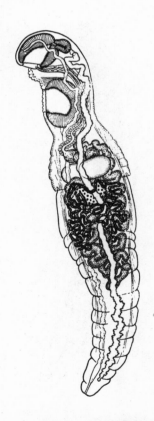

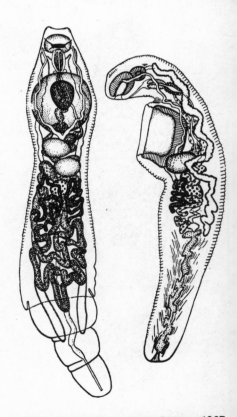

357. Chauhanurus microrchis
(Chauhan, 1945) (from Skrjabin and
Gushanskaya, 1954, after Chauhan,
1945)

358. Dinurus tornatus (Rudolphi,
1819) (from Skrjabin and Gushanskaya,
1954, after Looss, 1908)

359. Ectenurus lepidus Looss, 1907
(from Skrjabin and Gushanskaya, 1954,
after Looss, 1908)

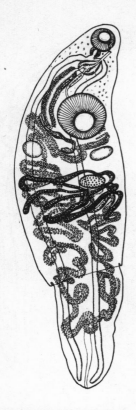

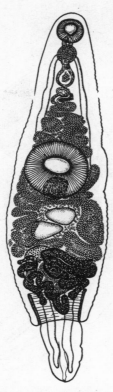

360. **Tubulovesicula spari** Yamaguti, 1934 (from Skrjabin and Gushanskaya, 1954, after Yamaguti, 1934)

361. **Uterovesiculuris hamati** (Yamaguti, 1934) (from Skrjabin and Gushanskaya, 1954, after Yamaguti, 1934)

362. **Erilepturus tiegsi** Woolcock, 1935 (from Skrjabin and Gushanskaya, 1954, after Woolcock, 1935)

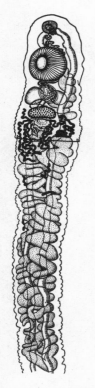

363. **Stomachicola muraenesocis** Yamaguti, 1934 (from Skrjabin and Gushanskaya, 1954, after Yamaguti, 1934)

364. **Pseudostomachicola rubea** (Linton, 1910) (from Skrjabin and Gushanskaya, 1954, after Linton, 1910)

365. **Clupenurus piscicola** Srivastava, 1935 (from Skrjabin and Gushanskaya, 1954, after Srivastava, 1935)

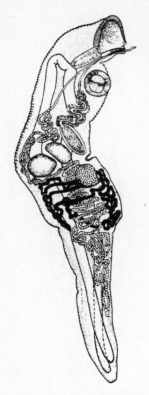

366. **Lecithocladium excisum**
(Rudolphi, 1819) (from Skrjabin and
Gushanskaya, 1954, after Markovsky,
1933)

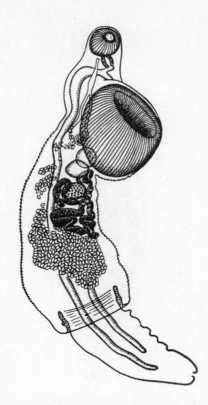

367. **Magnacetabulum trachuri**
Yamaguti, 1934 (from Skrjabin and
Gushanskaya, 1954, after Yamaguti,
1934)

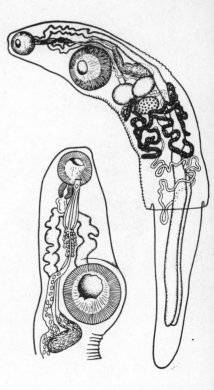

368. **Parectenurus americanus**
Manter, 1947 (from Skrjabin and
Gushanskaya, 1954, after Manter,
1947)

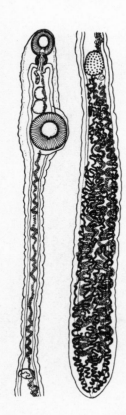

369. **Prosorchis psenopsis** Yamaguti,
1934 (from Skrjabin and Gushanskaya,
1954, after Yamaguti, 1934)

370. **Prosorchiopsis legendrei**
(Dollfus, 1947) (from Skrjabin and
Gushanskaya, 1954, after Dollfus,
1947)

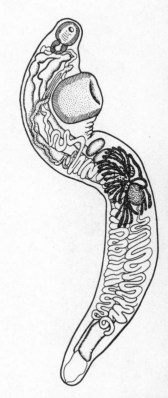

371. **Macradena perfecta**
Linton, 1910 (from Skrjabin and
Gushanskaya, 1954, after Manter,
1947)

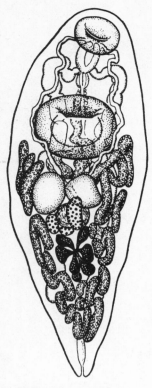

372. Lecithaster confusus
Odhner, 1905 (from Skrjabin and
Gushanskaya, 1954, after Looss,
1908)

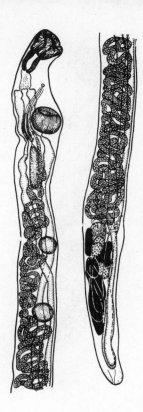

373. Trifoliovarium acanthocepolae
Yamaguti, 1940 (from Skrjabin and
Gushanskaya, 1954, after Yamaguti,
1940)

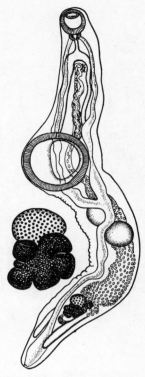

374. Hysterolecitha rosea
Linton, 1910 (from Skrjabin and
Gushanskaya, 1954, after Linton,
1910)

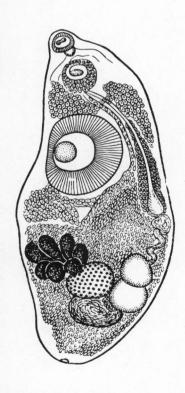

375. Dichadena acuta Linton, 1910
(from Skrjabin and Gushanskaya,
1954, after Linton, 1910)

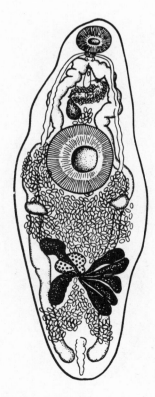

376. Brachadena pyriformis
Linton, 1910 (from Skrjabin and
Gushanskaya, 1954, after Manter,
1947)

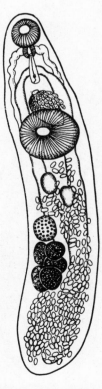

377. Lecithophyllium sphaerolecithum
(Manter, 1925) (from Skrjabin and
Gushanskaya, 1954, after Manter,
1926)

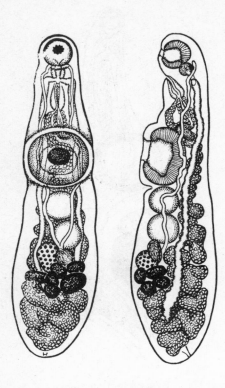

378. **Aponurus lagunculus** Looss, 1907 (from Skrjabin and Gushanskaya, 1954, after Looss, 1908)

379. **Hysterolecithoides epinepheli** Yamaguti, 1934 (from Skrjabin and Gushanskaya, 1954, after Yamaguti, 1934)

380. **Pronocephalus obliquus** Looss, 1901 (from Skrjabin, 1955, after Looss, 1902)

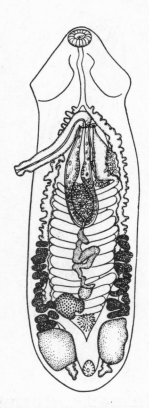

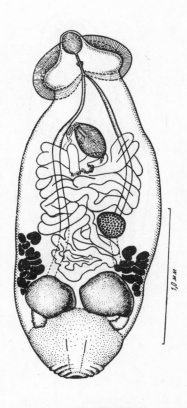

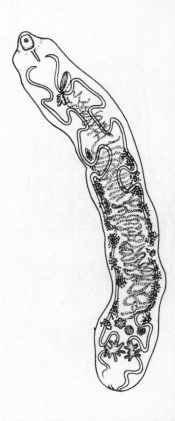

381. **Medioporus cheloniae** Oguro, 1936 (from Skrjabin, 1955, after Oguro, 1936)

382. **Ruicephalus minutus** (Ruiz, 1946) (from Skrjabin, 1955, after Ruiz, 1946)

383. **Astrorchis renicapite** (Leidy, 1856) (from Skrjabin, 1955, after Ruiz, 1946)

384. Pyelosomum cochlear Looss, 1899 (from Skrjabin, 1955, after Looss, 1899)

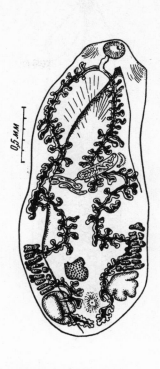

385. Barisomum erubescens Linton, 1910 (from Skrjabin, 1955, after Manter, 1947)

386. Cricocephalus albus (Kuhl and Hasselt, 1822) (from Skrjabin, 1955, after Looss, 1899)

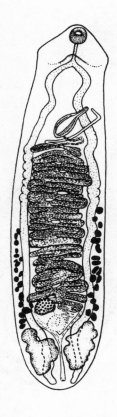

387. Epibathra crassa (Looss, 1901) (from Skrjabin, 1955, after Ruiz, 1946)

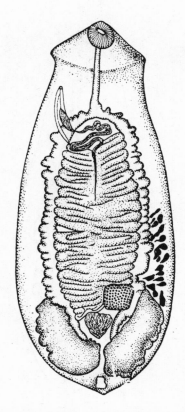

388. Renigonius orientalis Mehra, 1939 (from Skrjabin, 1955, after Mehra, 1939)

389. Pleurogonius longiusculus Looss, 1901 (from Skrjabin, 1955, after Looss, 1902)

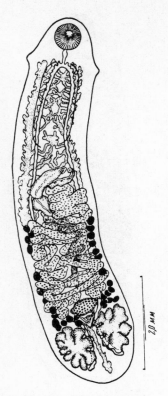

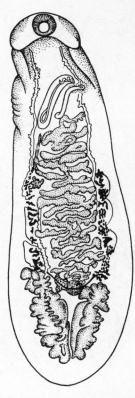

390. Iguanacola navicularis
Gilbert, 1938 (from Skrjabin, 1955,
after Gilbert, 1938)

391. Glyphicephalus solidus
Looss, 1901 (from Skrjabin, 1955,
after Looss, 1902)

392. Diaschistorchis pandus (Braun,
1901) (from Skrjabin, 1955, after
Braun, 1901)

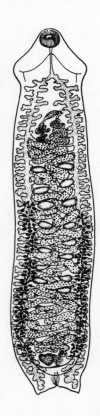

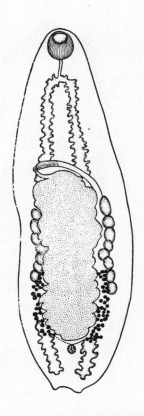

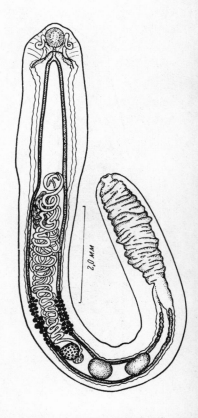

393. Charaxicephalus robustus
Looss, 1901 (from Skrjabin, 1955,
after Looss, 1902)

394. Desmogonius desmogonius
Stephens, 1911 (from Skrjabin, 1955,
after Stephens, 1911)

395. Cetiosaccus galapagensis
Gilbert, 1938 (from Skrjabin, 1955,
after Gilbert, 1938)

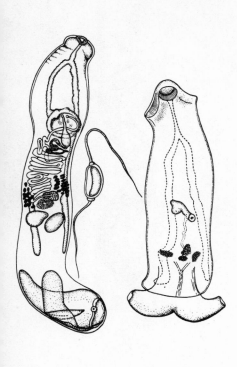

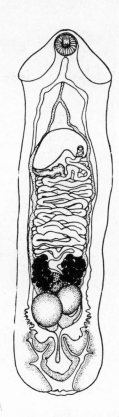

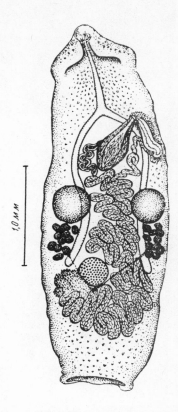

396. Choanophorus rovirosai Caballero, 1942 (from Skrjabin, 1955, after Caballero, 1942)

397. Macravestibulum obtusicaudum Mackin, 1930 (from Skrjabin, 1955, after Mackin, 1930)

398. Neopronocephalus triangularis Mehra, 1932 (from Skrjabin, 1955, after Mehra, 1932)

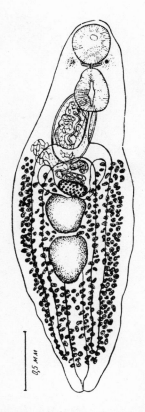

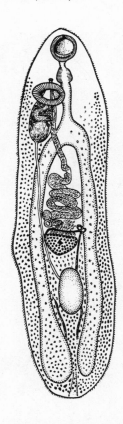

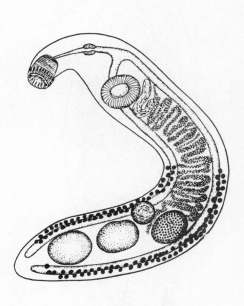

399. Megasolena estrix Linton, 1920 (from Skrjabin, 1955, after Manter, 1935)

400. Hapladena varia Linton, 1910 (from Skrjabin, 1955, after Linton, 1910)

401. Acanthostomum spiniceps (Looss, 1896) (from Morozov, 1955, after Pogoreltseva, 1952)

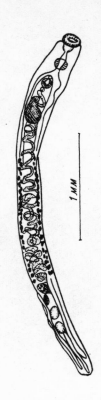

402. **Atrophecoeum burminis**
(Bhalerao, 1926) (from Morozov,
1955, after Bhalerao, 1940)

403. **Anisocoelium capitellatum**
(Rudolphi, 1819) (from Morozov,
1955, after Looss, 1901)

404. **Anisocladium fallax** (Rudolphi,
1819) (from Morozov, 1955, after
Looss, 1901)

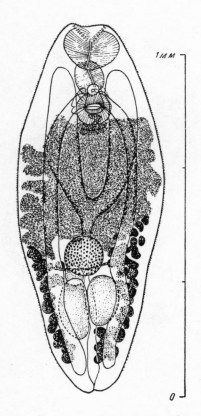

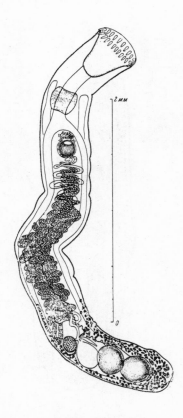

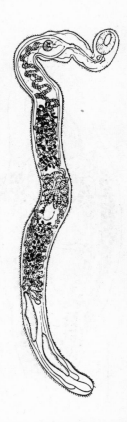

405. **Brientrema pelecani** Dollfus,
1950 (from Morozov, 1955, after
Dollfus, 1950)

406. **Gymnatrema gymnarcnii**
(Dollfus, 1950) (from Morozov,
1955, after Dollfus, 1950)

407. **Isocoelium mediolecithale**
Ozaki, 1927 (from Morozov, 1955,
after Ozaki, 1927)

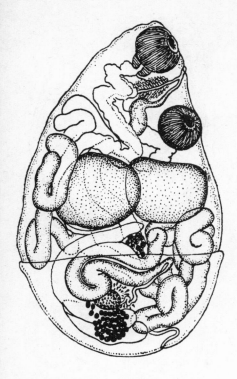

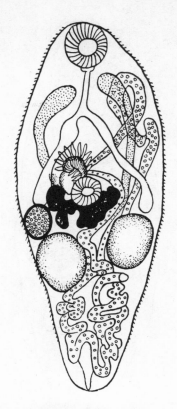

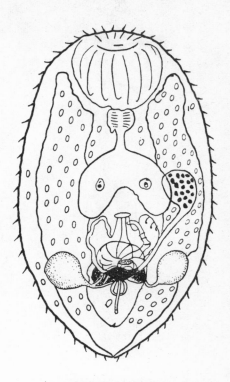

408. Aerobiotrema muraenesocis
Yamaguti, 1958 (from Skrjabin and
Gushanskaya, 1960, after Yamaguti,
1958)

409. Gymnophallus deliciosus
(Olsson, 1893) (from Morozov, 1955,
after Odhner, 1900)

410. Gymnophalloides tokiensis
Fujita, 1925 (metacercaria-from
Morozov, 1955, after Fujita, 1925)

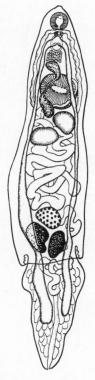

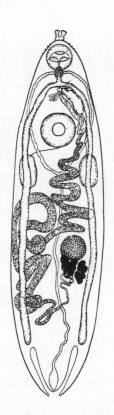

411. Dissosaccus laevis (Linton,
1898) (from Skrjabin and
Gushanskaya, 1955, after Manter,
1934)

412. Ceratotrema furcolabiata
Jones, 1933 (from Skrjabin and
Gushanskaya, 1955, after Jones, 1933)

413. Brachyphallus crenatus
(Rudolphi, 1802) (from Skrjabin and
Gushanskaya, 1955, after Lloyd, 1938)

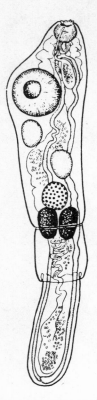

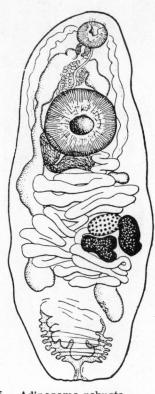

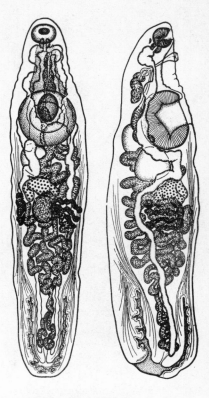

414. <u>Lethadena profunda</u>
(Manter, 1934) (from Skrjabin and
Gushanskaya, 1955, after Manter,
1934)

415. <u>Adinosoma robusta</u>
(Manter, 1934) (from Skrjabin and
Gushanskaya, 1955, after Manter,
1934)

416. <u>Plerurus digitatus</u>
(Looss, 1899) (from Skrjabin and
Gushanskaya, 1955, after Looss, 1908)

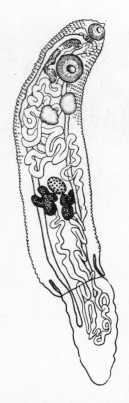

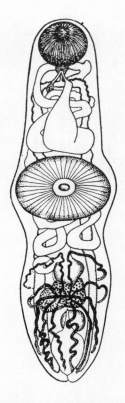

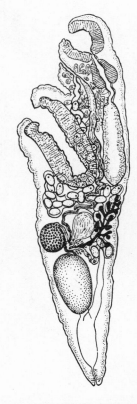

417. <u>Dinosoma rubra</u> Manter, 1934
(from Skrjabin and Gushanskaya,
1955, after Manter, 1954)

418. <u>Bathycotyle branchialis</u>
Darr, 1902 (from Skrjabin and
Gushanskaya, 1955, after Darr, 1902)

419. <u>Haplosplanchnus pachysomus</u>
(Eysenhardt, 1829) (from Skrjabin and
Gushanskaya, 1955, after Looss, 1902)

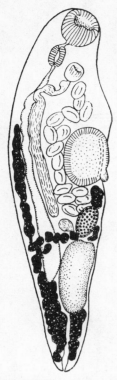

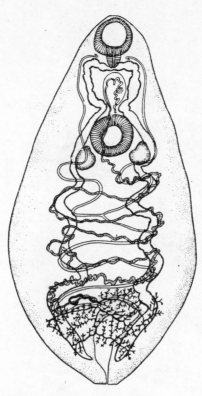

420.   Schikhobalotrema acuta
(Linton, 1910) (from Skrjabin and
Gushanskaya, 1955, after Manter,
1937)

421.   Isoparorchis trisimilitubis
Southwell, 1913 (from Skrjabin and
Gushanskaya, 1955, after Kobayashi,
1921)

422.   Diplotrema pelamydis
Yamaguti, 1938 (from Skrjabin,
1955, after Yamaguti, 1938)

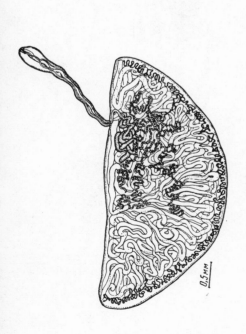

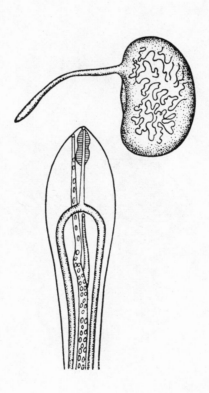

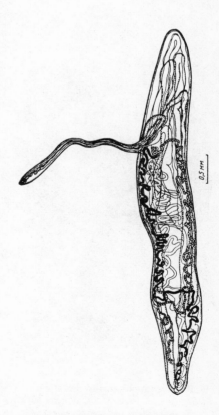

423.   Platocystis alalongae
Yamaguti, 1938 (from Skrjabin,
1955, after Yamaguti, 1938)

424.   Didymocystis thynni
(Taschenberg, 1879) (from Skrjabin,
1955, after Ariola, 1902)

425.   Didymozoon koti Yamaguti,
1938 (from Skrjabin, 1955, after
Yamaguti, 1938)

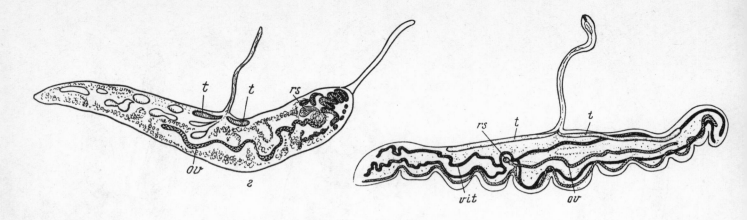

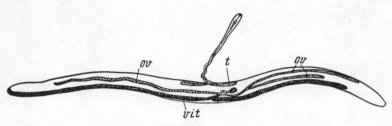

426. **Didymoproblema fusiforme**
Ishii, 1935 (from Skrjabin, 1955,
after Ishii, 1935)

427. **Lobatozoum multisacculatum**
Ishii, 1935 (from Skrjabin, 1955,
after Ishii, 1935)

428. **Didymocylindrus filiformis**
Ishii, 1935 (from Skrjabin, 1955,
after Ishii, 1935)

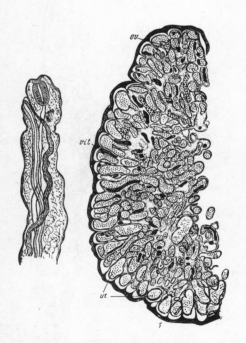

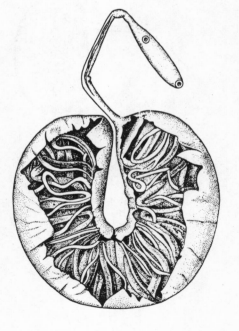

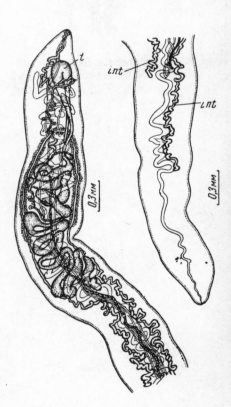

429. **Paragonapodasmius managatuwo**
Yamaguti, 1938 (from Skrjabin, 1955,
after Yamaguti, 1938)

430. **Gonapodasmius haemuli**
(MacCallum and MacCallum, 1916)
(Cepahlic end and cross section
through cyst of adult-from Skrjabin,
1955, after MacCallum and
MacCallum, 1916)

431. **Kollikeria filicollis** (Rudolphi,
1819) (dissection of female-from
Skrjabin, 1955, after van Beneden,
1858)

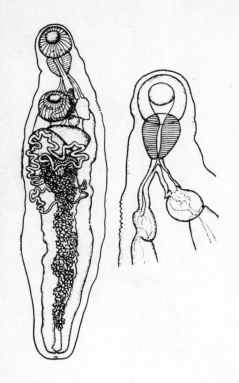

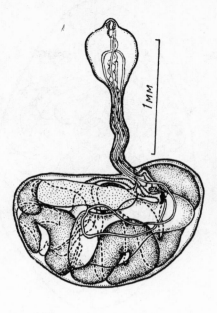

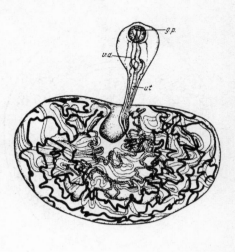

432. Profundiella skrjabini
A. Skriabin, 1958 (from Skrjabin and
Gushanskaya, 1960, after A. Skryabin,
1958)

433. Coeliotrema thynni Yamaguti,
1938 (male-from Skrjabin, 1955,
after Yamaguti, 1938

434. Wedlia bipartita (Wedl, 1855)
(female with male organs-from
Skrjabin, 1955, after Odhner, 1911)

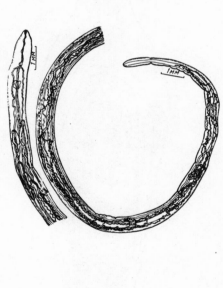

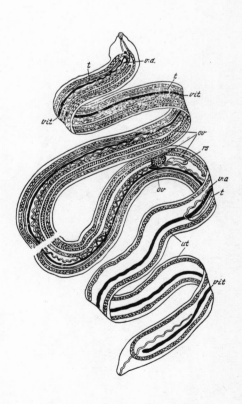

435. Nematobothrium faciale
(Baylis, 1938) (mature hermaphrodite-
from Skrjabin, 1955, after Baylis,
1938)

436. Metanematobothrium guernei
(Moniez, 1819)(from Skrjabin, 1955,
after Yamaguti, 1938)

437. Atalostrophion sardae
MacCallum, 1915 (from Skrjabin,
1955, after MacCallum, 1915)

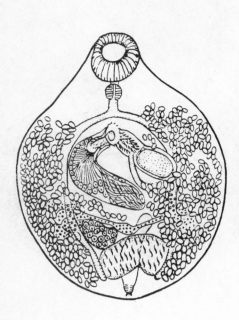

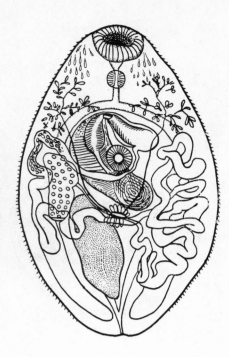

438. <u>Postmonorchis orthopristis</u> Hopkins, 1941 (from Sobolev, 1955, after Hopkins, 1941)

439. <u>Monorchis monorchis</u> (Stossich, 1890) (from Sobolev, 1955, after Looss, 1902)

440. <u>Genolopa ampullacea</u> Linton, 1910 (from Sobolev, 1955, after Hopkins, 1941)

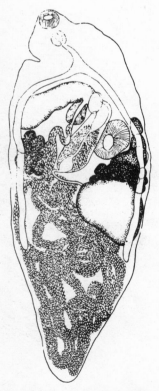

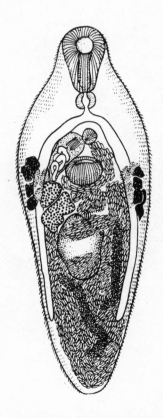

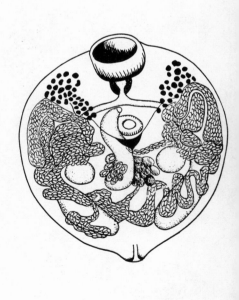

441. <u>Paraproctotrema fusiforme</u> Yamaguti, 1934 (from Sobolev, 1955, after Yamaguti, 1934)

442. <u>Proctotrema bacilliovatum</u> Odhner, 1911 (from Sobolev, 1955, after Odhner, 1911)

443. <u>Achoerus pauli</u> Wlasenko, 1931 (from Sobolev, 1955, after Vlasenko, 1931)

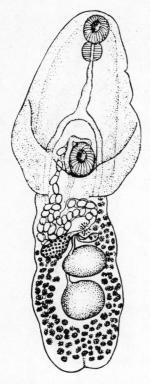

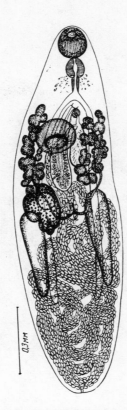

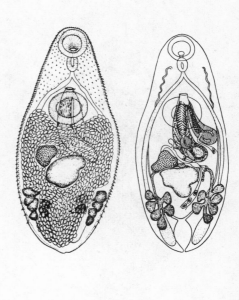

444. Diploproctodaeum haustrum (MacCallum, 1918) (from Skrjabin and Koval, 1960, after MacCallum, 1918)

445. Paramonorcheides awatati Yamaguti, 1938 (from Sobolev, 1955, after Yamaguti, 1938)

446. Telolecithus pugetensis Lloyd and Guberlet, 1932 (from Sobolev, 1955, after Lloyd and Guberlet, 1932)

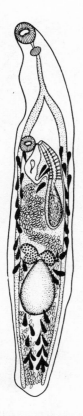

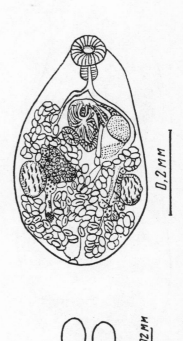

447. Hurleytrema ovocaudatum Srivastava, 1939 (from Sobolev, 1955, after Srivastava, 1939)

448. Monorcheides diplorchis Odhner, 1905 (from Sobolev, 1955, after Odhner, 1905)

449. Diplomonorchis leiostomi Hopkins, 1941 (from Sobolev, 1955, after Hopkins, 1941)

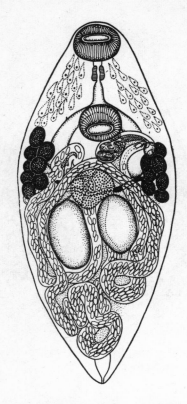

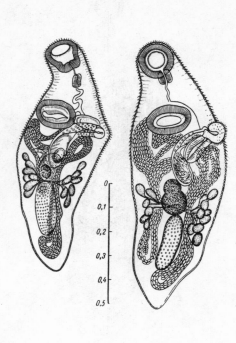

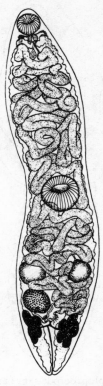

450. **Palaeorchis diplorchis**
(Yamaguti, 1936) (from Sobolev,
1955, after Yamaguti, 1936)

451. **Asymphylodora tincae**
(Modeer, 1790) (from Sobolev,
1955, after Szidat, 1943)

452. **Halipegus ovocaudatus**
(Vulpian, 1859) (from Skrjabin and
Gushanskaya, 1955, after Looss, 1894)

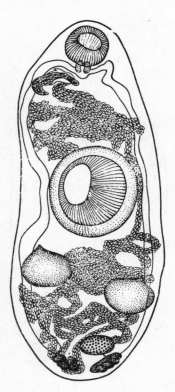

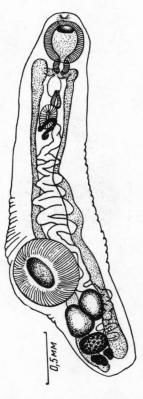

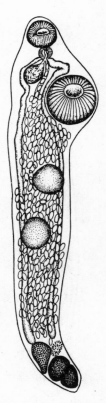

453. **Genarchella genarchella**
Travassos, Artigas and Pereira, 1928
(from Skrjabin and Gushanskaya,
1955, after Travassos, Artigas and
Pereira, 1928)

454. **Gonocercella pacifica**
Manter, 1940 (from Skrjabin and
Gushanskaya, 1955, after Manter,
1940)

455. **Indoderogenes purii**
Srivastava, 1941 (from Skrjabin and
Gushanskaya, 1955, after Srivastava,
1941)

258

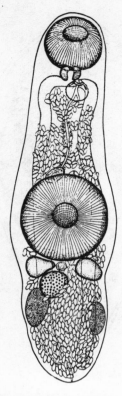

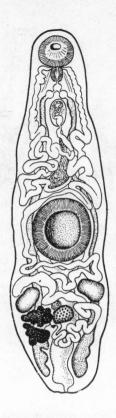

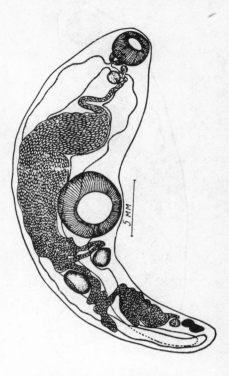

456. Derogenes macrostoma
Yamaguti, 1938 (from Skrjabin and
Gushanskaya, 1955, after Yamaguti,
1938)

457. Leurodera decora Linton, 1910
(from Skrjabin and Gushanskaya,
1955, after Manter, 1947)

458. Vitellotrema fusipora
Guberlet, 1928 (from Skrjabin and
Gushanskaya, 1955, after Guberlet,
1928)

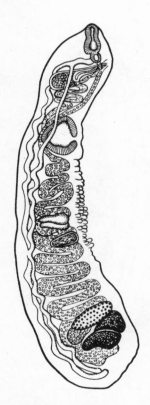

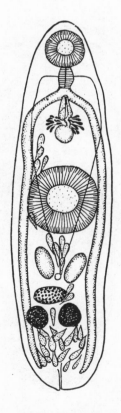

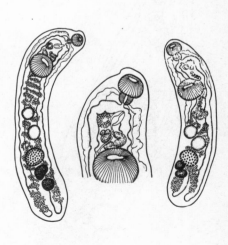

459. Theletrum fustiforme
Linton, 1910 (from Skrjabin and
Gushanskaya, 1955, after Linton, 1910)

460. Derogenoides ovacutus
Nicoll, 1912 (from Skrjabin and
Gushanskaya, 1955, after Nicoll, 1912)

461. Genolinea laticauda
Manter, 1925 (from Skrjabin and
Gushanskaya, 1955, after Manter,
1926)

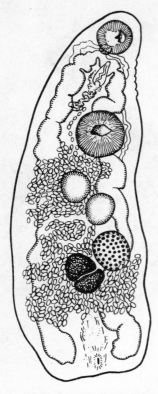

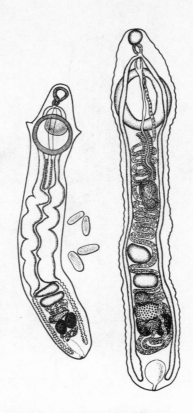

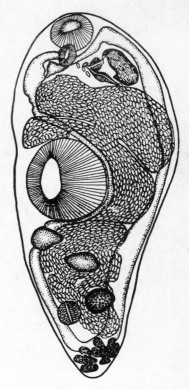

462. Parasterrhurus anurus Manter, 1934 (from Skrjabin and Gushanskaya, 1955, after Manter, 1934)

463. Opisthadena dimidia Linton, 1910 (from Skrjabin and Gushanskaya, 1955, after Linton, 1910)

464. Ophiocorchis lobatum Srivastava, 1933 (from Skrjabin and Gushanskaya, 1955, after Srivastava, 1933)

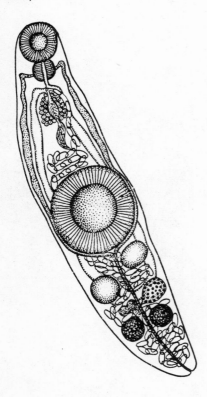

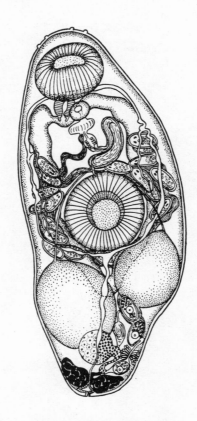

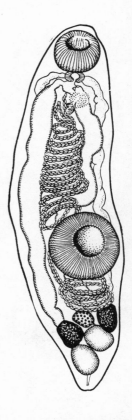

465. Genarches mulleri (Levinsen, 1881) (from Skrjabin and Gushanskaya, 1955, after Odhner, 1905)

466. Tangiopsis chinensis (Tang, 1951) (from Skrjabin and Gushanskaya, 1955, after Tang, 1951)

467. Hemiperina nicolli Manter, 1934 (from Skrjabin and Gushanskaya, 1955, after Manter, 1934)

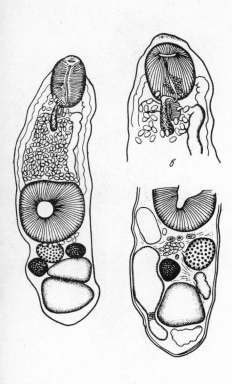

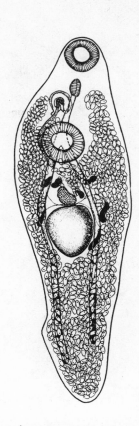

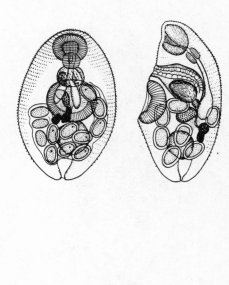

468. Gonocerca physidis
Manter, 1925 (from Skrjabin and
Gushanskaya, 1955, after Manter,
1926)

469. Paralecithobothrys brasiliensis
Freitas, 1948 (from Skrjabin, 1956,
after Freitas, 1948)

470. Dicrogaster perpusillus
Looss, 1902 (from Skrjabin, 1956,
after Looss, 1902)

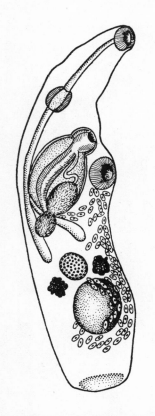

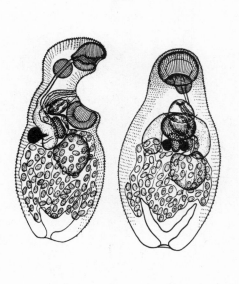

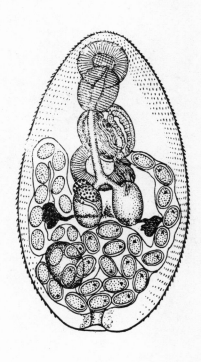

471. Wlassenkotrema longicollum
(Wlassenko, 1931) (from Skrjabin,
1956, after Vlasenko, 1931)

472. Haploporus benedeni (Stossich,
1887) (from Skrjabin, 1956, after
Looss, 1902)

473. Saccocoelium obesum Looss,
1902 (from Skrjabin, 1956, after
Looss, 1902)

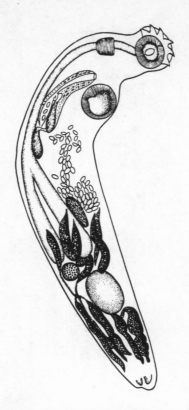

474. <u>Lecithobothrys putrescens</u>
Looss, 1902 (from Skrjabin, 1956,
after Looss, 1902)

475. <u>Waretrema piscicola</u>
Srivastava, 1939 (from Skrjabin,
1956, after Srivastava, 1939)

476. <u>Skrjabinolecithum spasskii</u>
Belouss, 1954 (from Skrjabin, 1956,
after Belous, 1954)

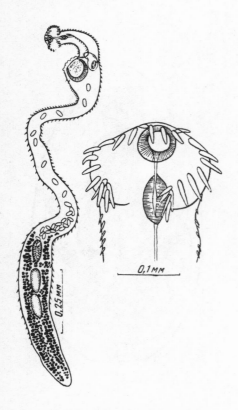

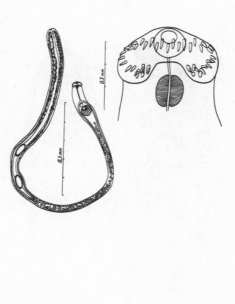

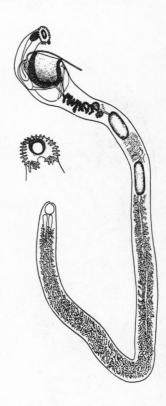

477. <u>Longicollia echinata</u>
Bychowskaja-Pawlowskaja, 1953
(from Skrjabin and Bashkirova, 1956,
after Bykovskaya-Pavlovskaya, 1953)

478. <u>Echinodollfusia stenon</u>
(Dollfus, 1950) (from Skrjabin and
Bashkirova, 1956, after Dollfus, 1950)

479. <u>Baschkirovitrema incrassatum</u>
(Diesing, 1850) (from Skrjabin and
Bashkirova, 1956, after Braun, 1901)

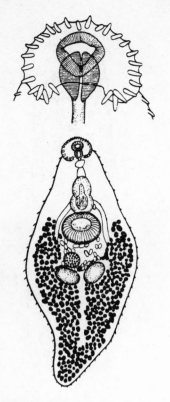

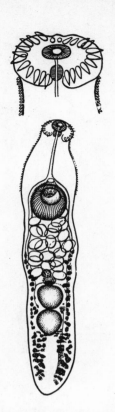

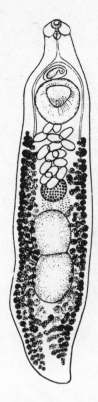

480. Parallelotestis horridus
Belopolskaia, 1954 (from Skrjabin and
Bashkirova, 1956, after Belopolskaya,
1954)

481. Dietziella deparcum (Dietz,
1909) (from Skrjabin and Bashkirova,
1956, after Dietz, 1910)

482. Ignavia inops Freitas, 1948
(from Skrjabin and Bashkirova, 1956,
after Dietz, 1910)

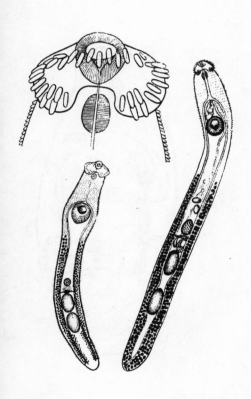

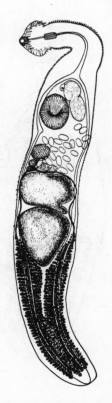

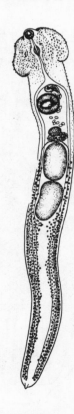

483. Moliniella anceps (Molin, 1859)
(from Skrjabin and Bashkirova, 1956,
after Dietz, 1910 and Hübner, 1939)

484. Stephanoprora ornata
Odhner, 1902 (from Skrjabin and
Bashkirova, 1956, after Dollfus, 1950)

485. Sobolevistoma graciosa
Sudarikov, 1950 (from Skrjabin and
Bashkirova, 1956, after Sudarikov,
1950)

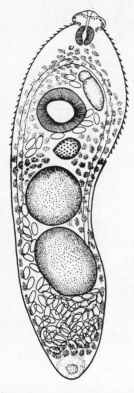

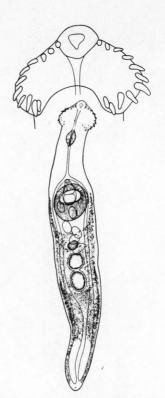

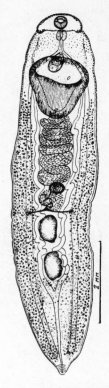

486. Saakotrema metatestis
(Saakova, 1952) (from Skrjabin and
Bashkirova, 1956, after Saakova, 1952)

487. Velamenophorus oligolecithosus
Mendheim, 1940 (from Skrjabin and
Bashkirova, 1956, after Mendheim,
1940)

488. Multispinotrema charadrii
(Tubangui and Masilungan, 1935)
(from Skrjabin and Bashkirova, 1956,
after Skrjabin, 1956)

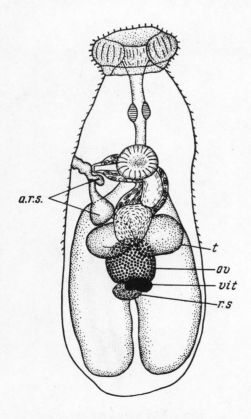

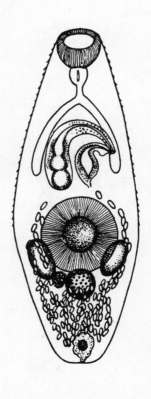

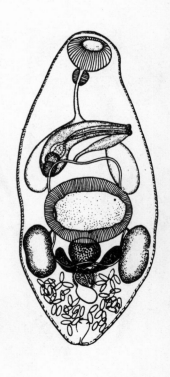

489. Neozoogonus californicus Arai,
1954 (from Skrjabin, 1957, after
Arai, 1954)

490. Zoonogenus vividus Nicoll, 1912
(from Skrjabin, 1957, after Nicoll,
1912)

491. Diphterostomum brusinae
(Stossich, 1889) (from Skrjabin,
1957, after Looss, 1901)

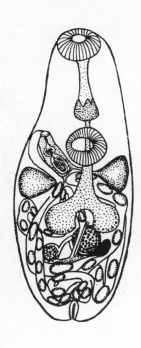

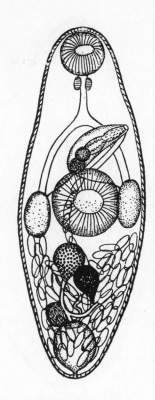

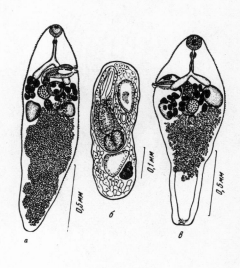

492. Zoogonus rubellus (Olsson, 1868) (from Skrjabin, 1957, after Stunkard, 1938)

493. Zoogonoides viviparus (Olsson, 1868) (from Skrjabin, 1957, after Odhner, 1902)

494. Brachyenteron peristedioni Manter, 1934 (adults and section through genital bursa-from Skrjabin, 1957, after Manter, 1934)

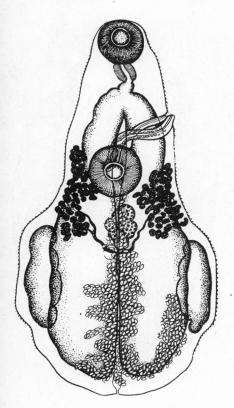

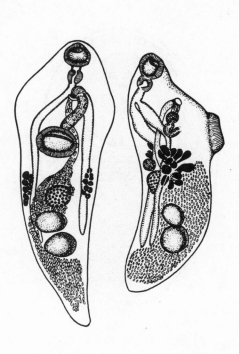

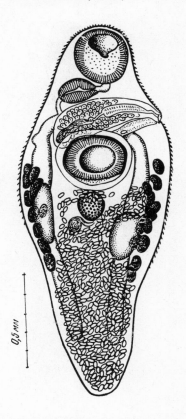

495. Urinatrema hispidum Yamaguti, 1934 (from Skrjabin, 1957, after Yamaguti, 1934)

496. Diplangus paxillus Linton, 1910 (from Skrjabin, 1957, after Linton, 1910)

497. Manteroderma parexocoeti (Manter, 1947) (from Skrjabin, 1957, after Manter, 1947)

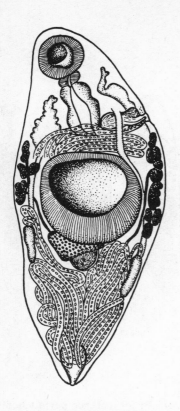

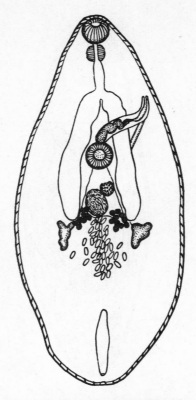

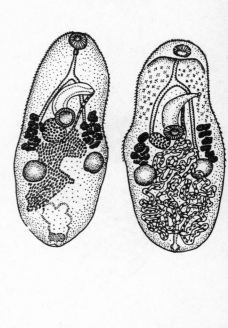

498. Deretrema fusillus Linton, 1910
(from Skrjabin, 1957, after Linton,
1910)

499. Lepidophyllum steenstrupi
Odhner, 1902 (from Skrjabin, 1957,
after Odhner, 1902)

500. Steganoderma formosum
Stafford, 1904 (from Skrjabin, 1957,
after Linton, 1940)

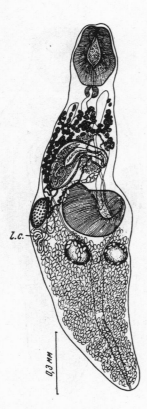

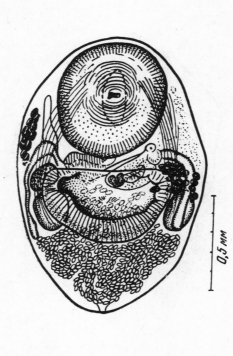

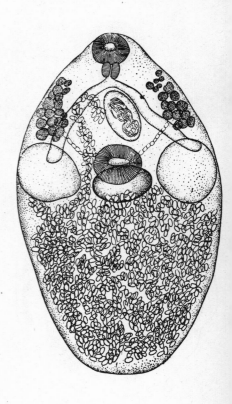

501. Pseudosteringophorus
hoplognathi Yamaguti, 1940 (from
Skrjabin and Koval, 1957, after
Yamaguti, 1940)

502. Megalomyzon robustus
Manter, 1947 (from Skrjabin and
Koval, 1957, after Manter, 1947)

503. Bacciger bacciger (Rudolphi,
1819) (from Skrjabin, 1957)

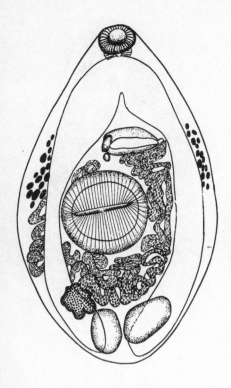

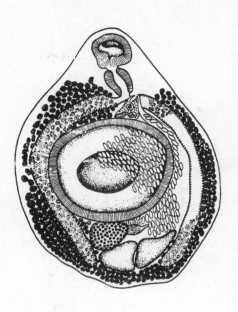

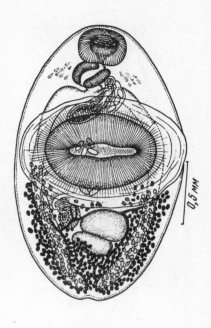

504. **Fellodistomum fellis** (Olsson, 1868) (from Skrjabin and Koval, 1957, after Chubrik, 1952)

505. **Pycnadena lata** (Linton, 1910) (from Skrjabin and Koval, 1957, after Linton, 1910)

506. **Pycnadenoides pagrosomi** Yamaguti, 1938 (from Skrjabin and Koval, 1957, after Yamaguti, 1938)

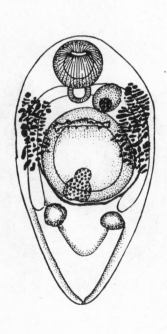

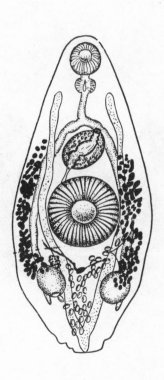

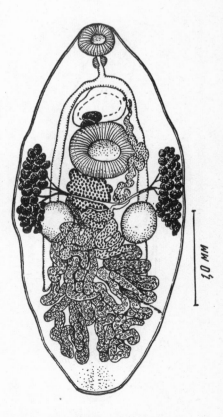

507. **Rhodotrema ovacutum** (Lebour, 1908) (from Skrjabin and Koval, 1957, after Odhner, 1911)

508. **Steringotrema cluthensis** (Nicoll, 1909) (from Skrjabin and Koval, 1957, after Nicoll, 1909)

509. **Steringophorus furciger** (Olsson, 1868) (from Skrjabin and Koval, 1957, after Polyansky, 1955)

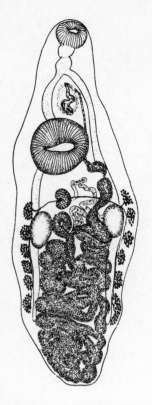

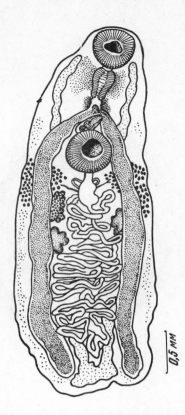

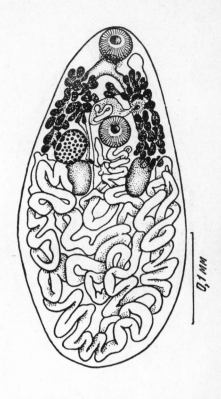

510. Lintonium vibex (Linton, 1900) (from Skrjabin and Koval, 1957, after Stunkard and Nigrelli, 1930)

511. Megenteron crassum Manter, 1934 (from Skrjabin and Koval, 1957, after Manter, 1934)

512. Benthotrema plenum Manter, 1934 (from Skrjabin and Koval, 1957, after Manter, 1934)

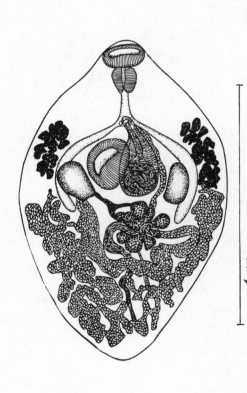

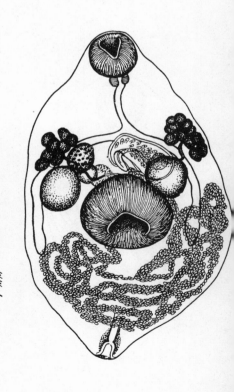

513. Antorchis urna (Linton, 1910) (from Skrjabin and Koval, 1957, after Linton, 1910)

514. Orientophorus brevichrus Srivastava, 1935 (from Skrjabin and Koval, 1957, after Srivastava, 1935)

515. Parantorchis chaetodonis Yamaguti, 1934 (from Skrjabin and Koval, 1957, after Yamaguti, 1934)

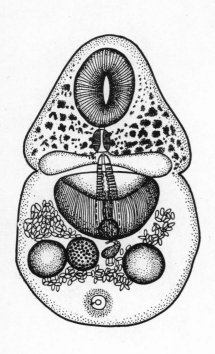

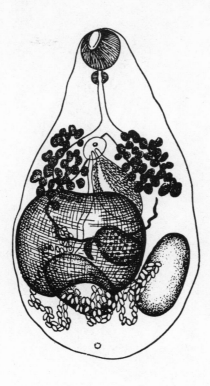

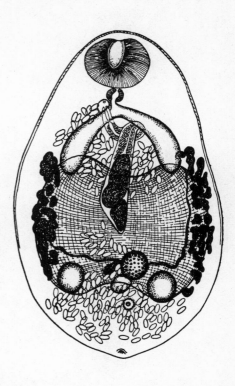

516. **Pseudodiscogasteroides indicum**
(Srivastava, 1939) (from Skrjabin and
Koval, 1957, after Srivastava, 1939)

517. **Paradiscogaster pyriformis**
Yamaguti, 1934 (from Skrjabin and
Koval, 1957, after Yamaguti, 1934)

518. **Discogasteroides ostracionis**
(Yamaguti, 1934) (from Skrjabin and
Koval, 1957, after Yamaguti, 1934)

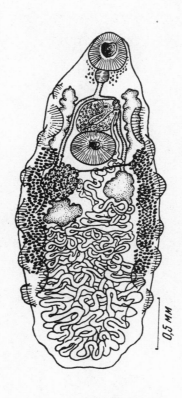

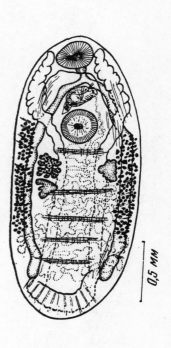

519. **Haplocladus typicus** Odhner,
1911 (from Skrjabin and Koval, 1957,
after Odhner, 1911)

520. **Lomasoma wardi** (Manter, 1934)
(from Skrjabin and Koval, 1957, after
Manter, 1934)

521. **Lissoloma brotulae** Manter,
1934 (from Skrjabin and Koval,
1957, after Manter, 1934)

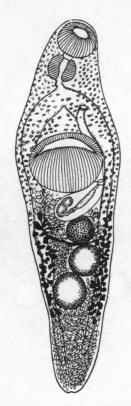

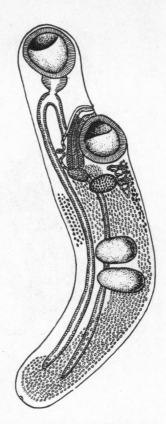

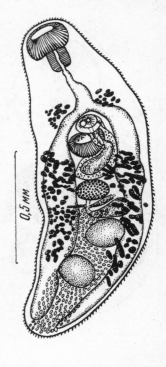

522. Proctoeces maculatus (Looss, 1901) (from Skrjabin and Koval, 1957, after Looss, 1901)

523. Mesolecitha linearis Linton, 1910 (from Skrjabin and Koval, 1957, after Linton, 1910)

524. Gauhatiana batrachii Gupta, 1953 (from Skrjabin and Koval, 1957, after Gupta, 1953)

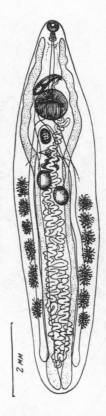

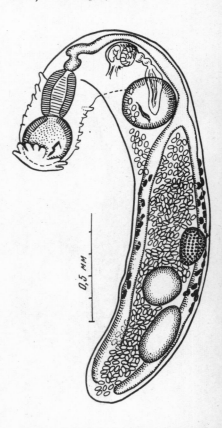

525. Urorchis goro Ozaki, 1927 (from Skrjabin and Koval, 1957, after Ozaki, 1927)

526. Symmetrovesicula chaetodontis Yamaguti, 1938 (from Skrjabin and Koval, 1957, after Yamaguti, 1938)

527. Tergestia laticollis (Rudolphi, 1819) (from Skrjabin and Koval, 1957, after Manter, 1947)

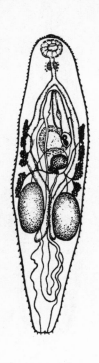

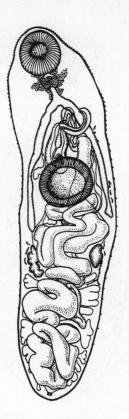

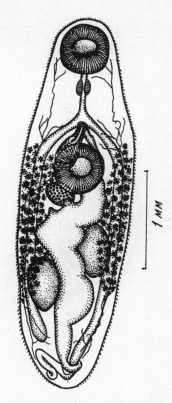

528. Lechriorchis primus Stafford, 1905 (from Skrjabin and Antipin, 1957, after Talbot, 1933)

529. Paralechriorchis syntomentera (Sumwalt, 1926) (from Skrjabin and Antipin, 1957, after Sumwalt, 1926)

530. Dasymetra conferta Nicoll, 1911 (from Skrjabin and Antipin, 1957, after Byrd and Denton, 1938)

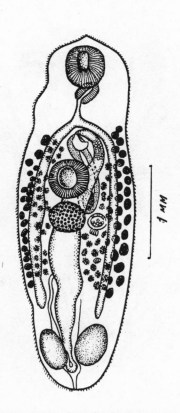

531. Pneumatophilus variabilis (Leidy, 1856) (from Skrjabin and Antipin, 1957, after Pratt, 1903)

532. Zeugorchis aequatus Stafford, 1905 (from Skrjabin and Antipin, 1957, after Byrd and Denton, 1938)

533. Natriodera verlatum (Talbot, 1934) (from Skrjabin and Antipin, 1957, after Byrd and Denton, 1938)

271

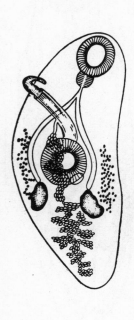

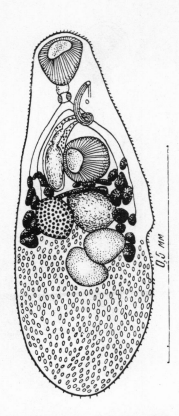

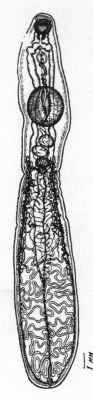

534. Ochetosoma monstruosum Braun, 1901 (from Skrjabin and Antipin, 1957, after Braun, 1902)

535. Oudhia horai Gupta, 1953 (from Skrjabin and Antipin, 1957, after Gupta, 1953)

536. Uroproctinella spinulosa (Yamaguti, 1938) (from Skrjabin and Gushanskaya, 1957, after Yamaguti, 1938)

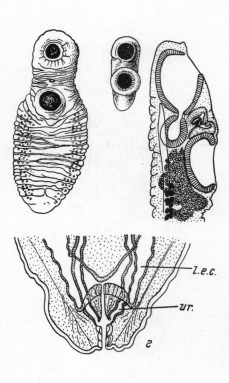

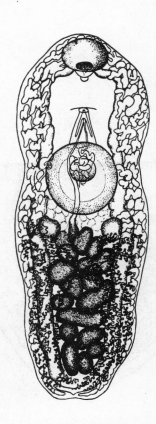

537. Hirudinella clavata (Menzies, 1791) (from Skrjabin and Gushanskaya, 1957, after Darr, 1902)

538. Ptychogonimus megastomus (Rudolphi, 1819) (from Skrjabin and Gushanskaya, 1957, after Dollfus, 1936)

539. Sclerodistomum italicum (Stossich, 1893) (from Skrjabin and Gushanskaya, 1957, after Looss, 1912)

272

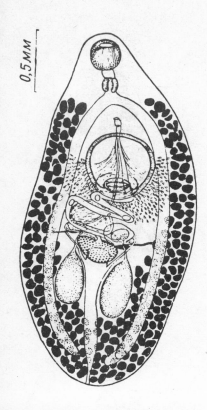

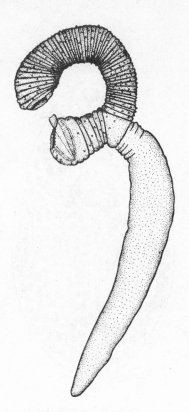

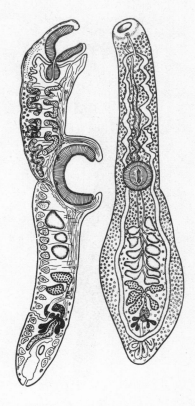

540. Marsupioacetabulum marinum Yamaguti, 1952 (from Skrjabin and Koval, 1960, after Yamaguti, 1952)

541. Capiatestes thyrsitae Crowcroft, 1948 (from Skrjabin and Gushanskaya, 1957, after Crowcroft, 1948)

542. Syncoelium ragazzii (Setti, 1897) (from Skrjabin and Gushanskaya, 1957, after Looss, 1899)

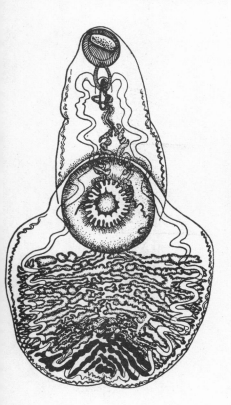

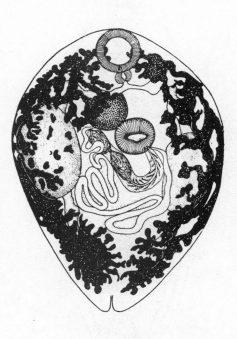

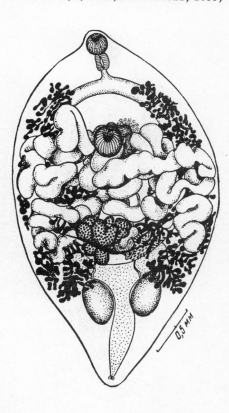

543. Paronatrema vaginicola Dollfus, 1937 (from Skrjabin and Gushanskaya, 1957, after Dollfus, 1937)

544. Troglotrema acutum (Leuckart, 1842) (from Skrjabin, 1958, after Baer, 1931)

545. Pholeter gastrophilus (Kossack, 1911) (from Skrjabin, after Delyamure, 1955)

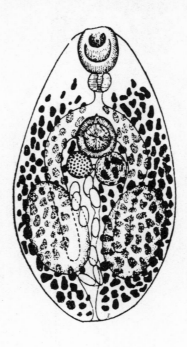

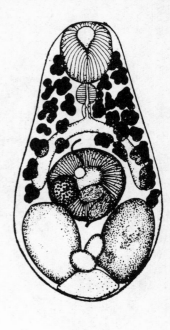

546. Allolepidapedon fistulariae Yamaguti, 1940 (from Skrjabin and Koval, 1960, after Yamaguti, 1940)

547. Nanophyetus salmincola (Chapin, 1926) (from Skrjabin, 1958, after Witenberg, 1932)

548. Sellacotyle mustelae (Wallace, 1932) (from Skrjabin, 1958, after Wallace, 1935)

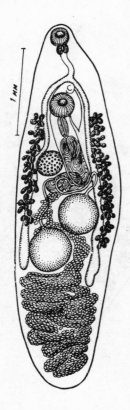

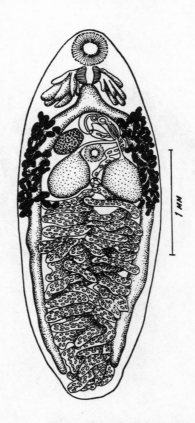

549. Astiotrema amydae Ogata, 1938 (from Skrjabin and Antipin, 1958, after Belous, 1958)

550. Glypthelmins quieta (Stafford, 1900) (from Skrjabin and Antipin, 1958, after Miller, 1930)

551. Haplometrana intestinalis Lucker, 1931 (from Skrjabin and Antipin, 1958, after Lucker, 1931)

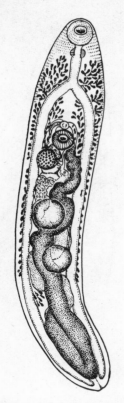

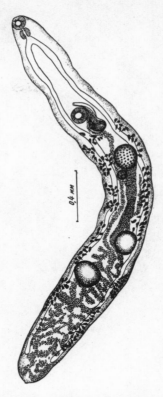

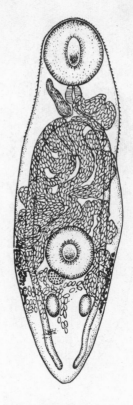

552. Haplometra cylindricea
(Zeder, 1800) (from Skrjabin and
Antipin, 1958, after Looss, 1894)

553. Microderma elinguis Mehra,
1931 (from Skrjabin and Antipin,
1958, after Mehra, 1931)

554. Dolichopera parvula Nicoll,
1914 (from Skrjabin and Antipin,
1958, after Nicoll, 1914)

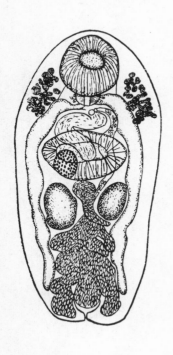

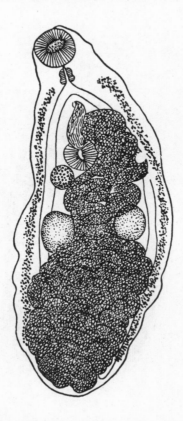

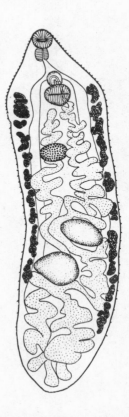

555. Stomatrema pusilla Guberlet,
1928 (from Skrjabin and Antipin,
1958, after Guberlet, 1928)

556. Bilorchis indicum Mehra, 1937
(from Skrjabin and Antipin, 1958, after
Mehra, 1937)

557. Ptyasiorchis mehrai (Gogate,
1935) (from Skrjabin and Antipin,
1958, after Gogate, 1935)

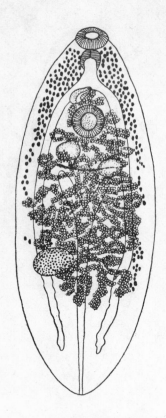

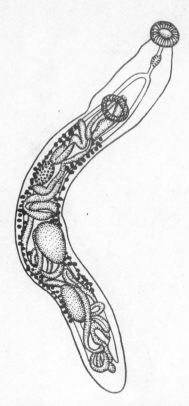

558. Xenopharynx solus Nicoll, 1912
(from Skrjabin and Antipin, 1958, after
Nicoll, 1912)

559. Macroderoides spiniferus
Pearse, 1924 (from Skrjabin and
Antipin, 1958, after Pearse, 1924)

560. Tremiorchis ranarum Mehra
and Negi, 1925 (from Skrjabin and
Antipin, 1958, after Bhalerao, 1926)

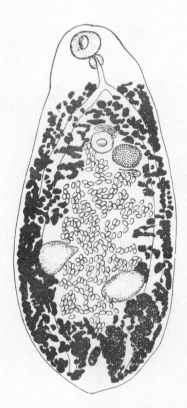

561. Haplometroides buccicola
Odhner, 1911 (from Skrjabin and
Antipin, 1958, after Odhner, 1911)

562. Rudolphitrema rudolphi
(Travassos, 1924) (from Skrjabin
and Antipin, 1958, after Travassos,
1924)

563. Plagiorchoides noblei (Park,
1936) (from Skrjabin and Antipin,
1958, after Park, 1936)

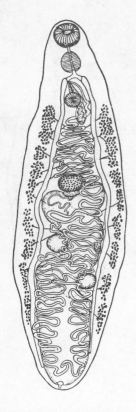

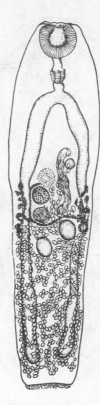

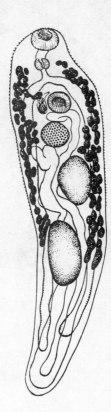

564. Megacutis multispinosus
Bennet, 1935 (from Skrjabin and
Antipin, 1958, after Bennet, 1935)

565. Eustomos chelydrae
MacCallum, 1921 (from Skrjabin
and Antipin, 1958, after MacCallum,
1921)

566. Alloglossidium corti (Lamont,
1921) (from Skrjabin and Antipin,
1958, after Mueller, 1930)

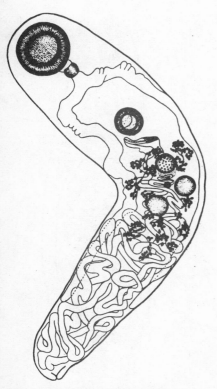

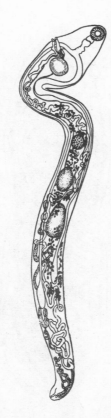

567. Liophistrema pulmonalis
Artigas, Ruiz and Leão, 1942 (from
Skrjabin and Antipin, 1958, after
Artigas, Ruiz and Leão, 1942)

568. Bieria artigasi Leão, 1946
(from Skrjabin and Antipin, 1958,
after Leão, 1946)

569. Otodistomum veliporum
(Creplin, 1837) (from Skrjabin and
Gushanskaya, 1958, after Manter,
1926)

277

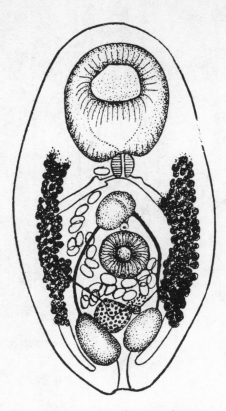

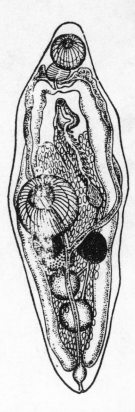

570. Azygia lucii (Müller, 1776)
(from Skrjabin and Gushanskaya,
1958, after Looss, 1894)

571. Proterometra macrostoma
(Faust, 1918) (from Skrjabin and
Gushanskaya, 1958, after Yamaguti,
1953)

572. Liocerca bonnieri (Monticelli,
1893) (from Skrjabin and Gushanskaya,
1958, after Monticelli, 1893)

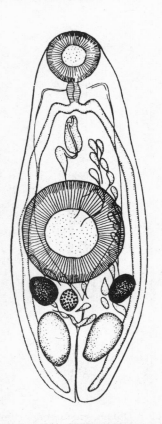

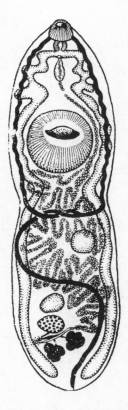

573. Hemipera ovocaudata Nicoll,
1912 (from Skrjabin and Gushanskaya,
1958, after Nicoll, 1912)

574. Arnola microcirrus (Vlassenko,
1931) (from Skrjabin and Gushanskaya,
1958, after Vlasenko, 1931)

575. Styphlodora serrata Looss, 1899
(from Skrjabin and Antipin, 1961, after
Looss, 1899)

 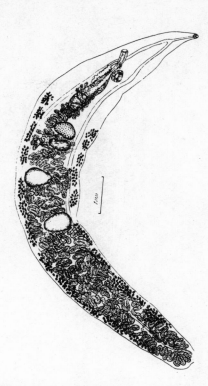 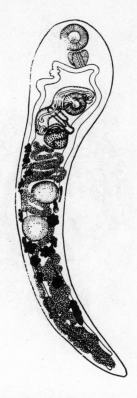

576. <u>Glossimetra orientalis</u> Mehra, 1937 (from Skrjabin and Antipin, 1961, after Mehra, 1937)

577. <u>Spinometra kachugae</u> Mehra, 1931 (from Skrjabin and Antipin, 1961, after Mehra, 1931)

578. <u>Glossidiella ornata</u> Travassos, 1927 (from Skrjabin and Antipin, 1961, after Travassos, 1927)

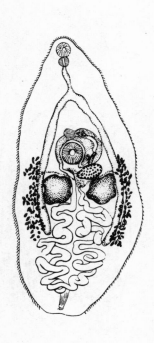 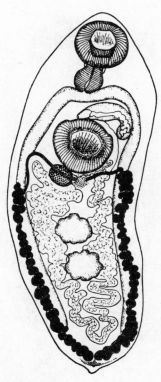 

579. <u>Styphlotrema solitaria</u> (Looss, 1899) (from Skrjabin and Antipin, 1961, after Looss, 1899)

580. <u>Encyclometra colubrimurorum</u> (Rudolphi, 1819) (from Skrjabin and Antipin, 1960, after Baylis and Cannon, 1924)

581. <u>Enodiotrema megachondrum</u> (Looss, 1899) (from Skrjabin and Antipin, 1960, after Looss, 1899)

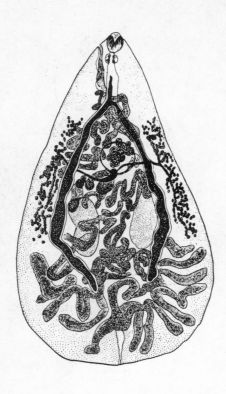

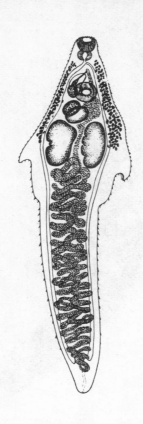

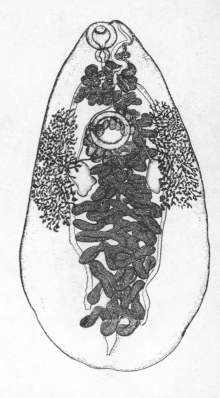

582. **Prosthogonimus ovatus** (Rudolphi, 1803) (from Skrjabin, 1961, after Braun, 1902)

583. **Oistosomum caduceus** Odhner, 1902 (from Skrjabin and Antipin, 1961, after Odhner, 1911)

584. **Schistogonimus rarus** (Braun, 1901) (from Skrjabin and Antipin, 1961, after Skrjabin, 1961)

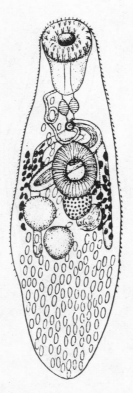

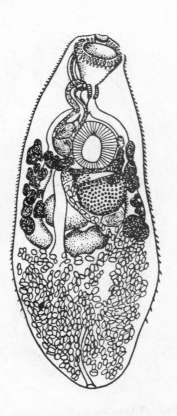

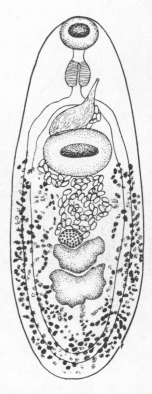

585. **Masenia collata** Chatterji, 1933 (from Skrjabin, 1958, after Chatterji, 1933)

586. **Eumasenia moradabadensis** Srivastava, 1951 (from Skrjabin, 1958, after Srivastava, 1951)

587. **Coitocaecum gymnophallum** Nicoll, 1915 (from Skrjabin and Petrov, 1958, after Nicoll, 1915)

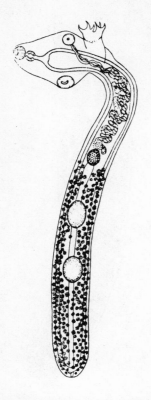

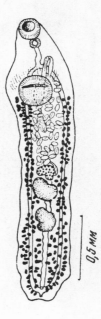

588. Anisoporus cobraeformis
Ozaki, 1928 (from Skrjabin and
Petrov, 1958, after Ozaki, 1928)

589. Opegaster ovatus Ozaki, 1928
(from Skrjabin and Petrov, 1958,
after Ozaki, 1928)

590. Opecoelina scorpanae Manter,
1934 (from Skrjabin and Petrov, 1958,
after Manter, 1934)

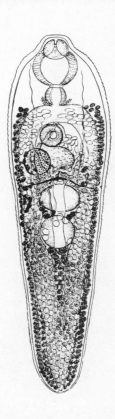

591. Opecoelus sphaericus Ozaki,
1925 (from Skrjabin and Petrov, 1958,
after Ozaki, 1928)

592. Dideutosaccus radifistuli
Acena, 1941 (from Skrjabin and
Petrov, 1958, after Acena, 1941)

593. Sphincterostoma branchiostegi
Yamaguti, 1937 (from Skrjabin and
Petrov, 1958, after Yamaguti, 1937)

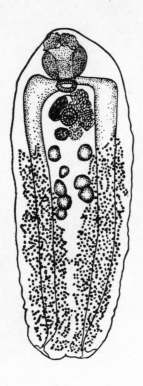

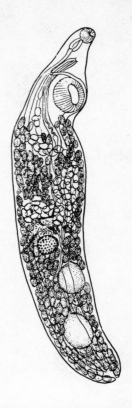

594. Megacreadium tetrodontis
Nagaty, 1956 (from Skrjabin and
Petrov, 1958, after Nagaty, 1956)

595. Lucknoides cavasiusi Gupta,
1953 (from Skrjabin and Petrov, 1958,
after Gupta, 1953)

596. Pseudopecoelina dampieriae
Yamaguti, 1942 (from Skrjabin and
Petrov, 1958, after Yamaguti, 1942)

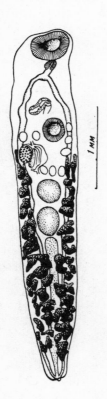

597. Neopecoelina saharanpurensis
Gupta, 1953 (from Skrjabin and
Petrov, 1958, after Gupta, 1953)

598. Pseudopecoeloides tenuis
Yamaguti, 1940 (from Skrjabin and
Petrov, 1958, after Yamaguti, 1940)

599. Opecoeloides furcatus
(Bremser, 1819) (from Skrjabin and
Petrov, 1958, after Janiszewska, 1953)

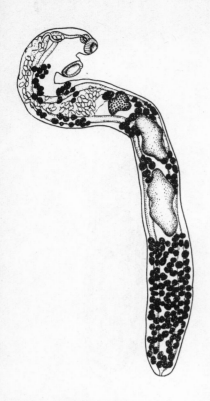

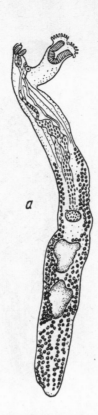

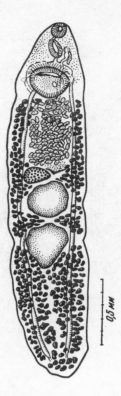

600. Anomalotrema putjatini
Zhukov, 1953 (from Skrjabin and
Petrov, 1958, after Zhukov, 1953)

601. **Fimbriatus fimbriatus**
(Linton, 1901) (from Skrjabin and
Petrov, 1958, after Linton, 1940)

602. Neopecoelus scorpaenae
Manter, 1947 (from Skrjabin and
Petrov, 1958, after Manter, 1947)

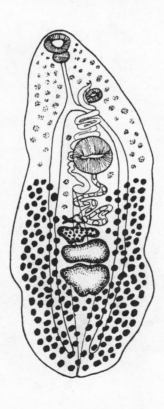

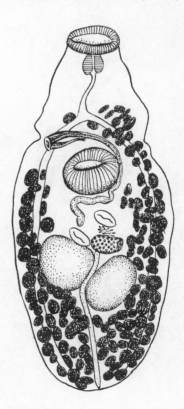

603. Pellamyzon sebastodis
Montgomery, 1957 (from Skrjabin and
Petrov, 1958, after Montgomery, 1957)

604. Genitocotyle acirrus Park, 1937
(from Skrjabin and Petrov, 1958, after
Park, 1937)

605. Horatrema pristipomatis
Srivastava, 1942 (from Skrjabin and
Petrov, 1958, after Srivastava, 1942)

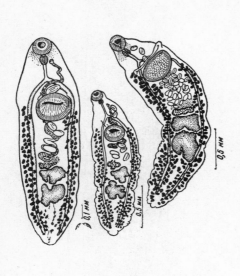

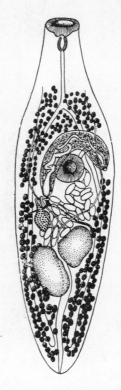

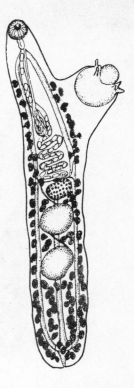

606. __Pseudopecoelus vulgaris__
(Manter, 1934) (from Skrjabin and
Petrov, 1958, after Manter, 1934)

607. __Neonotoporus trachuri__
(Yamaguti, 1938) (from Skrjabin and
Petrov, 1958, after Yamaguti, 1938)

608. __Dactylostomum gracile__
Woolcock, 1935 (from Skrjabin and
Koval, 1958, after Woolcock, 1935)

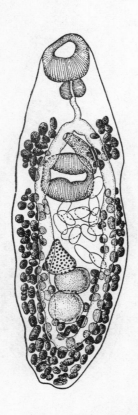

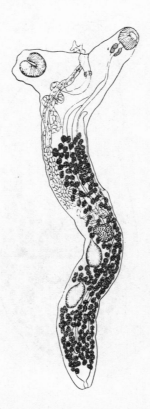

609. __Crowcrocaecum skrjabini__
(Iwanitzky, 1928) (from Skrjabin and
Koval, 1958, after Ivanitsky, 1927)

610. __Podocotyloides petalophallus__
Yamaguti, 1934 (from Skrjabin and
Koval, 1958, after Yamaguti, 1934)

611. __Pedunculacetabulum__
__opisthorchis__ Yamaguti, 1934 (from
Skrjabin and Koval, 1958, after
Yamaguti, 1934)

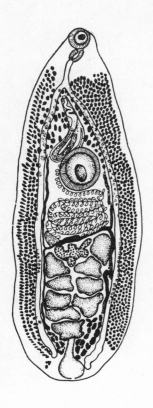

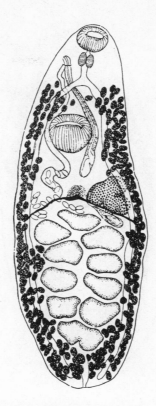

612. Helicometrina nimia Linton,
1910 (from Skrjabin and Koval, 1958,
after Linton, 1910)

613. Decemtestis sillagonis
Yamaguti, 1934 (from Skrjabin and
Koval, 1958, after Yamaguti, 1934)

614. Hysterogonia balistis Hanson,
1955 (from Skrjabin and Koval, 1958,
after Hanson, 1955)

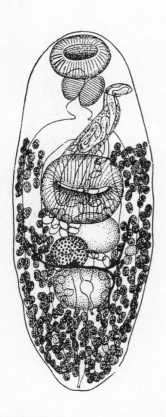

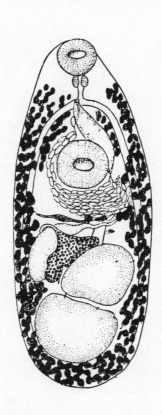

615. Pseudoplagioporus lethrini
Yamaguti, 1938 (from Skrjabin and
Koval, 1958, after Yamaguti, 1938)

616. Helicometra pulchella
(Rudolphi, 1819) (from Skrjabin and
Koval, 1958, after Odhner, 1902)

617. Stenopera equilata Manter, 1933
(from Skrjabin and Koval, 1958, after
Manter, 1933)

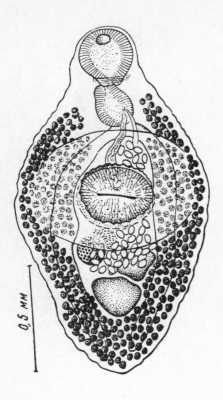

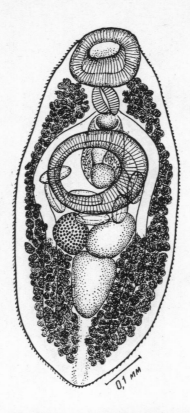

618. Pachycreadium gastrocotylum
(Manter, 1940) (from Skrjabin and
Koval, 1958, after Manter, 1940)

619. Spinoplagioporus minutus
(Poljansky, 1952) (from Skrjabin and
Koval, 1958, after Polyansky, 1952)

620. Eucreadium eucreadium Dayal,
1950 (from Skrjabin and Koval, 1958,
after Dayal, 1950)

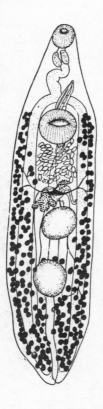

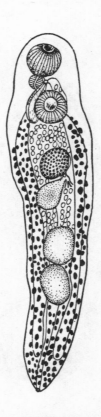

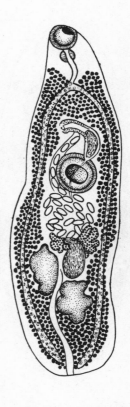

621. Podocotyle atomon (Rudolphi,
1802) (from Skrjabin and Koval,
1958, after Odhner, 1905)

622. Neopodocotyle indica Dayal,
1950 (from Skrjabin and Koval,
1958, after Dayal, 1950)

623. Hamacreadium mutabile
Linton, 1910 (from Skrjabin and
Koval, 1958, after Linton, 1910)

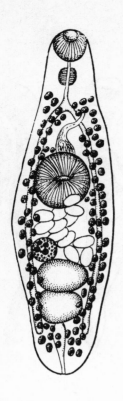

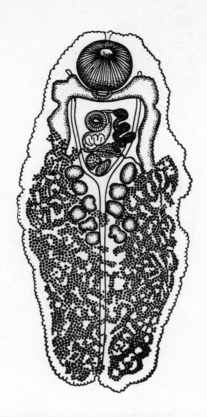

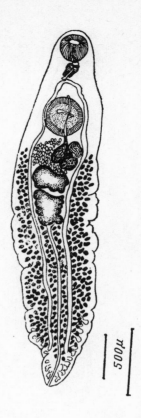

624. **Plagioporus serotinus**
Stafford, 1904 (from Skrjabin and
Koval, 1958, after Miller, 1940)

625. **Schistorchis carneus** Lühe, 1906
(from Skrjabin, 1959, after Lühe,
1906)

626. **Apocreadium mexicanum**
Manter, 1937 (from Skrjabin, 1959,
after Manter, 1937)

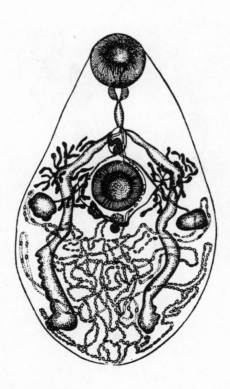

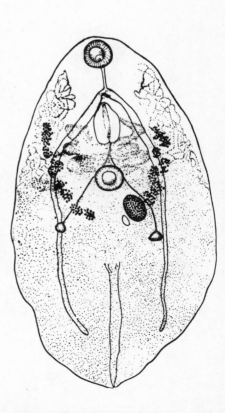

627. **Braunotrema pulvinata**
(Braun, 1899) (from Skrjabin,
1959, after Braun, 1899)

628. **Callodistomum diaphanum**
Odhner, 1902 (from Skrjabin, 1959,
after Odhner, 1911)

629. **Prosthenhystera obesa**
(Diesing, 1850) (from Skrjabin,
1959, after Travassos, 1922)

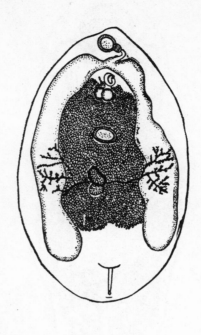

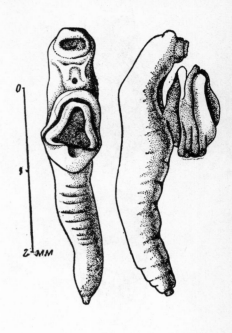

630. Cholepotes ovofarctus
(Odhner, 1902) (from Skrjabin,
1959, after Odhner, 1911)

631. Teratotrema dubia Travassos,
Artigas, and Pereira, 1928 (from
Skrjabin, 1959, after Travassos,
Artigas and Pereira, 1928)

632. Accacladocoelium petasiporum
Odhner, 1928 (from Skrjabin and
Gushanskaya, 1959, after Dollfus,
1935)

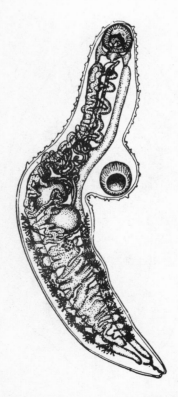

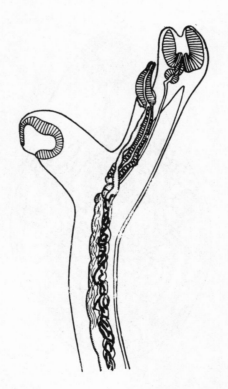

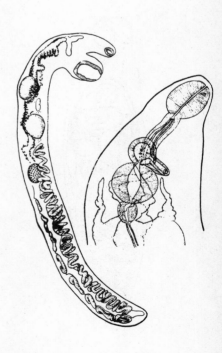

633. Accacoelium contortum
(Rudolphi, 1819) (from Skrjabin and
Gushanskaya, 1959, after Monticelli,
1893)

634. Accacladium serpentulum
Odhner, 1928 (from Skrjabin and
Gushanskaya, 1959, after Odhner,
1928)

635. Ryhnchopharynx paradoxa
Odhner, 1928 (from Skrjabin and
Gushanskaya, 1959, after Odhner,
1928)

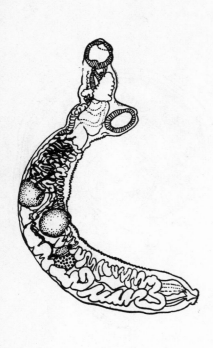

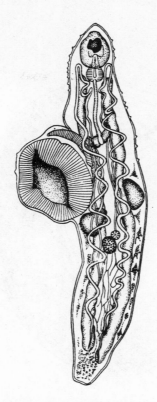

636. Paratetrochetus aluterae
Hanson, 1955 (from Skrjabin and
Gushanskaya, 1959, after Hanson,
1955)

637. Mneiodhneria calyptrocotyle
(Monticelli, 1893) (from Skrjabin and
Gushanskaya, 1959, after Monticelli,
1893)

638. Caballeriana lagodovsky
Skrjabin and Gushanskaya, 1959
(from Skrjabin and Gushanskaya,
1959, after Lloyd, 1938)

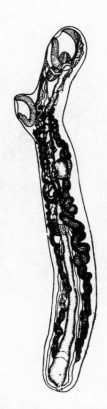

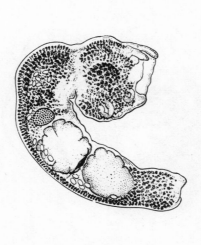

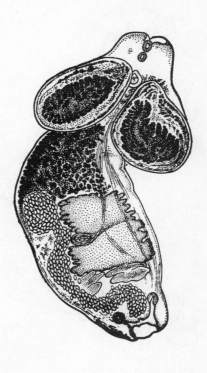

639. Tetrochetus raynerius
(Nardo, 1827) (from Skrjabin and
Gushanskaya, 1959, after Looss, 1912)

640. Apharyngostrigea cornu (Zeder,
1800) (from Sudarikov, 1959, after
Dubois, 1938)

641. Parastrigea cincta (Brandes,
1888) (from Sudarikov, 1959, after
Szidat, 1929)

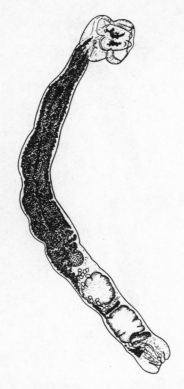

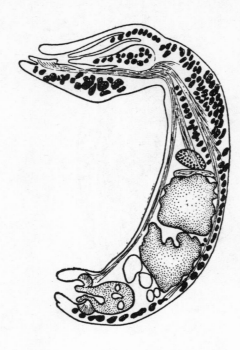

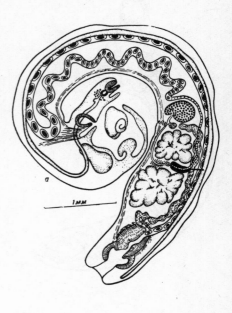

642. Ophiosoma patagiatum
(Creplin, 1846) (from Sudarikov,
1959, after Szidat, 1929)

643. Strigea strigis (Shrank, 1788)
(from Sudarikov, 1959, after Szidat,
1929)

644. Chaubaustrigea geoduboisi
(Chaubaud, Golvan and Rousselot,
1956) (from Sudarikov, 1959, after
Chaubaud, Golvan and Rousselot, 1956)

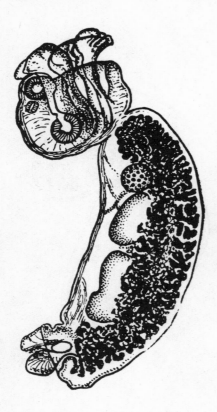

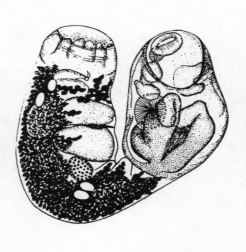

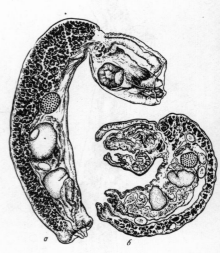

645. Cotylurus cornutus (Rudolphi,
1808) (from Sudarikov, 1959, after
Dubois, 1938)

646. Swartzitrema seamsteri
Chandler, 1951 (from Sudarikov,
1959, after Chandler, 1951)

647. Apatemon gracilis (Rudolphi,
1819) (from Sudarikov, 1959, after
Dubois, 1938)

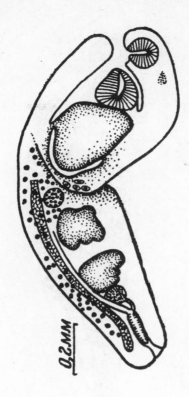

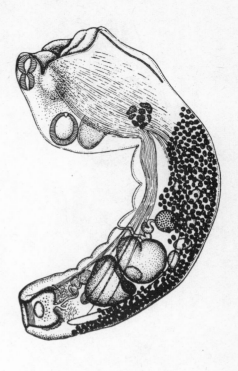

648.   Cardiocephalus longicollus
(Rudolphi, 1819) (from Sudarikov,
1959, after Szidat, 1929)

649.   Australapatemon intermedius
(Johnston, 1904) (from Sudarikov,
1959, after Johnston, 1904)

650.   Pseudostrigea buteonis
Yamaguti, 1933 (from Sudarikov,
1959, after Yamaguti, 1933)

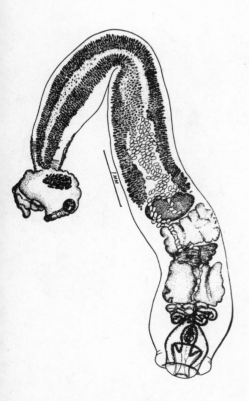

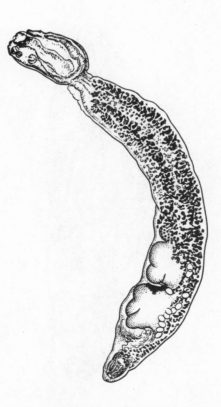

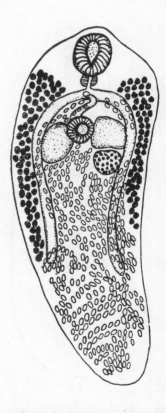

651.   Nematostrigea serpens
(Nitzch, 1819) (from Sudarikov, 1959)

652.   Cardiocephaloides brandesi
(Szidat, 1928) (from Sudarikov, 1959,
after Dubois, 1938)

653.   Mesocoelium sociale (Lühe,
1901) (from Sudarikov, 1959, after
Lühe, 1901)

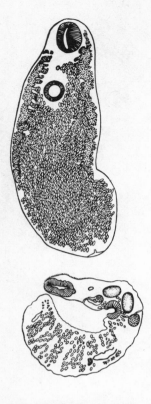

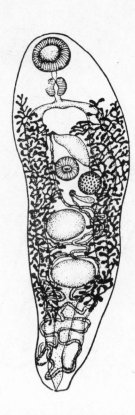

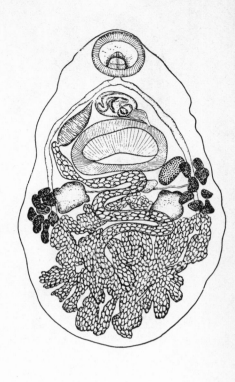

654. __Pintneria mesocoelium__
(Cohn, 1903) (from Sudarikov,
1959, after Cohn, 1903)

655. __Encyclobrephus robustus__
Sinha, 1949 (from Skrjabin and
Antipin, 1960, after Sinha, 1949)

656. __Travtrema stenocotyle__ (Cohn,
1902) (from Skrjabin and Antipin,
1960, after Pereira, 1929)

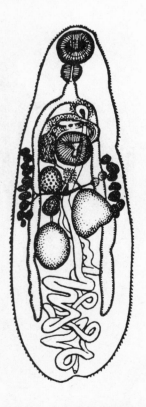

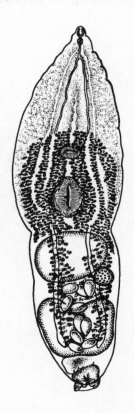

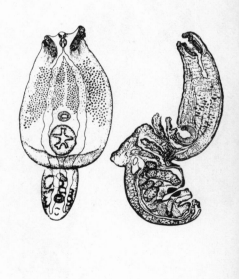

657. __Paurophyllum simplexus__ Byrd,
Parker and Reiber, 1940 (from
Skrjabin and Antipin, 1960, after Byrd,
Parker and Reiber, 1940)

658. __Mesoophorodiplostomum pricei__
(Krull, 1934) (from Sudarikov, 1960,
after Dubois, 1938)

659. __Sphincterodiplostomum
musculosum__ Dubois, 1936 (from
Sudarikov, 1960, after Dubois, 1936)

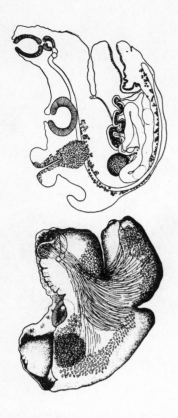

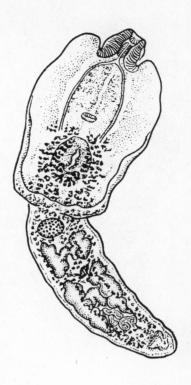

660. Harvardia sandgroundi Baer, 1932 (from Sudarikov, 1960, after Baer, 1932)

661. Adenodiplostomum triangulare (Johnston, 1904) (from Sudarikov, 1960, after Johnston, 1904)

662. Bolbophorus confusus (Krause, 1914) (from Sudarikov, 1960, after Dubois, 1938)

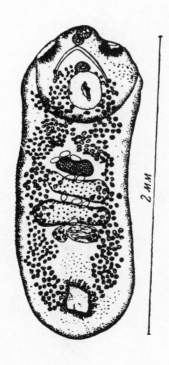

663. Diplostomum spathaceum (Rudolphi, 1819) (from Sudarikov, 1960, after Dubois, 1938)

664. Glossodiplostomoides hieraetii (Vidyarthi, 1938) (from Sudarikov, 1960, after Vidyarthi, 1938)

665. Tylodelphys clavata (Nordmann, 1832) (from Sudarikov, 1960, after Ciurea, 1928)

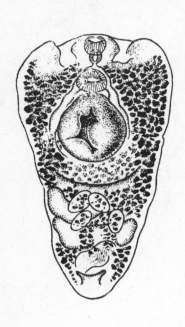

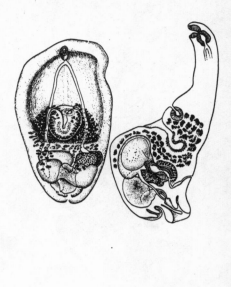

666. **Hysteromorpha triloba**
(Rudolphi, 1819) (from Sudarikov,
1960, after Dubois, 1938)

667. **Cylindorchis tenuicutis**
Southwell, 1913 (from Skrjabin,
1960, after Southwell, 1913)

668. **Ornithodiplostomum**
ptychocheilus (Faust, 1917) (from
Sudarikov, 1960, after Haitsma,
1930)

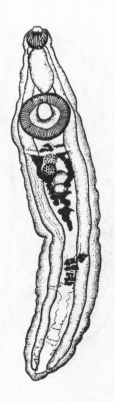

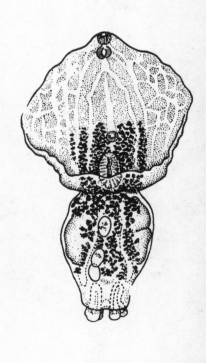

669. **Lophosicyadiplostomum**
saturnium Dubois, 1936 (from
Sudarikov, 1960, after Dubois, 1936)

670. **Aphanhystera monacensis**
Guiart, 1938 (from Skrjabin, 1960,
after Guiart, 1938)

671. **Posthodiplostomum cuticola**
(Nordmann, 1832) (from Sudarikov,
1960, after Ciurea, 1930)

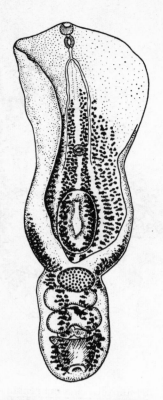

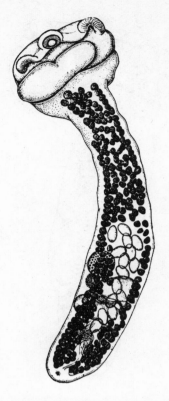

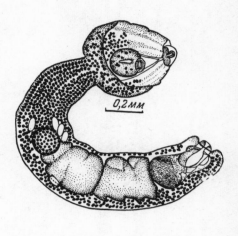

672. **Neodiplostomum spathoides**
Dubois, 1937 (from Sudarikov, 1960,
after Dubois, 1938)

673. **Pulvinifer singularis** Yamaguti,
1933 (from Sudarikov, 1960, after
Yamaguti, 1933)

674. **Subuvulifer halcyonae** (Gogate,
1940) (from Sudarikov, 1960, after
Gogate, 1940)

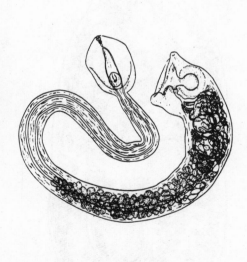

675. **Crassiphiala bulboglossa**
Haitsma, 1925 (from Sudarikov,
1960, after Haitsma, 1925)

676. **Cercotyla cerylis** Yamaguti,
1939 (from Sudarikov, 1960, after
Yamaguti, 1939)

677. **Uvulifer gracilis** Yamaguti,
1934 (from Sudarikov, 1960, after
Yamaguti, 1934)

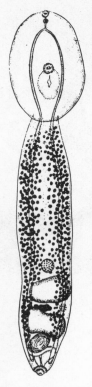

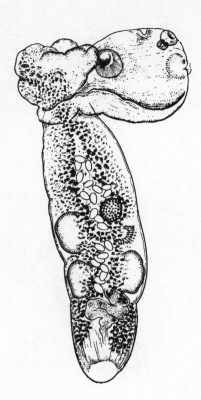

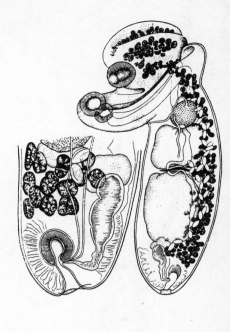

678. Pseudodiplostomum cochleariforme Yamaguti, 1934 (from Sudarikov, 1960, after Yamaguti, 1934)

679. Allodiplostomum scolopacis Yamaguti, 1935 (from Sudarikov, 1960, after Yamaguti, 1935)

680. Scolopacitrema cubrensis Sudarikov and Rykovsky, 1958 (from Sudarikov, 1960, after Sudarikov and Rykovsky, 1958)

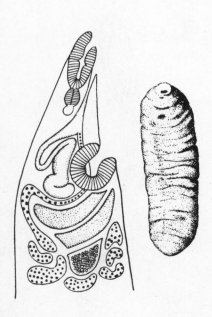

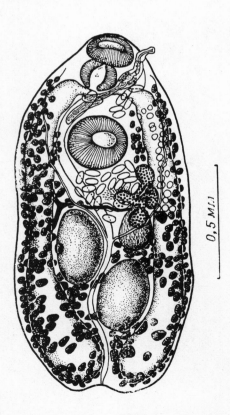

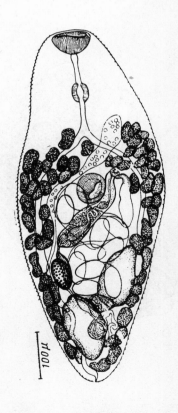

681. Botulus alepidosauri Guiart, 1938 (from Skrjabin, 1960, after Guiart, 1938)

682. Lepocreadioides zebrini Yamaguti, 1936 (from Skrjabin and Koval, 1960, after Yamaguti, 1936)

683. Opechonoides gure Yamaguti, 1940 (from Skrjabin and Koval, 1960, after Yamaguti, 1940)

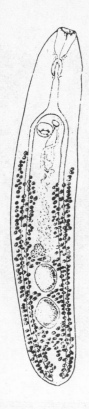

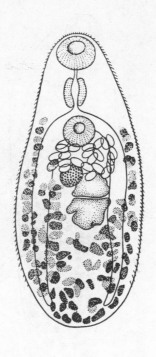

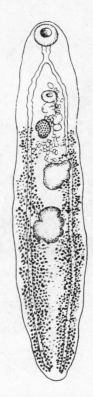

684. Opechona bacillaris (Molin, 1859) (from Skrjabin and Koval, 1960, after Markovsky, 1933)

685. Lepocreadium album (Stossich, 1890) (from Skrjabin and Koval, 1960, after Odhner, 1914)

686. Aephnidiogenes barbarus Nicoll, 1915 (from Skrjabin and Koval, 1960, after Nicoll, 1915)

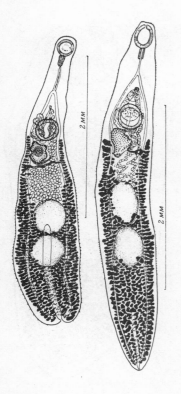

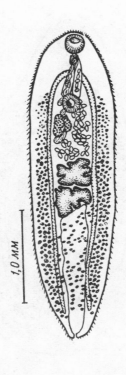

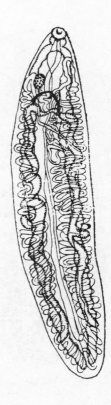

687. Holorchis legendrei Dollfus, 1946 (from Skrjabin and Koval, 1960, after Dollfus, 1946 and 1948)

688. Pseudholorchis pulcher (Manter, 1954) (from Skrjabin and Koval, 1960, after Manter, 1954)

689. Heronimus chelydrae MacCallum, 1902 (from Skrjabin, 1960, after Stunkard, 1919)

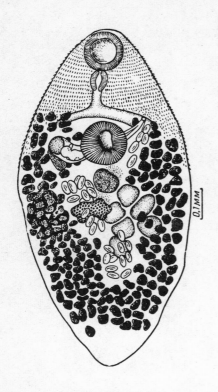

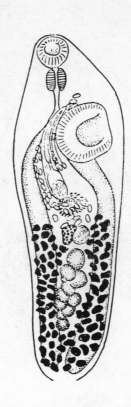

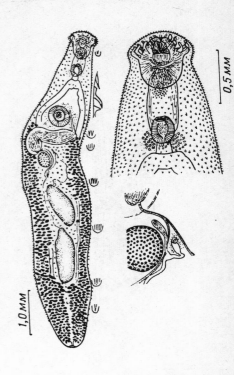

690.   Multitestis inconstans (Linton, 1905) (from Skrjabin and Koval, 1960, after Manter, 1931)

691.   Rhagorchis odhneri Manter, 1931 (from Skrjabin and Koval, 1960, after Manter, 1931)

692.   Dactylotrema squamatum Bravo and Manter, 1957 (from Skrjabin and Koval, 1960, after Bravo and Manter, 1957)

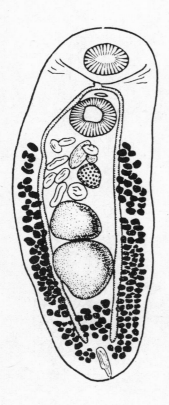

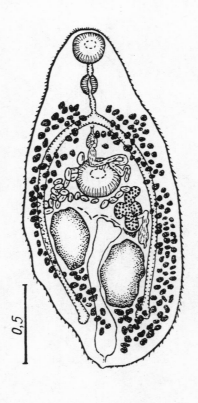

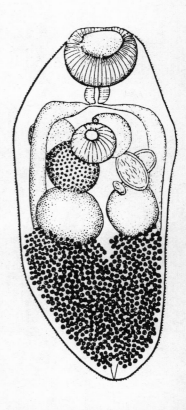

693.   Homalometron pallidum Stafford, 1904 (from Skrjabin and Koval, 1960, after Manter, 1926)

694.   Pancreadium otagoensis Manter, 1954 (from Skrjabin and Koval, 1960, after Manter, 1954)

695.   Microcreadium parvum Simer, 1929 (from Skrjabin and Koval, 1960, after Yamaguti, 1958)

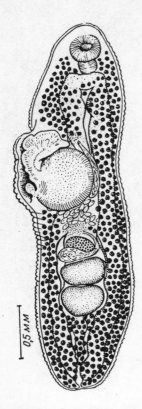

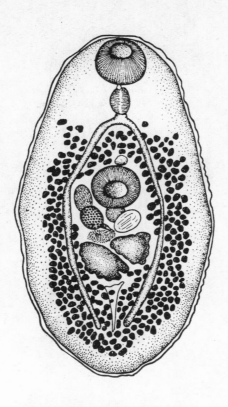

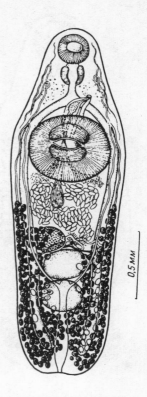

696. Myzotus vitellosus Manter, 1940 (from Skrjabin and Koval, 1960, after Manter, 1940)

697. Crassicutis cichlasomae Manter, 1936 (from Skrjabin and Koval, 1960, after Manter, 1936)

698. Labrifer semicossyphi Yamaguti, 1936 (from Skrjabin and Koval, 1960, after Yamaguti, 1936)

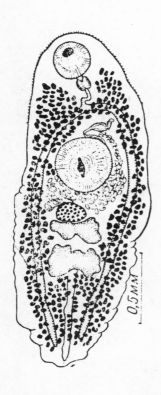

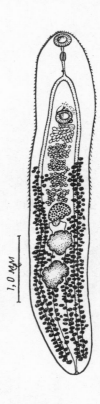

699. Myzoxenus vitellous Manter, 1934 (from Skrjabin and Koval, 1960, after Manter, 1934)

700. Lepidapedon rachion (Cobbold, 1858) (from Skrjabin and Koval, 1960, after Odhner, 1905)

701. Neolepidapedon polyprioni Manter, 1954 (from Skrjabin and Koval, 1960, after Manter, 1954)

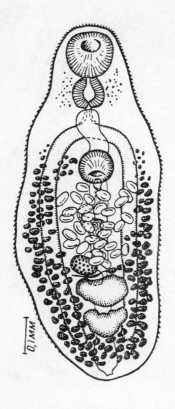

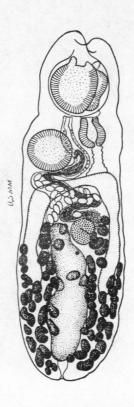

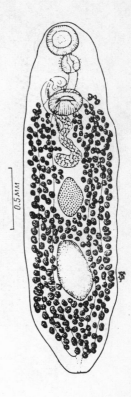

702. Postporus epinepheli (Manter, 1947) (from Skrjabin and Koval, 1960, after Manter, 1947)

703. Spiritestis arabii Nagaty, 1948 (from Skrjabin and Koval, 1960, after Nagaty, 1948)

704. Hairana sohali Nagaty, 1948 (from Skrjabin and Koval, 1960, after Nagaty, 1948)

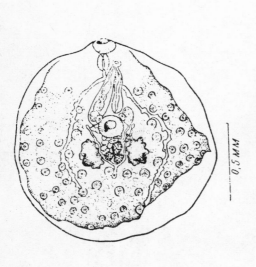

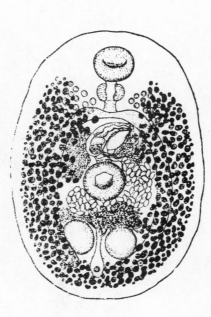

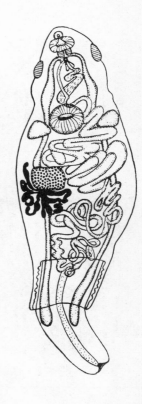

705. Dermadena lactophrysi Manter, 1945 (from Skrjabin and Koval, 1960, after Manter, 1945)

706. Pseudocreadium monocanthi Layman, 1930 (from Skrjabin and Koval, 1960, after Ozaki, 1936)

707. Grassitrema genypteri (Fife, 1954) (from Skrjabin and Gushanskaya, 1960, after Fife, 1954)

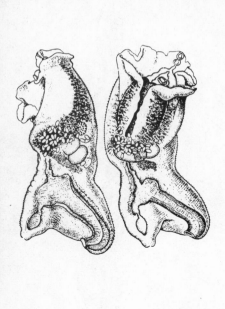

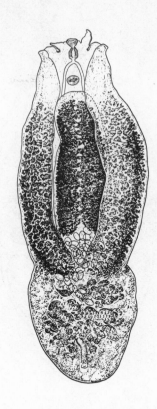

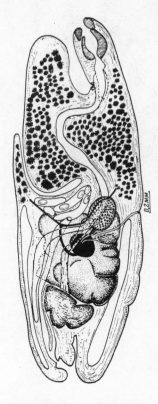

708. Podospathalium pedatum (Diesing, 1850) (from Sudarikov, 1960, after Dubois, 1938)

709. Alaria alata (Goeze, 1782) (from Sudarikov, 1960, after Dubois, 1938)

710. Pharyngostomum cordatum (Diesing, 1850) (sagittal section-from Sudarikov, 1960, after La Rue, 1926)

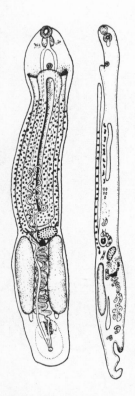

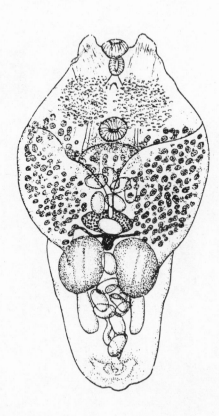

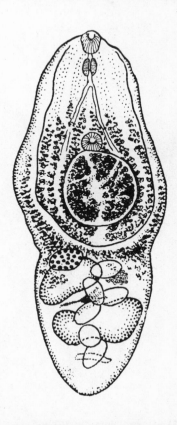

711. Procyotrema marsupiformis Harkema and Miller, 1959 (from Sudarikov, 1960, after Harkema and Miller, 1959)

712. Pharyngostomoides procyonis Harkema, 1942 (from Sudarikov, 1960 after Harkema, 1942)

713. Fibricola cratera (Barker and Noll, 1915) (from Sudarikov, 1960, after Dubois, 1938)

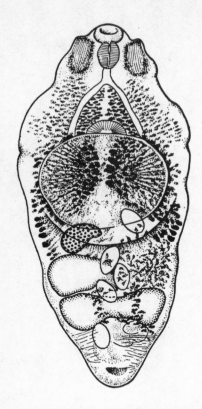 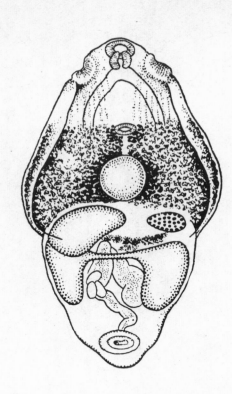 

714. Didelphodiplostomum variabile (Chandler, 1932) (from Sudarikov, 1960, after Dubois, 1938)

715. Cynodiplostomum azimi (Nazmi, 1933) (from Sudarikov, 1960, after Dubois, 1938)

716. Proterodiplostomum longum (Brandes, 1888) (from Sudarikov, 1960, after Dubois, 1936)

  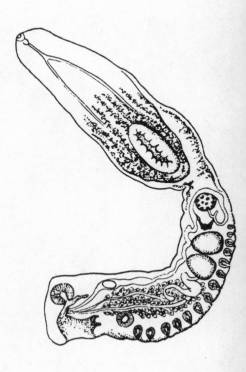

717. Archaeodiplostomum acetabulata (Byrd and Reiber, 1942) (from Sudarikov, 1960, after Byrd and Reiber, 1942)

718. Mesodiplostomum gladiolum Dubois, 1936 (from Sudarikov, 1960, after Dubois, 1936)

719. Polycotyle ornata Willemoes-Suhm, 1870 (from Sudarikov, 1960, after Poirier, 1886)

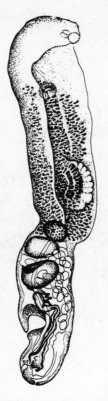

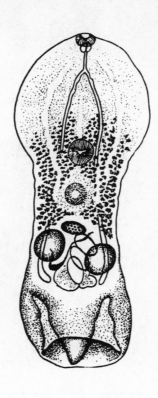

720. Cystodiplostomum hollyi
Dubois, 1936 (from Sudarikov, 1960,
after Dubois, 1936)

721. Paradiplostomum abbreviatum
(Brandes, 1888) (from Sudarikov,
1960, after Dubois, 1936)

722. Prolecithodiplostomum
constrictum Dubois, 1936 (from
Sudarikov, 1960, after Dubois, 1936)

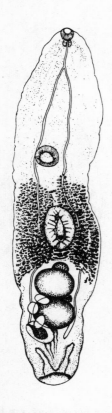

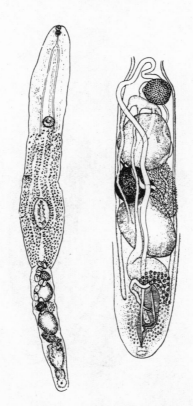

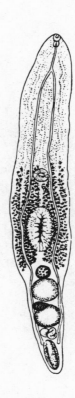

723. Herpetodiplostomum caimancola
(Dollfus, 1935) (from Sudarikov, 1960,
after Dubois, 1936)

724. Pseudocrocodilicola
americanense Byrd and Reiber, 1942
(from Sudarikov, 1960, after Byrd
and Reiber, 1942)

725. Crocodilicola pseudostoma
(Willemoes-Suhm, 1870) (from
Sudarikov, 1960, after Dubois, 1938)

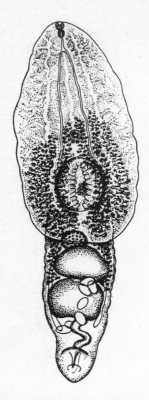

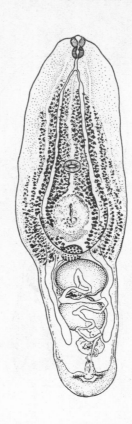

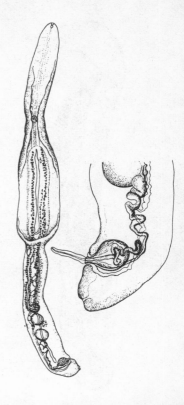

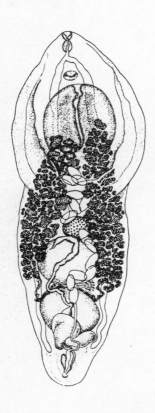

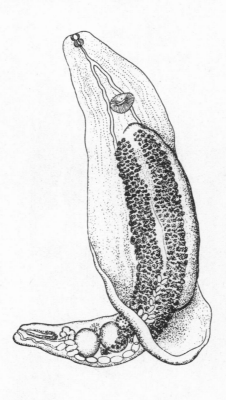

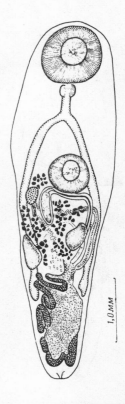

726. Pseudoneodiplostomum thomasi (Dollfus, 1936) (from Sudarikov, 1960, after Dubois, 1936)

727. Cheloniodiplostomum testudinis (Dubois, 1936) (from Sudarikov, 1960, after Dubois, 1936)

728. Heterodiplostomum lanceolatum Dubois, 1936 (from Sudarikov, 1960, after Dubois, 1936)

729. Ophiodiplostomum spectabile Dubois, 1936 (from Sudarikov, 1960, after Dubois, 1936)

730. Petalodiplostomum ancyloides Dubois, 1936 (from Sudarikov, 1960, after Dubois, 1936)

731. Opisthogonimus artigasi Ruiz and Leão, 1942 (from Skrjabin and Antipin, 1960, after Ruiz and Leão, 1942)

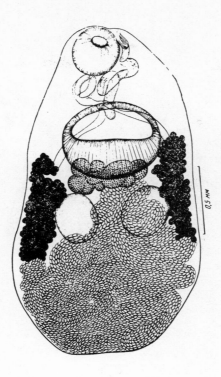

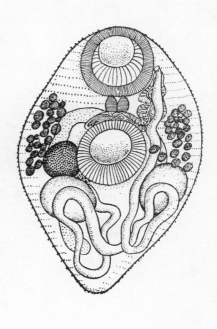

732. Westella sulina Artigas, Ruiz and Leão, 1942 (from Skrjabin and Antipin, 1960, after Artigas, Ruiz and Leão, 1942)

733. Opthalmogonimus sudarikovi Oschmarin, 1961 (from Skrjabin, 1961, after Oshmarin, 1961)

734. Cephalotrema minutum Baer, 1943 (from Skrjabin, 1961, after Baer, 1943)

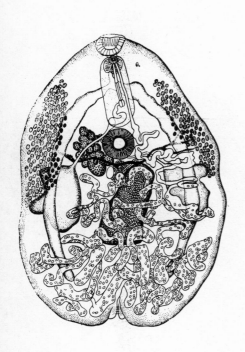

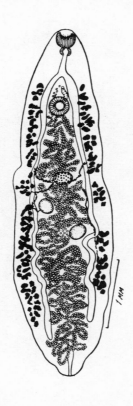

735. Mediogonimus olivacus Woodhead and Malewitz, 1936 (from Skrjabin, 1961, after Woodhead and Malewitz, 1936)

736. Allopharynx amudariensis (Strom, 1928) (from Skrjabin and Antipin, 1961, after Strom, 1928)

737. Glossidium pedatum Looss, 1899 (from Skrjabin and Antipin, 1961, after Looss, 1899)

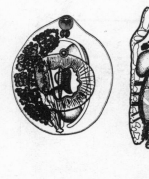

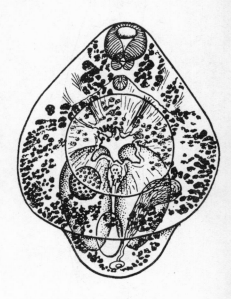

738.   Glossidioides loossi
(Travassos, 1927) (from Skrjabin
and Antipin, 1961, after Travassos,
1927)

739.   Cyathocotyle prussica Mühling,
1896 (from Sudarikov, 1961, after
Mühling, 1896)

740.   Pseudhemistomum unicum
Szidat, 1936 (from Sudarikov, 1961,
after Szidat, 1936)

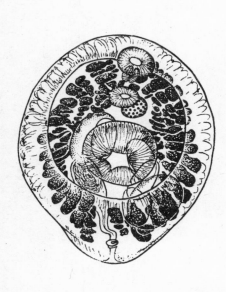

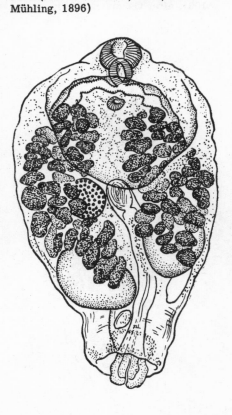

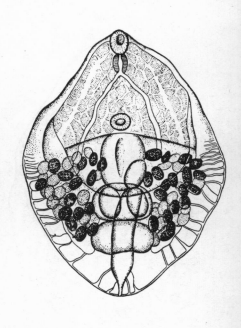

741.   Holostephanus luhei Szidat, 1936
(from Sudarikov, 1961, after Szidat,
1936)

742.   Duboisia syriaca (Dubois, 1934)
(from Sudarikov, 1961, after Dubois,
1934)

743.   Prohemistomum vivax
(Sonsino, 1892) (from Sudarikov,
1961, after Odhner, 1913)

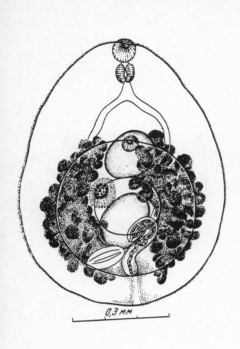

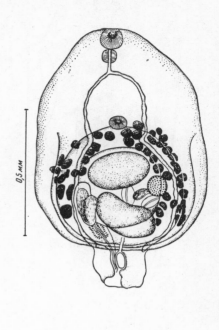

744. Paracoenogonimus ovatus Katsurada, 1914 (from Sudarikov, 1961, after Sudarikov, 1956)

745. Mesostephanus fajardensis (Price, 1934) (from Sudarikov, 1961, after Price, 1934)

746. Gelanocotyle milvi (Yamaguti, 1939) (from Sudarikov, 1961, after Vidyarthi, 1948)

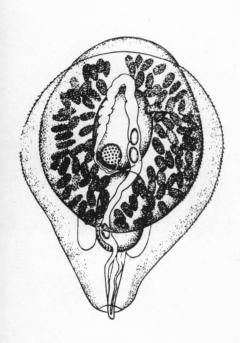

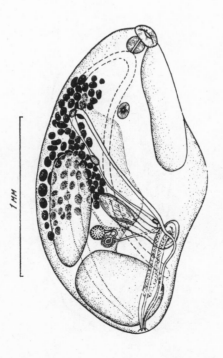

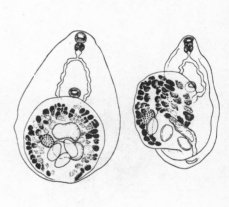

747. Prosostephanus industrius (Tubangui, 1922) (from Sudarikov, 1961, after Tubangui, 1922)

748. Tangiella parvovipara (Faust and Tang, 1938) (from Sudarikov, 1961, after Faust and Tang, 1938)

749. Serpentostephanus natricis (Dubois, 1958) (from Sudarikov, 1961, after Dubois, 1958)

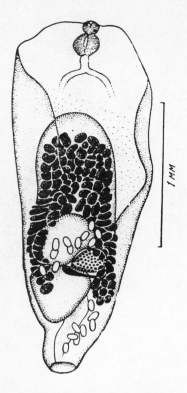

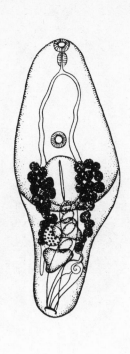

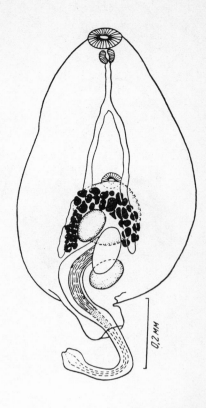

750. Neogogatea bubonis Chandler and Rausch, 1947 (from Sudarikov, 1961, after Chandler and Rausch, 1947)

751. Szidatia joyeuxi (Hughes, 1929) (from Sudarikov, 1961, after Langeron, 1924)

752. Mesostephanoides burmanicus (Chatterji, 1940) (from Sudarikov, 1961, after Chatterji, 1957)

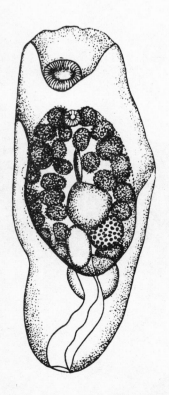

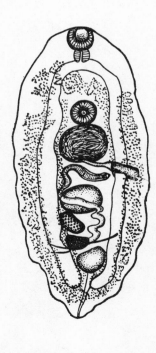

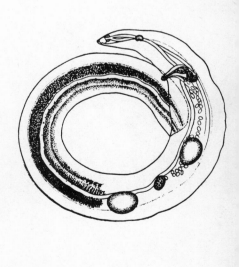

753. Gogatea serpentium (Gogate, 1932) (from Sudarikov, 1961, after Gogate, 1932)

754. Liolope copulans Cohn, 1902 (from Skrjabin, 1962, after Odhner, 1912)

755. Helicotrema magniovatum Odhner, 1912 (from Skrjabin, 1962, after Odhner, 1912)

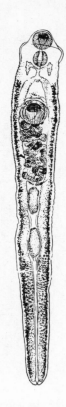

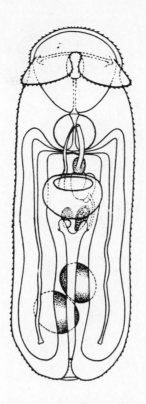

756. <u>Calycodes anthos</u> (Braun, 1899)
(from Skrjabin, 1962, after Looss,
1902)

757. <u>Auridistomum chelydrae</u>
(Stafford, 1900) (from Skrjabin,
1962, after Ralph, 1938)

758. <u>Patagium brachydelphium</u>
Heymann, 1905 (from Skrjabin,
1962, after Heymann, 1905)

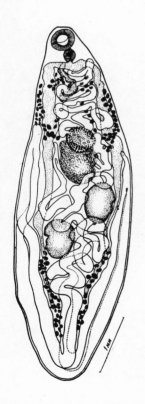

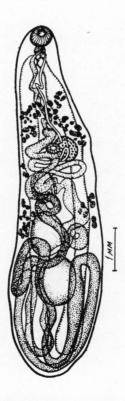

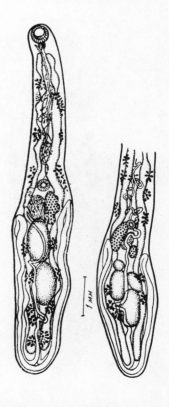

759. <u>Neohaematoloechus neivai</u>
(Travassos and Artigas, 1927) (from
Skrjabin and Antipin, 1962, after
Dobbin, 1957)

760. <u>Skrjabinoeces similis</u> (Looss,
1899) (from Skrjabin and Antipin,
1962, after Travassos and Darriba,
1930)

761. <u>Pneumonoeces variegatus</u>
(Rudolphi, 1819) (from Skrjabin
and Antipin, 1962, after Travassos
and Darriba, 1930)

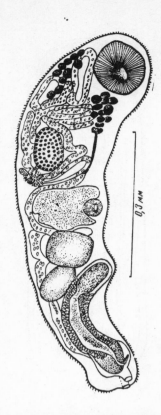

762. Ostiolum formosum Pratt, 1903
(from Skrjabin and Antipin, 1962,
after Pratt, 1903)

763. Neobucephalopsis bagarius
Dayal, 1948 (from Skrjabin and
Gushanskaya, 1962, after Dayal, 1948)

764. Bucephalus polymorphus
Baer, 1827 (from Skrjabin and
Gushanskaya, 1962, after Kozicka,
1959)

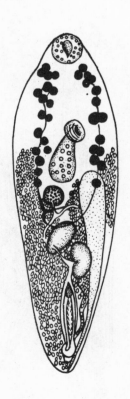

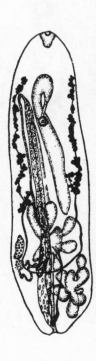

765. Bucephalopsis gracilescens
(Rudolphi, 1819) (from Skrjabin and
Gushanskaya, 1962, after Lebour)

766. Dolichoenterum longissimum
Ozaki, 1924 (from Skrjabin and
Gushanskaya, 1962, after Ozaki, 1924)

767. Paurorhynchus hiodontis
Dickerman, 1954 (from Skrjabin and
Gushanskaya, 1962, after Dickerman,
1954)

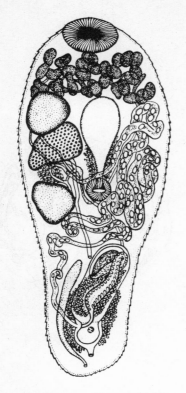

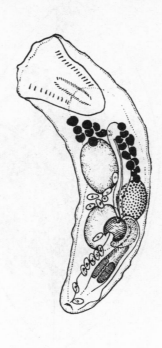

768. Pseudoprosorhynchus synodi Yamaguti, 1938 (from Skrjabin and Gushanskaya, 1962, after Yamaguti, 1938)

769. Neidhartia neidharti Nagaty, 1937 (from Skrjabin and Gushanskaya, 1962, after Nagaty, 1937)

770. Prosorhynchus crucibulus (Rudolphi, 1819) (from Skrjabin and Gushanskaya, 1962, after Nicoll, 1910)

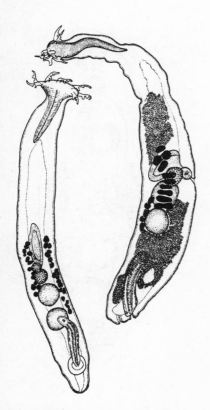

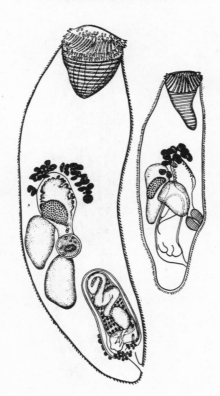

771. Alcicornis baylisi Nagaty, 1937 (from Skrjabin and Gushanskaya, 1962, after Nagaty, 1937)

772. Dollfustrema vaneyi (Tseng Shen, 1930) (from Skrjabin and Gushanskaya, 1962, after Tseng Shen, 1930)

773. Telorhynchus arripidis Crowcroft, 1947 (from Skrjabin and Gushanskaya, 1962, after Crowcroft, 1947)

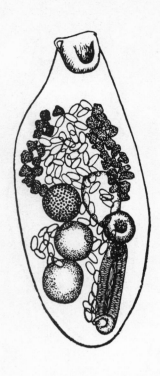

774. Rhipidocotyle galeata (Rudolphi, 1819) (from Skrjabin and Gushanskaya, 1962, after Eckmann, 1932)

775. Atractotrema fusum Goto and Ozaki, 1929 (from Skrjabin, 1947, after Goto and Ozaki, 1929)

776. Collyriclum faba (Bremser, 1831) (from Skrjabin, 1947, after Jegen, 1916)

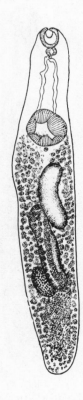

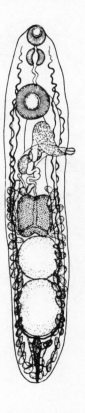

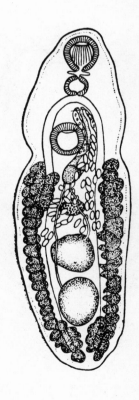

777. Mesotretes peregrinus M. Braun, 1900 (from Skrjabin, 1947, after Strom, 1935)

778. Opisthogonoporus amadai Yamaguti, 1937 (from Skrjabin, 1947, after Yamaguti, 1937)

779. Psilostomum brevicolle (Creplin, 1829) (from Skrjabin, 1947, after Braun, 1902)

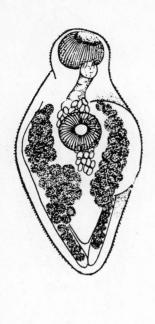

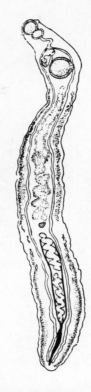

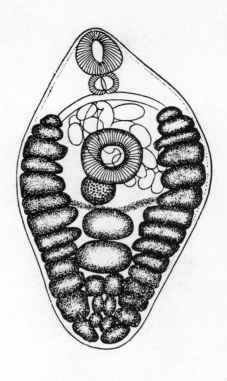

780. **Apopharynx bolodes** (Braun, 1902) (from Skrjabin, 1947, after Braun, 1902)

781. **Lyperorchis lyperorchis** Travassos, 1925 (from Skrjabin, 1947, after Travassos, 1925)

782. **Psilotrema marki** Skwortzow, 1934 (from Skrjabin, after Skvortsov, 1934)

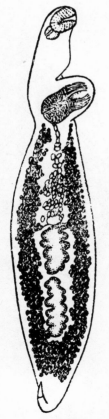

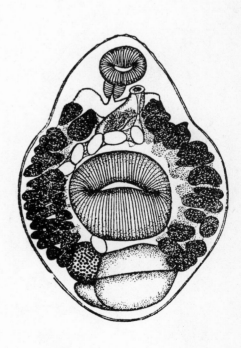

783. **Psilochasmus oxyurus** (Creplin, 1825) (from Skrjabin, 1947, after Braun, 1902)

784. **Skrjabinomerus desmane** Sobolev, Maschkov and Maschkov, 1939 (from Skrjabin, 1947, after Solonitsyn)

785. **Sphaeridiotrema globulus** (Rudolphi, 1819) (from Skrjabin, 1947, after Szidat, 1937)

313

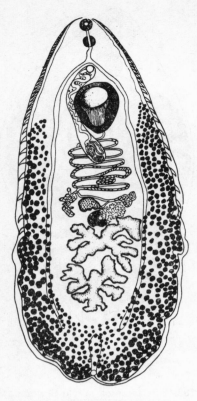

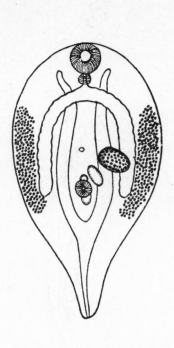

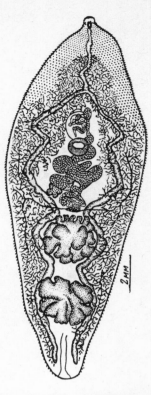

786. Testifrondosa cristata
Bhalerao, 1924 (from Skrjabin,
1947, after Bhalerao, 1924)

787. Renicola pinguis (Mehlis, 1831)
(from Skrjabin, 1947, after Cohn,
1904)

788. Pegosomum saginatum
(Ratz, 1898) (from Skrjabin and
Bashkirova, 1956, after Bykhovskaya-
Pavlovskaya, 1955)

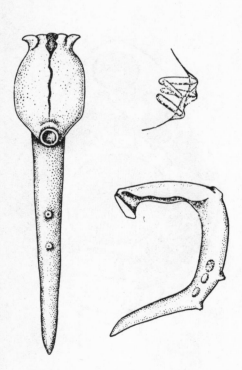

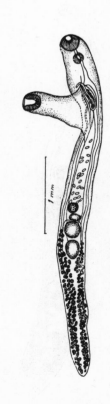

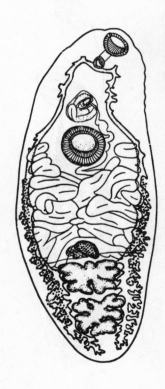

789. Sodalis spatulatus (Rudolphi,
1819) (from Skrjabin and Bashkirova,
1956, after Kovalevsky, 1899)

790. Stephanoproraoides lawi Price,
1934 (from Bashkirova, 1947, after
Price, 1934)

791. Cathaemasioides callis
Freitas, 1940 (from Skrjabin, 1947,
after Texeria and Freitas, 1940)

314

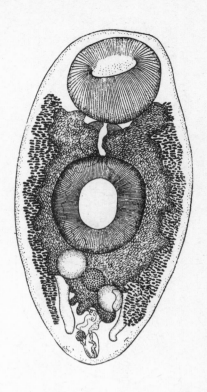

792. Protofasciola robusta (Lorenz, 1881) (from Skrjabin, 1948, after Odhner, 1926)

793. Nasitrema spathulatum Ozaki, 1935 (from Skrjabin, 1948, after Ozaki, 1935)

794. Leucochloridium macrostomum (Rudolphi, 1802) (from Skrjabin, 1948, after Witenberg, 1925)

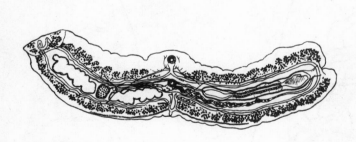

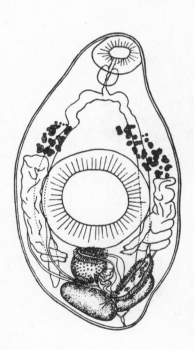

795. Moreania mirabilis Johnston, 1915 (from Skrjabin, 1948, after Johnston, 1915)

796. Leucochloridiomorpha constantiae (Müller, 1935) (from Skarbilovich, 1948, after Allison, 1943)

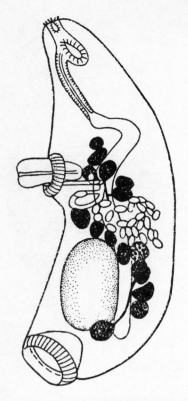

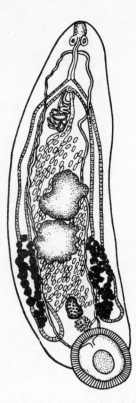

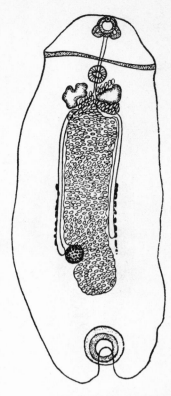

797. Balanorchis anastrophus
Fischoeder, 1901 (from Skrjabin,
1949, after Fischoeder, 1903)

798. Cleptodiscus reticulatus
Linton, 1910 (from Skrjabin, 1949,
after Linton, 1910)

799. Kalitrema kalitrema Travassos,
(from Skrjabin, 1949, after Travassos,
1934)

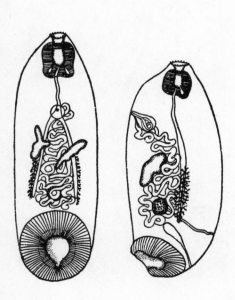

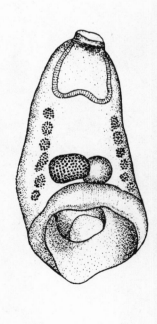

800. Pseudocladorchis cylindricus
(Diesing, 1836) (from Skrjabin, 1949,
after Daday, 1907)

801. Pseudodiscus collinsi (Cobbold,
1875) (from Skrjabin, 1949, after
Stiles and Goldberger, 1910)

802. Opisthodiscus diplodiscoides
Cohn, 1904 (from Skrjabin, 1949,
after Cohn, 1904)

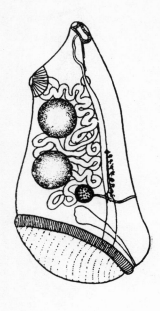 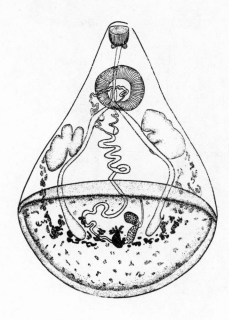 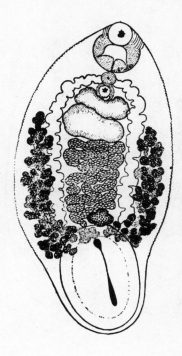

803. **Dadayius marenzelleri**
(Daday, 1907) (from Skrjabin,
1949, after Daday, 1907)

804. **Nicollodiscus gangeticus**
Srivastava, 1938 (from Skrjabin,
1949, after Srivastava, 1938)

805. **Schizamphistomum scleroporum**
(Creplin, 1844) (from Skrjabin, 1949,
after Looss, 1912)

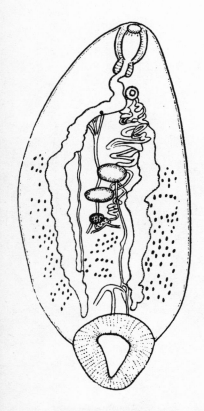 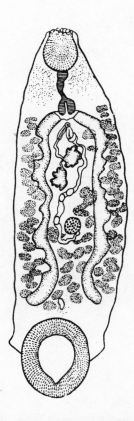 

806. <u>Allassostoma magnum</u>
Stunkard, 1917 (from Skrjabin,
1949, after Stunkard, 1917)

807. <u>Allassostomoides parvum</u>
(Stunkard, 1917) (from Skrjabin,
1949, after MacCallum, 1905)

808. <u>Chiorchis fabaceus</u> (Diesing,
1839) (from Skrjabin, 1949, after
Fischoeder, 1901)

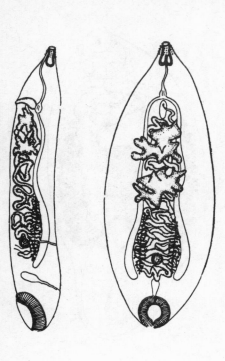

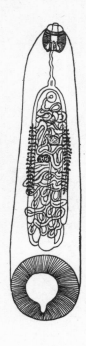

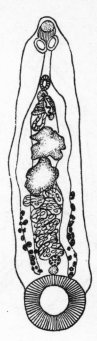

809. **Dadaytrema oxycephala**
(Diesing, 1836) (from Skrjabin,
1949, after Daday, 1907)

810. **Microrchis megacotyle**
(Diesing, 1836) (from Skrjabin,
1949, after Daday, 1907)

811. **Neocladorchis poonaensis**
Bhalerao, 1937 (from Skrjabin,
1949, after Bhalerao, 1937)

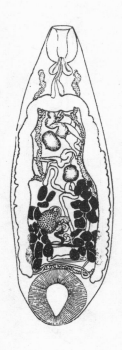

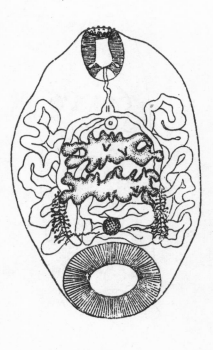

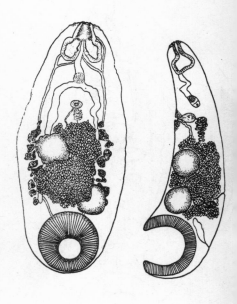

812. **Ophioxenos dienteros** Sumwalt,
1926 (from Skrjabin, 1949, after
Sumwalt, 1926)

813. **Travassosinia dilatata**
(Daday, 1907) (from Skrjabin,
1949, after Daday, 1907)

814. **Quasichiorchis purvisi**
(Southwell and Kirshner, 1937)
(from Skrjabin, 1949, after Southwell
and Kirshner, 1937)

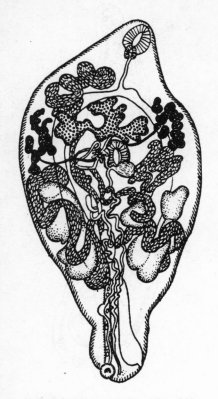

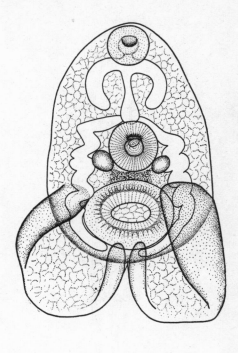

815.   <u>Cortrema corti</u> Tang, 1951
(from Skrjabin, 1960, after Tang,
1951)

816.   <u>Halltrema avitellina</u> Lent and
Freitas, 1939 (from Skrjabin, 1949,
after Lent and Freitas, 1939)

817.   <u>Brumptia bicaudata</u> (Poirier,
1908) (from Skrjabin, 1949, after
Stunkard, 1929)

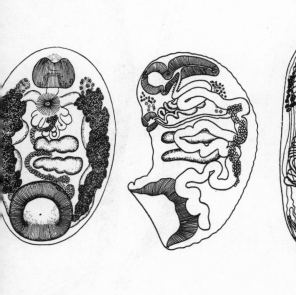

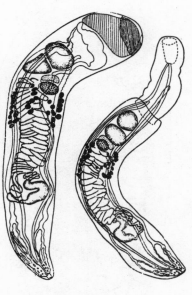

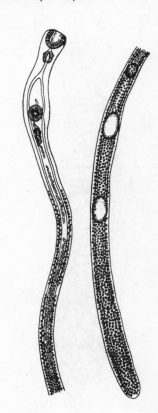

818.   <u>Stephanopharynx compactus</u>
Fischoeder, 1901 (from Skrjabin,
1949, after Fischoeder, 1901)

819.   <u>Metacetabulum invaginatum</u>
Freitas and Lent, 1938 (from Skrjabin,
1949, after Freitas and Lent, 1938)

820.   <u>Delphinicola tenuis</u> Yamaguti,
1933 (from Skrjabin and Petrov, 1950,
after Yamaguti, 1933)

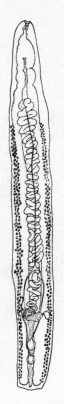

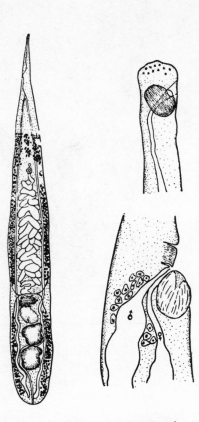

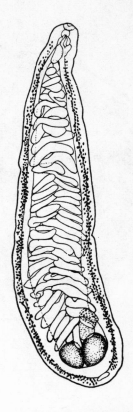

821. Plotnikovia podilymbae
(Olsen, 1938) (from Skrjabin and
Petrov, 1950, after Olsen, 1938)

822. Pseudamphimerus sterni
Gower, 1940 (from Skrjabin and
Petrov, 1950, after Gower, 1940)

823. Wardianum triangularum
(Harrah, 1922) (from Bashkirova,
1950, after Harrah, 1922)

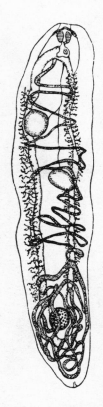

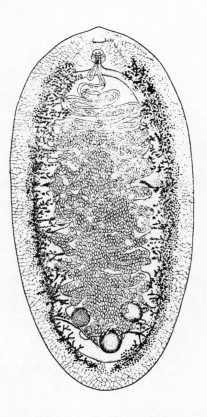

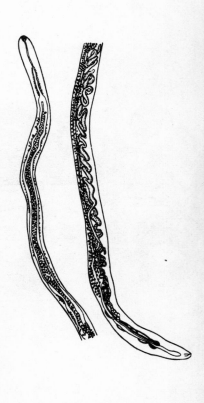

824. Spaniometra oculobia
(Cohn, 1902) (from Bashkirova,
1950, after Cohn, 1902)

825. Tracheophilus sisowi
Skrjabin, 1913 (from Bashkirova,
1950, after Skrjabin, 1913)

826. Neospirorchis
schistosomatoides Price, 1934 (from
Skrjabin, 1951, after Price, 1934)

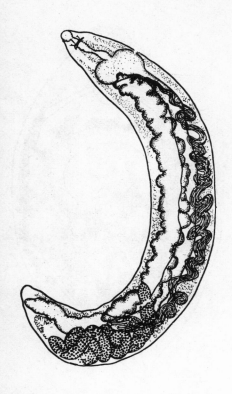

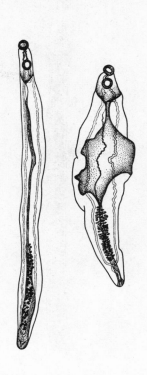

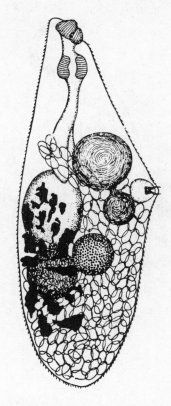

827. **Unicaecum ruszkowskii**
Stunkard, 1925 (from Skrjabin, 1951,
after Stunkard, 1927)

828. **Heterobilharzia americana**
Price, 1929 (males-from Skrjabin,
1951, after Price, 1929)

829. **Adleriella minutissima**
(Witenberg, 1929) (from Morozov,
1952, after Witenberg, 1929)

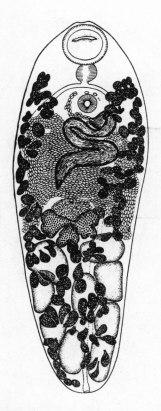

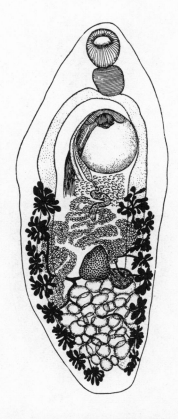

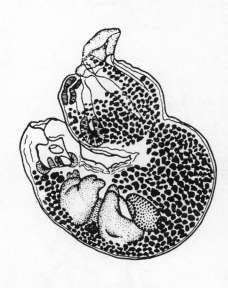

830. **Iheringtrema iheringi**
Travassos, 1947 (from Morozov,
1952, after Travassos, 1947)

831. **Polyorchitrema pisicola**
Srivastava, 1939 (from Morozov,
1952, after Srivastava, 1939)

832. **Neostrigea africana**
Bisseru, 1956 (from Sudarikov,
1959, after Bisseru, 1956)

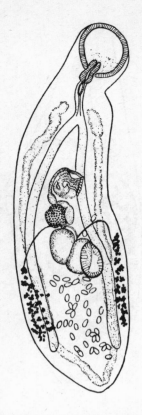

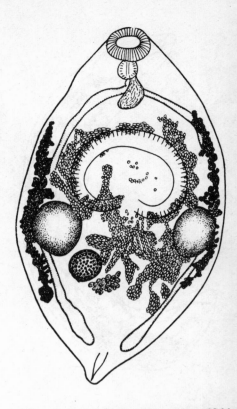

833. <u>Monodhelmis torpedinis</u>
Dollfus, 1937 (from Skrjabin, 1952,
after Dollfus, 1937)

834. <u>Brachylecithum filum</u>
(Dujardin, 1845) (from Skrjabin and
Evranova, 1952, after Strom and
Sondak, 1935)

835. <u>Canaania obesa</u> Travassos, 1944
(from Skrjabin and Evranova, 1952,
after Travassos, 1944)

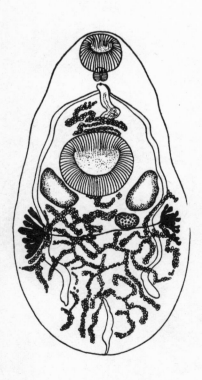

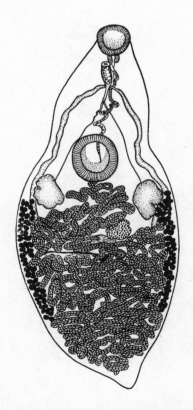

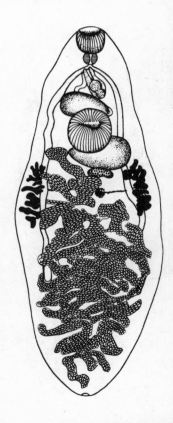

836. <u>Concinnum concinnum</u>
(Braun, 1901) (from Skrjabin and
Evranova, 1952, after Braun, 1901)

837. <u>Conspicuum conspicuum</u>
(Faria, 1912) (from Skrjabin and
Evranova, 1952, after Faria, 1912)

838. <u>Controrchis biliophilus</u> Price,
1928 (from Skrjabin and Evranova,
1952, after Price, 1928)

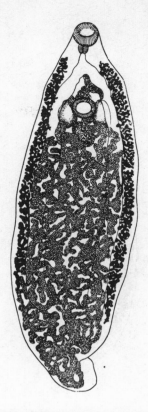

839. <u>Corrigia corrigia</u> (Braun, 1901)
(from Skrjabin and Evranova, 1952,
after Braun, 1902)

840. <u>Dictyonograptus dictyonograptus</u>
Travassos, 1919 (from Skrjabin and
Evranova, 1952, after Travassos,
1919)

841. <u>Euparadistomum varani</u>
Tubangui, 1931 (from Skrjabin and
Evranova, 1952, after Tubangui, 1931)

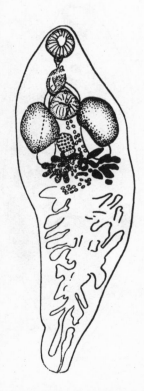

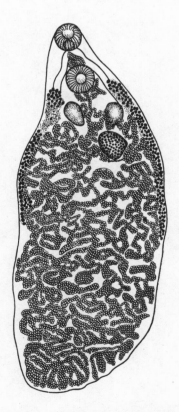

842. <u>Leipertrema rewelli</u>
Sandosham, 1951 (from Skrjabin and
Evranova, 1952, after Sandosham,
1951)

843. <u>Lubens lubens</u> (Braun, 1901)
(from Skrjabin and Evranova, 1952,
after Travassos, 1922)

844. <u>Lutztrema obliquum</u>
(Travassos, 1917) (from Skrjabin and
Evranova, 1952, after Travassos,
1917)

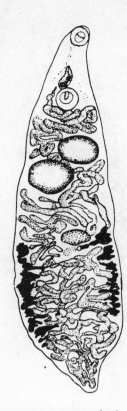

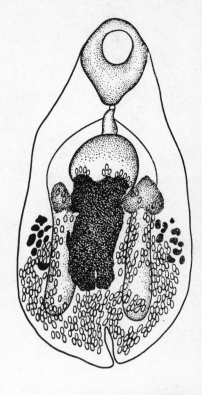

845.　Lyperosomum longicauda
(Rudolphi, 1809) (from Skrjabin and
Evranova, 1952, after Braun, 1902)

846.　Metadelphis evandroi
Travassos, 1944 (from Skrjabin and
Evranova, 1952, after Travassos,
1944)

847.　Paradistomum rabusculum
Kossack, 1910 (from Skrjabin and
Evranova, 1952, after Kossack, 1910)

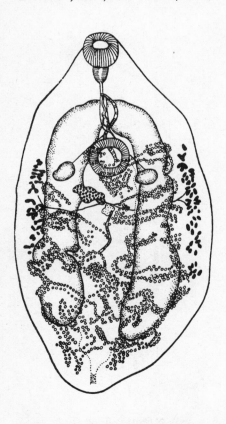

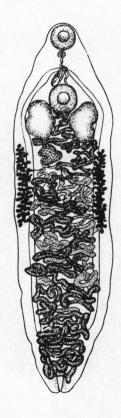

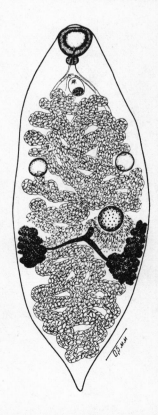

850.　Pancreatrema disacetabulum
Oschmarin, 1952 (from Skrjabin and
Evranova, 1952, after Oshmarin,
1952)

848.　Paradistomoides gregarium
(Tubangui, 1929) (from Skrjabin and
Evranova, 1952, after Tubangui, 1929)

849.　Platynosomum semifuscum
Looss, 1907 (from Skrjabin and
Evranova, 1952, after Looss, 1907)

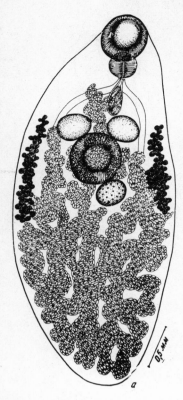

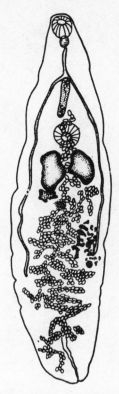

851.   Praeorchitrema praeorchis
Oschmarin, 1952 (from Skrjabin and
Evranova, 1952, after Oshmarin,
1952)

852.   Proacetabulorchis prashadi
Gogate, 1940 (from Skrjabin and
Evranova, 1952, after Yamaguti, 1941)

853.   Pseudathesmia paradoxa
Travassos, 1942 (from Skrjabin and
Evranova, 1952, after Travassos,
1944)

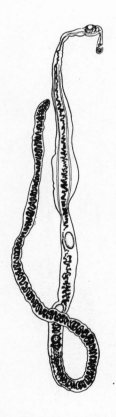

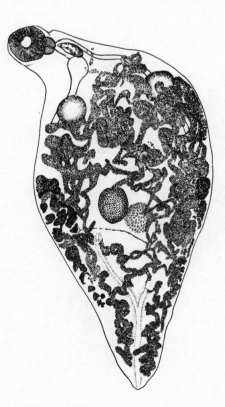

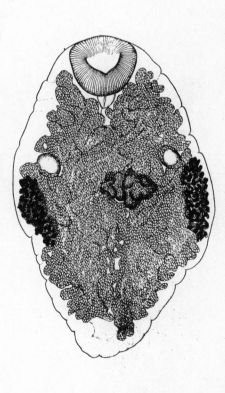

854.   Skrjabinosomum porrectum
(M; Braun. 1899) (from Skrjabin and
Evranova, 1952, after Braun, 1902)

855.   Skrjabinus skrjabini
(Issaitschikoff, 1920) (from Skrjabin
and Evranova, 1952, after Isaychikov,
1920)

856.   Stromitrema koshewnikowi
(Skrjabin and Massino, 1925) (from
Skrjabin and Evranova, 1952, after
Skrjabin and Massino, 1925)

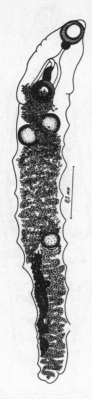

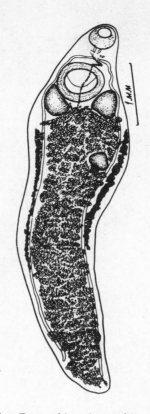

857.   Unilaterilecithum beloussi Oschmarin, 1952 (from Skrjabin and Evranova, 1952, after Oshmarin, 1952)

858.   Zonorchis microrchis (Travassos, 1916) (from Skrjabin and Evranova, 1952, after Travassos, 1944)

859.   Ogmocotyle pygargi Skrjabin and Schulz, 1933 (from Skrjabin, 1953, after Skrjabin and Schulz, 1933)

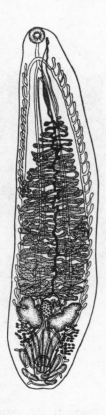

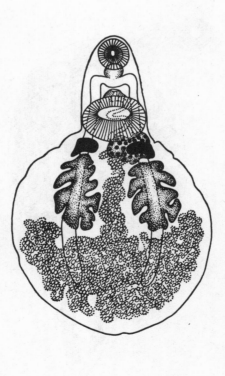

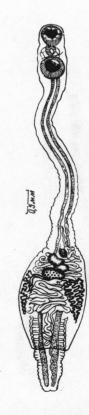

860.   Rhabdiopoeus taylori Johnston, 1913 (from Skrjabin, 1953, after Johnston, 1913)

861.   Plesiochorus cymbiformis (Rudolphi, 1819) (from Pigulevsky, 1953, after Stossich, 1895)

862.   Mecoderus oligoplitis Manter, 1940 (from Skrjabin and Gushanskaya, 1954, after Manter, 1940)

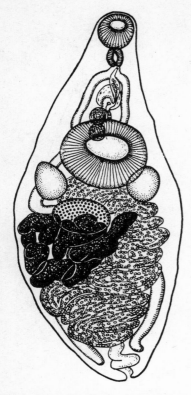

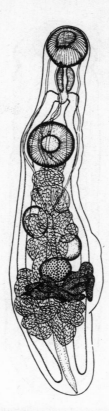

863. Hyophepaticola callionymi
Yamaguti, 1934 (from Skrjabin and
Gushanskaya, 1954, after Yamaguti,
1934)

864. Johniophyllum johnii (Yamaguti,
1938) (from Skrjabin and Gushanskaya,
1954, after Yamaguti, 1938)

865. Macradenina acanthuri Manter,
1947 (from Skrjabin and Gushanskaya,
1954, after Manter, 1947)

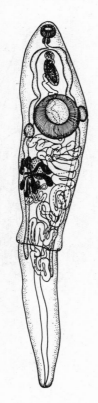

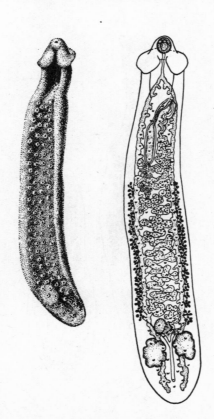

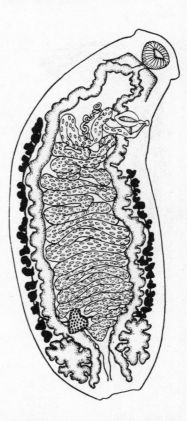

866. Musculovesicula gymnothoracis
Yamaguti, 1940 (from Skrjabin and
Gushanskaya, 1954, after Yamaguti,
1940)

867. Adenogaster serialis Looss,
1901 (from Skrjabin, 1955, after
Looss, 1902)

868. Myosaccus amblyrhynchi
Gilbert, 1938 (from Skrjabin, 1955,
after Gilbert, 1938)

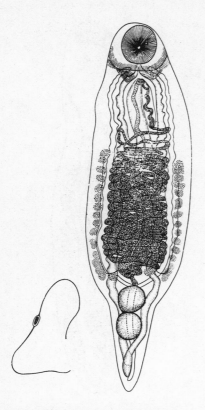

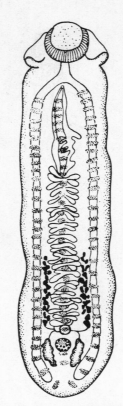

869. Teloporia aspidonectes (MacCallum, 1917) (from Skrjabin, 1955, after Stunkard, 1930)

870. Parapronocephalum symmetricum Belopolskaia, 1952 (from Skrjabin, 1955, after Belopolskaya, 1952)

871. Carassotrema koreanum Park, 1938 (from Skrjabin, 1955, after Park, 1938)

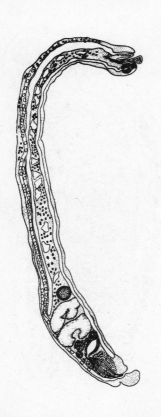

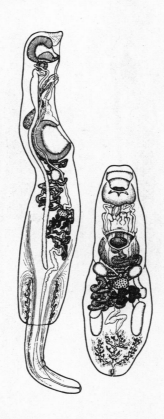

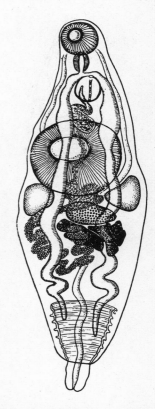

872. Duboisiella proloba Baer, 1938 (from Sudarikov, 1959, after Baer, 1938)

873. Lecithochirium rufoviride (Rudolphi, 1819) (from Skrjabin and Gushanskaya, 1955, after Looss, 1908)

874. Separogermiductus inimici (Yamaguti, 1934) (from Skrjabin and Gushanskaya, 1955, after Yamaguti, 1934)

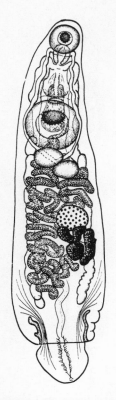

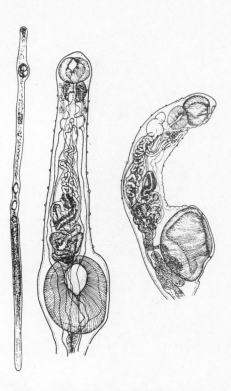

875. **Synaptobothrium caudiporum** (Rudolphi, 1819) (from Skrjabin and Gushanskaya, 1955, after Looss, 1908)

876. **Elytrophallus mexicanus** Manter, 1940 (from Skrjabin and Gushanskaya, 1955, after Manter, 1940)

877. **Lampritrema nipponicum** Yamaguti, 1940 (from Skrjabin and Gushanskaya, 1955, after Yamaguti, 1940)

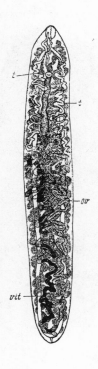

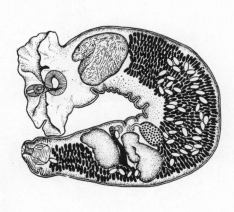

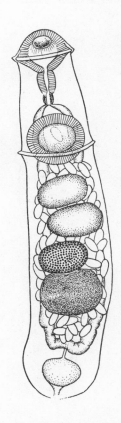

878. **Philopinna higai** Yamaguti, 1936 (from Skrjabin, 1955, after Yamaguti, 1936)

879. **Codonocephalus urinigerus** (Rudolphi, 1819) (from Sudarikov, 1959, after Ginetsinskaya, 1949)

880. **Bunocotyle cingulata** Odhner, 1928 (from Skrjabin and Gushanskaya, 1955, after Odhner, 1928)

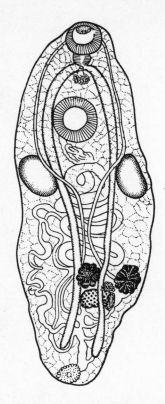

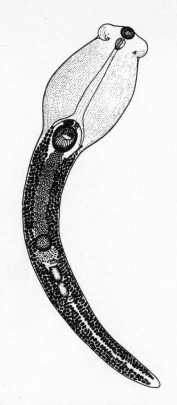

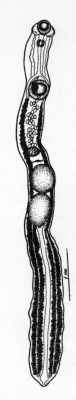

881. Dictysarca virens Linton, 1910
(from Skrjabin and Gushanskaya,
1955, after Manter, 1947)

882. Eurycephalus dogieli
Ovtscharenko, 1955 (from Skrjabin
and Bashkirova, 1956, after
Ovcharenko, 1955)

883. Nephroechinostoma aquilae
Oschmarin and Belouss, 1951 (from
Skrjabin and Bashkirova, 1956, after
Oshmarin and Belous, 1951)

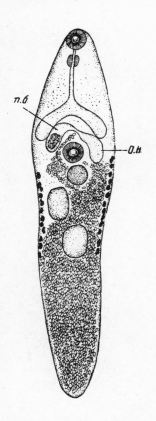

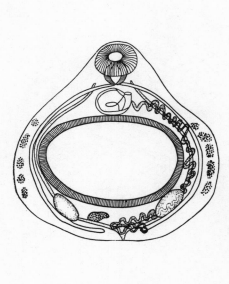

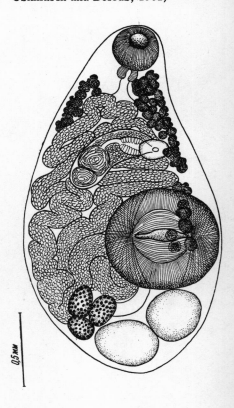

884. Ancylocoelium typicum Nicoll,
1912 (from Skrjabin and Koval, 1957,
after Koval, 1957)

885. Markevitschiella nakazawai
(Kobayashi, 1921) (from Skrjabin and
Koval, 1957, after Kobayashi, 1921)

886. Pyriforma macrorhamphosi
Yamaguti, 1938 (from Skrjabin and
Koval, 1957, after Yamaguti, 1938)

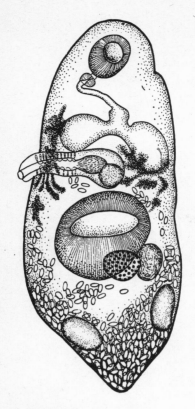

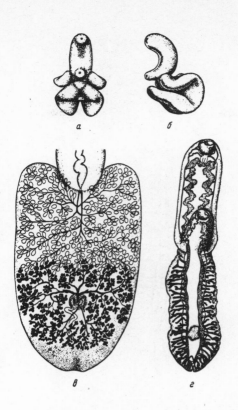

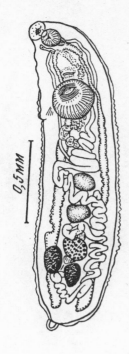

887. **Yamagutia lateroporus**
Srivastava, 1939 (from Skrjabin and
Koval, 1957, after Srivastava, 1939)

888. **Otiotrema torosum** Setti, 1897
(from Skrjabin and Gushanskaya,
1957, after Looss, 1899)

889. **Mitrostoma nototheniae** Manter,
1954 (from Skrjabin and Gushanskaya,
1957, after Manter, 1954)

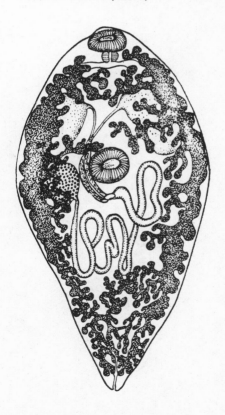

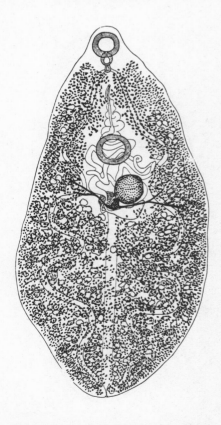

890. **Tricotyledonia genypteri** Fife,
1954 (from Skrjabin and Gushanskaya,
1957, after Fife, 1954)

891. **Nephrotrema truncatum**
(Leuckart, 1842) (from Skrjabin,
1958, after Baer, 1932)

892. **Achillurbainia nouveli** Dollfus,
1939 (from Skrjabin, 1958, after
Dollfus, 1939)

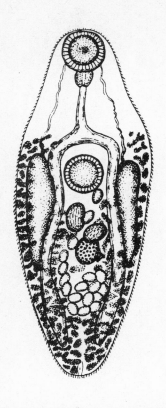

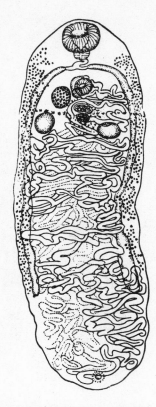

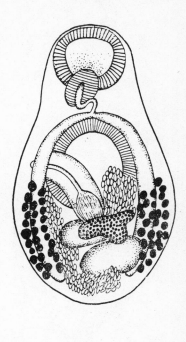

893. Macroorchis spinulosus Gotoz and Ando, 1919 (from Skrjabin, 1958, after Dollfus, 1935)

894. Alloglyptus crenshawi Byrd, 1950 (from Skrjabin and Antipin, 1958, after Byrd, 1950)

895. Alloplagiorchis garricki Simer, 1929 (from Skrjabin and Antipin, 1958, after Simer, 1929)

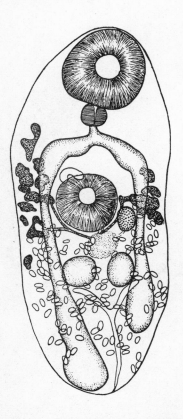

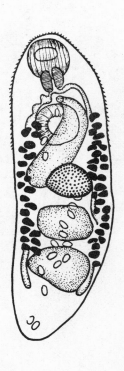

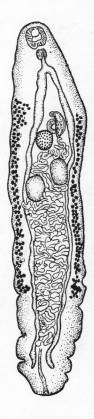

896. Paralepoderma cloacicola (Lühe, 1909) (from Skrjabin and Antipin, 1958, after Dollfus, 1950)

897. Parastiotrema ottawanensis Miller, 1940 (from Skrjabin and Antipin, 1958, after Miller, 1940)

898. Rauschiella tineri Babero, 1951 (from Skrjabin and Antipin, 1958, after Babero, 1951)

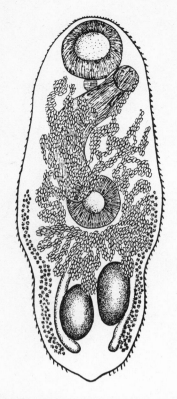

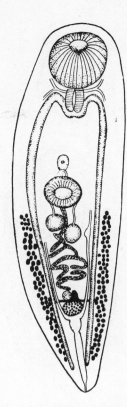

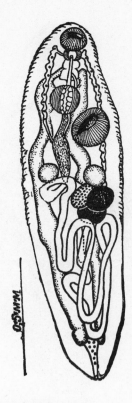

899.   Dolichoperoides macalpini
(Nicoll, 1914) (from Skrjabin and
Antipin, 1958, after Nicoll, 1918)

900.   Leuceruthrus micropteri
Marshal and Gilbert, 1905 (from
Skrjabin and Gushanskaya, 1958,
after Marshal and Gilbert, 1905)

901.   Myosaccium ecaude
Montgomery, 1957 (from Skrjabin and
Gushanskaya, 1959, after Montgomery,
1957)

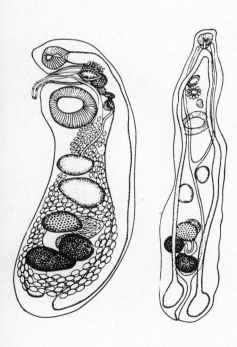

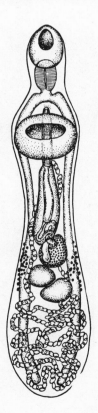

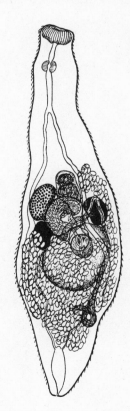

902.   Intuscirrus aspicotti Acena,
1947 (from Skrjabin and Gushanskaya,
1958, after Acena, 1947)

903.   Xenopera insolita Nicoll, 1915
(from Skrjabin and Gushanskaya,
1958, after Nicoll, 1915)

904.   Pseudoproctotrema parupenei
Yamaguti, 1942 (from Skrjabin and
Gushanskaya, 1958, after Yamaguti,
1942)

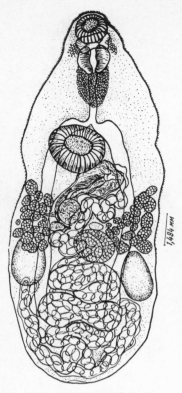

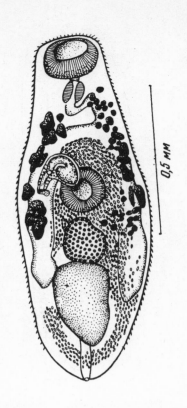

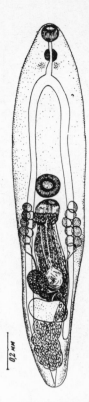

905. Botulisaccus pisceus Caballero, Bravo and Grocott, 1955 (from Skrjabin and Gushanskaya, 1958, after Caballero, Bravo and Grocott, 1955)

906. Brahamputrotrema punctata Gupta, 1953 (from Skrjabin and Gushanskaya, 1958, after Gupta, 1953)

907. Opisthomonorchis carangis Yamaguti, 1952 (from Skrjabin and Gushanskaya, 1958, after Yamaguti, 1952)

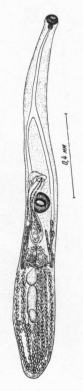

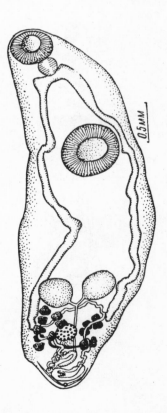

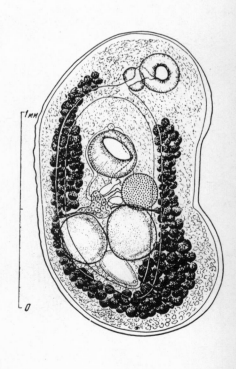

908. Diplolasiotocus chaetodontis Yamaguti, 1952 (from Skrjabin and Gushanskaya, 1958, after Yamaguti, 1952)

909. Thapariella anastomusa Srivastava, 1953 (from Skrjabin, 1958, after Srivastava, 1953)

910. Trematobrien haplochromios Dollfus, 1950 (from Skrjabin, 1958, after Dollfus, 1950)

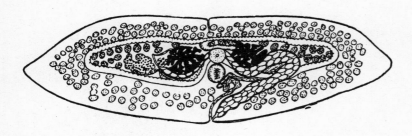

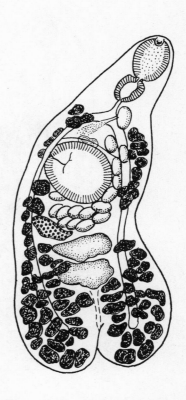

911.   Transversotrema haasi
Witenberg, 1944 (from Skrjabin,
1958, after Witenberg, 1944)

912.   Deropristis inflata (Molin, 1859)
(from Skrjabin, 1958, after Odhner,
1902)

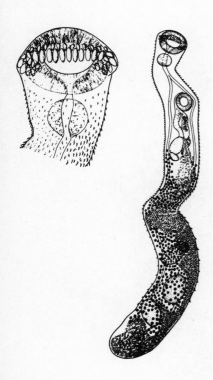

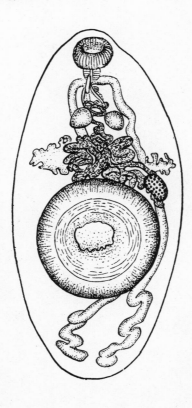

913.   Pristicola sturionis (Little,
1930) (from Skrjabin, 1958, after
Little, 1930)

914.   Prosogonotrema bilabiata
Vigueras, 1940 (from Skrjabin,
1958, after Vigueras, 1940)

915.   Parvacreadium bifidum Manter,
1940 (from Skrjabin and Petrov, 1958,
after Manter, 1940)

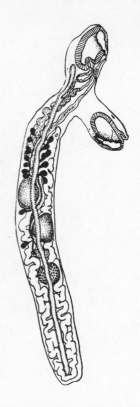

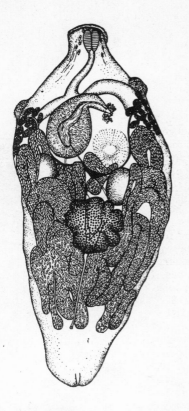

916. Orophocotyle planci (Stossich, 1899) (from Skrjabin and Gushanskaya, 1959, after Looss, 1902)

917. Faustula keksooni (MacCallum, 1918) (from Skrjabin, 1959, after Price, 1938)

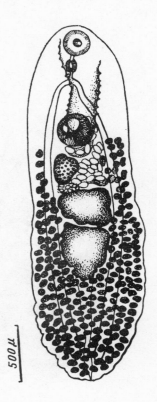

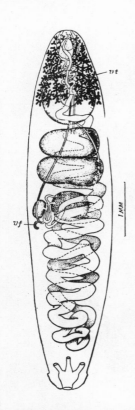

918. Choanodera caulolautili Manter, 1940 (from Skrjabin, 1959, after Manter, 1940)

919. Guschanskiana alveolata (Robinson, 1934) (from Skrjabin and Gushanskaya, 1959, after Robinson, 1934)

INDEX

37505